27 Nov 4[illegible]

4.00

Paul —

"Use this to figure the "interest."

Bill

Mathematics for the Million

The earliest geometrical problems arose from the need for a calendar to regulate the seasonal pursuits of settled agriculture. The recurrence of the seasons was recognized by erecting monuments in line with the rising, setting or transit of celestial bodies. This photograph, taken at Stonehenge, shows how the position of a stone marked the day of the summer solstice when the sun rises furthest north along the eastern boundary of the horizon.

Mathematics for the Million

by ***LANCELOT HOGBEN***

Illustrated by
J. F. HORRABIN

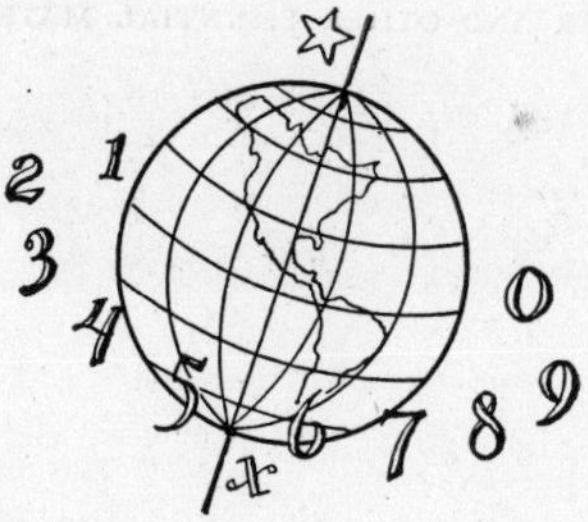

NEW, REVISED AND ENLARGED EDITION

New York

W. W. NORTON & COMPANY Inc.

Publishers

First Published, March 1937

Revised and Enlarged Editions July 1940, July 1943

Twenty-fifth Printing

A WARTIME BOOK

THIS COMPLETE EDITION IS PRODUCED IN FULL COMPLIANCE WITH THE GOVERNMENT'S REGULATIONS FOR CONSERVING PAPER AND OTHER ESSENTIAL MATERIALS.

PRINTED IN THE UNITED STATES OF AMERICA
FOR THE PUBLISHERS BY THE VAIL-BALLOU PRESS

TO

C. K. OGDEN

"It is a remarkable fact that the mathematical inventions which have proved to be most accessible to the masses are also those which exercised the greatest influence on the development of pure mathematics."

Tobias Dantzig in NUMBER. The Language of Science

Contents

Author's Excuse for Writing It

I WROTE this book in hospital during a long illness for my own fun. A few friends from among the million or so intelligent people who have been frightened by mathematics while at school persuaded me to publish it. I have agreed to do so on the understanding that they would relieve me of a task, which would interfere with my professional work, by correcting the proofs.

With no pretensions to be a specialist I want to make two things clear. The first is that I have written it in my capacity as a private citizen interested in education. The other is that, whatever objections may be raised against the approach adopted and views expressed in it, it will have fulfilled its aim if it stimulates the interest and removes the inferiority complex of some of the million or so who have given up hope of learning through the usual channels. Readers accustomed to the appearance of the heavens in the southern hemisphere will need to bear in mind that the illustrations are constructed from the standpoint of an observer living north of the Equator. The asides and soliloquies should not be taken too seriously. They are put in to sweeten the pill. Maybe many of them have as little nutritive value as saccharine.

The reader who wishes to know more about the place of mathematics in the history of culture may consult such works as the histories of Rouse Ball, Cantor, Heath, Sullivan, Dantzig, Cajori, the invaluable two volumes of Smith, and Neugebauer's recent treatise on early mathematics. Other useful books in which the relation of mathematics to the growth of scientific knowledge is indicated are Abel Rey's *La Science Orientale avant les Grecs*, Carl Snyder's *The World Machine*, Sir Norman Lockyer's *Stonehenge and other British Monuments*, and Wright's *Geographical Lore in the Time of the Crusades*. Two volumes which have appeared since this book was written are worth adding. One is Professor Farrington's *Science in Antiquity*. The other is Bell's *Search for Truth*. A good general text-book for the reader who wishes to get practice is Mann's *Practical Mathematics*.

If the book had any pretensions to be a work of scholarship, the writer would have documented it, and made it clear when, as often happens, the views expressed are not shared by others. It would then have been less lively, and therefore less adapted to fulfil the only aim which seemed to justify its publication.

Many helpful suggestions made by readers of the first edition have been incorporated in the new one, which has been carefully revised by Dr. J. C. P. Miller, Lecturer in Applied Mathematics in the University of Liverpool. One of the appendices was added at the suggestion of Professor E. Neville.

Foreword to the Second American Edition

In the foreword to the first edition of this book I explained how I wrote it for my own fun while in hospital during a long illness. I insisted that it was never intended to be regarded as the work of a specialist with academic pretensions to rank as an authoritative textbook. As I blended into the writing of it the gleanings of what I had read about the history of civilization and of mathematics from authors who know more than I am entitled to assess, I amused myself by recalling difficulties which I had painfully mastered before I understood difficulties which cleverer people had surmounted more tortuously and perhaps more painfully in earlier chapters of the romance of human enlightenment. So it would not be strictly true to say that no one was more surprised by the success of the book than the author. The real truth is that it was written in the conviction that the study of mathematics could be made exciting to ordinary people, as, for instance, myself.

When I left hospital, I had no intention of publishing it in its original form, and did so only because of the importunity of my publisher, Mr. Norton who is also—paradoxically—my friend. If the fact that non-mathematical readers for whom it was intended showed their appreciation in the way which is most congenial to an author who has family responsibilities did not surprise me as much as it surprised my friends, it is fair to say that I should have taken more trouble with the preparation of the first edition, had I realized the dimensions of the public it was destined to reach. What did surprise me was the cordiality and generosity with which critics who themselves were specialists commended such merits as it has and condoned its—to them—evident defects. Many of my reviewers wrote to me personally making suggestions for the improvement of a subsequent edition, and I have since received hundreds of letters from appreciative readers who have pointed out obscurities or errors in proof correcting. The result is that the present edition is in a real sense, a co-operative work, thanks in no small measure to the many American readers who have enjoyed the earlier edition or have wished to see the book prosper. Their names are too numerous to mention and I can only thank them collectively as one of the authors of what I have now come to regard as a work of collective American effort.

Besides the various improvements indicated in the foregoing paragraph the second edition has several new features, appendices added at the suggestion of Professor Neville, of Reading University, an index, and answers to problems and examples prepared by my friend J. C. P. Miller, Lecturer in Applied Mathematics in Liverpool University.

The existence of the second edition is sufficient evidence that the book has fulfilled its function of stimulating an interest among those whom the formal approach of school and college has failed to satisfy. I need not apologize for the defects which remain, because the reader who is able to get his inferiority complex cured painlessly can continue his studies with other books by writers who know more than I do. What I specially wish to express in this foreword is my gratitude to all the nameless co-authors who have contributed to the making, of what is at least a work of entertainment.

Lancelot Hogben

Mathematics for the Million

CHAPTER I

Mathematics, the Mirror of Civilization

THERE is a story about Diderot, the Encyclopaedist and materialist, a foremost figure in the intellectual awakening which immediately preceded the French Revolution. Diderot was staying at the Russian court, where his elegant flippancy was entertaining the nobility. Fearing that the faith of her retainers was at stake, the Tsaritsa commissioned Euler, the most distinguished mathematician of the time, to debate with Diderot in public. Diderot was informed that a mathematician has established a proof of the existence of God. He was summoned to court without being told the name of his opponent. Before the assembled court, Euler accosted him with the following pronouncement, which was uttered with due gravity: "$\frac{a + b^n}{n} = x$, donc Dieu existe répondez!" Algebra was Arabic to Diderot. Unfortunately he did not realize that was the trouble. Had he realized that algebra is just a language in which we describe the *sizes* of things in contrast to the ordinary languages which we use to describe the *sorts* of things in the world, he would have asked Euler to translate the first half of the sentence into French. Translated freely into English, it may be rendered: "A number x can be got by first adding a number a to a number b multiplied by itself a certain number of times, and then dividing the whole by the number of b's multiplied together. So God exists after all. What have you got to say now?" If Diderot had asked Euler to illustrate the first part of his remark for the clearer understanding of the Russian court, Euler might have replied that x is 3 when a is 1 and b is 2 and n is 3, or that x is 21 when a is 3 and b is 3 and n is 4, and so forth. Euler's troubles would have begun when the court wanted to know how the second part of the sentence follows from the first part. Like many of us, Diderot had stagefright when confronted with a sentence in size language.

He left the court abruptly amid the titters of the assembly, confined himself to his chambers, demanded a safe conduct, and promptly returned to France.

Though he could not know it, Diderot had the last laugh before the court of history. The clericalism which Diderot fought was overthrown, and though it has never lacked the services of an eminent mathematician, the supernaturalism which Euler defended has been in retreat ever since. One eminent contemporary astronomer in his Gifford lectures tells us that Dirac has discovered p and q numbers. *Donc Dieu existe.* Another distinguished astronomer pauses, while he entertains us with astonishing calculations about the distance of the stars, to award M. le grand Architecte an honorary degree in mathematics. There were excellent precedents long before the times of Euler and Diderot. For the first mathematicians were the priestly calendar makers who calculated the onset of the seasons. The Egyptian temples were equipped with nilometers with which the priests made painstaking records of the rising and falling of the sacred river. With these they could predict the flooding of the Nile with great accuracy. Their papyri show that they possessed a language of measurement very different from the pretentious phraseology with which they fobbed off their prophecies on the laity. The masses could not see the connection between prophecy and reality, because the nilometers communicated with the river by underground channels, skilfully concealed from the eye of the people. The priests of Egypt used one language when they wrote in the proceedings of a learned society and another language when they gave an interview to the "sob sisters" of the Sunday press.

In the ancient world writing and reading were still a mystery and a craft. The plain man could not decipher the Rhind papyrus in which the scribe Ahmes wrote down the laws of measuring things. Civilized societies in the twentieth century have democratized the reading and writing of *sort language*. Consequently the plain man can understand scientific discoveries if they do not involve complicated measurements. He knows something about evolution. The priestly accounts of the creation have fallen into discredit. So mysticism has to take refuge in the atom. The atom is a safe place not because it is small, but because you have to do complicated measurements and use underground channels to find your way there. These underground channels are concealed from the eye of the people because the plain man has not been taught to read and write *size language*. Three centuries ago, when priests conducted their services in Latin, Protestant reformers founded grammar schools so that people could read the open bible. The time has now come for another Reformation. People must learn to read and write the language of measurement so that they can understand the open bible of modern science.

In the time of Diderot the lives and happiness of individuals might still depend on holding the correct beliefs about religion. Today the lives and happiness of people depend more than most of us realize upon the correct interpretation of public statistics which are kept by Government offices. When a committee of experts announce that the average man can live on his unemployment allowance, or the average child is getting sufficient milk, the mere mention of an average or the citation of a list of figures is enough to paralyse intelligent criticism. In reality half or more than half the population may not be getting enough to live on when the *average* man or child has enough. The majority of people living today in civilized countries cannot read and write freely in size language, just as the majority of people living in the times of Wycliff and Luther were ignorant of Latin in which religious controversy was carried on. The modern Diderot has got to learn the language of size in self-defence, because no society is safe in the hands of its clever people.

Long before clever people started reading and writing the ordinary languages in which we describe different sorts of things, other people who were not so terribly clever had learnt to talk. The plain man of today, that is to say, the reader or the writer of this book, has a great advantage over the audiences who listened to the priestly oracles of the ancient world. Though we may not read or write it, we have all learned to talk in *size language*. If we were asked what distinguishes the men of today, the men of the machine age, from the men who lived before the American or French Revolution, we might give many answers. Very few would give the answer that Burke gave. About forty years after the incident we have been discussing, Burke wrote a vitriolic denunciation of the social revolution heralded by the Encyclopaedists. With this difference that Burke wrote elegant, sonorous, and commanding prose, many passages in it recall familiar descriptions of current events in Russia, as they are reflected in the dented mirror of the daily press. In one of the most resonant and also the silliest passages of his reflections, Burke pronounces an eloquent obituary on the *ancien régime*. What raises his anger to white heat is not that Europe will become a continent of shopkeepers. It is that Europe will become a continent of calculators. "The Age of Chivalry is gone. That of sophists, economists, and *calculators* has succeeded, and the glory of Europe is extinguished for ever . . ."

The first men who dwelt in cities were *talking* animals. The man of the machine age is a *calculating* animal. We live in a welter of figures: cookery recipes, railway time-tables, unemployment aggregates, fines, taxes, war debts, overtime schedules, speed limits, bowling averages, betting odds, billiard scores, calories, babies' weights, clinical temperatures, rainfall, hours of sunshine, motoring records, power indices, gas-meter readings, bank rates, freight rates, death rates, discount, interest, lotteries, wave lengths, and tyre pressures. Every night, when he winds up his watch, the modern man adjusts a scientific instrument of a precision and delicacy unimaginable to the most cunning artificers of Alexandria in its prime. So much is commonplace. What escapes our notice is that in doing these things we have learnt to use devices which presented tremendous difficulties to the most brilliant mathematicians of antiquity. Ratios, limits, acceleration, are not remote abstractions, dimly apprehended by the solitary genius. They are photographed upon every page of our existence. In the course of the adventure upon which we are going to embark we shall constantly find that we have no difficulty in answering questions which tortured the minds of very clever mathematicians in ancient times. This is not because you and I are very clever people. It is because we inherit a social culture which has suffered the impact of material forces foreign to the intellectual life of the ancient world. The most brilliant intellect is a prisoner within its own social inheritance.

An illustration will help to make this quite definite at the outset. The Eleatic philosopher Zeno set all his contemporaries guessing by propounding a series of conundrums, of which the one most often quoted is the paradox of Achilles and the tortoise. Here is the problem about which the inventors of school geometry argued till they had speaker's throat and writer's cramp. Achilles runs a race with the tortoise. He runs ten times as fast as the tortoise. The tortoise has 100 yards' start. Now, says Zeno, Achilles runs 100 yards and reaches the place where the tortoise started. Meanwhile the tortoise has gone a tenth as far as Achilles, and is therefore 10 yards ahead of Achilles. Achilles runs this 10 yards. Meanwhile the tortoise has run a tenth as far as Achilles, and is therefore 1 yard in front of him. Achilles runs this 1 yard. Meanwhile the tortoise has run a tenth of a yard and is therefore a tenth of a yard in front of Achilles. Achilles runs this tenth of a yard. Meanwhile the tortoise goes a tenth of a tenth of a yard. He is now a hundredth of a yard in front of Achilles. When Achilles has caught up this hundredth of a yard, the tortoise is a thousandth of a yard in front. So, argued Zeno, Achilles is always getting nearer the tortoise, but can never quite catch him up.

You must not imagine that Zeno and all the wise men who argued the point failed to recognize that Achilles really did get past the tortoise. What troubled them was, where is the catch? You may have been asking the same question. The important point is that you did not ask it for the same reason which prompted them. What is worrying you is why they thought up funny little riddles of that sort. Indeed, what you are really concerned with is an *historical* problem. I am going to show you in a minute that the problem is not one which presents any *mathematical* difficulty to you. You know how to translate it into size language, because you inherit a social culture which is separated from theirs by the collapse of two great civilizations and by two great social revolutions. The difficulty of the ancients was not an historical difficulty. It was a mathematical difficulty. They had not evolved a size language into which this problem could be freely translated.

The Greeks were not accustomed to speed limits and passenger-luggage allowances. They found any problem involving division very much more difficult than a problem involving multiplication. They had no way of doing division to any order of accuracy, because they relied for calculation on the mechanical aid of the counting frame or abacus, shown in Fig. 6. They could not do sums on paper. For all these and other reasons which we shall meet again and again, the Greek mathematician was unable to see something that we see without taking the trouble to worry about whether we see it or not. If we go on piling up bigger and bigger quantities, the pile goes on growing more rapidly without any end as long as we go on adding more. If we can go on adding larger and larger quantities indefinitely without coming to a stop, it seemed to Zeno's contemporaries that we ought to be able to go on adding smaller and still smaller quantities indefinitely without reaching a limit. They thought that in one case the pile goes on for ever, growing more rapidly, and in the other it goes on for ever, growing more slowly. There was nothing in their number language to suggest that when the engine slows beyond a certain point, it chokes off.

To see this clearly we will first put down in numbers the distance which the tortoise traverses at different stages of the race after Achilles starts. As we have described it above, the tortoise moves 10 yards in stage 1, 1 yard in stage 2, one-tenth of a yard in stage 3, one-hundredth of a yard in stage 4, etc. Suppose we had a number language like the Greeks and Romans, or the Hebrews, who used letters of the alphabet. Using the one that is familiar to us because it is still used for clocks, graveyards, and law-courts, we might write the total of all the distances the tortoise ran before Achilles caught him up like this:

$$X + I + \frac{I}{X} + \frac{I}{C} + \frac{I}{M} \text{ and so on.*}$$

We have put "and so on" because the ancient peoples got into great difficulties when they had to handle numbers more than a few thousands. Apart from the fact that we have left the tail of the series to your imagination (and do not forget that the tail is most of the animal if it goes on for ever), notice another disadvantage about this script. There is absolutely nothing to suggest to you how the distances at each stage of the race are connected with one another. Today we have a number vocabulary which makes this relation perfectly evident, when we write it down as:

$$10 + 1 + \frac{1}{10} + \frac{1}{100} + \frac{1}{1{,}000} + \frac{1}{10{,}000} + \frac{1}{100{,}000} + \frac{1}{1{,}000{,}000} \text{ and so on.}$$

In this case we put "and so on" to save ourselves trouble, not because we have not the right number-words. These number-words were borrowed from the Hindus, who learnt to write number language after Zeno and Euclid had gone to their graves. A social revolution, the Protestant Reformation, gave us schools which made this number language the common property of mankind. A second social upheaval, the French Revolution, taught us to use a reformed spelling. Thanks to the Education Acts of the nineteenth century, this reformed spelling is part of the common fund of knowledge shared by almost every sane individual in the English-speaking world. Let us write the last total, using this reformed spelling, which we call decimal notation. That is to say:

$$10 + 1 + 0{\cdot}1 + 0{\cdot}01 + 0{\cdot}001 + 0{\cdot}0001 + 0{\cdot}00001 + 0{\cdot}000001 \text{ and so on.}$$

* The Romans did not actually have the convenient method of representing proper fractions used above for illustrative purposes.

We have only to use the reformed spelling to remind ourselves that this can be put in a more snappy form:

$$11\cdot 111111 \text{ etc.,}$$

or still better:

$$11\cdot\dot{1}.$$

We recognize the fraction $0\cdot\dot{1}$ as a quantity that is less than $\frac{2}{10}$ and more than $\frac{1}{10}$. If we have not forgotten the arithmetic we learned at school, we may even remember that $0\cdot\dot{1}$ corresponds with the fraction $\frac{1}{9}$. This means that, the longer we make the sum, $0\cdot 1 + 0\cdot 01 + 0\cdot 001$, etc., the nearer it gets to $\frac{1}{9}$, and it never grows bigger than $\frac{1}{9}$. The total of all the yards the tortoise moves till there is no distance between himself and Achilles makes up just $11\frac{1}{9}$ yards, and no more.

You will now begin to see what was meant by saying that the riddle presents no mathematical difficulty to you. You have a number language constructed so that it can take into account a possibility which mathematicians describe by a very impressive name. They call it the convergence of an infinite series to a limiting value. Put in plain words, this only means that, if you go on piling up smaller and smaller quantities as long as you can, you *may* get a pile of which the size is not made measurably larger by adding any more. The immense difficulty which the mathematicians of the ancient world experienced when they dealt with a process of division carried on indefinitely, or with what modern mathematicians call infinite series, limits, transcendental numbers, irrational quantities, and so forth, provides an example of a great social truth borne out by the whole history of human knowledge. Fruitful intellectual activity of the cleverest people draws its strength from the common knowledge which all of us share. Beyond a certain point clever people can never transcend the limitations of the social culture they inherit. When clever people pride themselves on their own isolation, we may well wonder whether they are very clever after all. Our studies in mathematics are going to show us that whenever the culture of a people loses contact with the common life of mankind and becomes exclusively the plaything of a leisure class, it is becoming a priestcraft. It is destined to end, as does all priestcraft, in superstition. To be proud of intellectual isolation from the common life of mankind and to be disdainful of the great social task of education is as stupid as it is wicked. It is the end of progress in knowledge. History shows that superstitions are not manufactured by the plain man. They are invented by neurotic intellectuals with too little to do. The mathematician and the plain man each need one another. Maybe the Western world is about to be plunged irrevocably into barbarism. If it escapes this fate, the men and women of the leisure state which is now within our grasp will regard the democratization of mathematics as a decisive step in the advance of civilization.

In such a time as ours the danger of retreat into barbarism is very real. We may apply to mathematics the words in which Cobbett explained the uses of grammar to the working men of his own day when there was no public system of free schools. In the first of his letters on English grammar for a working boy, Cobbett wrote these words: "But, to the acquiring of this branch of knowledge, my dear son, there is one motive, which, though it ought, at all times, to be strongly felt, ought, at the present time, to be so felt in an extraordinary degree. I mean that desire which every man, and especially every young man, should entertain to be able to assert with effect the rights and liberties of his country. When you come to read the history of those Laws of England by which the freedom of the people has been secured . . . you will find that tyranny has no enemy so formidable as the pen. And, while you will see with exultation the long-imprisoned, the heavily-fined, the banished William Prynne, returning to liberty, borne by the people from Southampton to London, over a road strewed with flowers: then accusing, bringing to trial and to the block, the tyrants from whose hands he and his country had unjustly and cruelly suffered; while your heart and the heart of every young man in the kingdom will bound with joy at the spectacle, you ought all to bear in mind, that, without a knowledge of grammar, Mr. Prynne could never have performed any of those acts by which his name has been thus preserved, and which have caused his name to be held in honour."

Today economic tyranny has no more powerful friend than the calculating prodigy. Without a knowledge of mathematics, the grammar of size and order, we cannot plan the rational society in which there will be leisure for all and poverty for none. If we are inclined to be a little afraid of the prospect, our first step towards understanding this grammar is to realize that the reasons which repel many people from studying it are not at all discreditable. As mathematics has been taught and expounded in schools no effort is made to show its social history, its significance in our own social lives, the immense dependence of civilized mankind upon it. Neither as children nor as adults are we told how the knowledge of this grammar has been used again and again throughout history to assist in the liberation of mankind from superstition. We are not shown how it may be used by us to defend the liberties of the people. Let us see why this is so.

The educational system of North-Western Europe was largely moulded by three independent factors in the period of the Reformation. One was linguistic in the ordinary sense. To weaken the power of the Church as an economic overlord it was necessary to destroy the influence of the Church on the imagination of the people. The Protestant Reformers appealed to the recognized authority of scripture to show that the priestly practices were innovations. They had to make the scriptures an open book. The invention of printing was the mechanical instrument which destroyed the intellectual power of the Pope. Instruction in Latin and Greek was a corollary of the doctrine of the open bible. This prompted the great educational innovation of John Knox and abetted the more parsimonious founding of grammar schools in England. The ideological front against popery and the wealthy monasteries strengthened its strategic position by new translations and critical inspection of the scriptural texts. That is one reason why classical scholarship occupied a place of high honour in the educational system of the middle classes.

The language of size owes its position in Western education to two different social influences. While revolt against the authority of the Church was gathering force, and before the reformed doctrine had begun to have a wide appeal for the merchants and craftsmen of the medieval boroughs, the mercantile needs of the Hansa had already led to the founding of special schools in Germany for the teaching of the new arithmetic which Europe had borrowed from the Arabs. An astonishing proportion of the books printed in the three years after the first press was set up were commercial arithmetics. Luther vindicated the four merchant gospels of addition, subtraction, multiplication, and division with astute political sagacity when he announced the outlandish doctrine that every boy should be taught to calculate. The grammar of numbers was chained down to commercial uses before people could foresee the vast variety of ways in which it was about to invade man's social life.

Geometry, already divorced from the art of calculation, did not enter into Western education by the same route. Apart from the stimulus which the study of dead languages received from the manufacture of bibles, classical pursuits were encouraged because the political theories of the Greek philosophers were congenial to the merchants who were aspiring to a limited urban democracy. The appeal of the city-state democracy to the imagination of the wealthier bourgeois lasted till after the French Revolution, when it was laid to rest in the familiar funeral urns of mural decoration. The leisure class of the Greek city-states played with geometry as people play with crossword puzzles and chess today. Plato taught that geometry was the highest exercise to which human leisure could be devoted. So geometry became included in European education as a part of classical scholarship, without any clear connection with the contemporary reality of measuring Drake's "world encompassed." Those who taught Euclid did not understand its social use, and generations of schoolboys have studied Euclid without being told how a later geometry, which grew out of Euclid's teaching in the busy life of Alexandria, made it possible to measure the size of the world. Those measurements blew up the pagan Pantheon of star-gods and blazed the trail for the great navigations. The revelation of how much of the surface of our world was still unexplored was the solid ground for what we call the faith of Columbus.

Plato's exaltation of mathematics as an august and mysterious ritual had its roots in dark superstitions which troubled, and fanciful puerilities which entranced, people who were living through the childhood of civilization, when even the cleverest people could not clearly distinguish the difference between saying that 13 is a "prime" number and saying that 13 is an unlucky number. His influence on education has spread a veil of mystery over mathematics and helped to preserve the queer freemasonry of the Pythagorean brotherhoods, whose members were put to death for revealing mathematical secrets now printed in school books. It reflects no discredit on anybody if this veil of mystery makes the subject distasteful. Plato's great achievement was to invent a religion which satisfies the emotional needs of people who are out of harmony with their social environment, and just too intelligent or too individualistic to seek sanctuary in the cruder forms of animism. The curiosity of the men who first speculated about atoms, studied the properties of the lodestone, watched the result of rubbing amber, dissected animals, and catalogued plants in the three centuries before Aristotle wrote his epitaph on Greek science, had banished personalities from natural and familiar objects. Plato placed animism beyond the reach of experimental exposure by inventing a world of "universals." This world of universals was the world as God knows it, the "real" world of which our own is but the shadow. In this "real" world symbols of speech and number are invested with the magic which departed from the bodies of beasts and the trunks of trees as soon as they were dissected and described.

The *Timaeus* is a fascinating anthology of the queer perversities to which this magic of symbolism could be pushed. Real earth, as opposed to the solid earth on which we build houses, is an equilateral

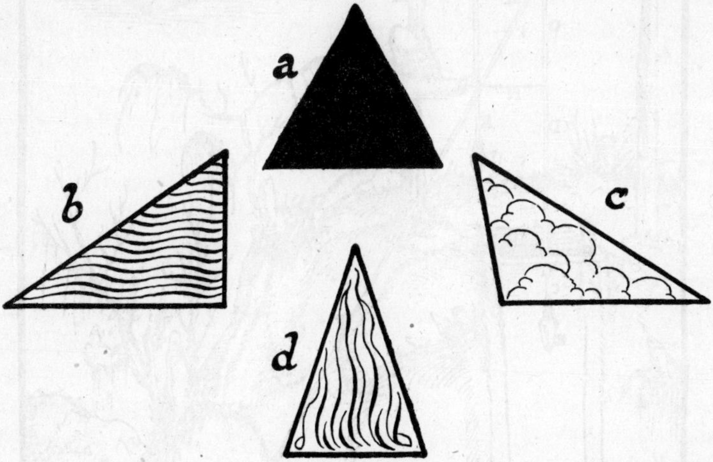

FIG. 1.—PLATO TOOK MEASUREMENT OUT OF GEOMETRY AND PUT MAGIC IN ITS PLACE

The real world of Plato was a world of form from which matter was banished.

(*a*) An equilateral triangle (i.e. one of which all three sides are equal) is the elemental earth form.
(*b*) A right-angled triangle is the spirit of water. (To find spirit in water is the most advanced kind of magic.)
(*c*) A scalene triangle with no equal sides is the spirit of the air.
(*d*) An isosceles triangle (i.e. one of which only two sides are equal) is the elemental fire.

(If you do not know these names, note their meaning. You may meet them again. You have been warned.)

triangle. Real water, as opposed to what is sometimes regarded as a beverage, is a right-angled triangle. Real fire, as opposed to fire against which you insure, is an isosceles triangle. Real air, as opposed to the air which you pump into a tyre, is a scalene triangle (Fig. 1). Lest you should find this hard to credit, read how Plato turned the geometry of the sphere into a magical explanation of man's origin. God, he tells us, "imitating the spherical shape of the universe, enclosed the two divine courses in a spherical body, that, namely, which we now term the head." In order that the head "might not tumble

FIG. 1A.—MATHEMATICS IN EVERYDAY LIFE

This figure is taken from Agricola's famous sixteenth-century treatise on mining technology. At that time the miners were the aristocrats of labour, and the book called attention to a host of new scientific problems which had been neglected in the slave civilizations of antiquity, when there was little co-operation between theoretical specu-

about among the deep and high places of the earth, but might be able to get out of the one and over the other," it was provided with "the body to be a vehicle and means of locomotion, which consequently had length and was furnished with four limbs extended and jointed. . . ." This supremacy of the head is very flattering to intellectuals who have no practical problems to occupy them. So it is not surprising that Plato's peculiar metaphysics retained its influence on education after his daring project for a planned society ceased to be thought a suitable doctrine for young people to study. An educational system which was based on Plato's teaching is apt to entrust the teaching of mathematics to people who put the head before the stomach, and who would tumble about the deep and high places of the earth if they had to teach another subject. Naturally this repels healthy people for whom symbols are merely the tools of organized social experience, and attracts those who use symbols to escape from our shadow world in which men battle for the little truth they can secure into a "real" world in which truth seems to be self-evident.

The fact that mathematicians are often like this may be why they are so inclined to keep the high mysteries of their Pythagorean brotherhood to themselves. To ordinary people, the perfection of their "real" world savours of unreality. The world in which ordinary people live is a world of struggle and failure, trial and error. In the mathematical world everything is obvious—once you have got used to it. What is rarely explained to us is that it may have taken the human race a thousand years to see that one step in a mathematical argument is "obvious." How the nilometer works is obvious to you if you are a priest in the temple. If you are outside the temple, it can only become obvious through tracing out the subterranean channel which connects the temple with the river of man's social experience. Educational

---

Caption continued]

lation and practical experience. Having measured the distance HG which is the length of the stretched rope, you can get the distance you have to bore horizontally to reach the shaft, or the depth to which the shaft must be sunk, if you want to reach the horizontal boring. You will see easily with a scale diagram that the ratio of the horizontal cutting to the measured distance HG is the ratio of the two measurable distances N:M. Likewise the ratio of the shaft depth to HG is O:M. When you have done Dem. 7 it will be easier to see. The line N was made with a cord set horizontally by a spirit level. So it is at right angles to either of the two plumb lines. When you have read Chapter VI you will see that the extra plumb line and the spirit level are not necessary, if you have a protractor to measure the angle at the top, and a table of sine and cosine ratios of angles.

methods which are mixed up with priestcraft and magic have contrived to keep the rising and falling, the perpetual movement of the river from our scrutiny. So they have hidden from us the romance of what might be the greatest saga of man's struggle with the elements. Plato, in whose school our teachers have grown up, did not approve of making observations and applying mathematics to arrange them and co-ordinate them. In one of the dialogues he makes Socrates, his master, use words which might equally well apply to many of the text-books of mechanics which are still used. "The starry heavens which we behold is wrought upon a visible ground and therefore, although the fairest and most perfect of visible things, must necessarily be deemed inferior far to the true motions of absolute swiftness and absolute intelligence. . . . These are to be apprehended by reason and intelligence but not by sight. . . . The spangled heavens should be used as a pattern and with a view to that higher knowledge. But the astronomer will never imagine that the proportions of night to day . . . or of the stars to these and to one another can also be eternal . . . and it is equally *absurd to take so much pains in investigating their exact truth. . . . In astronomy as in geometry we should employ problems, and let the heavens alone*, if we would approach the subject in the right way and so make the natural gift of reason to be of any use."

This book will narrate how the grammar of measurement and counting has evolved under the pressure of man's changing social achievements, how in successive stages it has been held in check by the barriers of custom, how it has been used in charting a universe which can be commanded when its laws are obeyed, but can never be propitiated by ceremonial and sacrifice. As the outline of the story develops, one difficulty which many people experience will become less formidable. The expert in mathematics is essentially a technician. So his chief concern in teaching is to make other technicians. Mathematical books are largely packed with exercises which are designed to give proficiency in workmanship. This makes us discouraged because of the immense territory which we have to traverse before we can get insight into the kind of mathematics which is used in modern science and social statistics. The fact is that modern mathematics does not borrow so very much from antiquity. To be sure, every useful development in mathematics rests on the historical foundation of some earlier branch. At the same time every new branch liquidates the usefulness of clumsier tools which preceded it. Although algebra, trigonometry, the use of graphs, the calculus all depend on the rules of Greek geometry, scarcely more than a dozen from the two hundred propositions of Euclid's elements are essential to help us in understanding how to use them. The remainder are complicated ways of doing things which can be done more simply when we know later branches of mathematics. For the mathematical technician these complications may provide a useful discipline. The person who wants to understand the place of mathematics in modern civilization is merely distracted and disheartened by them. What follows is for those who have been already disheartened and distracted, and have consequently forgotten what they may have learned already or fail to see the meaning or usefulness of what they remember. So we shall begin at the very beginning.

Two views are commonly held about mathematics. One comes from Plato. This is that mathematical statements represent eternal truths. Plato's doctrine was used by the German philosopher, Kant, as a stick with which to beat the materialists of his time, when revolutionary writings like those of Diderot were challenging priestcraft. Kant thought that the principles of geometry were eternal, and that they were totally independent of our sense organs. It happened that Kant wrote just before biologists discovered that we have a sense organ, part of what is called the internal ear, sensitive to the pull of gravitation. Since that discovery, the significance of which was first fully recognized by the German physicist, Ernst Mach, the geometry which Kant knew has been brought down to earth by Einstein. It no longer dwells in the sky where Plato put it. We know that geometrical statements when applied to the real world are only approximate truths. The theory of Relativity has been very unsettling to mathematicians, and it has now become a fashion to say that mathematics is only a game. Of course, this does not tell us anything about mathematics. It only tells us something about the cultural limitations of some mathematicians. When a man says that mathematics is a game, he is making a private statement. He is telling us something about himself, his own attitude to mathematics. He is not telling us anything about the public meaning of a mathematical statement.

If mathematics is a game, there is no reason why people should play it if they do not want to. With football, it belongs to those amusements without which life would be endurable. The view which we shall explore is that mathematics is the language of size, and that it is an essential part of the equipment of an intelligent citizen to understand this language. If the rules of mathematics are rules of grammar, there is no stupidity involved when we fail to see that a mathematical truth is obvious. The rules of ordinary grammar are not obvious. They have to be learned. They are not eternal truths. They are conveniences without whose aid truths about the sorts of things in the world cannot be communicated from one person to another. In Cobbett's memorable words, Mr. Prynne would not have been able to impeach Archbishop Laud if his command of grammar had been insufficient to make himself understood. So it is with mathematics, the grammar of size. The rules of mathematics are rules to be learned. If they are formidable, they are formidable because they are unfamiliar when you first meet them—like gerunds or nominative absolutes. They are also formidable because in all languages there are so many rules and words to memorize before we can read newspapers or pick up radio news from foreign stations. Everybody knows that being able to chatter in several foreign languages is not a sign of great social intelligence. Neither is being able to chatter in the language of size. Real social intelligence lies in the use of a language, in applying the right words in the right context. It is important to know the language of size, because entrusting the laws of human society, social statistics, population, man's hereditary make-up, the balance of trade, to the isolated mathematician without checking his conclusions is like letting a committee of philologists manufacture the truths of human, animal, or plant anatomy from the resources of their own imaginations.

You will often hear people say that nothing is more certain than that two and two make four. The statement that two and two make four is not a mathematical statement. The mathematical statement to which people refer, correctly stated, is as follows:

$$2 + 2 = 4.$$

This can be translated: "to 2 add 2 to get 4." This is not necessarily a statement of something which always happens in the real world. The illustration (Fig. 2) shows that in the real world you do not always find that you have 4 when you have added 2 to 2. To say $2 + 2 = 4$ merely illustrates the meaning of the verb "add," when it is used to translate the mathematical verb "+". To say that $2 + 2 = 4$ is a true statement is just a grammatical convention about the verb "+" and the nouns "2" and "4." In English grammar it is true in the same sense to say that the plural of "mouse" is "mice," or, if you prefer it, "add mouse to mouse to get mice." In English grammar it is untrue to say that the plural of "house" is "hice." Saying "2 + 2 = 2" is false in precisely the same sense. A slight change in the meaning of the word "add," as used to translate "+", makes it a perfectly correct statement about the apparatus in Fig. 2. Such changes of meaning

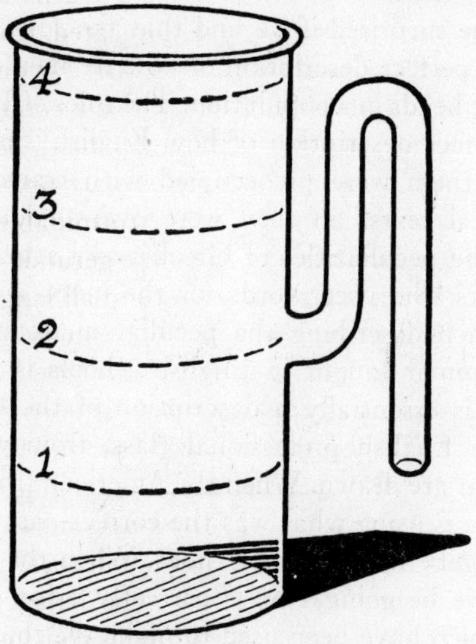

FIG. 2

In the real world you do not always find that you have got FOUR, when you add TWO and TWO.

Try filling this with water. Its laws of "addition" would be:

1 +. 1 = 2
1 +. 2 = 3
1 +. 3 = 2
2 +. 2 = 2 etc.

The dot is put in to show that the kind of addition used here is not the kind of addition (+ without a dot) which applies to a vessel which cannot leak, and is so large that it cannot be filled.

are confusing. The object of grammar is to control the freedom of words so that there is no congestion of the intellectual traffic. As a statement about the real world, saying that the British Houses of Parliament are in Glasgow, is a plain lie. As a statement of grammar, it is a true example of how the plural of "house" is formed. If a British Radical member said that the Hice of Parliament were treating the unemployed of Glasgow with shameless frivolity, he might convey a profound and important truth about the real world to a few bright people. As a statement of grammar, it would be false. Many would miss the point and wonder whether he were certifiable. Unlike Mr. Prynne, who understood grammar, he would fail to advance the liberties of the people.

We must not be surprised if we find that the rules of mathematics are not always a perfect description of how we measure the distance of a star, or count heads in a population. The rules of English grammar are a very imperfect description of how English is used. The people who formulated them were preoccupied with translating the bible and other classical texts. So they were over-anxious to find exact equivalents for the peculiarities of Greek and Latin. They were like the first zoologists who used words for the limbs and organs of the human body, when describing the peculiar anatomy of the insect. The English grammar taught in English schools is rather primitive zoology. Also it is essentially a description of the habits of speech prevailing in the English professional class, from which writers of books on grammar are drawn. When the American from New England says "gotten," he is using what was the correct past participle of the strong verb "to get" in *Mayflower* times. When the English country labourer says "we be going," he is correctly using one of the three original verbs which have been used to make the roots of the modern mixed verb "to be." When he says "yourn," he is using one of two once equally admissible and equally fashionable forms introduced by analogy about the time when Chaucer wrote the *Canterbury Tales*. To say that "are" and "yours" are grammatically correct is merely to say that we have agreed to adopt the habits of the more prosperous townspeople. When Mr. Shaw is dead, and hence a topic for grammarians, we shall say that "dont" is the correct way to write "do not." Almost certainly we shall soon admit "it is me" as correct grammar. The rules of mathematical grammar also change. In modern vector analysis the rules for using "+" are not the rules we learned at school.

If we can unearth milestones of man's social pilgrimage in the language of everyday life, it is much more easy to do so when we study the grammar of mathematics. The language in which people describe the different *sorts* of things there are in the world is vastly more primitive and more conservative than the *size* languages which have been multiplied to cope with the increasing precision of man's control over nature. In the world which is open to public inspection, the world of inorganic and organic nature, man was not compelled to enlarge the scope of language to describe any new *sorts* of phenomena between 2000 B.C. and the researches of Faraday and Hertz, the father of radio. Even electric and magnetic attractions were recognized as a special sort of thing before there were any historians in the world. In the seventh century B.C. Thales recorded the attraction of small particles to a piece of amber (Greek "electron") when rubbed. The Chinese already knew about the lodestone or natural magnet. Since about 1000 B.C., when some men broke away from picture writing or script like the Chinese which associates sounds with picture symbols, and first began to use an alphabet based purely on how words sound, there has only been one conspicuous invention introduced for describing the qualities of things in the world. This was made by biologists in the eighteenth century, when the confusion existing in the old herbals of medicinal plants forced them to invent an international language in which no confusion is possible. The clear description of the immense variety of organic beings has been made possible by the deliberate introduction of unfamiliar words. These words, like "Bellis perennis," the common daisy, or "Pulex irritans," the common flea, are taken from dead languages. Any meaning for which the biologist has no use lies buried in a social context forgotten long ago. In much the same way the North Europeans had borrowed their alphabet of sound symbols from the picture scripts, and buried the associations of distracting metaphors in the symbols used by the more sophisticated people of the ancient world.

The language of mathematics differs from that of everyday life, because it is essentially a rationally planned language. The languages of size have no place for private sentiment, either of the individual or of the nation. They are international languages like the binomial nomenclature of natural history. In dealing with the immense complexity of his social life man has not yet begun to apply inventiveness to the rational planning of ordinary language when describing different kinds of institutions and human behaviour. The language of everyday life is clogged with sentiment, and the science of human nature has not advanced so far that we can describe individual sentiment in a clear way. So constructive thought about human society is hampered by the same conservatism as embarrassed the earlier naturalists. Nowadays people do not differ about what sort of animal is meant by Cimex or Pediculus, because these words are only used by people who use them in one way. They still can and often do mean a lot of different things when they say that a mattress is infested with bugs or lice. The study of man's social life has not yet brought forth a Linnaeus. So an argument about the "withering away of the State" may disclose a difference about the use of the dictionary when no real difference about the use of the policeman is involved. Curiously enough, people who are most sensible about the need for planning other social amenities in a reasonable way are often slow to see the need for creating a rational and international language.

The technique of measurement and counting has followed the caravans and galleys of the great trade routes. It has developed very slowly. At least four thousand years intervened between the time when men could calculate when the next eclipse would occur and the time when men could calculate how much iron is present in the sun. Between the first recorded observations of electricity produced by friction and the measurement of the attraction of an electrified body two thousand years intervened. Perhaps a longer period separates the knowledge of magnetic iron (or lodestone) and the measurement of magnetic force. Classifying things according to size has been a much harder task than recognizing the different sorts of things there are. It has been more closely related to man's social achievements than to his biological equipment. Our eyes and ears can recognize different sorts of things at a great distance. To measure things at a distance, man has had to make new sense organs for himself, like the astrolabe, the telescope, and the microphone. He has made scales which reveal differences of weight to which our hands are quite insensitive. At each stage in the evolution of the tools of measurement man has refined the tools of size language. As human inventiveness has turned from the counting of flocks and seasons to the building of temples, from the building of temples to the steering of ships into chartless seas, from seafaring plunder to machines driven by the forces of dead matter, new languages of size have sprung up in succession. Civilizations have risen and fallen. At each stage a more primitive, less sophisticated culture breaks through the barriers of custom thought, brings fresh rules to the grammar of measurement, bearing within itself the limitation of further growth and the inevitability that it will be superseded in its turn. The history of mathematics is the mirror of civilization.

The beginnings of a size language are to be found in the priestly civilizations of Egypt and Sumeria. From these ancient civilizations we see the first-fruits of secular knowledge radiated along the inland trade routes to China and pushing out into and beyond the Mediterranean, where the Semitic peoples are sending forth ships to trade in tin and dyes. The more primitive northern invaders of Greece and Asia Minor collect and absorb the secrets of the pyramid makers in cities where a priestly caste is not yet established. As the Greeks become prosperous, geometry becomes a plaything. Greek thought itself becomes corrupted with the star worship of the ancient world. At the very point when it seems almost inevitable that geometry will make way for a new language, it ceases to develop further. The scene shifts to Alexandria, the greatest centre of shipping and the mechanical arts in the ancient world. Men are thinking about how much of the world remains to be explored. Geometry is applied to the measurement of the heavens. Trigonometry takes its place. The size of the earth, the distance of the sun and moon are measured. The star gods are degraded. In the intellectual life of Alexandria, the factory of world religions, the old syncretism has lost its credibility. It may still welcome a god beyond the sky. It is losing faith in the gods within the sky.

In Alexandria, where the new language of star measurement has its beginnings, men are thinking about numbers unimaginably large compared with the numbers which the Greek intellect could grasp. Anaxagoras had shocked the court of Pericles by declaring that the sun was as immense as the mainland of Greece. Now Greece itself had sunk into insignificance beside the world of which Eratosthenes and Poseidonius had measured the circumference. The world itself sank into insignificance beside the sun as Aristarchus had measured it. Ere the dark night of monkish superstition engulfed the great cosmopolis of antiquity, men were groping for new means of calculation. The bars of the counting frame had become the bars of a cage in which the intellectual life of Alexandria was imprisoned. Men like Diophantus and Theon were using geometrical diagrams to devise crude recipes for calculation. They had almost invented the third new language of algebra. That they did not succeed was the nemesis of the social culture they inherited. In the East the Hindus had started from a much lower level. Without the incubus of an old-established vocabulary of number, they had fashioned new symbols which lent themselves to simple calculation without mechanical aids. The Moslem civilization which swept across the southern domain of the Roman Empire brought together the technique of measurement, as it had evolved in the hands of the Greeks and the Alexandrians, adding the new instrument for handling numbers which was developed through the invention of the Hindu number symbols. In the hands of Arabic mathematicians like Omar Khayyám, the main features of a language of calculation took shape. We still call it by the Arabic name, algebra. We owe algebra and the pattern of modern European poetry to a non-Aryan people who would be excluded from the vote in the Union of South Africa.

Along the trade routes this new arithmetic is brought into Europe by Jewish scholars from the Moorish universities of Spain and by Gentile merchants trading with the Levant, some of them patronized by nobles whose outlook had been unintentionally broadened by the Crusades. Europe stands on the threshold of the great navigations. Seafarers are carrying Jewish astronomers who can use the star almanacs which Arab scholarship had prepared. The merchants are becoming rich. More than ever the world is thinking in large numbers. The new arithmetic or "algorithm" sponsors an amazing device which was prompted by the need for more accurate tables of star measurement for use in seafaring. Logarithms were among the cultural first-fruits of the great navigations. Mathematicians are thinking in maps, in latitude and longitude. A new kind of geometry (what we call graphs in everyday speech) was an inevitable consequence. This new geometry of Descartes contains something which Greek geometry had left out. In the leisurely world of antiquity there were no clocks. In the bustling world of the great navigations mechanical clocks are displacing the ancient ceremonial function of the priesthood as timekeepers. A geometry which could represent time and a religion in which there were no saints' days are emerging from the same social context. From this geometry of time a group of men who were studying the mechanics of the pendulum clock and making fresh discoveries about the motion of the planets devise a new size language to measure motion. Today we call it "the" calculus.

For the present this crude outline of the history of mathematics as a mirror of civilization, interlocking with man's common culture, his inventions, his economic arrangements, his religious beliefs, may be left at the stage which had been reached when Newton died. What has happened since has been largely the filling of gaps, the sharpening of instruments already devised. Here and there are indications of a new sort of mathematics. We see a hint of it in social statistics and the study of the atom. We begin to see possibilities of new languages of size transcending those we now use, as the calculus of movement gathered into itself all that had gone before.

INSTRUCTIONS FOR READERS OF THIS BOOK

The customary way of writing a book about mathematics is to show how each step follows logically from the one before without telling you what use there will be in taking it. This book is written to show you how each step follows historically from the step before, and what use it will be to you or someone else if it is taken. The first method repels many people who are intelligent and socially alive, because intelligent people are suspicious of mere logic, and people who are socially alive regard the human brain as an instrument for social activity.

Although the greatest care has been taken to see that all the logical, or, as we ought to say, the grammatical, rules are put in a continuous sequence, you must not expect that you will necessarily follow every step in the argument the first time you read it. An eminent Scottish mathematician gave a very sound piece of advice for lack of which many people have been discouraged unnecessarily. "Every mathematical book that is worth anything," said Chrystal, "must be read backwards and forwards . . . the advice of a French mathematician, *allez en avant et la foi vous viendra.*"

So there are two INDISPENSABLE CAUTIONS which you must bear in mind, if you want to enjoy reading this book.

The FIRST IS READ THE WHOLE BOOK THROUGH ONCE QUICKLY TO GET A BIRD'S-EYE VIEW OF THE SOCIAL INTERCONNECTIONS OF MATHEMATICS, and when you start reading it for the second time to get down to brass tacks, read each chapter through before you start working on the detailed contents.

The SECOND IS ALWAYS HAVE PEN AND PAPER, PREFERABLY SQUARED PAPER, in hand, also PENCIL AND RUBBER, when you read the text for serious study, and WORK OUT ALL THE NUMERICAL EXAMPLES AND FIGURES as you read. Almost any stationer will provide you with an exercise book of squared paper for a very small sum. WHAT YOU GET OUT OF THE BOOK DEPENDS ON YOUR CO-OPERATION IN THE SOCIAL BUSINESS OF LEARNING.

CHAPTER II

First Steps in Measurement

OR

MATHEMATICS IN PREHISTORY

SOME people will tell you that mathematics did not begin until there was a class with leisure to play with figures and numbers. Later on we shall find abundant evidence for the view that mathematics has advanced when there has been real work for the mathematician to do, and that it has stagnated whenever it has become the plaything of a class which is isolated from the common life of mankind. Whether this is true or false, it is a fact that mathematical brainwork, like other kinds of brainwork, depends on our biological and cultural inheritance, our social and physical environment. The Greeks, who were the foremost mathematical writers of antiquity, lived in a world in which they saw people measuring the angles between the stars, building temples with the aid of diagrams traced on the sand, reckoning heights by the length of shadows, designing figures on clay, and making tiles. The men who first wrote books on mathematics lived in a world in which the priestly architecture of the Pyramids, magical games with numbers, Cyprian vases ornamented with geometrical patterns, walls and floors covered with mosaic tiles, were familiar objects. There were merchants counting out coins. There were tax-gatherers exacting tribute by measure. There were craftsmen slaves building with set-square, plumb-line, and water level. There were mariners taking their bearings from the Pole star. At best leisure can only provide men with the opportunity to reflect upon a world whose features are being transformed by those who lack leisure.

In fact, it is quite wrong to imagine that mathematics was invented by leisurely and idealistic Athenians out of sheer fascination with its utter uselessness. The Babylonians and Egyptians were able to obtain results which represent no mean order of performance. In the art of calculation Babylonian technique was far superior to that of the Attic Greeks. The great antiquity of such achievements and the close association of primitive scripts with the social activity of timekeeping suggest that we must retrace our footsteps a long way beyond the Nippur tablets and the Great Pyramid of Cheops, if we wish to understand the social origins of mathematical studies. By the time when people first began to write books on mathematics, mankind had found ways and means of answering several sorts of questions to which the answer is a number. We shall be able to see how the need for mathematics took shape when we have examined some of these questions.

1. HOW MANY INDIVIDUALS MAKE UP A GROUP?

The extinct Tasmanian aborigines, who had scarcely passed beyond the Palaeolithic level in cultural evolution, did not count beyond four. We may assume that the need for counting large numbers of things was not felt until men began to keep herds and flocks. The shepherd and the herdsman must count the numbers of their sheep and cows to see that none is missing, and long before men began to dwell in cities they had hit on the device of counting them in groups. In our number system we group objects for enumeration in tens, tens of tens (hundreds), or tens of tens of tens (thousands). This is what is meant when we say that *ten* is the *base* or group number of our system.

Some multiple of five (five, ten, or twenty) recurs as the base or fundamental way of grouping numbers in nearly all systems of numerals throughout the world. This is due to the fact that primitive man, like a child, uses his fingers as a tally to check off the things he counts. In the New World he sometimes uses his toes. A tribe of Paraguayan aborigines have names corresponding to the numbers one to four, five (one hand), ten (two hands), fifteen (two hands and a foot), twenty (both hands and feet). The ancient Maya calendar numerals (Fig. 106, Chapter 7) included separate signs for the units one to four, for five, for twenty, and for four hundred (twenty twenties).* There are traces of this hand and foot counting in our own language as seen in the frequent use of the "score" in the Old Testament. An even earlier way of grouping numbers in twos and fours (two hands and feet) is seen in the base *two* of the Syriac numerals (Fig. 3). In English we distinguish between once, twice and three times, four times, etc., or eleven, twelve and thirteen, fourteen, etc.

2. HOW LONG AGO WAS IT?

We cannot say whether the use of numbers for counting objects like sheep or cows actually preceded another use which man found for numbers as soon as he passed beyond the hunting and food-gathering stage. When he learned to sow grain and keep beasts which bear at certain periods of the year, he had to take stock of the seasons.

* The same symbol was used sometimes for 360 and sometimes for 400 (see p. 335).

He noticed that the moon rises a little later and sets a little later each night between one full moon and the next, and began to group days in moons or months of thirty days. He also recognized, as do nearly all primitive peoples, that the constellations of the night sky change with the seasons, rising a little earlier and setting a little earlier every

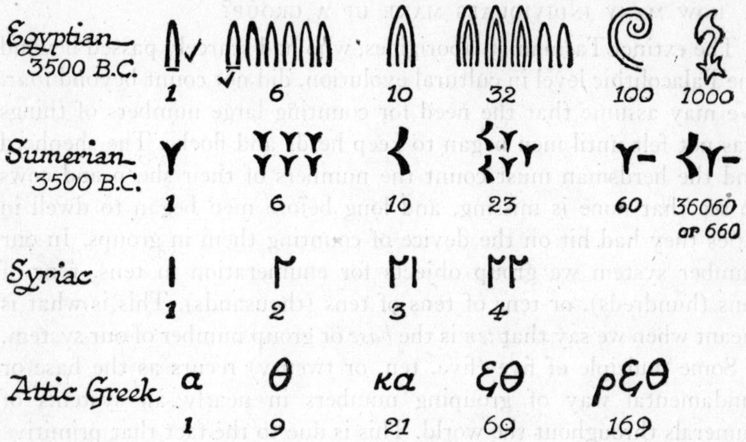

FIG. 3.—ANCIENT NUMBER SCRIPTS

These will be referred to again in later chapters. As stated at the end of this one, the zero bar was rarely used at the end of the number series in the sexagesimal Babylonian script. When put in as shown here the number 60 is 1(60) + 0(1). The number 36060 is $10(60^2) + 1(60) + 0(1)$. The number 660, which is 11(60) + 0(1), would be written in the same way. A gap between the symbols or the context told you which was intended.

night. Nearly all living peoples can keep track of the seasons by recognizing which constellations are first seen to rise immediately after sunset, and are able to reckon the number of moons which intervene between one dry or wet season and another. The Egyptians had already fixed the length of the year as 365 days before 4000 B.C. by counting the days which intervened between two successive occasions when the dog star, Sirius, was just visible at its rising immediately before sunrise.

The grouping of days to make a year was also recognized by the behaviour of the sun's shadow. The sun's shadow always pointed in one direction at midday when it was shortest. The noon shadow divided the horizon by a line, the meridian, going from what we call north to south. At different seasons the sun rose and set far towards the north or south of the horizon, when the noon shadow was respectively shortest and longest. The day of the shortest noon shadow (June 21st in our calendar) was the summer solstice. A year was also recog-

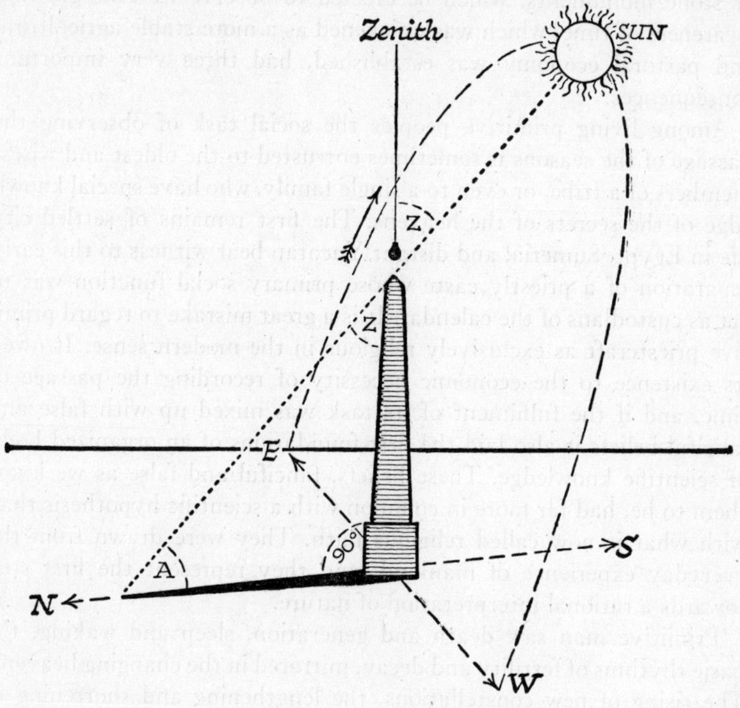

FIG. 4

Noon on the equinoxes (March 21st and September 23rd), when the sun rises due east and sets due west. The sun's shadow at noon always lies along the line which joins the north and south points of the horizon. This is also the observer's meridian of longitude which joins the north and south poles.

The zenith is the name which astronomers give to the spot in the heavens directly overhead.

Note that the angle (A) of the sun above the horizon (called the sun's "altitude") and the angle (Z) which the sunbeam makes with the plumb line or vertical (called the sun's *zenith distance*) make up a right angle or 90°, so that $A = 90° - Z$ and $Z = 90° - A$.

nized as the number of days between one summer solstice and the next. The days of the vernal and autumnal equinoxes, when the sun rises and sets exactly half-way between the north and south points on the horizon (i.e. due east and due west), were the occasions of special rites. Side by side with the observation of the sun's shadow throughout the seasons, Neolithic man was also learning to keep track of his meals and hours of labour by the length of the sun's shadow cast by poles or stone monuments, which he erected to observe it. This growing awareness of time, which was quickened as a more stable agricultural and pastoral economy was established, had three very important consequences.

Among living primitive peoples the social task of observing the passage of the seasons is sometimes entrusted to the oldest and wisest members of a tribe, or even to a single family, who have special knowledge of the secrets of the heavens. The first remains of settled city life in Egypt, Sumeria, and distant Yucatan bear witness to this early separation of a priestly caste whose primary social function was to act as custodians of the calendar. It is a great mistake to regard primitive priestcraft as exclusively religious in the modern sense. It owed its existence to the economic necessity of recording the passage of time, and if the fulfilment of its task was mixed up with false and fanciful beliefs it also laid the first foundations of an organized body of scientific knowledge. These beliefs, fanciful and false as we know them to be, had far more in common with a scientific hypothesis than with what is now called religious faith. They were drawn from the everyday experience of mankind, and they represent the first step towards a rational interpretation of nature.

Primitive man saw death and generation, sleep and waking, the basic rhythms of fertility and decay, mirrored in the changing heavens. The rising of new constellations, the lengthening and shortening of the sun's shadow announced the time of lambing, seed-sowing, and the drying cornstalk. The recurring phases of the moon coincided with the rhythm of woman's fertile life. Sundown and sunrise were the signals of sleep and the physical tension of awakening. Nowadays, we are beginning to understand how these cycles of natural events become stimuli for rhythmical changes regulated by nervous impulses in our own bodies. We know that light brings into action the pituitary gland which controls the reproductive cycle, and the Soviet Union is applying such knowledge extensively to increase egg production by keeping fowls in continuous electric light. Pastoral man did not as yet realize that light can do without the hen, though the hen cannot do without the light. He was not yet able to understand that this great crude clock for seed-scattering and tending his beasts was not a great chief, an old man of the tribe, who could be enticed or kept off by

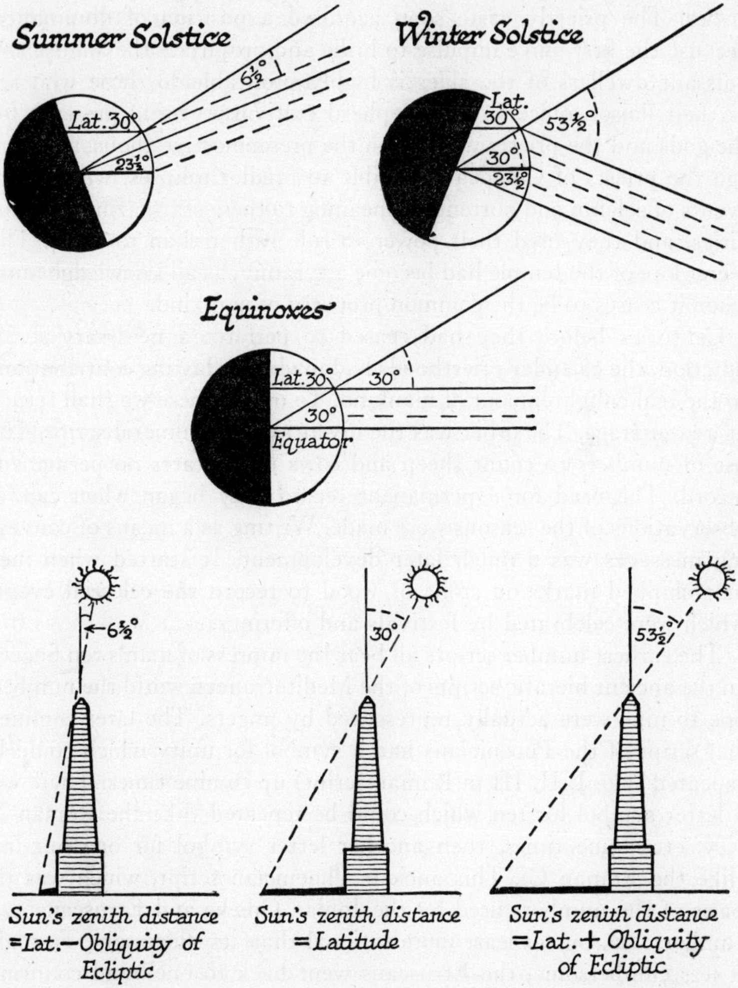

FIG. 5.—EGYPTIAN MEASUREMENT OF THE OBLIQUITY OF THE ECLIPTIC FROM THE SUN'S NOON SHADOW

At noon the sun is highest. The Pole, the earth's centre, the observer, and the sun are all in the same plane (or flat surface). On the equinoxes (March 21st and September 23rd) the sun's zenith distance at noon is the observer's latitude, (30° at Memphis). If the obliquity of the ecliptic is E,

L + E = sun's zenith distance on winter solstice (December 21st).

L − E = sun's zenith distance on summer solstice (June 21st).

So the obliquity of the ecliptic is

½ (sun's z.d. on December 21st − sun's z.d. on June 21st).

This will be explained more fully on p. 356.

bribes. The priestly caste soon acquired a position of dominance, because the first naïve impulse to bribe and propitiate the august and puissant dwellers of the skies is highly profitable to those who act as their liaison officers. The shepherd cultivators bring presents for the gods and the priests wax fat on the presents. Five thousand years ago the priests of Chaldea were able to predict eclipses, which were events of solemn and portentous meaning to these star-gazing communities, and they used their power to rule rather than to serve. The secret lore of the temple had become a tyranny, as all knowledge must when it ceases to be the common property of mankind.

Centuries before they had ceased to perform a necessary social function, the calendar priesthoods had made two lasting contributions to the real enlightenment of mankind. To one of these we shall return at a later stage. The other was the invention of a numeral script. The use of numbers to count sheep and cows necessitates no permanent record. The need for a permanent record only began when careful observations of the seasons were made. Writing as a means of conveying messages was a much later development. It started when men first chipped marks on stone or wood to record the celestial events which were celebrated by festivals and offerings.

The earliest number scripts all bear the impress of man's ten fingers. In the ancient hieratic scripts of the Mediterranean world the numbers one to nine were actually represented by fingers. The later commercial script of the Phoenicians had a symbol for unity which could be repeated (like I, II, III in Roman script) up to nine times. There was a letter symbol for ten which could be repeated (like the Roman X, XX, etc.) nine times, then another letter symbol for one hundred (like the Roman C). This ancient Phoenician script, which was the basis of the numbers used by the Ionian Greeks and Etruscans, was cumbersome, but at least more rational than its successors. To make it less cumbersome, the Etruscans went back to one-hand counting, and added the symbols which in Roman numeration represent 5, 50, 500 (V, L, D). The later Greeks rejected the Ionian script, adopting and bequeathing to the Alexandrians a number system which exhausted all the letters of the alphabet, like the Hebrew numeral system. While this was compact, it had two consequences which proved to be disastrous. One, which we shall study in Chapter 5, was that it encouraged the peculiar kind of number magic called "gematria." The other, which is of greater importance, will be studied in Chapter 7. The introduction of a literal system for numbers made it impossible

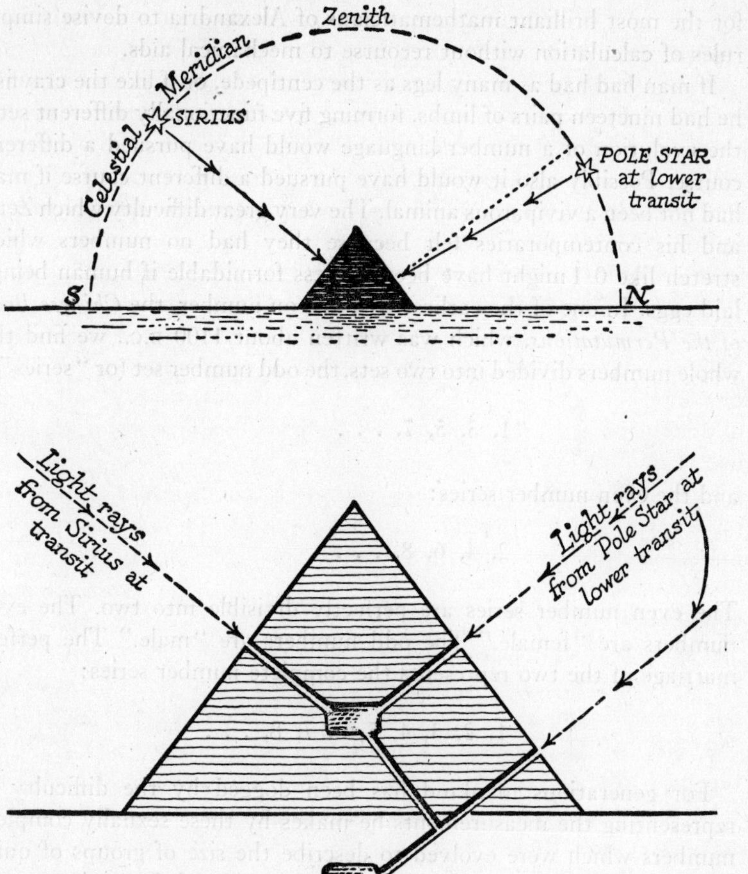

FIG. 5A.—THE ASTRONOMICAL ORIENTATION OF THE GREAT PYRAMID

The Pyramid of Cheops and that of Sneferu are constructed on a common geometrical plan. The perimeter of the four sides, which face exactly the north, south, east, and west, has the same ratio to the height as the ratio of the circumference to the radius of a circle, i.e. $2 \times 3\frac{1}{7}$, or 2π. According to Flinders Petrie: "The squareness and level of the base is brilliantly true, the average error being less than a ten-thousandth of the side in equality, squareness and level." At its transit across the meridian, the rays of Sirius, the dog star, whose heliacal rising announced the beginning of the Egyptian year and the flooding of the sacred river which brought prosperity to the cultivators, were at right angles to the south face of the Great Pyramid, and shone straight down the ventilating shaft into the royal chamber, illuminating the head of the dead Pharaoh. The main opening and a second shaft leading to the lower chamber conveyed the light of the Pole star, which was then the star *a* in the constellation *Draco*, at its lower transit, three degrees below the true celestial pole.

for the most brilliant mathematicians of Alexandria to devise simple rules of calculation without recourse to mechanical aids.

If man had had as many legs as the centipede, or if like the crayfish he had nineteen pairs of limbs, forming five functionally different sets, the evolution of a number language would have pursued a different course. Possibly also it would have pursued a different course if man had not been a viviparous animal. The very great difficulty which Zeno and his contemporaries felt because they had no numbers which stretch like $0\cdot\dot{1}$ might have been far less formidable if human beings laid eggs. In one of the earliest treatises on number, the *Chinese Book of the Permutations*, which was written about 1100 B.C., we find the whole numbers divided into two sets, the odd number set (or "series"):

1, 3, 5, 7, . . .

and the even number series:

2, 4, 6, 8, . . .

The even number series are perfectly divisible into two. The even numbers are "female." The odd numbers are "male." The perfect marriage of the two represents the complete number series:

1, 2, 3, 4, 5, 6, 7, 8, . . .

For generations mankind has been dogged by the difficulty of representing the measurements he makes by these sexually complete numbers which were evolved to describe the size of groups of quite separate and distinct things. The clever people of the ancient world could not tackle the idea of a number like the square root of two (see p. 204), which is like an unhatched egg. A number had to be either a boy or a girl.

This seemingly irrelevant association of number and sex need not surprise us. Number script was a by-product of an organized calendar, the need for which came from man's preoccupation with his own fertility and that of his flocks. Another strain of phallicism can be detected in the number scripts of the ancient world. The prominence given to three was probably suggested by the male organs of generation. In many languages three times is used as a symbol of potency as in "thrice armed is he." In the ancient systems of numeration we see signs of retrogression to these primitive preoccupations with fertility.

An example may be the interval of three introduced by the Romans, who took over the Etruscan numerals, thus:

I	II	III	IV	V	. . .	(Renaissance)
X	XX	XXX	XL	L	. . .	(Roman)
C	CC	CCC	CD	D	. . .	"

The original Phoenician and Sumerian systems of numeration foreshadowed this development by favouring the grouping of signs in threes. The inversion of four, etc., is analogous to the old-fashioned habit of saying ten to five instead of four fifty. It proved to be a great inconvenience because it made it more difficult for the Romans to devise rules of calculation. Possibly the Romans would not have hampered themselves by this unfortunate inversion if human beings reproduced by external fertilization like frogs.

Civilized mankind developed written symbols for numbers long before the need for rapid and simple means of calculation arose. In fashioning their number script men had no prevision of the requirements of a script with which simple arithmetical performances could be carried out. As men were forced to deal with larger numbers they came to rely upon a piece of physical apparatus which circumscribed their whole horizon of number and measurement. Idealists make our problems unnecessarily abstruse by concealing the difficulties which beset these mathematicians of antiquity. The elasticity of their mental processes was continually cramped by the rigidity of their material equipment. They are given credit for being mysteriously profound when they were merely being unavoidably clumsy. When man got beyond the stage of relying entirely upon tally sticks, representing numbers by notches, he hit on the practice of using pebbles or shells which could be rapidly discarded or used over and over again. So came the counting frame. At first it was probably a series of grooves on a flat surface. Then it was a set of upright sticks on which pierced stones, shells, or beads could be placed. Finally the closed frame seen in the lower part of Fig. 6 superseded the earlier type seen in the upper part of the figure. The counting frame or *abacus* (Fig. 6) was a very early achievement of mankind. It follows the megalithic culture routes all round the world. The Mexicans and Peruvians were using the abacus when the Spaniards got to America. The Chinese and the Egyptians already possessed the abacus several millennia before the Christian era. The Romans took it from the Etruscans. Till about the beginning

ADDITION WITH THE ABACUS

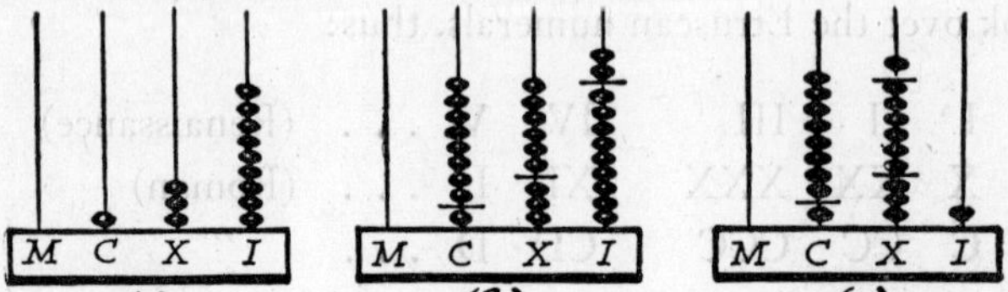

(a) 139

(b) 139 + 862

(c) Add 1 to column X for 10 thrown out of column I

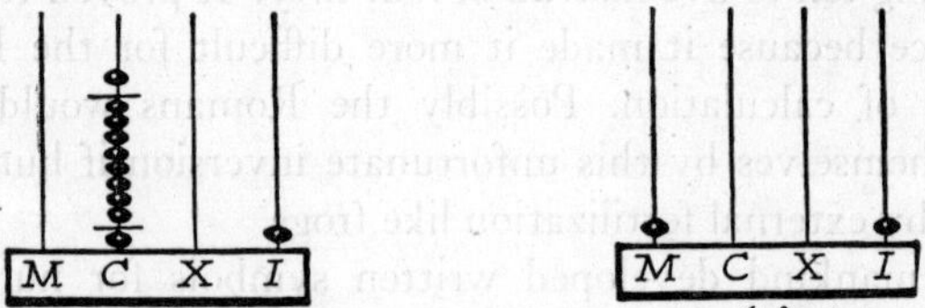

(d) Add 1 to column C for 10 thrown out of column X

(e) Add 1 to column M for 10 thrown out of column C

(Answer MI = 1001)

LATER METHOD OF CARRYING OVER

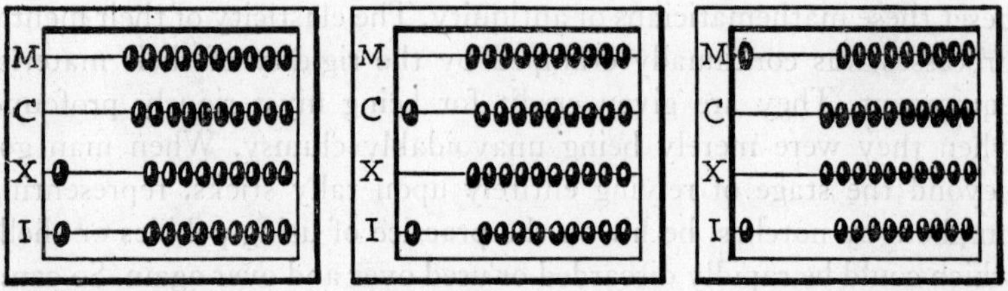

2 + 9 = 10 + 1
Add units, and carry over to X one for each ten thrown out

60 + 30 + 10 + 1 = 101
Add tens, and carry over to C one for each ten thrown out

100 + 800 + 100 + 1 = 1001
Add hundreds, and carry over to M one for each ten thrown out

FIG. 6.—ADDING 139 TO 862 ON THE COUNTING FRAME

of the Christian era, this fixed frame remained the only instrument for calculation that mankind possessed.

To us figures are symbols with which sums can be done. This

conception of figures was completely foreign to the most advanced mathematicians of ancient Greece. The ancient number scripts were merely labels to record the result of doing work with an abacus, instead of doing work with a pen or pencil. In the whole history of mathematics there has been no more revolutionary step than the one which the Hindus made when they invented the sign "0" to stand for the empty column of the counting frame. You will see more clearly why this was important, and how it made possible simple rules of calculation, when you get to Chapter 7. Here we can notice two things about the discovery of "nothing." The first is that if your base is 10, you only require nine other numbers to express any number as large as you like. Your ability to represent numbers is not limited by the number of letters in your alphabet. You do not have to introduce new signs, like the Roman X, C, and M, every time you multiply by ten. The other important thing about "nothing" you may begin to see if you look at the lower diagram. The new number vocabulary of the Hindus allows you to add on paper in the same way as you add on the abacus. How the invention was made and how it affected the after-history of mathematics must be left for the present. The important thing to realize is that the mathematicians of classical antiquity inherited a social culture which was equipped with a number script before the need for laborious calculations was felt. So they were completely dependent upon mechanical aids which have now been banished to the nursery.

It is customary to distinguish between two ways in which numbers are used, cardinal numbers which signify how many individuals make up a group, and ordinal numbers which indicate the position of an event in a sequence. This distinction is not so important as another which resulted from the earliest attempts to record the passage of time. When we say there are 100 sheep in a flock, we mean the same thing as saying that the last sheep is the hundredth when they are all arranged in single file. Seasons recorded on the tally stick stretched across the horizon of experience in the earliest stages of human culture like sheep arranged in single file. In treating each sheep as equivalent to another for the purpose of enumerating the flock all we mean is that each is qualitatively the same kind of individual as any other. Quantitatively, as regards height, weight, volume, and the number of fibres in its fleece, one sheep is not the same kind of individual as another. The earliest calendars were not based on the measurement of time in equivalent intervals. They recorded the ordinal succession of events sharply marked off by natural phenomena. One day is separated from another by a varying amount of darkness just as one sheep is separated from another of different size by a varying amount of fresh air.

Whatever is said about the use of numbers to represent the size of a group of individuals which can be arranged in single file applies equally to the use of numbers to signify the order which an event or thing occupies in some natural or artificial sequence. We can arrange a set of twenty-eight sticks of different sizes in a definite order of greater or less without having any information about how the length of any one of them corresponds with the scale divisions on a foot-rule. So likewise primitive tribes may fix the age of initiation in the fourteenth dry season without realizing whether the intervals between one dry season and another are truly equivalent. There is not much difference between the way we use a number when we say that there are seven sheep in a field, and when we say that Saturday is the seventh day in the week. There is a very big difference in the way we use numbers when we say that there are 365 days in a year and 24 hours make a day. When people began to divide up the day by the position of the sun's shadow they started to use the old distinct numbers in a way which was quite novel. An hour is not separated from another hour by any natural event like the period of moisture between one dry season or another, or the succession of lunar aspects between two full moons. Hours and minutes only correspond with *measurements* on a scale, which we can use with greater or less precision according to the care we take in making the scale and in observing the pointer, i.e. the angle of the shadow, when the last grain of sand falls in the sand glass, or where the hand of the clock is.

3. IN WHAT DIRECTION DOES IT LIE?

The need for accurate measurement grew naturally from the practice of time-keeping, which was an essential prerequisite of settled city life. It is fairly certain that people began to measure angles long before they troubled themselves very much with measuring lengths. The number of days in a year had been fixed by the heliacal rising of Sirius at the very beginning of settled city life along the Nile. Watching for the rising of a particular star or constellation involves knowing at what point of the horizon it will appear, and we have ample evidence that Neolithic man had learned to set up crude monuments to fix the direction of celestial phenomena, before there were cities which have

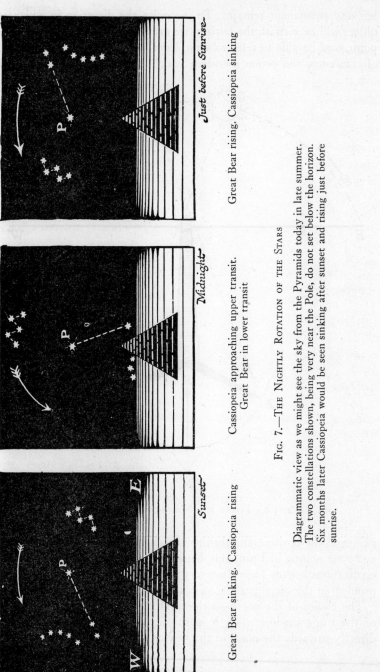

Great Bear sinking. Cassiopeia rising

Cassiopeia approaching upper transit. Great Bear in lower transit

Great Bear rising. Cassiopeia sinking

FIG. 7.—THE NIGHTLY ROTATION OF THE STARS

Diagrammatic view as we might see the sky from the Pyramids today in late summer. The two constellations shown, being very near the Pole, do not set below the horizon. Six months later Cassiopeia would be seen sinking after sunset and rising just before sunrise.

left any permanent remains. To recognize the direction in which an object will be seen on the horizon we must observe it from some fixed point, and be able to refer to some fixed line. Two fundamental lines of reference, the prime meridian which joins the north and south

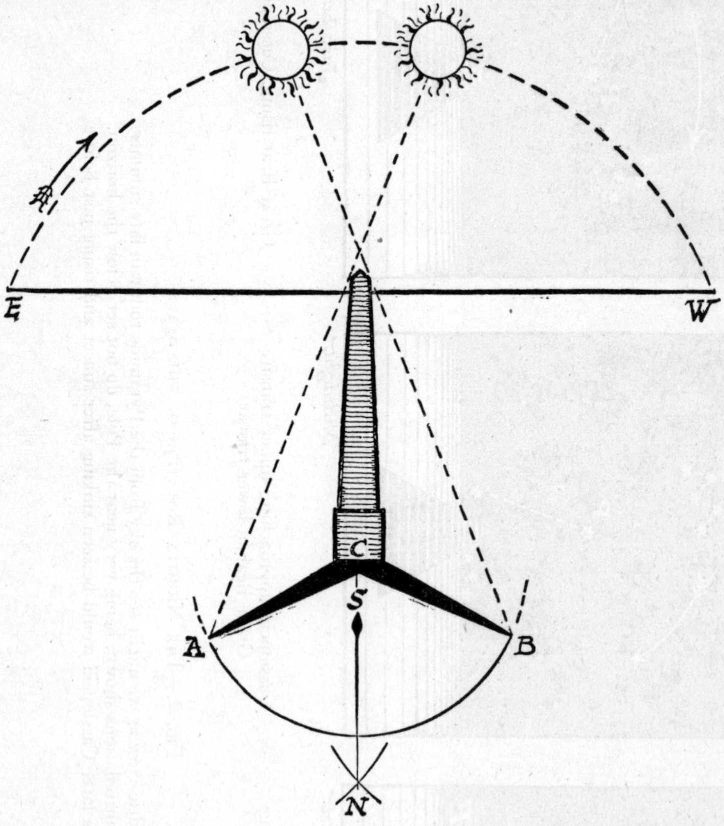

FIG. 8.—FIXING THE NORTH-SOUTH MERIDIAN

points on the horizon, and the line at right angles to it joining the east and west points, had probably been settled before the great calendar civilizations began. Their discovery constitutes the first mathematical problem in the social practice of mankind.

The choice of the north-south meridian was based on the position of the sun's shadow when it is shortest at midday. It also points directly towards the place in the heavens around which the stars revolve by night. At the time when the Pyramids were built, a bright star in the constellation of Draco revolved in a tiny circle (of three degrees) round it. The position of the constellations changes in the course of centuries, and today the celestial pole is recognized by the star Polaris, our Pole star, which is only one degree off. We have a

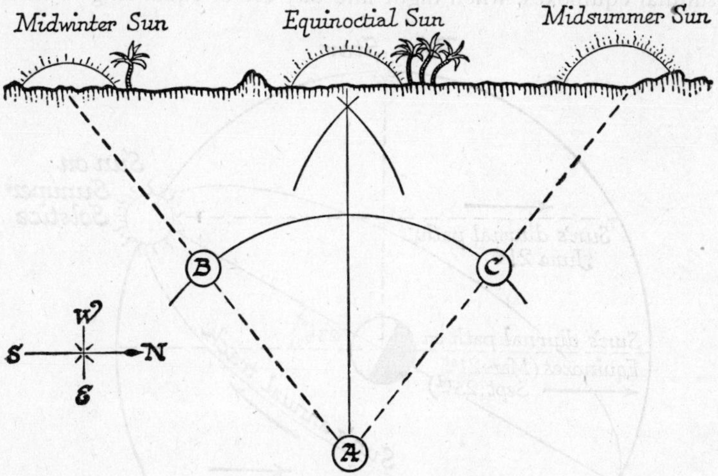

FIG. 9.—FIXING THE EQUINOX

Some early calendrical monuments suggest that the equinox was fixed by observations on the rising or setting sun of the solstices (December 21st and June 21st), when the sun rises and sets at its most extreme positions towards the south and north respectively. In the figure A and B are two poles placed in alignment with the setting sun of the winter solstice. The distance between A and C in line with the setting sun of the summer solstice is the same as the distance between A and B. Midway between its journey between the two extremes the sun rises and sets due East and West, and the lengths of day and night are equal. Hence these two days (March 21st and September 23rd) are called the Equinoxes. In ancient ritual they were days of great importance. The east and west points on the horizon can be obtained by bisecting the angle BAC (See p. 133).

record of the way in which the exact location of the noon shadow was fixed in ancient times. In the sand or soft earth around the shadow pole or obelisk, which was the public clock, a circle was traced with a piece of cord. The two points where the shadow just touched the circle were marked and the angle between these two points and the shadow pole was bisected first, perhaps, by stretching a cord between them and folding it in halves, later by tracing arcs of equal radius about the two points (Fig. 8).

The recognition of the east and west meridian or *equinoctial* presented a similar problem, and the orientation of burial sites shows that it also antedates any city life. We are so accustomed to be taught that the sun rises in the east and sets in the west that many of us do not realize that it only does so on two days of the year—the vernal and autumnal equinoxes, when night and day are of equal length. In our

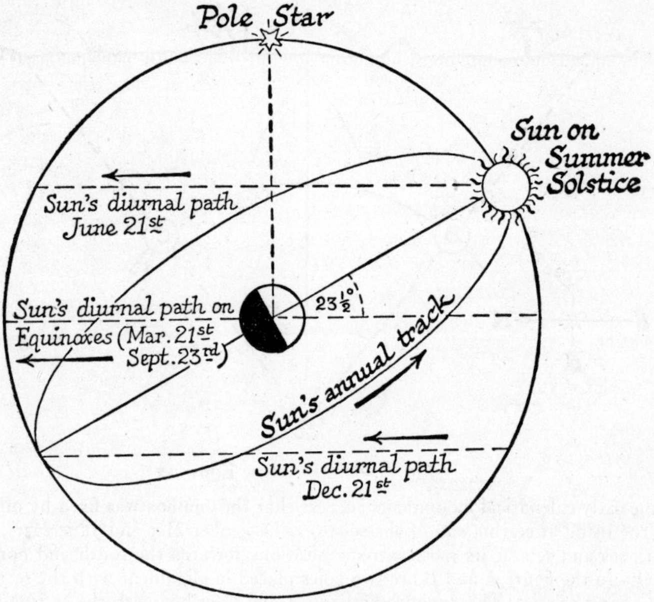

FIG. 10.—THE SUN'S (APPARENT) ANNUAL MOTION IN THE CELESTIAL SPHERE (see p. 58)

winter the sun rises and sets in the south-east and south-west, in summer in north-east and north-west. The great fertility festival of the spring equinox was fixed for the day when the sun rises and sets midway between the two extreme positions which it occupies on the winter and summer solstices. Ancient monuments like Stonehenge, and remains of the Maya calendar culture, show how the sun's position at sunrise or sunset on the solstices was fixed by alignment with two pillars of different height. Possibly the position of the equinoctial sun at rising or setting was located by bisecting the angle shown in Fig. 9. Alternatively it may have been fixed by making a line at *right angles* to the north-south meridian (see p. 133).

By the time when we first have written testimony to the cultural achievements of the ancient world, the priesthood had been long familiar with the precise direction of stars when they reached their highest altitude (transit) above the horizon. The south face of the

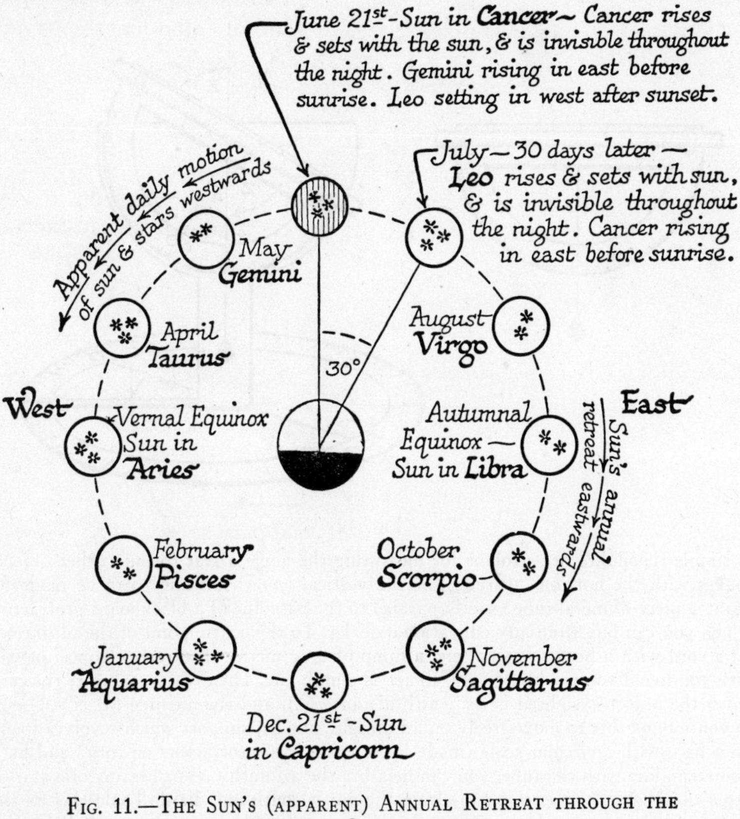

FIG. 11.—THE SUN'S (APPARENT) ANNUAL RETREAT THROUGH THE ZODIACAL CONSTELLATIONS

Great Pyramid which was built about 2800 B.C. was so placed that the rays of Sirius at its transit struck it at right angles. One ventilating shaft leading to the royal chamber was so accurately placed that the dead Pharaoh was illuminated by the Dog star when it crossed the meridian. The main opening and a second shaft let in the light of the Pole star, α Draconis, at its lower transit. The astonishing accuracy of these constructive feats was the fruit of centuries of recorded observations, and the means of recording the direction in which something lies still bear the impress of the physical reality from which the measurement of the angle took its origin.

In the ancient priestly lore the whole orb of heaven revolved around an axis passing through the celestial pole. Sun, moon, planets, and

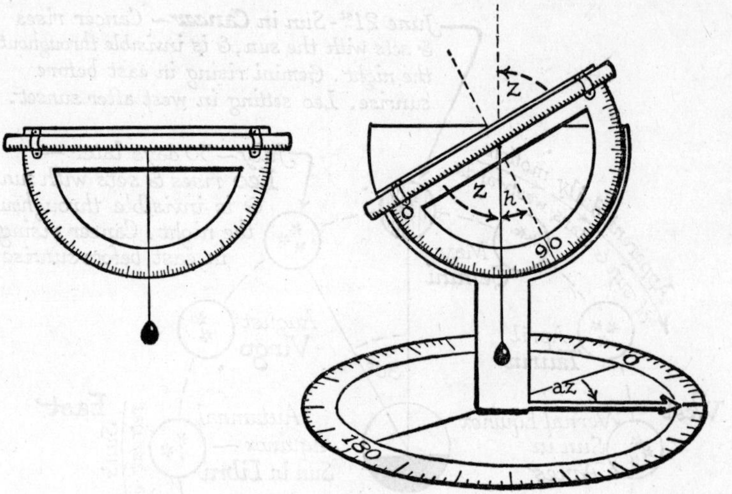

FIG. 12

A simple theodolite or astrolabe for measuring the angle a star (or any other object) makes with the horizon (altitude), or the vertical (zenith distance) can be made by fixing a piece of metal tube exactly parallel to the base line of a blackboard protractor, which you can buy from any educational dealer. To the centre point of the protractor fix a cord with a heavy weight (e.g. a lump of type metal which any compositor will give you free if you ask him nicely) to act as plumb line. The division opposite the cord when the object is sighted is its zenith distance (Z), and the altitude (h) is $90° - Z$. If you mount this to move freely on an upright wooden support which revolves freely on a base with a circular scale (made by screwing two protractors on to it) and fix a pointer in line with the tube, you can measure the azimuth (*az*) or bearing of a star or other object (e.g. the setting sun) from the north–south meridian. To do this fix the scale so that it reads 0° when the sighter is pointed to the noon sun or the Pole star. This was a type of instrument used to find latitude and longitude in the time of the Great Navigations. You can use it to find the latitude and longitude of your house (Chapter 4, p. 171), or make an ordnance survey of your neighbourhood (Chapters 4, p. 162, and 6, p. 251).

stars revolved about it in parallel circles. Each day the moon slipped back a little in the celestial sphere so that it rises later and sets later as it waxes and wanes. Each day the sun seemed to slip back a little slantwise across the celestial sphere, so that the same stars rise earlier on successive nights, and some are invisible at seasons when the sun occupies the same position in the heavens. The slanting track of the sun through the belt of zodiacal constellations accounted for the fact that it was higher at some seasons in the noontide heavens than at others. Finding the length of a year demands accurate measurement, and it is not surprising that first estimates were not as good as later ones. The Babylonian year was at first 360 days, and the addition of five feast days to twelve Egyptian months of thirty days suggests that the Egyptian year had also been at one time 360 days. Thus the circular track of the sun in the ecliptic belt of the celestial sphere was mapped out in 360 steps, each corresponding with a day and a night. There is little doubt that the degree had its origin in these 360 natural divisions of the sun's journey through the whole angle described in its complete circular track (Fig. 11). Two millennia before the Christian era the priesthoods of the ancient Mediterranean world knew the angle which the sun's slanting track (Figs. 5 and 10) makes with the equinoctial ("obliquity of the ecliptic") within a fraction of a degree. Babylonian relics show that they possessed instruments essentially similar to the astrolabes (Fig. 12) or primitive theodolites which remained in use till the telescope was invented. With these they mapped out the local heavens, circles of altitude and azimuth (compare Figs. 13 and 118).

You will now be able to see more clearly why the measurement of direction put numbers to a new use. Numbers had been invented to describe separate things, and they fitted these separated things exactly. This can never be true about measurements. However hard you may try to divide the boundary of a circle into 360 equal parts, they will not really be equal. They will only be as nearly equal as your instruments allow you to make them. Then again, even if you use your astrolabe, the ancient form of sextant, or the modern sextant which has a telescope and a vernier, as carefully as you can, the direction will never exactly correspond with one of the divisions marked. In practice you have to take the nearest division as the correct mark. In one way or another the same complication about the use of numbers arises in connection with all the remaining questions.

4. HOW FAR DOES IT STRETCH?

Men built hotels for their celestial visitors and earthly representatives long before they had the sagacity to think about making houses fit for themselves to dwell in. The construction of calendar monuments for sighting the direction of heavenly bodies and of burial edifices for the embalmed remains of the sky-born Pharaoh entailed accurate measurements of distance. The two pyramids of Cheops and Sneferu at Gizeh are constructed on the same geometrical plan, which is explained in the legend of Fig. 5A with Petrie's comments. The accuracy of construction which is characteristic of the temple architecture is bound up

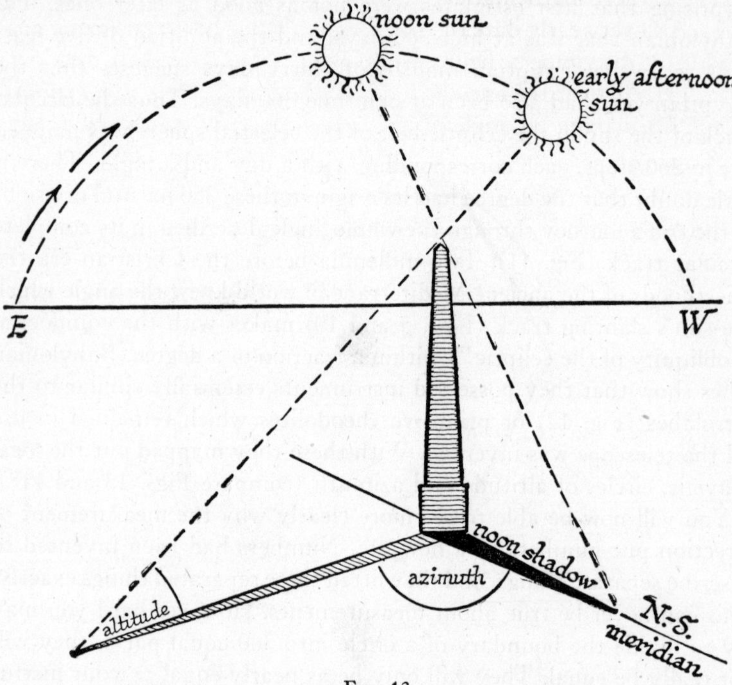

FIG. 13

The direction of a celestial body can be fixed by two angles, the angle it makes with the horizon or the vertical (altitude or zenith distance) and the angle it makes with the meridian (azimuth).

with their essential social function. Being built to receive their heavenly guests, these ancient monuments had to have a very precise orientation, which has been illustrated by the arrangement of the ventilating shafts in the Great Pyramid at Gizeh. For many millennia men were content to use crude anatomical units of length for most practical purposes. The Semitic peoples used the cubit or distance from the tip of the middle finger to the elbow, as farmers still use their legs to pace out a field in "feet" or yards. For ordinary purposes they were content with a unit of length which varied from one individual to another. Temple architecture demanded a far higher standard of precision, and was based on the long-lost art of shadow reckoning in the sunnier climates where civilization began. Heights were reckoned by the length of the shadow and the angle of the sun above the horizon, and reckoning heights in this way depends on certain simple truths about the relation between the lengths of the sides of a triangle.

The earliest mathematical discoveries belong to this class of problems. At a very early date the Babylonians knew how to make an angle of 60° by inscribing a figure of six equal sides (hexagon) in a circle (Fig. 14). All over the ancient world we find evidence of a very simple recipe for making an angle of 90°, which depends on the fact that a

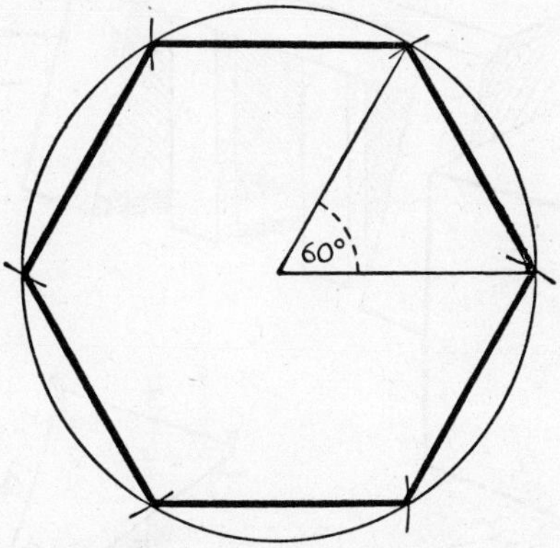

FIG. 14

A regular *hexagon* (figure with six sides of equal length) inscribed in a circle by marking off along the boundary intersecting arcs with the same radius.

triangle with sides 3, 4, and 5 units of length is right-angled. According to one legend the priestly architects of Egypt laid out a right angle by knotting together three pieces of rope as in Fig. 15, the lengths of the pieces being in the ratio 3 : 4 : 5. If this is pegged down at the knots, a perfect set square is obtained. Five or six thousand years ago the Egyptians and Babylonians had discovered at least one case of a general rule about the sides of a right-angled triangle (see Fig. 16). Geometry books state it in these words: "the square on the longest side (hypotenuse) of a right-angled triangle is equal to the sum of the squares on the other two sides." Thus a right-angled triangle is also formed if we knot together three pieces of rope, 5 yards, 12 yards, and 13 yards long, stretch it out, and peg it down at the knots as in Fig. 15. You can see at once that

$$25 + 144 = 169$$

$$\text{i.e.} \quad 5^2 + 12^2 = 13^2$$

The use of the degree or three hundred and sixtieth part of the circle as a unit of angular measurement may also help explain the early discovery of another important truth. The Egyptians and Babylonians both knew that the circumference of a circle always has the same ratio

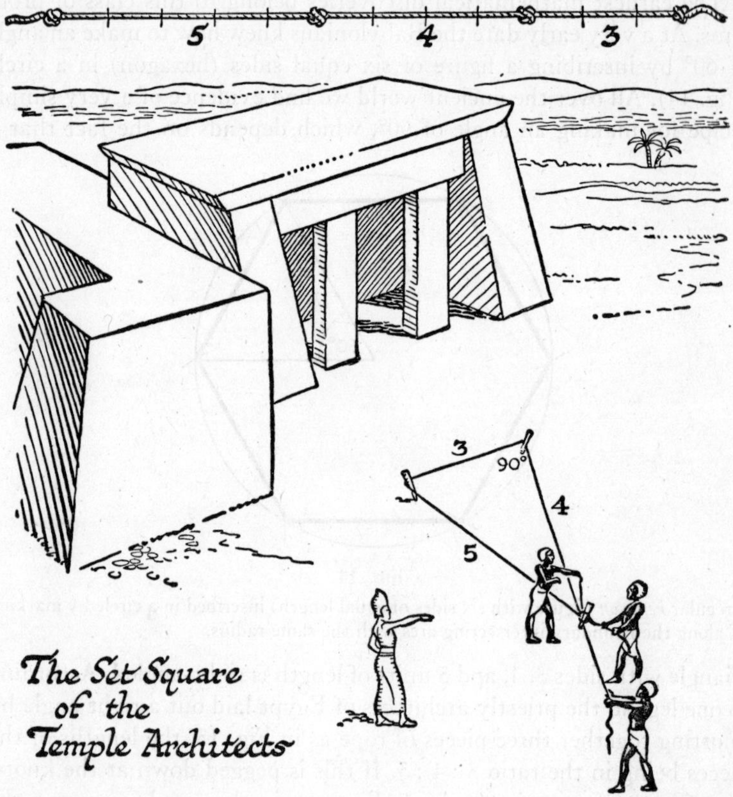

FIG. 15

to its diameter. This ratio, which we represent by the Greek letter π, is roughly $3\frac{1}{7}$ or correct to 4 decimals in our number script $3 \cdot 1416$. The Babylonians used a crude approximation, reckoning it to be $3 \cdot 0$. The Egyptians, on the other hand, gave a much closer approximation. The sides of the pyramids at Gizeh and their heights are in the ratio 11 : 7, making the ratio of half the perimeter to the height $3\frac{1}{7}$. The Ahmes papyrus (about 1600 B.C.) gives the ratio of the circumference to the diameter as $3 \cdot 16$ in our notation. The Moscow papyrus gives a formula for the area of a sphere making π equivalent to $3 \cdot 14$. Thus the Egyptian mensuration of the circle was correct within 1 per cent.

The great antiquity of a simple recipe for making an angle of 60° gives us a clue to the reason for selecting the hour as a unit. Dividing the working day by the direction of the sun's shadow into intervals which are not separated by any natural break depends on choosing a suitable angle as unit for calibrating the shadow clock (Fig. 17). In one hour the celestial sphere (or, as we would say, the earth) turns on its axis through 360 ÷ 24 = 15°. In Chapter 4 you will see that of

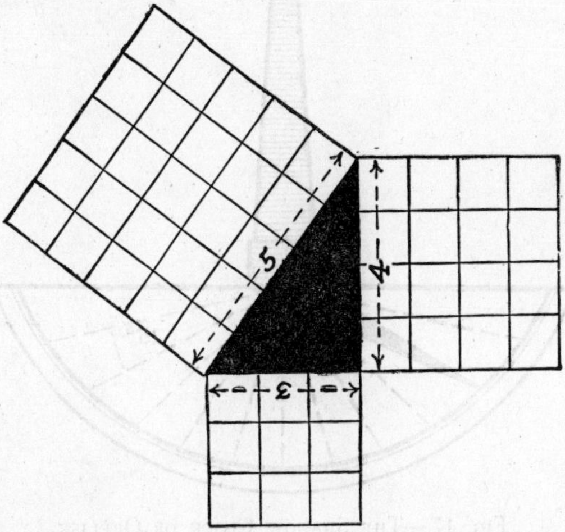

FIG. 16.—THE RIGHT-ANGLED TRIANGLE OF THE TEMPLE BUILDERS

Long side, 5 feet	.. .. ..	(5^2 = 25 square feet)
Short sides, 4 feet	.. .. ..	(4^2 = 16 square feet)
3 feet	.. .. ..	(3^2 = 9 square feet)

$$25 = 16 + 9$$

or $$5^2 = 4^2 + 3^2$$

all angles less than 90° the easiest to make are 30°, 60°, and 45°. Once we have found how to make angles of this size we can get fractions of them by repeated division into two. Of the three angles mentioned 60° alone can be divided so as to give a whole number of degrees. It can in fact be divided successively twice, giving four angles of 15°, the arc (see p. 131) through which the sun rotates about the axis of the celestial sphere in one hour.

With the progress of building, the right angle of 90° based on the plumb line and water level became increasingly important as a measure of the size of an angle. The urban angle of the builder was such and such a fraction of a right angle instead of so many degrees (see Fig. 18). As temple construction became a mania which exhausted the resources of these old priest-ridden communities, the priests relinquished their greatest cultural achievement, the measurement of the angle, to a craftsman class of slaves and freed slaves. The knowledge of architectural mensuration which this subject class possessed has left no records other than the geometrical perfection of their achievements. The only

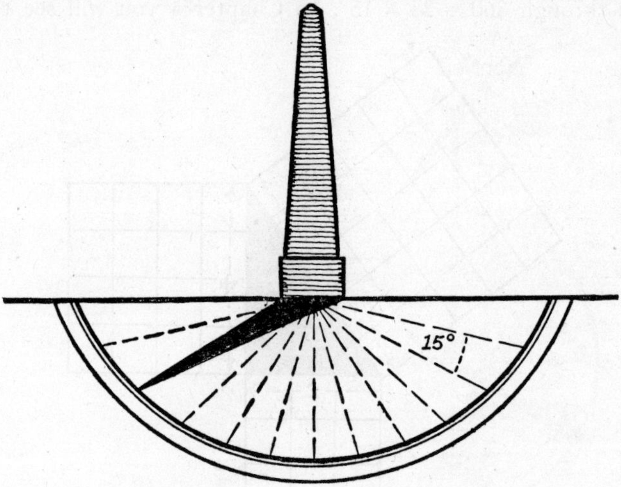

FIG. 17.—THE SHADOW CLOCK OR OBELISK

reason why we customarily speak of the Greeks as the first mathematicians is that the Egyptians have left practically no literature telling how they achieved what are still some of the most astounding feats of measurement in the history of mankind. Such fragments as we have, like the Rhind papyrus of the scribe Ahmes, show that the state of their arithmetic was at the same level as that of the Greeks who came later. They left so small a literature because the literate class had no disposition to broadcast its priestly secrets, and the craftsman class of surveyors, engineers, architects, and mariners, not being scribes, passed on their knowledge by oral tradition. The class basis of education in the ancient times led to much loss and wastage of valuable knowledge.

5. HOW MUCH FLAT SPACE DOES IT ENCLOSE?

The pillage of the cultivators by the ruling caste which ordained the building of these vast temples and tombs led to a system of taxation of the land in Egypt. Herodotus tells us that the Nile was constantly overflowing and washing away landmarks, and so giving rise to dispute over taxes due and property rights. This brought into being a craft of surveyors. Side by side with the craft of surveying, the Egyptians paid great attention to schemes of irrigation, especially in con-

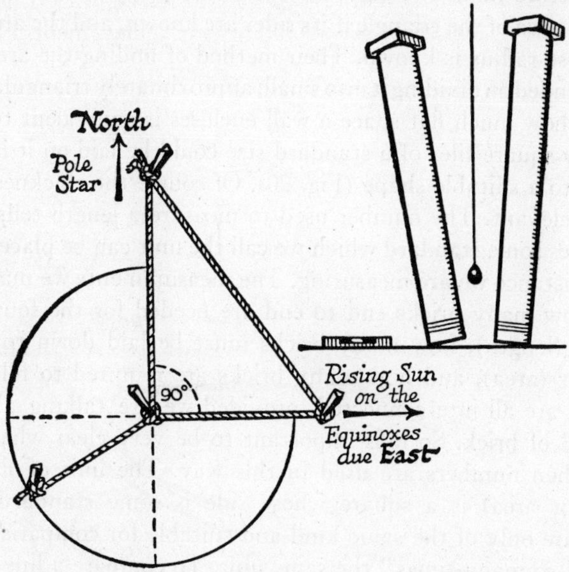

FIG. 18.—THE URBANIZATION OF THE ANGLE

In placing the Temple with reference to the four cardinal points in the great circle of the horizon, the angle of the quarter year ($\frac{1}{4}$ of $360 = 90$) and the angle of the set-square are seen to be one and the same thing. PLUMB-LINE and WATER LEVEL gave us the definition of the right angle as an independent unit of measurement. The pillar of the Temple is upright when it inclines equally to the horizon line on either side like the plumb line. A right angle is also the angle the plumb line makes with the horizon.

nection with the prophesying of the flooding of the sacred river. Here, again, the priesthood could only increase their power by parting with the secrets of power. Egyptian surveying supplemented the measurement of the angle with the measurement of *area*. We do not know exactly how people hit on the square as the unit of area. A variety of equally plausible explanations offer themselves. One is that it was suggested by the way we fill up a space to mend a piece of basketwork —a craft which preceded weaving. Another is that it grew out of the use of mosaic tiles, or was suggested by the checker-board pattern seen on early Babylonian pottery. There are some grounds for supposing that one very early discovery about area was made by drawing on square-tiled floors. One of the first examples of block printing (Fig. 19) in China seems to be based on a copy of such a drawing which illustrated the so-called theorem of Pythagoras possibly known to the Chinese before him. The Egyptians and the Babylonians knew how to find the area of the triangle if its sides are known, and the area of the circle whose radius is known. Their method of finding the area of the circle depended on dividing it into small, approximately triangular strips.

Asking how much flat space a wall encloses is equivalent to asking how many square tiles of a standard size could be laid on it if it were squeezed to a suitable shape (Fig. 20). Of course the thickness of the tiles is irrelevant. The number used to measure a length tells us how many times some standard which we call the unit can be placed alongside the distance we are measuring. The measurements we make when we say how many bricks end to end are needed for the foundations of a wall (length), how many bricks must be laid down to make a brick floor (area), and how many bricks are required to fill a space (volume), are all interconnected, provided we are talking about the same kind of brick. So it is important to be very clear what unit is chosen when numbers are used in this way. The unit of flat space (surface or area) is a square whose side is some standard length. Lengths are only of the same kind and suitable for comparison when they are "so many times" the same unit. To compare a line 3 inches long with a line 5 feet long, we must express them both as inches (3 and 60), or feet ($\frac{1}{4}$ and 5), or use some independent standard (e.g. 7·5 and 150 centimetres). So likewise to compare areas we must keep to the same standard of length. A square with a side 10 inches long encloses 100 square inches, and is four times the area of a square with sides 5 inches long enclosing 25 square inches. A square with a side 10 inches long is only one thirty-sixth of a square whose side is 5 feet.

6. HOW MUCH SOLID SPACE DOES IT FILL?

When exchange was confined to barter, grain, wine, and oil were measured in vessels. Social custom dictated a more or less constant shape and size of the vessels used. Relics of these crude measures are still used in England. For instance, the hogshead is a large cask the size of which differs according to the kind of beer or wine sold. The English system has advanced very little from the Bronze Age level. The pint and the gallon (vessel measures) are still used more than the

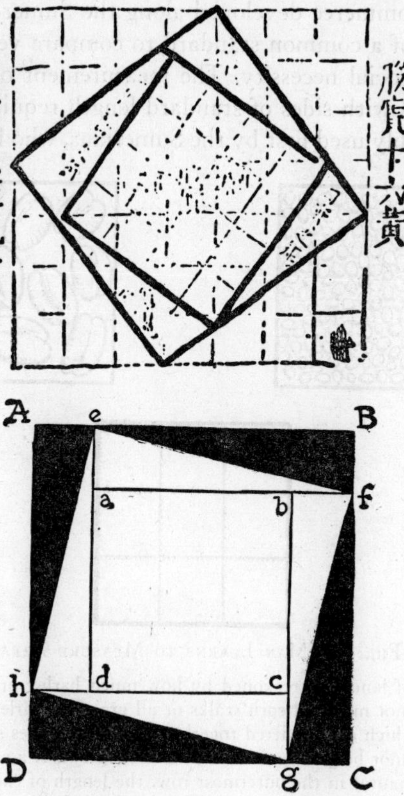

FIG. 19

The *Book of Chou Pei Suan King*, probably written about A.D. 40, is attributed by oral tradition to a source before the Greek geometer taught what we call the Theorem of Pythagoras, i.e. that the square on the longest side of a right-angled triangle is equivalent to the sum of the squares on the other two. This very early example of block printing from an ancient edition of the *Chou Pei*, as given in Smith's *History of Mathematics*, demonstrates the truth of the theorem. By joining to any right-angled triangle like the black figure *eBf* three other right-angled triangles just like it, a square can be formed. Next trace four oblongs (rectangles) like *eaf*B, each of which is made up of two triangles like *ef*B. When you have read Chapter 4 you will be able to put together the Chinese puzzle, which is much less puzzling than Euclid. These are the steps:

$$\text{Triangle } ef\text{B} = \tfrac{1}{2} \text{ rectangle } eaf\text{B} = \tfrac{1}{2}\, \text{B}f \,.\, e\text{B}$$

$$\text{Square ABCD} = \text{Square } efgh + 4 \text{ times triangle } ef\text{B}$$

$$= ef^2 + 2\text{B}f \,.\, e\text{B}$$

$$\text{Also Square ABCD} = \text{B}f^2 + e\text{B}^2 + 2\text{B}f \,.\, e\text{B}$$

So $ef^2 + 2\text{B}f \,.\, e\text{B} = \text{B}f^2 + e\text{B}^2 + 2\text{B}f \,.\, e\text{B}$

Hence $ef^2 = \text{B}f^2 + e\text{B}^2$

cubic foot. As commerce developed along the Sumerian trade routes, the acceptance of a common standard to compare vessels of different sizes became a social necessity. The measurement of volume by the number of cubes with sides of standard length required to fill a solid space was probably used first by the Sumerians, who built with bricks.

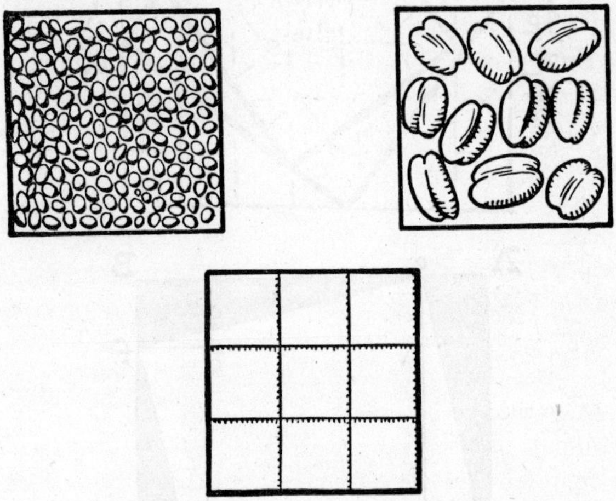

FIG. 20.—MAN LEARNS TO MEASURE AREAS

At first the value of land was reckoned by how much barley or rice could be grown on it. Nature does not make all corn stalks or all grains of barley alike, but man can make square tiles which can be fitted together to make patches so nearly of the same shape that they cannot be distinguished by the naked eye. If a square is made with n tiles (n is 3 in our figure) in the outermost row, the length of each side is n times the length of the side of a single square tile. The number of tiles which go to make the square is n rows of n tiles, that is to say, n times n tiles. That is why we call n multiplied by itself n squared, written n^2. The fundamental rule of area is based on the tiled floor. The rule is that n^2 units of area make up the area of a square the side of which is n units of length.

7. HOW MUCH MATTER DOES IT CONTAIN?

We still measure solids which can be packed tightly by volume. For instance, we speak of so many bushels of flour and barley. Such a measure was obviously useless to the Phoenician traders who first visited our shores for tin. The Sumerians and their Semitic successors in Asia Minor took to trading at an early date. The founding of great trading ports like the city of Tyre was followed by the colony of Carthage on the west border of the Mediterranean. Phoenician ships were plying north to barter with the megalithic communities of Brittany, Cornwall, and Devon by 1500 B.C. About 500 B.C. the Carthaginian Hanno had tacked along the African coast beyond the equator. So soon as ships began to steer beyond sight of land, the priestly economy of the ancient civilizations was doomed. Star measurement had become part of seafaring lore.

To a trading people, as the Bible reminds us, the false weight is an abomination. So it is not surprising that the civilizations of Mesopotamia and Asia Minor outstripped that of Egypt in devising a system of weights and measures. The need for constant reckoning in commercial undertakings is associated with a very high development of arithmetic. At Nippur fifty thousand tablets of a large library, most of which was destroyed by the Elamites about 2000 B.C., have been recovered. There was already a school of commercial arithmetic for traders.

Babylonian arithmetic just fell short of being an instrument of computation as efficient as our own. The principle of position, which will be explained in Chapter 7, was used consistently on a sexagesimal scale of 60. Repetitive combinations of the symbols for one and ten were used to make the fundamental numbers from 1 to 59, corresponding to our use of the symbols for 1 to 9 as fundamental numbers. Above that position indicated *so many times* 60 or 3600 or other powers of 60, just as we represent *so many times* ten or a hundred or higher power of ten. Like the Hindu and Maya notations, it employed a zero, which was intercalated to represent a gap in the sexagesimal series, as we might distinguish between 33 and 303. However, it rarely appears to have been used in the terminal position, as when we distinguish 33 and 330. This step seems to be all that was lacking to make the notation amenable to the Arabic devices we ourselves use. Babylonian arithmetic never actually advanced to the invention of a system of "algorithms," though it might well have done so. For rapid calculation tables of multiplication, addition, subtraction, division, squares and progressions were compiled with a thoroughness in keeping with the apparatus of modern computing. The tradition of Greek arithmetic rooted in Pythagorean number magic had far less in common with our own; and the Attic numerals, if less cumbersome than this vastly more ancient number script, were totally incapable of giving birth to the algorithms or calculating rules, of which every child of twelve is now the fortunate possessor. Another feature of Babylonian arithmetic is essentially modern. In expressing fractions, denominators were not specified. Sexagesimal fractions were used in the same way as we use decimal fractions, except that there was no device like our dot (comma on the Continent) to signify the precise meaning to be attached to a set of figures. Babylonian arithmetical tables, like modern tables of logarithms, left the order of magnitude implied by the symbols to be inferred from the context.

What has been said about the measurement of direction applies equally to length, to area, to volume, and to weight. The use of numbers in measuring weight is to tell us how many times a standard weight balances a particular object when they are placed in opposite pans on the scales. This is not the same kind of thing as counting sheep in a flock or days in a year. Two objects may balance one another on one pair of scales, though one of them may be seen to be the heavier if a more sensitive balance is used. Whatever units we choose, whatever instruments we use, the male and female, odd and even numbers which we use to count coins or cattle can never convey an exact description of the weight or volume of an object, the area of its surface, the length of its sides, or the angle at which it is placed. We shall find it easier to solve some of our difficulties, and difficulties which perplexed the cleverest people in ancient times, if we realize at the beginning that numbers were first used to denote the exact order which an object or event occupies in a series, and that the need for rules in using numbers first arose in applying them to measurements which can never be exact.

Exercises on Chapter II

DISCOVERIES TO MAKE

1. Find several circular objects, such as a dustbin lid, clock face. Measure the circumference and diameter of each and find the value of the circumference divided by the diameter in each case as accurately as you can.

The following sets of instructions relate to triangles. Notice in each instance what conclusions are suggested by them.

2. (*a*) Draw a triangle with sides 10 centimetres, 8 centimetres, and 6 centimetres. The way to do this is to draw a straight line anywhere on the paper and mark off a distance AB equal to 10 centimetres. Adjust your compasses so that the distance between the point and the pencil is 8 centimetres. Place the point of the compasses at A and with the pencil draw an arc which will have a radius of 8 centimetres. In

the same way draw an arc with a radius of 6 centimetres with centre at B. Join C, the point where the two arcs cut, to A and B, and you will have the triangle you want.

Draw triangles with sides:

(*b*) 9 centimetres, 15 centimetres, 12 centimetres.
(*c*) 17 centimetres, 8 centimetres, 15 centimetres.

3. In all three triangles measure the angle between the two shorter sides of the triangle.

4. The Egyptian method of laying out a right angle is still in use. The following is a quotation from Bulletin Number 2 of the Ministry of Agriculture and Fisheries (1935). It is part of a set of directions for laying out a plantation of fruit trees.

"The easiest method of chaining a right angle is as follows: The 24th link is pegged at the point from which the right angle is to be set out, the nought end of the chain and the 96th link are pegged together, back along the base line, so that the piece of chain 0–24 is taut. If the 56th link is taken in the direction required until both the sections 24–56 and 56–96 are taut, then the point reached will be at right angles to the base line."

If you can find a convenient space, peg out the Egyptian rope triangle and the surveyor's triangle. The link referred to is 7·9 inches long. Satisfy yourself that these are both ways of setting out a right angle.

5. (*a*) Draw a right angle. Measure off on the arms of the angle distances of 5 centimetres and 12 centimetres. Join the ends to form a triangle. Measure the other side.

(*b*) In the same way draw a right-angled triangle with sides 12 centimetres and 16 centimetres long, and measure the third side.

(*c*) Draw a right-angled triangle with sides of 7 centimetres and 24 centimetres, and measure the third side.

6. Draw a triangle with one side 2 inches long, and the angles at either end of this side equal to 30°. Draw triangles with one side 3 inches and 4 inches respectively, and the adjoining angles 30°. Measure the other sides in all three triangles.

7. Draw three triangles with one side 2 inches, 3 inches, and 4 inches respectively, and the adjoining angles 45°. Measure the sides and test the rule of Fig. 16.

8. Draw three triangles of different sizes, each with two equal sides, and measure all the angles.

9. Find out what the sum is of all the three angles added together in all the triangles you have drawn.

10. Draw two triangles and try to make their shapes different from any you have drawn before. Measure the angles and add them together in each triangle.

TESTS ON TRIANGLES

1. Look back at the right-angled triangles you drew in the last section numbered 2 (*a*), (*b*), (*c*), and 5 (*a*), (*b*), (*c*). In each triangle call the longest side c, the next longest side a, and the shortest b. Find a^2, b^2, and c^2 for each triangle, and verify in each case that the following statements are true:

$$c^2 = a^2 + b^2$$
$$a^2 = c^2 - b^2$$
$$b^2 = c^2 - a^2$$

2. If in any right-angled triangle
$c = 26$ and $a = 24$, what is b?
If $a = 24$ and $b = 18$, what is c?
If $c = 34$ and $b = 16$, what is a?

If in any triangle two angles are 45°, what is the third angle?
If two angles are 30°, what is the third angle?
If one angle is 30° and the other is 60°, what is the third angle?
If one angle is 75° and the other is 15°, what is the third angle?

THINGS TO MEMORIZE

1. In a right-angled triangle, if c is the longest side and a and b are the other two sides:

$$c^2 = a^2 + b^2$$
$$a^2 = c^2 - b^2$$
$$b^2 = c^2 - a^2$$

2. In any triangle, if A, B, C are the angles:

$$A + B + C = 180°$$

CHAPTER III

The Grammar of Size, Order, and Number

OR

TRANSLATING NUMBER LANGUAGE

SPEAKING of mathematics as the language of size and the rules of mathematics as rules of grammar is something more than a mere figure of speech. It helps us to understand mathematics if we recognize how fundamentally alike are the languages with which mankind is able to describe the different *sorts* and the different *sizes* of things in the world. In every aspect of mathematics the similarity is very close. If you are interested in the structure of language, you will find that a close study of the grammatical resemblance between mathematics and the languages of everyday life repays the space we shall devote to it in this chapter. If you think grammar is a dull subject, it will be wiser to skim through the pages which follow and return to them later, when occasion arises.

In communicating information about different *sorts* of things in the world, primitive man first learned to substitute crude pictures for speech to record seasonal occurrences for future use. These pictures gradually came to serve for objects denoted by the same sound as the thing depicted. Chinese writing appears to have evolved mainly on these lines. As time went on the pictorial character of writing became less recognizable. When the illiterate peoples of the Western world started to write, they used the pictorial symbols of their teachers and conquerors to represent sounds. Writing ceased to have any pictorial significance. The correspondence between the message and the event could only be recognized when the message was translated into speech. This broad division between two kinds of writing, picture-writing or hieroglyphics and alphabetic-writing or letter script, has its parallel in mathematics. The literature of mathematics begins with the pictorial or hieroglyphic language which we call geometry. In the course of time geometry evolved along a line which recalls the evolution of the Chinese language. Figures were first used as diagrams for shapes and surfaces or volumes. They also came to be used as charts for the solution of arithmetical problems. At a much later date people stopped using nothing but pictures to record how numbers behave. They began to use letters, and compiled dictionaries in which you can find the meaning of the words used. Such dictionaries are called tables. There is nothing more mysterious about understanding the meaning of sin 15° than the meaning of the French word "écoutille." Sin 15° is found by looking up the number given for 15° in the tables of natural sines. This is an essential part of a ship's equipment. In the tables it is given as 0·2588, just as the meaning of "écoutille" is given as "companion-hatch" in the French dictionary. True, this does not tell you how to use sin 15°. Neither does knowing that "écoutille" means "companion-hatch" tell you how to use the word "écoutille," unless you happen to know what part of a ship a companion-hatch is. In both cases, knowing how to use the word is part of knowing all about a ship.

Dictionary language, or, as mathematicians call it, "analysis," came later than hieroglyphic language, and grew out of it; but it has never supplanted the need for it completely. Even in ordinary language we have not outgrown the hieroglyphic method. A good cartoon is worth a whole volume of political oratory. Today there are many different dictionary languages. Each has its own peculiar merit. The French language is especially suitable for the exercise of ironical wit. The English language is especially suitable to convey scientific truths concisely. The tortuous prolixity of German diction can be used to befuddle sensible and decent people till they believe that Hegel's dialectic makes sense and Jew-baiting makes a nation prosperous. So different kinds of analysis which go by such names as "the infinitesimal calculus," "vector notation," "matrix algebra" are severally used for different ways of counting and measuring things. The fundamental similarity of all grammar, whether it is the grammar of *sort* or the grammar of *size*, is shown by the two fundamental parts of speech common to languages of each type. One part of speech is the *noun*, which represents the things referred to in a sentence. The other part of speech is the *verb*, which tells you what to do with things, or what the things are doing.

NOUN.—The nouns of mathematical grammar are called numbers. Just as we can recognize different kinds of nouns which we call proper nouns, common nouns, abstract nouns, collective nouns, and pronouns, we can recognize corresponding ways in which numbers can be classified. It took the human race a very long while to recognize the different uses to which numbers had been put, and many difficulties which arise in learning how to apply the rules of mathematical grammar are due to the fact that we do not grasp at the outset two fundamentally distinct ways in which numbers are used.

As long as man counted time in days and measured wine in flagons, he was not bothered about the fact that he was pressing the same words into service of two radically different ways of describing size. We can call these two different ways of using numbers: *counts* or proper numbers, and *estimates* or common numbers. We count half-pennies, votes, apples, quarter-days, and population. We estimate heights, voltages, areas, quarts, and pulse-rates. We may call numbers used to measure the size of a group *proper* numbers, because there is only one such number which correctly describes the size of the group. If you say that there are 15 sheep running in a field, you mean that there are 15 sheep, and not 15·001 or 14·999 sheep. The number 15 stands for something quite definite, just as the proper noun "Abraham B. Stubbins" stands for a perfectly definite person. If you say that the height of your room is 15 feet 3 inches, all you can mean is that it is nearer to the mark 15 feet 3 inches than it is to the marks 15 feet 2 inches and 15 feet 4 inches on a scale divided in inches. If you like to take a smaller scale marked in tenths of an inch, you can give another estimate. With a finer scale and a vernier you could give a figure correct to the nearest hundredth of an inch. The microscope of the bacteriologist can measure to a hundred thousandth of an inch without difficulty. The spectroscope can detect differences of one hundred-billionth, i.e. 0·00000000000001 centimetres. There is no reason to suppose that our present spectroscopes are the most accurate instruments that human beings can ever make. Discrepancies between estimates of the size of an electron made during the last thirty years are far greater than the discrepancies between present estimates of the size of the earth and those made two thousand years ago. To speak of astronomy and physics as the exact sciences is merely a misnomer. Perhaps it is popular because it helps idealist philosophers to overlook the existence of biological science which deals with the imperfections of their own brains.

The point to be clear about when you talk of the size of a room is that the number you give is only one of an enormously large class of numbers near to one another, just as the common noun "men" stands for a large number of animals very much alike, and including among their number Tom, Dick, and Harry. Tom, Dick, and Harry remind us that the distinction between proper nouns and common nouns in ordinary grammar is not nearly as clear-cut as the definitions of school books seem to indicate. In the fable of the big bad wolf, Mr. Wolf is a proper noun. When we use "Tom, Dick, and Harry" together idiomatically, they are really common nouns. The fact is that there are a good many Toms, Dicks, and Harrys in the world. We rely on the context to tell us which particular Tom, Dick, or Harry is meant. Nowadays we have several means of indicating when a number is being used as a common noun. If the smallest divisions of my measuring rod are inches, the statement that the room is 15 feet 3 inches or 183 inches high means that it is nearer to the 183 than to the 182- or to the 184-inch mark, i.e. it lies between $182\frac{1}{2}$ ($183 - \frac{1}{2}$ inches) and $183\frac{1}{2}$ ($183 + \frac{1}{2}$ inches). So what we really mean by saying that it is 183 inches high can be stated more precisely by saying that it is $183 \pm \frac{1}{2}$ inches. In applying mathematics to the real world, proper nouns like 183 or whole numbers only correctly describe the size of groups made up of separate individuals, like the membership of a trade union, or the contents of a ballot box. For all other uses, when numbers correspond with common nouns, we need numbers which stretch, like $183 \pm 0{\cdot}5$. Otherwise we rely wholly on the context to make clear what we mean. A height of "183 inches" measured with a rod marked in tenths of an inch really means $183 \pm 0{\cdot}05$ inches.

The difficulties which have arisen in the history of size language because numbers were first used for separate things recalls a corresponding stage in the history of ordinary speech. Some linguists hold that primitive man made separate noises when he pointed to a black cow, a white cow, or a brown cow. Development along this line was prevented by the constant need to manufacture new words. Civilized peoples have dealt with the difficulty of distinguishing individuals and groups of individuals in different ways. One is by inventing separate noises which we call adjectives, like black, brown, or white. This enables us to go on recognizing more and more things without multiplying our vocabulary beyond practicable dimensions. We have also invented other devices. If an individual happens to have the surname "Smith," his parents may give him the Christian names "Morris Marmaduke Mornington." It is not likely that there will be two persons named Morris Marmaduke Mornington Smith in the same street. In the English language—not in Russian—Christian names are now essentially adjectives.

The dual use of numbers for counts and estimates has been the source of continual misunderstanding between the practical man and the mathematician. In the next two chapters we shall see how it produced the first crisis in the history of mathematics. When confronted with the difficulty of making whole numbers fit measurements which imperfect human beings, using imperfect sense organs, make with imperfect instruments in an imperfect and changing world, the practical man was long content to go on adding fresh divisions to his scale of measurement. You can see that this works very well up to a point

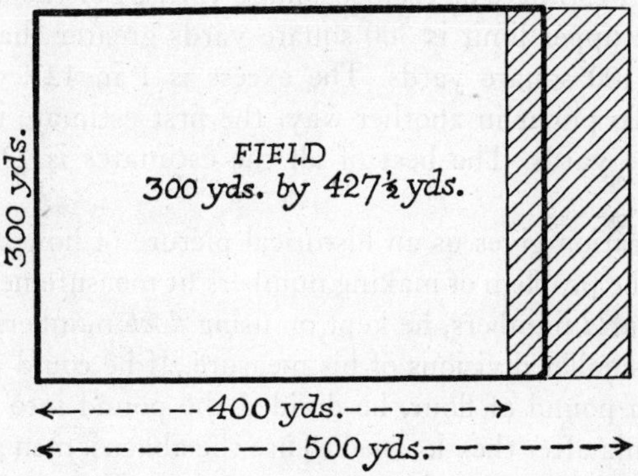

FIG. 21

by examining the following illustration. Suppose four men are asked to measure the area of an oblong field which is 300 yards broad and 427½ yards long. We will assume for the time being, as the practical man himself does assume, that it is actually possible for a field to be exactly 300 yards broad or exactly 427½ yards long. Suppose also that the first man has a rope of 100 yards, the second has a tape of 10 yards, the third has a pole of 3 yards, and the fourth a rule 1 yard long. None of them finds any difficulty with the first side. Their measures can be placed along it just 3 times, 30 times, 100 times, and 300 times respectively. The trouble begins with the side 427½ yards long. The first man finds that this is more than 4 and less than 5 times his measure, so his estimate of the area lies between that of a field of 300 × 500 square yards, or 150,000 square yards, and that of a field 300 × 400, or 120,000 square yards (see Fig. 21). The second finds that it is more than 42 and less than 43 times his measure. His estimate lies between 420 × 300 and 430 × 300 square yards. Let us make a table of all their estimates:

Measure	*Lower Limit (square yards)*	*Upper Limit (square yards)*
100 yards	300 × 400 = 120,000	300 × 500 = 150,000
10 „	300 × 420 = 126,000	300 × 430 = 129,000
3 „	300 × 426 = 127,800	300 × 429 = 128,700
1 yard	300 × 427 = 128,100	300 × 428 = 128,400

If you look at these results you will see that the upper estimate of the first crude measure is 30,000 square yards (or 25 per cent) bigger than the lower estimate of 120,000 square yards. For the last and best estimate, the upper limit is 300 square yards greater than the lower limit of 128,100 square yards. The excess is 1 in 427, or less than $\frac{1}{4}$ per cent. To put it in another way, the first estimate is 135,000 ± 15,000 square yards. The best of all the estimates is 128,250 ± 150 square yards.

This illustration gives us an historical picture of how the practical man solved the problem of making numbers fit measurements. Instead of inventing *field* numbers, he kept on using *flock* numbers by making smaller and smaller divisions of his measure. If he could not measure out exactly a pound of flour, he divided the pound into ounces. For many millennia after they learned to use the abacus, men always dealt with fractions as small units of measurement. Even three hundred years ago, mathematicians used degrees ($\frac{1}{60}$), minutes ($\frac{1}{3600}$), and seconds ($\frac{1}{216000}$), to represent fractions of lengths, weights, or even sums of money, because it was difficult to think of a fraction as a real number without a metaphorical scale divided into clear-cut segments. A real number was a whole number like 2 sheep or 5 cows.

The Greeks, who wrote books about the sort of figures which the architects and surveyors of Egypt traced upon the sand to guide them in their work, were the first to bother themselves about the fact that practical men were using number in two different ways. In comparing figures which they drew with two very imperfect instruments, the compass and the ruler, they soon found that they were not always able to represent sizes by sheepish and cowlike numbers, which must be either odd or even, male or female, like sheep or cows. In a different social context this might have been a first step to planning a rational number language. Actually it led to stagnation. Greek mathematics was not financed by the Air Ministry like modern aerodynamics. It did not have to produce results which could be used. Instead of seeking to perfect the language of number, the Greeks sought perfection in the skies. They banished number and units of measurement from geometry, and exalted mathematics as an aid to spiritual perfection. Mathematics was only able to take another step forward when the Alexandrians began to look for measurements instead of perfection in the skies.

The story of this crisis will be told later on. Here we shall only refer to a curious trick which made confusion worse confounded. To dodge the imperfections of Greek number language, Eudoxus introduced into the study of figures a custom which recalls the triangular simplicities which hypnotized the Hittites in 1936 B.C., and still befuddle the followers of Hegel in A.D. 1936. To avoid using units like "cubits" or "centimetres" they said that the size of a figure, line, or angle must be one of three things. Either it is greater than ($>$), less than ($<$), or "equal" to ($=$) another figure, line, or angle. The Athenian intellectual did not examine the sort of things about which these words can be used. If he had actually done so, he would have seen that the seeming perfection and exactitude of his geometrical proofs was suppositious.

There are three ways of describing the size of a group or object. The first and crudest is the statement of a single *limit*. For instance, I know that the "stolen bacillus" is smaller than Mr. Wells. As I cannot recognize a bacillus with my eyes and can recognize an object 1/1000th of the size of Mr. Wells, I can say that the bacillus is less than 1/1000th of the size of Mr. Wells. In mathematical language, $b < W/1000$. Unless I happen to remember the dimensions of the hydrogen atom, or the size of a molecule of egg-white, or the limits of visibility of the microscope, I cannot state any quantity than which the stolen bacillus is greater ($b >$?). Conversely, I know that the distance (S) from Southport to the star Sirius is greater than the distance (s) from Southport to Syracuse. I even know that it is more than a thousand times greater. In mathematical language, $S > 1000\ s$. Unless I have a book on astronomy I have no way of recalling the distance of any star which is farther away than Sirius, i.e. any distance than which the distance from Southport of Sirius is smaller ($S <$?). Statements which involve only one limit can often be made about measurements of objects. They can sometimes be made about groups. For instance, I may know that the number of blood corpuscles in the human body is much greater than the number of inhabitants in London, or that the number of fleas in the world is greater than the number of men in the world, without being able to give a number for the upper limit in either case.

Such crude statements are the first step in measurement. True measurement involves the statement of two limits. We have already illustrated this by what has been said about the height of a room or the area of a field. One limit is a number of units greater, the other limit is a number of units less, than the number of units we take as mean estimate. We may also describe the size of a group in this way. For instance, we may be told that the population of London is 11 million, that the population of Liverpool is 1 million, and that the population of Moscow is somewhere in between. We can then give a plus or minus estimate for the population of Moscow as 6 ± 5 million. As long as we are only using numbers to represent units of measurement, statements like this are the most that we can ever make. All we can hope to do is to narrow the margin of uncertainty which is bounded by the number in front of which the $\pm$ sign is put.

In comparing groups we can sometimes make a third kind of statement. If every hen in a run lays 4 eggs per week, the number (n) of hen's eggs laid per week is exactly four times as great as the number (N) of hens in the run. In mathematical language this sentence reads

$$n = 4\text{N}.$$

The important thing to notice about this sentence is that it is exactly true when, and only when, it is made about the size or arrangement (order) of a group of separate things, like individual hens and individual eggs. When we are talking about the size of anything we can actually trace on sand or model in wax like a figure in Euclid's geometry, exact equality has no place. If the geometrical line is really something which can stand for the height of a stone wall, and the geometrical rectangle is a figure which can stand for an oblong field, the best that we can say about either of them is that it is less than so many times and greater than so many times another line or rectangle. For instance, if they are very nearly the same size, I may be able to say that the line is less than $1 \cdot 001$ times and greater than $0 \cdot 999$ times another line.

One of the great cultural advantages of our own century is that we now possess fractions that stretch as well as fractions that do not. A fraction that does not stretch, like $\frac{2}{3}$, is perfectly satisfactory for describing the ratio of a group of individuals or objects to one another. If 300 voters go to the poll in one ward and 100 ballot papers are wrongly filled in, the number of votes counted will be $\frac{2}{3}$ the number of voters. If one wall is 15 feet long, and is only covered with wallpaper up to 10 feet, we cannot say that $\frac{2}{3}$ is papered in exactly the same sense.

Our measurements of 15 feet and 10 feet, like all measurements, are fallible beyond a certain point. This can be easily expressed in a compact form by using the decimal fraction $0{\cdot}\dot{6}$. $0{\cdot}\dot{6}$ means a quantity

$$> \frac{6}{10} \qquad < \frac{7}{10}$$

$$> \frac{66}{100} \qquad < \frac{67}{100}$$

$$> \frac{666}{1000} \qquad < \frac{667}{1000}$$

$$> \frac{6666}{10000} \qquad < \frac{6667}{10000}$$

$$> \frac{66666}{100000} \qquad < \frac{66667}{100000} \quad \text{and so on.}$$

In using the decimal fraction $0{\cdot}\dot{6}$ we can stop short at any point according to the accuracy of which our instruments are capable. If our error of measurement is 1 in 100, it is pointless to go on adding more sixes after $0{\cdot}66$. Since $0{\cdot}67$ exceeds $\frac{2}{3}$ by $\frac{1}{300}$, which is one two-hundredth of the latter, and $\frac{2}{3}$ exceeds $0{\cdot}66$ by $\frac{1}{150}$, which is one hundredth of the former, either $0{\cdot}66$ or $0{\cdot}67$ corresponds to the fraction $\frac{2}{3}$ in so far as it can represent a measurement made by a scale with a 1 per cent margin of error. The decimal fraction gives us the means for expressing just how much we know and how much we do not know. Decimal fractions have only been in general use for a century. We have to thank the National Assembly of the French Revolution for this part of our social heritage. Till about five hundred years ago one practical man had no such simple way of expressing how much his observations might differ from those of another practical man.

It happens that we can make the decimal fraction $0{\cdot}\dot{6}$ as near to $\frac{2}{3}$ as we like by putting down sixes till we get too tired to add more. Once we are used to the practice of going on as long as we like, we have no difficulty in seeing that there may be plenty of numbers for which we can find no simple ratio of two male numbers, or of one male and one female number like $\frac{2}{3}$. The decimal fraction $0{\cdot}\dot{6}$ can be written in number symbols because it simply consists of a decimal series of sixes. If it consisted of numbers that did not make any obvious pattern, we should have to find a substitute for a number noun. In modern mathematics, as in ordinary speech, there are pronouns. Two of the most important are π and e, both of which we shall hear more about later. The first is the ratio of the boundary to the diameter of a circle. We use the Greek letter π (pronounced PIE) because the exact value we give depends upon the use to which we put it. If we wish to make a cylinder head true within an error of, say, 1 per cent, it is good enough to take it as 3·14. If we want to make a cylinder head that is true to an error less than 1 in 10,000, it is good enough to take it as 3·1416. How long we make the tail of the fraction depends upon whether we are designing a Roman chariot wheel, the piston of Puffing Billy, or a modern aeroplane engine. Like $0\cdot\dot{6}$, π is really a family of numbers all very near to one another. We use the pronoun π because there is no convenient way of expressing the family resemblance by a common noun of number language.

In mathematics letters are generally used for nouns in a somewhat different way. In addition to proper nouns and common nouns, grammar books distinguish between abstract nouns like "justice" and collective nouns like "people." This distinction has added to the congestion of intellectual traffic instead of preventing it. Indeed, one of the greatest cultural revolutions in human history was the recognition that the abstract noun of the grammarian is a mixed bag. Sometimes it is indistinguishable from a collective noun. Sometimes it is just a compact way of writing out a collection of adjectives. Often it is nothing but what the anthropologist calls "magic gesture." The idealist philosopher Plato gave abstract nouns like "justice" an existence independent of the social circumstances of the people who describe a social action as just or unjust. Plato's curious views about such words were closely connected with his curious views about numbers. Both were wafted into his firmament of universals which the scholastic theologians believed to be as definite a place as hell itself. Modern science began when men like Roger Bacon and Francis Bacon rejected the world of "universals" and set about making words describe the solid earth of human experience. We do not need to draw a distinction between abstract and collective nouns in mathematics because mathematics is a language of action. The letters of the alphabet which are used for whole families of numbers having something definite in common, correspond with what we call collective nouns and the better sort of abstract nouns. In ordinary speech the value of such nouns is that they save time and space. The same is true of size language. Take the following ways of stating the same rule as an example.

(i) "The area of an oblong floor in square units (e.g. square feet) is found by multiplying the length by the breadth in corresponding units (e.g. feet)."

More shortly this may be written thus:

(ii) Area = length × breadth.

This can be boiled down to the still more compact form:

(iii) A = *lb*.

Using the letters A, *l*, *b* shows us how to find the area of rooms of different lengths and breadths, so that we do not have to write the rule out again for every different size of room, and writing *l* next to *b* means that *l* and *b* have to be multiplied together. The use of abstract or collective numbers like *n* to stand for any number of the particular things we are talking about, just as the abstract noun "colour" stands for red, blue, green, etc., in different contexts, is not confined to providing us with a compact way of stating a rule. It also helps us to *find* simple rules of calculation. Here is an example of a simple rule of this sort shown in Fig. 22.

Suppose we have a set of chairs arranged in rows, each of which contains one more chair than the preceding row and one less than the one which follows. If we want to know how many chairs there are altogether, or to use the word generally applied to an addition, the *sum* of all the chairs, we have no need to go to the trouble of counting them one by one. We can find the sum by a simple rule which applies to adding up a big family of sets of numbers like the numbers of chairs in each row. If the first row consists of one chair, the twelfth will consist of twelve, and the sum of all the chairs in the first twelve rows will be:

$$1 + 2 + 3 + 4 + 5 + 6 + 7 + 8 + 9 + 10 + 11 + 12$$

We can rearrange the numbers in this sum like this:

$$(1 + 12) + (2 + 11) + (3 + 10) + (4 + 9) + (5 + 8) + (6 + 7)$$

Each of these pairs adds up to 13, and there are six pairs in all, making the whole sum 6 times 13, i.e. 78. Now let us write out what we have done without using proper numbers. We had a certain number of numbers to add together. Call it *n*. We arranged them in pairs, making half as many pairs as *n* itself, i.e. $\frac{1}{2}n$ pairs. The sum of each pair of numbers added up to the same as the sum of the *f*irst number (*f*) and the *l*ast number (*l*) in the set, i.e. the sum of each pair was briefly

$(f+l)$, and since there were $\frac{1}{2}n$ pairs altogether the total was $\frac{1}{2}n(f+l)$. Before you go any farther you can add up the first twenty and the first thirty numbers and you will find that you get the same result by the very much quicker method of applying the simple rule we have just built up. For instance, if you add up all the first thirty numbers

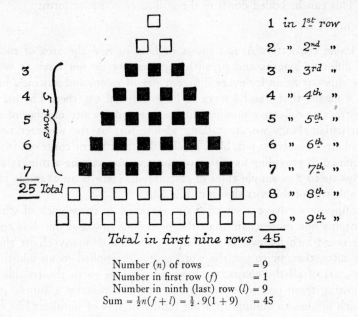

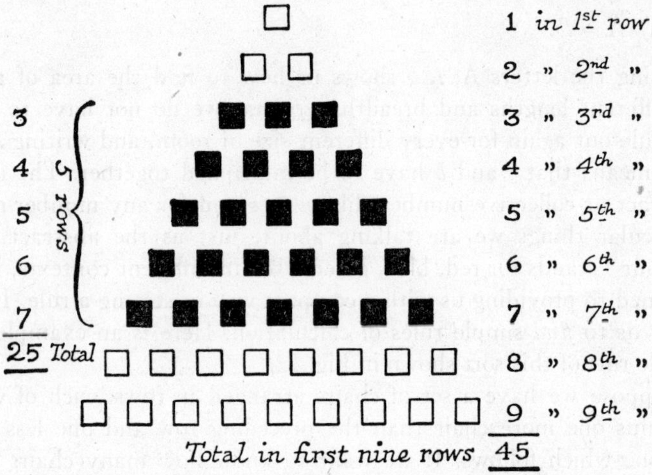

Number (n) of rows $= 9$
Number in first row (f) $= 1$
Number in ninth (last) row (l) $= 9$
Sum $= \frac{1}{2}n(f+l) = \frac{1}{2}.9(1+9) = 45$

FIG. 22.—SUM OF FIRST NINE NUMBERS

Note that the formula works equally well for counting all the chairs in rows 3 to 7 inclusive. In this case the number of rows (n) is 5, the first number (f) is 3, the last (l) is 7. So the sum is

$$\tfrac{1}{2}.5(3+7) = \tfrac{1}{2}(5 \times 10) = 25$$

(1 to 30) you will find the sum is 465. There are 30 numbers ($n = 30$) of which the first is 1 and the last is 30. So according to our rule the sum should be $\frac{1}{2}.30\ (1+30) = 15 \times 31 = 465$.

The next thing to notice is that the rule given applies whether we start with the first row of chairs or any other one. For instance, we might have started with the third row (in which there are 3 chairs), and gone on to the twelfth. In that case there would be ten rows, i.e. ten numbers to count ($n = 10$), of which the first $f = 3$ and the last $l = 12$. The sum would be $\frac{1}{2}.10(3+12) = 75$, three less than

78, a result which is obviously right, since we have only left out the one chair of the first row and the two chairs of the second row. Or test the rule like this. The sum of the numbers from 1 to 30 (all the chairs in the first thirty rows) is the sum of the numbers from 1 to 12 (i.e. 78), and the eighteen numbers which follow from 13 to 30.

□ □ □	3
■ ■ ■ ■ ■ ■	6
■ ■ ■ ■ ■ ■ ■ ■ ■	9
■ ■ ■ ■ ■ ■ ■ ■ ■ ■ ■ ■	12
□ □ □ □ □ □ □ □ □ □ □ □ □ □ □	15

Total- 45

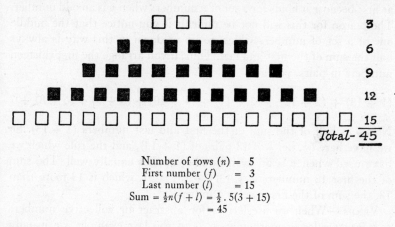

Number of rows (n) = 5
First number (f) = 3
Last number (l) = 15
Sum = $\frac{1}{2}n(f + l) = \frac{1}{2} \cdot 5(3 + 15)$
= 45

Fig. 23.—Sum of the Set 3, 6, 9, 12, 15

Note.—(1) The formula works because the numbers can be arranged in a "series" increasing or decreasing by the same amount (3) each time.
(2) The formula saves you the trouble of actually counting any rows except the first and last if you know that the series grows in this way.

The sum of the first twelve is 78, the sum of the next eighteen should be $\frac{1}{2} \cdot 18(13 + 30) = 9 \times 43 = 387$, and 387 added to 78 makes 465, which was what we got by direct addition.

Another thing to notice is that the usefulness of this rule for cutting out laborious addition is not confined to sets of numbers which increase by one at a step. Take for example the set of numbers:

$$7 \quad 12 \quad 17 \quad 22 \quad 27 \quad 32$$

We can add these in pairs thus:

$$(7 + 32) + (12 + 27) + (17 + 22)$$

Each of these three pairs adds up to the sum of the first (7) and last (32) numbers, i.e. to 39, and the sum of all the six is therefore $\frac{1}{2} \cdot 6(7 + 32)$. The reason why we can arrange them in such pairs is that each number differs from the one before by the same amount.

So the result of adding the second to the last but one, the third to the last but two, etc., is just the same as adding the first to the last. The rule therefore holds for all sets of numbers arranged so that the difference between the second and the first is the same as the difference between the third and the second, and so on. You may be worried at first because it holds for a set of n numbers when n is an odd number. The reason for this will not be difficult if you notice that the middle one of a set of numbers which go up or down in this way is always half the sum of the first and last. Thus, if you arrange the first thirteen numbers in pairs, you get

$$(1 + 13) + (2 + 12) + (3 + 11) + (4 + 10) + (5 + 9) + (6 + 8) + 7$$

Now 7 is half of the sum of the first and last numbers $(1 + 13)$. So we have here $6\frac{1}{2}$, i.e. $\frac{1}{2}$ of 13 pairs of $(1 + 13)$, and the rule which we have used when n is an even number applies equally well. The sum of the first 13 numbers is $\frac{1}{2}.13(1 + 13) = 91$, which is 13 more than 78, the sum of the first twelve numbers.

VERBS.—When we use letters for abstract or collective numbers to convey rules in mathematics as in the last example, we usually indicate multiplication by putting the numbers multiplied next to one another. To show that a whole collection of numbers is included in what is to be multiplied we use brackets. For instance, the number phrase $a(b + c)$ means that a is multiplied by the sum formed by adding b to c. Thus $3(5 + 2)$ means 21, i.e. (3×7). This is not the same thing as $ab + c$. Using the same numbers, the last statement would mean $(3 \times 5) + 2$, i.e. 17. We have to use the less compact form 3×5 when writing numbers because the more compact form had already been used for something quite different. For instance, 35 means thirty-five and not fifteen, and $2\frac{1}{2}$ does not mean $\frac{1}{2}$ of 2. We are now going to look more closely at the meaning of signs like "×" and "+," or putting two numbers next to one another like l and b in the rule for area. Perhaps it is better to write the rule in the somewhat more familiar form:

$$l \times b = \text{A}$$

We have seen what this statement means as a sentence expressed in ordinary language. As it stands it is a mathematical sentence. Sentences in mathematics are called equations. An equation is nothing more than a complete sentence in size language. As we all know, a sentence must contain a verb, and the verb tells you what the noun does. We have already seen that A, *l*, and *b* are nouns. The marks "×" and "+" are number verbs. Because mathematics is a practical language and not a sentimental language, there is one peculiarity of mathematical sentences or equations. They always contain the verb infinitive "to get," which is written in the mathematical alphabet " = ." Mathematicians themselves do not call marks like "×" and "—" verbs, they call them operators, just as Americans call workmen operatives. This means that they are not simply there for ornament, like dukes or beefeaters. They do real work. The complete translation of the mathematical sentence

$$l \times b = A$$

would read thus:

"the *l*ength *must be multiplied* by the *b*readth *to get* the *A*rea."

You have now no difficulty in seeing that what mathematicians call operators are exactly the same thing as useful verbs in grammar. C. K. Ogden, inventor of Basic English and one of the most practically minded intellectuals of our time, deserves our gratitude for building a bridge between grammar and mathematics by foreshadowing a rational language in which there is a clear correspondence between the rules of grammar for size and sort. Once you understand this correspondence there is nothing mystifying about an equation. We will make sure that we understand it by putting the two ways of saying the same thing in two columns.

Verbal Statement (Rhetorical algebra)	*Mathematical Equation* (Symbolic algebra)
The *l*ength	l
must be multiplied by	$\times$
the *b*readth	b
to get	$=$
the *A*rea	A

Having got this clear, we can now examine the verb or operator "×." This we can do more clearly by taking the case of the sentence which describes a room 3 yards by 4 yards and area 12 square yards. There are two different ways in which the sentence can be translated. The first is the hieroglyphic or cartoon method, which in mathematics is called geometry. This is to make a scale drawing of the floor, say

3 inches by 4 inches, divide the length and breadth into inches, fill in the number of squares and count them, as in Fig. 24. You will find that there are 12 of them. The other way is to remember that the multiplication table tells you that 3 times 4 or 4 times 3 are 12. This is dictionary language, or, as mathematicians say, "analysis." The multiplication table is a dictionary. Four hundred years ago nobody learned the multiplication table beyond two times. Till we had schools to meet the needs of a merchant class whose livelihood depended on the art of

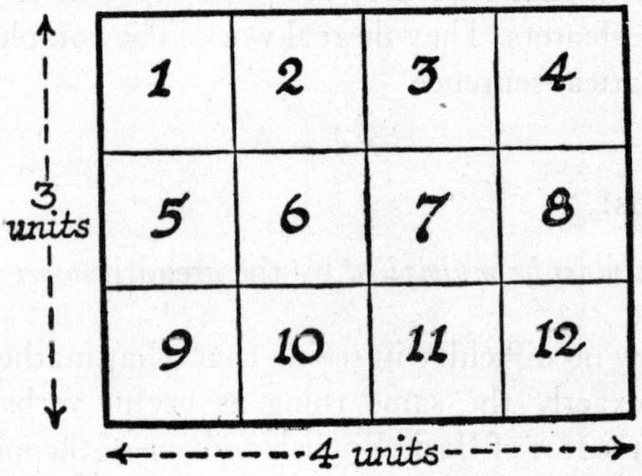

FIG. 24.—HIEROGLYPHIC MULTIPLICATION

In the picture language of geometry we can represent the operator (or mathematical verb) "×" in the mathematical sentence 3 × 4 = 12 by the direction "*make a rectangle* 3 units of length by 4 units of length *and count* the number of squares."

calculation, the multiplication table was a work of reference like the dictionary (Fig. 25). Drawing a scale diagram may seem to you a very roundabout method. That is only because the multiplication table is part of your social heritage. The hieroglyph "×," which means "draw a rectangle to scale and count the unit squares," is the older mathematical language for translating the verb "multiply," just as hieroglyphics are older than the alphabet. The dictionary method of translating "×," which is equivalent to saying "recall to mind or look up such-and-such a line and column in the multiplication table," was a late social acquirement.

This very simple example discloses one very important fact about the history of mathematics. The progress of mathematics has depended very largely upon discovering more socialized and less individualistic ways of dealing with numbers (see Fig. 25). The hieroglyphic or geometrical translation of "×" involves doing something new for

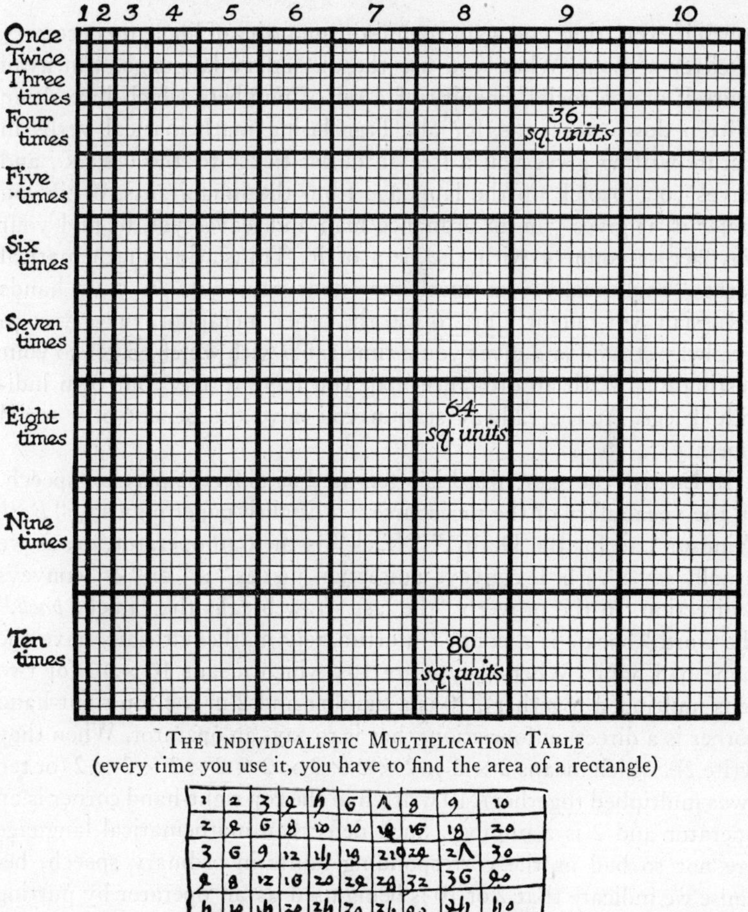

THE INDIVIDUALISTIC MULTIPLICATION TABLE
(every time you use it, you have to find the area of a rectangle)

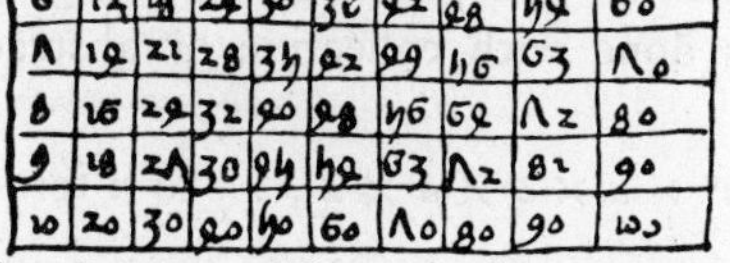

THE SOCIALIZED TABLE OF MULTIPLICATION

From a very early book on Arithmetic using Arab numerals (fifteenth-century copy of Holywood's *Algorism*).

FIG. 25

In the socialized table of multiplication the area of each rectangle is seen at once by the number which has the position corresponding vertically with one side and horizontally with the other. The counting of the square units of area has been done once for all. All you have to do is to read the result, and learn it. In the fifteenth century people did not learn it, they referred to it, as a modern mathematician refers to a table of logarithms.

yourself every time you want to find the quantity of linoleum necessary to cover a room. When you use the dictionary language, you avail yourself of the social amenity of a set of numbers which have been written down once and for all. Translating mathematical verbs in picture-writing gives you a free Intourist ticket to the U.S.S.R., and leaves you to pick up the language from the inhabitants, or, if you prefer it, it gives you an ordnance map and leaves you to find your way across country with the help of it. Translating mathematical verbs "analytically," as mathematicians say, puts in your hands "Russian Self-taught," or, to use the other metaphor, takes you to a railway station and gives you a time-table with which to get to your destination. With an ordnance map you have to use your own individual legs. At the railway station you have the benefit of a social amenity.

In English the same word is often used as different parts of speech. In the vocabulary of the racecourse, an English paper may say "*Back* Windsor Lad for the Derby." "Back" is then an operator, or, as we usually say, a verb. It conveys a direction, just as "×" or "+" conveys a direction. In the proverb "the last straw breaks the camel's *back*," the word "back" is a noun. Unfortunately mathematicians have the same bad habit. When they write 10^2, which means 10×10 (or two tens multiplied together), 10 is a number and 2 in the top right-hand corner is a direction for action, that is to say, an operator. When they write 2^{10}, which means $2 \times 2 \times 2 \times 2 \times 2 \times 2 \times 2 \times 2 \times 2 \times 2$ (or ten twos multiplied together), 10 written in the top right-hand corner is an operator and 2 is a number. Such defects in mathematical language are not so bad as the corresponding faults in ordinary speech, because we indicate that 2 or 10 is being used as an operator by putting it in an unusual position and printing or writing it in smaller type. The same thing is done with collective or abstract numbers. The statement:

$$a^n = a \times a \times a \times a \ldots \text{ to } n \text{ terms}$$

(or n a's multiplied together) is a sentence which tells us what kind of action we are expected to take when a number is put in the top right-hand corner. In this equation n is an operator, and a is a number. The same recipe could be expressed by putting

$$n^a = n \times n \times n \times n \ldots \text{ to } a \text{ times}$$

$$\text{or} \quad n^a = a \; n\text{'s multiplied together}$$

In the last *n* stands for a number and *a* for an operator. The second sentence also tells you what to do when a number is written in the top right-hand corner.

Dictionary language can convey a good deal that could never be expressed by hieroglyphics alone. So also number language can convey directions which cannot always be communicated by figure language. You can see this at once by examining the meaning of 10^2, 10^3, 10^4, as in the table below:

Operator	*Figure Language of Greeks*	*Dictionary Language of Hindus*
2	Find the area of the square of side 10 = 100 square units	Multiply 10 by 10 (two tens multiplied together) = 100
3	Find the volume of the cube of side 10 = 1,000 cube units	Multiply 10 by 10 by 10 (three tens multiplied together) = 1,000
4	No meaning	Multiply $10 \times 10 \times 10 \times 10$ (four tens multiplied together) = 10,000

A phrase (or "expression") like 7^3 provides us with another example of the socialization of the mathematical verb. The operator 3 written in the top right-hand corner may convey one of the following directions:

(*a*) Find the volume of a cube with side 7 units long.
(*b*) Multiply three 7's together.
(*c*) Look up 7 in the table of "cubes."

In Chapter 10 we shall find another meaning more completely collectivized than (*c*) expressed by a sentence with four verbs:

$$7^3 = \text{antilog } (3 \log 7)$$

All this means is: "*Look up* 7 in the table of logarithms, *multiply* what you find there by 3, and then *look up* the result in the table of antilogarithms to get 7^3." Going through two tables would not be a great saving of time if you intended to find 7^3, but it would be an immense saving of time if you wanted 777^3.

We have seen that a letter like "*x*" in an "expression" (or phrase) like 10^x is not a collective or abstract noun. It is a verb which includes the meaning of a lot of other verbs. It stands for any particular verb like 2 or 5 in expressions like 10^2 or 10^5. There is nothing outside the realm of ordinary speech in this way of manufacturing collective or abstract verbs. When I say that I am *putting up* at a boarding house, I generally mean that I am *sleeping*, *washing*, *dressing*, *eating* my breakfast, and *paying* my bill at the end of the week. I can go into higher orders of abstractions. Mathematicians do the same. If I say that I am going to stay in Moscow, I mean among other things that I am going to get a ticket from Intourist, pack my trunks, and take a steamer, as well as *put up* (with all that that includes) in Moscow. We need not give an equivalent illustration of these higher abstractions in size language at this stage. We shall meet them later on.

There is always a danger of carrying this so far that we get lost in a maze of symbols. The mathematician then does what the sensible editor does. He brightens up the discussion by bringing in a cartoon. He goes back to his hieroglyphs, to geometry, whenever he can. To go back is not quite the right expression, because new kinds of hieroglyphs such as "graphs" have been devised (like business advertisements) to give a vivid picture of operations which could not be conveyed by the earlier kinds. For instance, Fig. 26 shows how the geometry of the Reformation could give us a clear picture of the race of Achilles and the tortoise. Euclid's geometry could not. It left out time. The operation x^2—squaring x—can be represented in Greek geometry, which could not make a diagram or model corresponding to x^5. When we come to the Reformation geometry in Chapter 9, we shall see that the graph of x^5 is just as easy to draw as that of x^2.

This tendency of number language to come back to the firm earth of figures and models, when doubts arise, has played a great part in building up the rules of what mathematicians call proof. In one sense proof has much the same relation to discovery as art criticism has to authorship. Mathematical truths are usually *discovered* by experimenting with individual cases first and "*proved*" afterwards. The proof is then an obituary notice on a praiseworthy statement. It exposes how it is connected with all the other mathematical rules we have learned to use. As we are always learning other rules, the methods first used to justify a rule in mathematics are nearly always held to be lacking in "rigour" by mathematicians who come later. This is how one of our most abstract mathematicians, Professor G. H. Hardy, speaks of one of the most abstract branches of mathematics: "The theory of numbers, more than any other branch of mathematics, began by being an experimental science. Its most famous theorems have all been conjectured, sometimes a hundred years or more before they were proved; and they have been suggested by the evidence of a mass of computations." One aspect of what is called proof is close to what the Apostle Paul

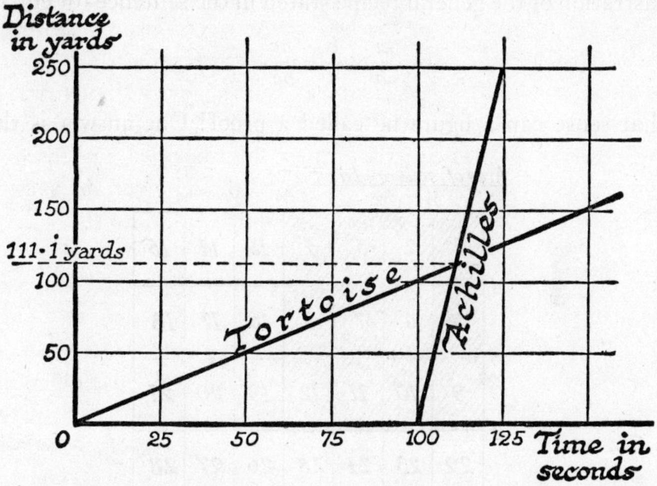

FIG. 26.—THE RACE OF ACHILLES AND THE TORTOISE

Greek geometry, like Greek number language, could not catch up with the tortoise of Zeno. This was because Greek geometry took *space* from the temple architects and the tax surveyor, and left *time* to the priests who made the calendars. The Reformation, which did away with saints' days, came about when merchants were prospering from the Great Navigations. The Great Navigations were possible when the world was being mapped out in latitude and longitude. The new geometry of the Reformation was based on the MAP method. It put time into geometry. So it can tell you at once when Achilles did pass the tortoise. This will be explained in Chapter IX.

meant when he advocated experimental ethics in advising us to "prove all things and hold fast to that which is good." It is the testing of particular results obtained from using a new kind of script by reference to earlier methods of getting similar results.

For instance, measurement of areas was studied centuries before rules for dealing with fractions were invented. The proof of the rule illustrated by the equation

$$\frac{3}{5} \times \frac{4}{7} = \frac{12}{35}$$

shows how the Arabs and the first calculators sought to justify the rules governing fractions. We turn back to the geometrical operation

"×" to seek an area (Fig. 27). To do this we make 3 segments of a line divided into 5 segments of unit length represent the fraction $\frac{3}{5}$, and 4 segments of a line divided into 7 equal segments of unit length represent the fraction $\frac{4}{7}$. The example represented by the figure is an illustration of the general recipe stated in the sentence (or equation)

$$\frac{a}{b} \times \frac{c}{d} = \frac{ac}{bd}$$

In what sense can a figure be called a proof? One answer is that it

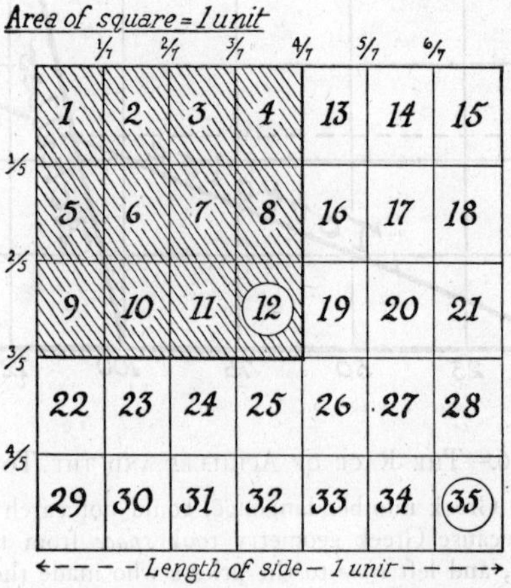

FIG. 27.—PICTURE-WRITING CAN BE USED FOR TESTING THE RULE ILLUSTRATED BY THE MATHEMATICAL SENTENCE (OR "EQUATION")

$$\frac{3}{5} \times \frac{4}{7} = \frac{12}{35}$$

exposes the historical relation between what is already known, the way to measure areas, and what is in process of becoming known, the correct way in which to use fractions. We have seen that such fractions can only represent areas in an approximate sense. What, then, do we mean by saying that the rule is proved by the figure? One answer is that the rule fits the figure as closely as our method of drawing a figure justifies us in expecting it to do. There is nothing absolute in the correspondence. We get the same kind of relief in looking at the figure as in seeing a good cartoon.

In the grammar of European languages, like our own, verbs are classified in conjugations by the way in which they are used to express the time at which an action takes place. Different kinds of mathematical verbs cannot be classified in this way. In so far as time is expressed by operators (Chapter 9) we have to use different ones, just as the perfect tenses (completed time) and imperfect tenses (continued time) of our verb "to speak" have to be translated by two totally different verbs in the Russian language. We need not be discouraged to find imperfect correspondence in all details of size grammar and sort grammar. An Englishman is surprised to find that Russian verbs have gender like French nouns. Before Ogden and Jespersen we had no real grammar of English. What we have been taught as English grammar is a pretence that every rule in Latin must have some equivalent rule in English. Apart from the vestigial genitive used for animate objects, *case* has no meaning applied to nouns in modern English. Just as English grammar differs in some respects from Latin grammar, the grammar of size is not identical with the grammar of sort in every detail. Hence the similarities which we are now recognizing must not be interpreted in a hard-and-fast sense.

There are various ways of classifying mathematical verbs. Two of them are worth recognizing early. Before doing so, we may note that there are no intransitive verbs in mathematics. All mathematical verbs must have an object, because size language is not a language of reflection, but a language of participation in the world's work. The first way of classifying mathematical verbs depends on their relation to the rest of the sentence. One class of operators might be loosely compared with reflexive verbs like "I *wash myself* when I get up." The phrases "$3 + 4$" or "3×4" mean just the same thing as "$4 + 3$" or "4×3" respectively. We only need to know one-half of the multiplication table. Now "$\frac{3}{4}$" or "$3 \div 4$" and "$3 - 4$" do not mean the same thing as "$\frac{4}{3}$" or "$4 \div 3$" and "$4 - 3$." If you like the analogy, they are not reflexive verbs. A sentence like

$$4 \div 3 = 1\tfrac{1}{3}$$

or

$$\frac{4}{3} = 1\tfrac{1}{3}$$

has the structure. "With something do something to something to get some result." This reminds one of a statement like "Take this letter to the post-office to get it registered." Such a sentence has not the same structure as the equation

$$3 \times 4 = 12$$

or as

$$3 + 4 = 7$$

because taking a letter to the post-office is not the same thing as taking the post-office to a letter. Mathematicians call operators like "×" or "+" commutative operators, and operators like "÷" or "−" non-commutative operators. Some kinds of mathematics only use the latter, just as some languages like English have practically eliminated reflexive verbs. Notice in this connexion that the operators "÷" and the bar "−" written with one number above and the second below, mean the same thing just as the verbs "to talk with" and "to converse" mean the same thing.

The other important distinction in classifying operators depends on their relation to one another. This is a more important one to know. Like the foregoing it has no exact parallel in grammar. In one way it is rather like our distinction between the active verb and the passive verb. In another way it is rather like the distinction between a verb like "to assert" and a verb like "to deny." We say that the operator "÷" is the *inverse* operator to "×", and the operator "−" is the inverse operator to "+". What this means is really very easy to understand if you remember what you do when you subtract. If

$$3 + 4 = 7$$

it is also true that $\quad 7 - 4 = 3$

and that $\quad 7 - 3 = 4$

Instead of translating the last sentence by "From 7 *take away* 3 to get 4," you may render it "Find the number which *has to be added* to 3 to get 7." From this point of view it represents addition in the passive voice. The same relation exists between multiplication and division. Multiplying 3 by 4 is adding up 4 lots of 3. Dividing 4 by 3 is finding out how many times 3 can be subtracted from 4 till you cannot take away another whole set of 3 on the counting frame. Putting it in another way we can translate the equation

$$4 \div 3 = 1\tfrac{1}{3}$$

or $\quad \frac{4}{3} = 1\frac{1}{3}$

by the sentence "4 is obtained when $1\frac{1}{3}$ *is multiplied by* 3." When you put this sentence in the active voice, it reads "Multiply $1\frac{1}{3}$ by 3 to get 4," or

$$1\tfrac{1}{3} \times 3 = 4$$

You will probably know another example of an operator and its inverse operator. In the equation

$$7^2 = 49$$

the operator is 2. It reads "Multiply two sevens together to get 49." Exactly the same statement may be translated in another form, thus:

$$\sqrt{49} = 7$$

This means "Find the number which when it *is multiplied* by itself gives 49, to get 7." The operator "$\sqrt{}$" is called the square root of 49. Similarly the inverse operator to 4 written in the top right-hand corner is "$\sqrt[4]{}$." "I *wrote* this chapter" (active voice) means the same as "this chapter *was written* by me" (passive voice). The same thing is meant by the two equations: $2^5 = 32$ and $\sqrt[5]{32} = 2$.

However, there is another grammatical analogy which is more important in practice. An inverse operator put in front of its corresponding operator cancels the meaning of the latter. In the same way "I deny that I assert" leaves you where you were, not knowing what my view is. Keeping to the last illustration you will not find it difficult to see that

$$\sqrt[3]{27} = \sqrt[3]{3^3} = 3$$

$$\text{or} \quad \sqrt[5]{32} = \sqrt[5]{2^5} = 2$$

That is to say, the inverse operator $\sqrt[n]{}$ wipes out the meaning of the operator represented by *n* put in the top right-hand corner. We have already met another example of this. "Antilog (log 5)" means "look up the number corresponding to 5 in the table of logarithms, and then find the number corresponding to this in the table of antilogarithms." The number you would get would be 5. *Antilog* put before *log* leaves you where you were before. You can translate for yourself in the dictionary language of the square and square-root tables a statement like

$$\sqrt{289} = \sqrt{17^2}$$

So far we have not explained how to get the numbers given in the tables of logarithms and antilogarithms. This will be explained in Chapter 10. You can make a table of squares for yourself (e.g. $1^2 = 1$, $2^2 = 4$, $3^2 = 9$).

This leads to another way of looking at the inverse operator. A table of square roots can be built up once you have made a table of squares by turning the table of squares inside out. You should do this as an exercise. When you do it you will get some insight into something at which we have only hinted, and shall explain more fully in the next chapter. In hieroglyph mathematics, a square root is the length of a line corresponding with an area represented by the number whose square root we are finding. That is to say, the square root of 49, or 7 (see Fig. 20), is the number of units of length in the side of a square enclosing 49 square units of area. You will remember how we said earlier that in studying figures the Greeks came up against sizes which could not be described exactly by whole numbers or fractions of the older sort. The same is true of the square root of 2. Although we can find a number for the square root of 2 as near as we need in order to draw a square of 2 square feet as accurately as we can draw it, we cannot translate the phrase $\sqrt{2}$ *exactly* by sheepish or cowlike numbers. There is no reason why we should, because the wall of the sheepfold or cowpen is not made up of separate individual sheep or cows. (See Fig. 75, chapter 5).

As you will need tables of square roots before long, one way of making such a table may be given here. With a table of squares, such as we have printed at the end of this book, you will not find it difficult to get a value for $\sqrt{2}$ which is good enough for most practical purposes. You know that $\sqrt{1}$ is 1 and $\sqrt{4}$ is 2. So $\sqrt{2}$ is less than 2 and greater than 1. As a first guess take 1·5. The table shows that $15^2 = 225$, or $1 \cdot 5^2 = 2 \cdot 25$. So 1·5 is too big. $14^2 = 196$, so $1 \cdot 96 = 1 \cdot 4^2$, and 1·4 is too small. As 1·96 is much nearer to 2 than is 2·25, 1·4 is better than 1·5. By multiplying out you will find that 1·42 is too big and 1·41 is too small. If you only want an estimate suitable for ordinary drawing instruments, which cannot be relied upon to give successive results within 1 per cent, $1 \cdot 415 \pm 0 \cdot 005$ is good enough. To make the error less than 1 per cent you could take any number between 1·414 and 1·415. Another way of getting a good value for these roots, which mathematicians call *surds* or *irrationals*, is this. If you want to find the square root of 10, look through the table of squares for two numbers one of which is nearly ten times the other. For instance, 9,604 is 98^2 and 961 (which differs from $\frac{1}{10}$ of 9,604 by roughly 6 in 10,000, or 0·06 per cent) is 31^2. So $(\frac{98}{31})^2$ is very nearly 10, and the square root of 10 is therefore very nearly $\frac{98}{31}$. This gives the square root of 10 as 3·16. Multiply it out and see how close it is.

SYNTAX.—Books on grammar divide their rules into two kinds. Those which deal with the individual parts of speech, nouns, verbs, etc., are called *accidence*. Besides these there are the rules about how words are put together in complete sentences. These are the rules of *syntax*. The fundamental rules of mathematical syntax are very simple because, as we have seen, the language of size is not a language in which sentiment can be expressed. So all its sentences have essentially the same structure. They always contain "to get," which is written "=." This divides the sentence into two parts, which we call the two *sides* of the equation. The fundamental rules of mathematical syntax concern how you can change one side of the equation or both sides of the equation simultaneously.

The only point which we need notice about changing one side only is the order of words. Some words are interchangeable, and others are not. In English the sentence "The Pope is the Head of the Roman Church" means the same thing as "Of the Roman Church the Pope is the Head." It does not mean the same thing as "The Head is the Pope of the Roman Church," or "The Roman Church is the Head of the Pope." The only difficulty of this kind which need worry us in dealing with size language has already been made clear. When numbers are connected by verbs like "$\times$" or "$+$", they are interchangeable. For instance

$$ab = ba$$

e.g. $$3 \times 7 = 21 = 7 \times 3$$

$$a(b + c) = a(c + b) = (b + c)a = (c + b)a$$

e.g. $$7(3 + 2) = 7(2 + 3) = 35 = (3 + 2)7 = (2 + 3)7$$

One-sided changes can be made when they do not affect the meaning of the side changed. If they do affect the meaning, exactly the same change has to be made on the other side. For instance, if $x = y$, we may also write

(i) $x + a = y + a$

(ii) $x - a = y - a$

(iii) $ax = ay$

(iv) $\frac{x}{a} = \frac{y}{a}$, (unless $a = 0$)

Translation in size language is just putting on one side of an equation (usually the right side) all the quantities you know, and on the other side all the quantities you do not know. The equation then reads: "Put down such and such to get what you want to find." Since what you know is customarily put on the right side, a more literal rendering would be: "What you want can be got by putting down such and such." This rearrangement of quantities (or "terms") can be done by using one of the four rules given above. The application of the first two rules is summarized in the rule that *a quantity added to the rest of one side of an equation can be shifted to the other side if the sign (+ or −) is changed.* For instance, if

$$p + b = q$$

e.g. $3 + 4 = 7$

it is also true that $p + b - b = q - b$

or $p = q - b$

e.g. $3 = 7 - 4$

Similarly if $p - c = q$

e.g. $9 - 5 = 4$

it is also true that $p - c + c = q + c$

or $p = q + c$

e.g. $9 = 4 + 5$

The shorter rule which combines (iii) and (iv) will be illustrated by a class of quantities which are now familiar features of social life. Notice before we do so that (iii) might also be written: $\frac{ax}{1} = \frac{ay}{1}$. We shall see later that a great deal of time and labour can be saved in studying geometry if we do not handicap ourselves by the very great difficulty which ratios presented to the mathematicians of antiquity. The word "ratio" is used for quantities connected by the words "per" or "to the." Familiar examples are: *income* (so much per annum), *wages* (so much per week), *interest* (so much per cent). Other ratios in everyday life are prices, overtime pay, petrol consumption (miles to the gallon), speed (miles per hour), batting averages (runs to the completed innings).

Take first petrol consumption. The petrol consumption of an automobile is alleged to be 35 miles to the gallon. Assuming, as is unlikely, that the salesman is not lying, this means that if you divide the number of miles (m) by the number of gallons (g), the result is 35, i.e.:

$$m \div g = 35$$

or $$\frac{m}{g} = 35$$

The amateur detective might use this as a recipe for three kinds of behaviour: (*a*) if he is about to chase a fugitive on a non-stop journey London to Brighton, or Woods Hole to Boston, he knows how many miles he will have to go without filling up, and can get how many gallons he must put in his tank, i.e.:

$$g = \frac{m}{35}$$

In other words "Divide the miles you have to go by 35 to get the number of gallons you have to put in the tank."

(*b*) If he wishes to detect whether the suspect is lying about how far he drove the automobile in the night, and knows from a garage proprietor how much the tank held yesterday, he can look at the petrol indicator, and so deduce how many miles the automobile has travelled in the intervening time, i.e.

$$m = 35g$$

In other words "Multiply the gallons used up by 35 to get how far the suspect really travelled."

(*c*) Suppose the suspect says that he had driven to Brighton or Boston, as the case may be, in the night, and that the petrol consumption tallies with the statement. The detective may suspect the alibi, and want to satisfy himself that there is no leak in the petrol tank. He can do this by taking the automobile for a run. The alibi holds if the number of miles run divided by the number of gallons consumed is 35. If the original statement is correct:

$$35 = \frac{m}{g}$$

All three ways of writing down the petrol consumption of an automobile can be summarized by using broad arrows:

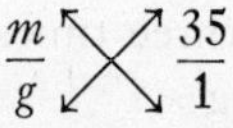

This rule is much easier to handle than deciding when you can interchange subject, direct object, and indirect object in sentences like the three following:

(*a*) The bishop gave a bun to the baboon.
(*b*) A bun was given to the baboon by the bishop.
(*c*) The baboon was given a bun by the bishop.

All these three mean the same thing, and do not mean "The baboon gave the bishop a bun."

Cookery-book recipes illustrate the rule better by showing us why we wrote the number 35 in the unusual way $\frac{35}{1}$. In ratios the "so many" in "so many to the something" may be a fraction. For instance, in making jelly we may be told to add $1\frac{1}{2}$ ($\frac{3}{2}$) lbs. of sugar to 1 quart of juice. Let us compare the three different recipes for action in the statement.

$$\frac{p}{q} = \frac{3}{2}$$

meaning $$\frac{\text{pounds of sugar added}}{\text{quarts of juice}} = \frac{3}{2}$$

(*a*) Suppose I have first measured out my juice. The number of pounds of sugar I have to add is $\frac{3}{2}$ of the number of quarts, or

$$p = \frac{3Q}{2}$$

(*b*) If I only have a certain amount of sugar and want to make as much jelly as I can, I must measure out a number of quarts equivalent to $1 \div \frac{3}{2}$ or two-thirds the number of pounds of sugar. This is the same thing as writing

$$q = \frac{2P}{3}$$

(*c*) If I am not a good arithmetician, and am given the recipe in the form 6 pounds of sugar to every 4 quarts of juice, I might measure out 6 pounds of sugar and 4 quarts of juice, and repeat the performance until all the juice was used up. Twice the number of pounds would then be the same number as three times the number of quarts. This would be equivalent to writing

$$2p = 3Q$$

All these ways of using the recipe boil down to the same diagonal rule,

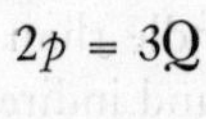

OTHER PARTS OF SPEECH.—You may have asked yourself whether there is anything in the language of size corresponding with other parts of speech. Of course there are no interjections in mathematics

because interjections have no place in the language of work. They are survivals of the noises which our monkey ancestors made before they learned the social use of noises. There are exact equivalents of adjectives and adverbs, but it would take us into higher realms than we have reached at present to explain what they are intelligibly. If your curiosity is whetted, here is an example of the adverb. The symbol 3 in the sign $\sqrt[3]{}$ modifies the meaning of the sign $\sqrt{}$. Standing alone the latter means that so many of some quantity have to be multiplied together to get the number marked by the sign $\sqrt{}$. The number 3 tells us *how many* times. When no number is put in front of the sign, it is taken to be 2. In a later chapter you will see how nouns can be modified. If I use x for all the quantities measured along one line and y for all the quantities measured along another line, I may write x_a or y_b to mean some particular value of x, or some particular value of y, just as the "red" cow tells me which cow, a and b written underneath may be regarded as adjectives. You need not worry about this now. There is only one other part of speech which is worth mentioning. There are some words which combine the characteristics of nouns and verbs. We call them gerunds. An example is the word "working" in the sentence "Working more than four hours a day will not be necessary in a rationally planned society." Mathematicians often speak of a similar sort of mathematical word as negative numbers (or back numbers) like -3, and imaginary numbers (or drunk numbers) like $\sqrt{-3}$. Now -3 is not simply a number. It is a number with a direction attached to it. It combines the characteristics of a mathematical verb and a mathematical noun. It is a size gerund. A good deal of the mystification which surrounds the "imaginary" numbers on which we depend for the alternating current of our electric light circuit simply arises from the habit of talking of them as if they were simply numbers. As they are not really numbers, this makes them seem to be merely imaginary in spite of the hard work they do at the power station. There are two *conjunctions* sometimes used in mathematics. One is $\therefore$ (therefore), and the other is $\because$ (because). Remember them.

STYLE.—A last similarity between size language and ordinary language is easy to grasp. A common defect of everyday speech is called being redundant, i.e. using several words where one would do. When this happens in the same sentence it always obscures its meaning. The only person who has any excuse for doing so is the chairman of an open-air meeting, when he has to collect a crowd for the principal speaker. Mathematics is not used for discussion in the open air. So redundancy is never allowed. Two tricks used to remove mere verbosity are called collecting terms and cancellation. Collecting terms is illustrated by this sentence:

$$3a - c + b + a - 2c + b = 4a + 2b - 3c$$

You will see that this is right if you substitute actual numbers for *a*, *b*, *c*. The other trick is called cancelling, i.e. removing a quantity which is both added and subtracted, or a quantity by which we are dividing and multiplying at the same time. For instance:

$$3a + b - b = 3a$$

This rule is so simple that we have already taken it for granted. Adding and taking away the same quantity leaves you as before. The other kind of cancellation is the one used in dealing with fractions, e.g.

$$\frac{6}{16} = \frac{2 \times 3}{2 \times 8} = \frac{3}{8}$$

Similarly, using collective numbers to convey the general rule:

$$\frac{ab}{bc} = \frac{ab}{cb} = \frac{a}{c}$$

This is easy to see, because it follows from the rule for multiplying fractions, thus

$$\frac{b}{b} = 1$$

$$\text{So} \quad \frac{b}{b} \times \frac{a}{c} = \frac{a}{c} \times 1$$

$$\therefore \frac{ba}{bc} = \frac{a}{c}$$

There is one other rule about style to notice at the outset. In everyday speech we have to interest as well as instruct the audience; otherwise they become restless or bored. Using the same word often is tedious, like the dripping of a tap. We avoid doing so when we have words which mean the same thing. We sacrifice logical simplicity for psychological adequacy. The strong prejudice felt against a simplified international language, in spite of the urgent need for one, has some justification owing to the fact that old languages are rich in alternatives. In the international language of mathematics we sacrifice everything else to making a statement as clear as possible. This means that we avoid writing the same operation in different ways. The rule has been broken in the last example. The excuse is that perhaps you are not yet used to the two different ways of translating the word "multiply."

ELLIPSIS.—In the language of everyday life we sometimes leave out words. In the imperative mood, biblical English often inserts the subject of the verb, as in "Go thou and do likewise," but in modern English we invariably leave out the subject. In French the word "not" is translated by *ne* before the verb and *pas* after it. After the verbs *pouvoir* and *savoir*, we may omit the *pas*. In the same way as we omit the subject after the imperative of the verb in English, because the mode of address leaves no doubt about the identity of the subject, we usually omit the number 1 when it occurs as a divisor or multiplier in mathematical language, because multiplying or dividing by 1 does not affect the result, i.e.

$$\frac{a}{1} = a; \quad 1 \times a = a; \quad a^1 = a$$

By remembering this you can apply the diagonal rule to an expression like:

$$ax = by$$
$$\frac{ax}{1} = \frac{by}{1}$$
$$\frac{a}{b} = \frac{y}{x}; \quad \frac{x}{y} = \frac{b}{a}; \quad \frac{x}{b} = \frac{y}{a}$$

Another context in which it is sometimes important to bear in mind this omission is when we are looking for connexions between sets of numbers. In the set of products

$$3, \quad 2(3), \quad 4(3), \quad 8(3), \quad 16(3)$$

the numbers 2, 4, 8, 16 are called coefficients of 3. The first number, if written 1(3), would bring out the connexion between the coefficients more clearly. Again you will see the connexion between these numbers:

$$x, \quad 3x^3, \quad 5x^5, \quad 7x^7$$

more clearly if you rewrite them as:

$$1x^1, \quad 3x^3, \quad 5x^5, \quad 7x^7$$

Another important thing to remember about the number 1 is that

$$\frac{a}{a} = 1$$

So we see the connexion between the numbers

$$1; \quad \tfrac{4}{5}, \quad \tfrac{2}{3}, \quad \tfrac{4}{7}$$

much better if we rewrite them:

$$\tfrac{4}{4}, \quad \tfrac{4}{5}, \quad \tfrac{4}{6}, \quad \tfrac{4}{7}$$

A last thing to remember about 1 is that

$$1^n = 1 = \sqrt[n]{1}$$

So if $a = 1$ and $b = 1$ in the equation

$$d^2 = a^2 + b^2$$
$$d^2 = 1 + 1 = 2$$
$$\therefore \quad d = \sqrt{2}$$

IDIOM.—In drawing attention to the fundamental likeness of the languages of size and sort, we have left out one important topic—the idiom of word order—to be dealt with in Chapter 7, when we shall give historical examples to illustrate how the symbolism of size language has grown by imperceptible stages out of the language of everyday life.

A piece of translation work which is always cropping up in stating simple laws of scientific measurement (such as how volts and amperes or amperes and ohms vary in an electric circuit, or how the volume of a gas changes when the pressure is increased or diminished) is worth noticing before we pass on. When we say that petrol consumption is directly proportional to the distance covered we mean that the ratio of the two is a fixed quantity or *constant*, in this case the number of miles per gallon. So the statement x is directly proportional to y, which is written shortly $x \propto y$, also means $x \div y =$ constant, or $x = y \times$ constant, written briefly in the form $x = ky$. Similarly, if we say that something is *inversely* proportional to another, e.g. in a circuit the amperage is inversely proportional to the resistance (ohms), we mean that if one is increased the other decreases so that the product remains fixed. Thus if we treble the number of ohms the current is reduced to a third. So the statement x is inversely proportional to y, written $x \propto \frac{1}{y}$, is equivalent to $xy =$ constant, or more shortly $xy = k$.

Bacon tells us that while "we falsely admire and extol the powers of the human mind, we neglect to seek for its true *helps*." If you want to get the best out of this book, do not make the mistake of teachers who multiply our difficulties by extolling the powers of the human mind. Make the fullest use of two helps, one of which has been illustrated in this chapter. If you are looking for a numerical rule or are trying to apply one to solve a practical problem, test the rule or its application by making up a simple example or analogous problem to see whether you get the right answer. This will help you to see whether you understand the rule, which is the same thing as being able to use it, or whether you understand the problem, which is equivalent to knowing what sort of rule to apply. Most tests given at the end of the chapters in this book can be checked. So no answers are given. An analogous help applies to problems in hieroglyphic mathematics. Do not miss a clue which would be obvious in a good drawing by making your figures less accurately than you can, and if the object is to find a rule of measurement, measure what you are looking for and satisfy yourself that your rule holds.

Exercises on Chapter 3

DISCOVERIES

1. Diagrams like those in Figs. 24 and 27 can be used to illustrate the meaning of many different kinds of expressions. For example, the following diagrams illustrate the meaning of $a(a + b)$ and $a(a - b)$.

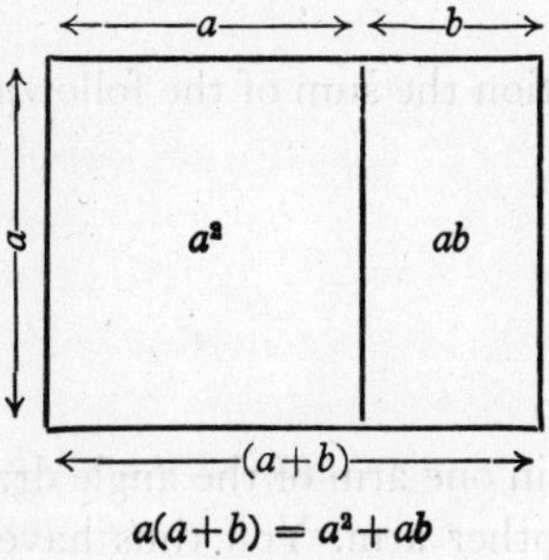

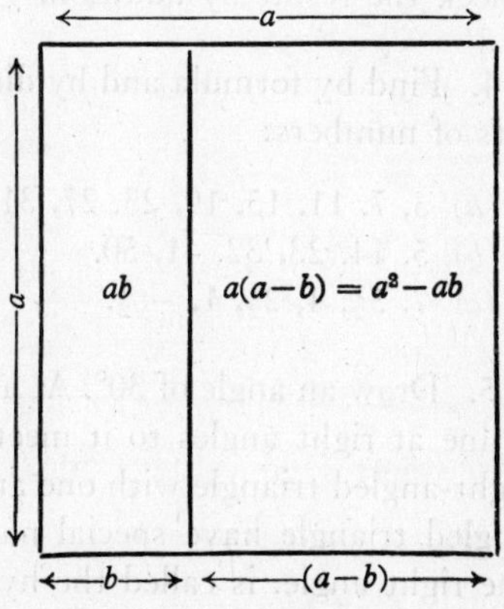

Draw diagrams on squared paper to illustrate the following:

$$(a+b)\ (a+b)$$
$$(a-b)\ (a-b)$$
$$(a+b)\ (a-b)$$

In your diagrams make a and b whole numbers. Write down your results in the form:

$$a(a+b) = a^2 + ab \text{ etc.}$$

Check your results in two ways.

(*a*) Replace a and b in your formula by the numbers you chose for them and see that both sides of your equation are identical.

(*b*) Count the number of squares in the area indicated by your diagrams.

2. Make figures to illustrate the statements:

$$(x+y+z)^2 = x^2 + y^2 + z^2 + 2xy + 2xz + 2yz$$
$$(g+f)\ (a+b+c+d) = g(a+b+c+d) + f(a+b+c+d)$$
$$(g+f)\ (a+b+c+d) = ga + gb + gc + gd + fa + fb + fc + fd$$

Check the former by putting $x = 2$, $y = 4$, $z = 7$, etc.

3. Find the sum of all the numbers:

(*a*) From 7 to 21.
(*b*) From 9 to 29.
(*c*) From 1 to 100.

Check the result by addition.

4. Find by formula and by direct addition the sum of the following sets of numbers:

(*a*) 3, 7, 11, 15, 19, 23, 27, 31, 35.
(*b*) 5, 14, 23, 32, 41, 50.
(*c*) 7, $5\frac{1}{2}$, 4, $2\frac{1}{2}$, 1, $-\frac{1}{2}$.

5. Draw an angle of 30°. At any point in one arm of the angle draw a line at right angles to it meeting the other arm. You thus have a right-angled triangle with one angle equal to 30°. The sides of a right-angled triangle have special names. The longest side, that opposite the right angle, is called the hypotenuse. The other sides are named

with reference to one of the other angles. At present we are interested in the angle of 30°, so we call the side opposite to it the perpendicular, and the other short side the base. Draw several right-angled triangles with one angle of 30°, each a different size and in different positions on the paper, and see that you can recognize the perpendicular, base, and hypotenuse immediately in any position.

6. In each triangle measure the following ratios:

$$\frac{\text{perpendicular}}{\text{hypotenuse}}, \quad \frac{\text{base}}{\text{hypotenuse}}, \quad \frac{\text{perpendicular}}{\text{base}}.$$

7. In the same way draw several triangles with an angle of 60° and several with an angle of 45°. Measure the ratios in each triangle. These ratios have been given names. If A is any angle the hypotenuse and base are the lines which enclose it, and the perpendicular is the side *opposite* A. The ratio $\frac{\text{perpendicular}}{\text{hypotenuse}}$ is then called the SINE of the angle A. The ratio $\frac{\text{base}}{\text{hypotenuse}}$ is called the COSINE of A. The ratio $\frac{\text{perpendicular}}{\text{base}}$ is called the TANGENT of A. These ratios are written for brevity: sin A, cos A, and tan A. By drawing right-angled triangles of various sizes you will see that each of these ratios has the same value for any particular angle.

8. By drawing two or three right-angled triangles and taking the mean of your measurements make a table of the sines, cosines, and tangents of 15°, 30°, 45°, 60°, 75°.

Find out by looking at the triangles you have drawn why

(*a*) $\sin (90° - A) = \cos A$.
(*b*) $\cos (90° - A) = \sin A$.
(*c*) $\tan A = \frac{\sin A}{\cos A}$.

9. Draw a circle with radius of 1 inch. Draw two radii enclosing an angle of 15°. One way of measuring an angle is by the ratio of the arc bounding it to the radius of the circle. This is called the number of *radians*, so that when the arc equals the radius, the angle is *one radian*. You have already found an approximate value for the ratio of the circumference to the diameter of a circle, and have learnt to call this ratio π. If you look at your diagram, you will see that you can get 24 angles

of 15° into the circle, and that therefore the arc bounding it is $\frac{1}{24}$ of the circumference. So the arc will be $\frac{\pi}{24}$ times the diameter, and as the radius is half the diameter it will be $\frac{\pi}{12}$ times the radius. We have drawn a circle of unit radius, so we see that an angle of 15° can also be described as an angle of $\frac{\pi}{12}$ radians.

10. In the same way find the values of angles of 30°, 60°, 90°, and 180° in radians.

11. How many degrees are there in a radian (take $\pi = 3\frac{1}{7}$)? What fraction of a radian is a degree?

TESTS ON MEASUREMENT

1. Suppose you want to measure accurately the length of a garden plot. To get first an approximate measure you would pace it out. Distances of this sort are reckoned by surveyors in chains and links. A chain is 66 feet, and a link is $\frac{1}{100}$ part of a chain, that is 7·92 inches. A natural pace is considered to be about $2\frac{2}{3}$ feet, so that the surveyor's rule is to multiply the number of paces by 4 and point off two figures from the right-hand end to stand for links. So if the length of a fence is 120 paces this would be taken as being 4 chains and 80 links ($4 \times 120 = 480$). You thus obtain the required distance in chains and links.

(*a*) Imagine you have paced the length of your garden plot and found it to be exactly 80 paces. According to the surveyor's rule it should measure 3 chains 20 links, or 211 feet 2·4 inches. Now mark one of your own paces with chalk on the floor and measure it with a foot-rule. How would you correct your estimate of the length of the garden plot on account of the difference between your pace and the standard pace? N.B.—If you are not fully-grown, your pace will have to be rather a long one, or you will be a long way out.

(*b*) Land surveyors measure distances along a straight line with a Gunter's chain. This is a chain 66 feet long, divided up into 100 links. Each link is 7·92 inches long. Within what limits would you expect the measurement of your garden by this chain to lie? Remember that what you know about the length so far is that it is 211 feet 2·4 inches corrected by the difference between your pace and the standard pace.

(*c*) A metallic tape 66 feet long, divided into feet and inches, is sometimes used. Such a tape was once found to have shrunk to 65 feet 4 inches after being used on wet grass. If you were so unlucky as to use a tape in such a state and later discovered the amount of shrinkage, how would you correct your measurements?

2. The division marks on a dressmaker's tape may be as much as $\frac{5}{8}$ of a millimetre thick. A millimetre is about $\frac{1}{25}$ of an inch. A careless person might take his measurements from the outsides of the marks, or from the insides of the marks. Measuring in this way, what could be the highest and lowest estimates of the length of

(*a*) the side of a curtain about 6 feet long;

(*b*) a space of about $\frac{1}{2}$ inch between 2 buttons on a baby's frock?

What percentage of the mean is the difference between two pairs of measurements in (*a*)?

TABULATION

3. By the method of approximation given in this chapter, make a table of the square roots of all the numbers from 1 to 20 inclusive correct to 3 decimal places.

4. Tabulate 2^n from $n = 1$ (when $2^n = 2$) to $n = 12$ (when $2^n = 4{,}096$). Do the same with 3^n from $n = 1$ to $n = 10$. Use these results to tabulate $(1\frac{1}{2})^n$ and $(\frac{2}{3})^n$ from $n = 1$ to $n = 8$, correct to 3 decimal places.

TRANSLATION INTO SIZE LANGUAGE

5. Translate the following into mathematical language.

(*a*) Multiply twice the length added to twice the breadth (measured in yards) by the price of fencing per yard to find the cost of fencing a plot.

(*b*) Take one spoonful of tea per person and add one spoonful for the pot to get the amount of tea required to make a pot for a party (call the number of people n).

(*c*) If you know that the weight of a crate containing n eggs is W and the weight of the empty crate is w, then you must subtract w from W and divide the result by n to get the average weight of one egg.

(*d*) Multiply the base by the perpendicular height and divide by 2 to get the area of a triangle.

(*e*) Write down the rule for finding the amount if a sum of money (£a) is left to accumulate for n years at r per cent simple interest.

ALGEBRAIC MANIPULATION

6. When learning how to use symbols, it is very useful to check all your work arithmetically, as in the following example.

$$\text{Simplify: } a + 2b + 3c + 4a + 5c + 6b$$

In algebra to simplify an expression means to change it to a convenient form for doing further work with it. We can simplify this expression by adding together all the *a*'s, all the *b*'s, and all the *c*'s. We then have

$$a + 2b + 3c + 4a + 5c + 6b = 5a + 8b + 8c$$

To check our work by arithmetic, put $a = 1$, $b = 2$, and $c = 3$. Then

$$\begin{aligned} a + 2b + 3c + 4a + 5c + 6b &= 1 + 2 \times 2 + 3 \times 3 + 4 \times 1 + 5 \times 3 + 6 \times 2 \\ &= 1 + 4 + 9 + 4 + 15 + 12 \\ &= 45 \end{aligned}$$

$$\begin{aligned} \text{Also} \quad 5a + 8b + 8c &= 5 \times 1 + 8 \times 2 + 8 \times 3 \\ &= 5 + 16 + 24 \\ &= 45 \end{aligned}$$

Check your results in this way in the following tests and whenever in doubt if you have dealt correctly with an algebraic expression.

Simplify:

(*a*) $x(x + 2y) + y(x + y)$.
(*b*) $(x + 2y + 3z) + (y + 3x + 5z) + (2z + 3y + 2x)$.
(*c*) $(a + 1)(a + 2) + (a + 2)(a + 3) + (a + 3)(a + 1) + 1$.
(*d*) $(x - 1)^2 - (x - 2)^2$.
(*e*) $a^2 - ab - (b^2 + ab)$.
(*f*) $(zx)(xy) + (xy)(yz) + (yz)(zx)$.
(*g*) $(2ab)(3a^2b^3)$.
(*h*) $(x^3)^2 + (x^2)^3$.
(*i*) $(a - b)(a + 2b) - (a + 2x)(a + x) - (a - 2x + 2b)(a - x - b)$.
(*j*) $\dfrac{2x^4y^5}{4x^3y^2}$.
(*k*) $\dfrac{(3ab^2)^3}{9a^2b^5}$.
(*l*) $\dfrac{2ab}{3c} \times \dfrac{4cd}{8b}$.

7. Satisfy yourself that the statements (*a*) *x* is inversely proportional

to y when z is kept the same; and (*b*) x is directly proportional to z when y is kept the same are both contained in the single equation:

$$xy = kz$$

This is very important to remember. (*Clue:*—replace the quantity kept the same by some other letter, e.g. C or c to represent a "constant.")

SIMPLE EQUATIONS

8. In each case make sure that the value you have found for x satisfies the equation.

(*a*) $3x + 7 = 43$
(*b*) $2x - 3 = 21$
(*c*) $17 = x + 3$
(*d*) $3(x + 5) + 1 = 31$
(*e*) $2(3x - 1) + 3 = 13$
(*f*) $x + 5 = 3x - 7$
(*g*) $4(x + 2) = x + 17$
(*h*) $\frac{x}{4} = \frac{1}{8}$
(*i*) $\frac{x + 2}{5} = \frac{x - 1}{2}$
(*j*) $\frac{x}{2} - \frac{x}{3} + 7 = \frac{5x}{6} - 5$
(*k*) $\frac{3}{x} = 3$
(*l*) $4 + \frac{15}{x} = 7$
(*m*) $-2x - 5 + 12x - 3 - 4 = 8$

Find x in terms of a and b in the following:

(*n*) $x - a = 2x - 7a$
(*o*) $2(x - a) = x + b$
(*p*) $a(a - x) = 2ab - b(x + b)$

SIMPLE PROBLEMS INVOLVING AN EQUATION

Check all your results.

9. Divide £540 between A and B so that A gets £30 more than B. (Call B's share x. A's will be $x + 30$.)

10. Divide £627 between A and B and C so that A gets twice as much as B and three times as much as C. (Call C's share x.)

11. Tom walks at a rate of 4 miles per hour, and Dick at a rate of 3 miles per hour. If Dick has half an hour's start, how long will it be before Tom catches up with him? (Call time from Dick's start till he is caught up x.)

12. A page of print contains 1,200 words if in large type, and 1,500 in small type. If an article of 30,000 words is to occupy 22 pages, how many pages must be in small type?

13. Automobile A does 30 miles to a gallon of petrol and 500 miles to a gallon of oil. Automobile B does 40 miles to a gallon of petrol and 400 miles to a gallon of oil. If oil costs as much as petrol, which will be the cheaper automobile to run?

14. A 60-foot row of early peas yields 12 pecks. An 80-foot row of maincrop peas yields 18 pecks. If maincrop peas fetch 1s. 4d. a peck, what price must early peas fetch to make them equally profitable?

THINGS TO MEMORIZE

1.
$$(a + b)(a + b) = a^2 + 2ab + b^2$$
$$(a - b)(a - b) = a^2 - 2ab + b^2$$
$$(a + b)(a - b) = a^2 - b^2$$

2. If A is any angle:

$$\sin A = \frac{\text{perpendicular}}{\text{hypotenuse}} \qquad \sin(90^\circ - A) = \cos A$$

$$\cos A = \frac{\text{base}}{\text{hypotenuse}} \qquad \cos(90^\circ - A) = \sin A$$

$$\tan A = \frac{\text{perpendicular}}{\text{base}} \qquad \tan A = \frac{\sin A}{\cos A}$$

3. If $x \propto z$, y being fixed and $x \propto \frac{1}{y}$, z being fixed, $xy = kz$.

CHAPTER IV

Euclid without Tears

OR

WHAT YOU CAN DO WITH GEOMETRY

We have attempted to form a picture, in part conjectural, of the ancient world in which men were learning to talk about size. Till about 2000 B.C. men had made very little progress in devising general principles about counting and measuring things. There was the beginning of a language of size. As yet there can hardly be said to have been a literature. The constructive achievements of these people are far more impressive than a few tablets on commercial arithmetic which have been unearthed at Nippur, or the papyri which tell us all we know about the priestly lore of the Nile. The Great Pyramid of Cheops is their enduring monument to truths about triangles passed on from mouth to mouth by priest to novitiate, by master craftsman to apprentice, by slave artificers to their children. Maybe it will stand when we have ceased to learn how the Greeks built a great pyramid of logic not less stiff or unyielding. We may be sure that the temple architects and the tax surveyors had already begun the practice of tracing models on the sand to guide them in the art of shadow-reckoning and mensuration long before there were people who set about recording diagrams of figures and trying to piece together the guiding principles. Sand tracings remained for centuries the method of working out geometrical problems. Archimedes, the greatest mathematician of antiquity, was butchered by the Roman storm troopers while drawing diagrams on sand. The steps by which men made the first geometrical constructions with cord and peg, plumb-line and water level, are more remarkable than the writing of books about them.

The Chinese must be given some credit for laying the foundations of a literature of size. As time goes on we may learn more about how much we owe to them. The illustration reproduced in Fig. 19 is sufficient to justify us in believing that they had established important general rules about figures half a millennium before the Greeks. They had hit upon some very interesting things about numbers, mixed up with a great deal of nonsense. It seems probable that they knew families of numbers, which play a fundamental role in modern statistics. Most of their knowledge is lost. Like the two libraries of Alexandria, the early Chinese libraries were burned. This calamity was not due to the fortunes of war. It was deliberate, like Hitler's destruction of German culture. The burning of the books was ordered by an emperor who believed, like Bernard Shaw, that people would write better if they read less. At first the Chinese had an advantage over the earlier civilization of Europe. Their calendar makers were to a less extent a *ceremonial* caste. They were of a more secular type. We do not know why the Chinese failed to achieve their early promise; we can only make guesses about some of their handicaps. One reason may have been that they began their education too early. They were saddled with a corrupt hieroglyphic script which is not suitable to express simple things in a simple way. They have never got out of it.

The Greeks, who possibly learned much from them, had neither the handicap of a priestly caste nor that of an expensive education. When the Chinese were writing the first mathematical textbooks, the mainland of Greece was invaded by nomadic savages from the north. These Aryan invaders came from steppes where there were no brilliant stars in cloudless skies. They had no script. They had not learned the arts of building or commerce. They had no weights and measures. They overran the seaboard of Asia Minor, setting up small kingdoms like Lydia and city-states like Miletus on the fringe of a chain of trading ports founded by the greatest merchants and navigators of antiquity. With these Semitic Phoenicians Nordic man contracted his first debt to the Jews. It was a debt for school fees. He learned to read and to write and to calculate. His very ignorance helped him to break away from the clumsy picture-writing and ideograms which hampered the earlier civilizations of Egypt and China. He used the old symbols to represent the sounds of his own simple language. He acquired a sound alphabet with which he began to write simple, clear sentences. With no tradition of elaborate ceremonial he could probe the secrets of the priests with curiosity instead of reverence. He had not been taught to believe "in the beginning was God." In the beginning was chaos. He was making order where he had been used to chaos.

We do not know whether these northern savages who overran the north-eastern portion of the Mediterranean really were blue-eyed or really had fair hair. We know that there is not a particle of justification for the belief that the scientific achievements of Greek civilization were the fruit of their racial equipment. Two men who are reputed to be the founders of Greek geometry, Thales (640–546 B.C.) and Pythagoras (582–507 B.C.), were both of Phoenician parentage. Science and mathematics did not reach the mainland of Greece until it was already nearing the end of its formative period. It was brought to the court of Pericles at the behest of Aspasia, his mistress, a woman of Miletus from the coast of Asia Minor. From Miletus, the native city of Thales himself, Anaxagoras came at her invitation. Pythagoras and Empedocles, who first wrote about the vacuum, lived in Italy and Sicily. Democritus, who speculated about atoms, lived on the coast midway between Asia Minor and the mainland of Greece at Abdera. The star of Greek science had set when the cult of Athenian philosophy began. It had never been Greek in the continental sense. In its beginning it was not even Greek in a racial sense.

The Tyrian parentage of Pythagoras gives us a clue to the clear signs of Chinese influence in his teachings, which we shall deal with in the next chapter. He travelled in Asia. By upbringing he was in touch with the great commercial community which was the gateway to the inland Asiatic trade-routes. Thales was a merchant with a knowledge of engineering. He travelled far afield and visited Egypt; he used the principles he worked with to compute the height of the Great Pyramid in the course of his travels, and predicted an eclipse on May 28, 585 B.C.; he made experiments with amber, the first record of observations on electrical attractions, and studied the lodestone or natural magnet. He did not cultivate mathematics as an aid to spiritual perfection. Probably he would have been surprised to hear that it is. Their geographical situation gave to these Ionian Greeks like Thales, who lived in island or coastal communities with no pre-existing caste of ecclesiastical commissioners, a great advantage over their Chinese contemporaries. We get a vivid glimpse of it in a fragment from the first great materialist about whom Karl Marx wrote his doctoral thesis. Here are the words of Democritus:

"Of all my contemporaries, it is I who have traversed the greatest part of the earth, visited the most distant regions, studied climates the most diverse, countries the most varied, and listened to the most men. There is no one who has surpassed me in geometrical constructions and demonstrations, no not even the geometers of Egypt, among whom I passed five full years of my life."

Well might Plato, who taught that geometry is an exercise of disembodied intellect, express the wish to have all the works of

Democritus burned. Shaw has praised the wisdom of the Fascist Caesar who looked on while the first library of Alexandria was burned. With it perished the eighty works of Democritus and all the great astronomical achievements of the Alexandrians. Maybe a great deal of rubbish perished. The evils of Greek intellectualism have survived the havoc of the flames. The good is interred with their bones. The substantial remains are the corrupt science of Aristotle and the Platonic geometry which Euclid brought to Alexandria. It was Euclid who said that there is no royal road to mathematics. He said it to a ruler, but no doubt he also said the same thing to his pupils. When one of them wanted to know the use of geometry he told a slave to give the youth a coin, so that he might have something for his pains. The active cosmopolitan community of Alexandria found a use for Euclid's geometry in spite of their teacher. We shall do the same.

THE LIMITATIONS OF EUCLID

In our generation there has come a change of outlook about geometry. We associate it especially with the names of Ernst Mach and Einstein. We now know that the geometry of Euclid does not give us the best possible way of measuring space. This does not mean that it is not a useful branch of knowledge. It was and still is. New discoveries have simply taught us that it has its limitations. It is quite easy to see some of them at the beginning, instead of putting them in at the end. For many things Greek geometry remains the best tool we have. A grocer's scale is more useful in the household than the most delicate chemical balance. The very delicacy of the balance which makes it capable of giving us estimates of the size of atoms makes it unsuitable for domestic use. We shall still have to learn Euclid's geometry for domestic use in the most literal sense of the term. The geometry of his Ionian teachers was originally based on watching how people built and cut up land into allotments. It ceases to be useful when we want to know the position of the furthest nebulae in the constellation of Ursa major. These nebulae are more than three hundred light-years away from us. It takes light, travelling at roughly eleven million miles a minute, three hundred years to traverse the space between them and the earth on which we live.

Now this limitation need not surprise us at all when we see how Greek geometry was circumscribed by its social context. We have already seen that Greek arithmetic could not catch up with the tortoise. Neither could Greek geometry. It arose from the practice of making sand diagrams of relatively permanent things like buildings and land and vessels. It did not take *time* into account. Its lines and angles and figures were fixed. So when we use its changeless figures to guide us in measuring a changing world, we have to recollect what we have left out of the picture. Nothing is so solid that it remains exactly the same for ever. When we say that the area of the Soviet Union is 8,242,900 square miles, we assume that its boundaries are not going to change during the period in which we intend to use our information, and

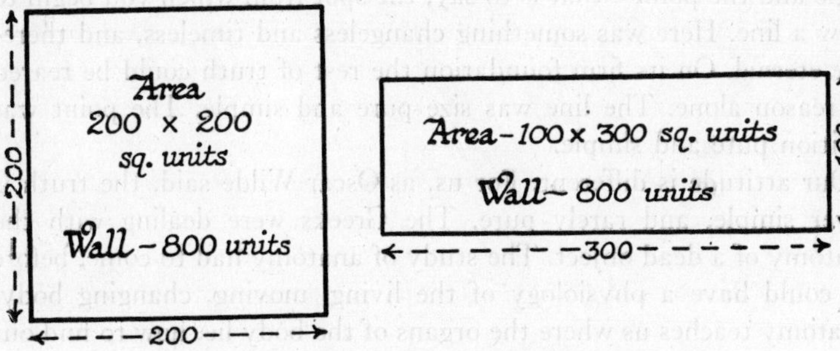

FIG. 28.—THE RELATIVITY OF SIZE AND SOCIAL USE

that the volume of the earth has not appreciably changed in the meantime. Actually the world is getting smaller as it cools. It shrinks quite a lot during a lapse of time occupying several geological epochs.

When we say that a box has such-and-such a volume, we are talking about a measurement which remains the same for the time between its manufacture and destruction for firewood. Time is not relevant for the social use to which our information will be put. So we isolate solid space from time. When we say that a field has a certain amount of surface or area, we also leave out of account the fact that the earth is shrinking as it cools, and we make a further approximation. Even if we are interested in mineral rights, we cannot dig down to the centre of the earth or interfere with our neighbours on the opposite side of the globe. So we leave out depth. The first men who measured surfaces were not interested in mineral rights. They were concerned about how many grains you can scatter on or reap from a field, or how many sheep and cows you can graze on it. When they had to build a wall to protect their flocks and vineyards or a temple in which to propitiate the gods who regulated rain and seasons and sunlight they had a different problem. In Fig. 28 you will see that a wall of the same size may enclose two fields or plots of different area. In one the amount of grain grown or the number of sheep which can be penned together is a third greater than in the other. In measuring length you leave this out. It is not socially relevant to the business of building a wall. Length is size used for making a wall. Area is size used for growing crops and grapes. Volume is size used for bartering milk and wine. The Greek intellectual did not grasp this relativity of size and social usefulness. The first anatomists of figures believed that they had got down to bedrock when they had isolated the line and the angle and the point—that is to say, the spot from which you begin to draw a line. Here was something changeless and timeless, and therefore eternal. On its firm foundation the rest of truth could be reared by reason alone. The line was size pure and simple. The point was position pure and simple.

Our attitude is different. For us, as Oscar Wilde said, the truth is never simple, and rarely pure. The Greeks were dealing with the anatomy of a dead object. The study of anatomy had to come, before we could have a physiology of the living, moving, changing body. Anatomy teaches us where the organs of the body lie, how to find our way about the inside of a body. The geometry of the flat figure tells us how to find our way about flat figures. Anatomy exposes the nature of the cadaver by dissection. Geometry exposes the nature of flat figures by dissection. Books on anatomy do not always start from the same point. Neither need the study of geometry. In seeing how the organs of the flat figure—lines and angles and surfaces—are connected with one another, we have to please ourselves about where we start, i.e. what we take for granted. There is no eternal truth about where to start. Rules about flat figures or bulky figures are approximate truths in so far as they are of any use in measuring a world of change. They are good models to guide us in building and dividing land. Up to a point they are good models for describing the larger world of stars. Democritus was not wasting time when he spent five full years of his life watching how the Egyptians did such things, so that he could demonstrate the principles to his fellow-countrymen. The geometry of this chapter is about actual figures which you can draw with a compass and rule (as Plato prescribed). So perfect equality such as exists between the male and female whole numbers of Greek arithmetic has nothing to do with it. The angles, lines and areas which come into it can only be represented by numbers of the stretchable kind which apply to real measurements. The statement AB = CD does not mean "the line AB is exactly equal to the line CD," because no one knows how to make exactly equal lines with any actual compass or rule. Its correct translation is "*measure* AB *to get* the length of CD as accurately as you need it."

The Greeks were not familiar with radical and rapid change in social custom. They reckoned time with sundial and sandglass. They had no physical instruments for measuring time in shorter intervals than the time taken to boil an egg. It was natural to think that measuring space and measuring time had nothing to do with one another. Architecture and surveying and commerce had secularized space. Time-keeping was still predominantly the prerogative of the priests in the countries where the Greek mathematicians travelled. Greek geometry left them with time. Even Archimedes, who learned his geometry in Alexandria and applied it to constructing levers and wheels, believed that a line is necessarily straight because it is the shortest distance between two points. For most practical purposes this is true. It is not inevitably and eternally true. One reason why it is not true the biologist can tell us. Part of the internal ear in our bodies records the influence of gravity. This is why a cat falls on its feet and a fish keeps the right way up in swimming. If we set the fluid of the internal ear in motion by turning round several times quickly, we become dizzy. We do not know "which way up" we are. There is a similar organ in the shrimp. If it is filled with tiny steel filings, the shrimp will respond to a magnet instead of responding to the pull of gravitation. If the lines of magnetic force are curved, it can never swim in a straight line. For such a shrimp the shortest distance between two points is a curved line. The simplest estimates which you and I can make about the size of lines involves *movement* of the eye muscles. They depend on time and space. Optical illusions about distance depend on forcing the eyes to move in an unusual way. Size and movement in time are inseparable in the real world of the biologist.

Closely connected with the fact that Euclid left out time is another limitation of his method. This will crop up again when we see how the Arabs began to make mathematical sentences in dictionary language. When the Arabs used flat figures, as the Greeks drew them, to make scale diagrams for solving problems of calculation, they soon noticed a curious discrepancy. Their models could only answer a question in one way. To some questions more than one answer is possible, and they knew enough about numbers to realize that two numbers could be equally good answers for some of the questions they asked. This dilemma arose for a simple reason. The separate figures of Euclid have no particular position. In effect Greek geometry said that some things which are manifestly different are the same thing. Along with time position was left out. When a new geometry was suggested by the position of a moving ship at sea, it also gave us a way of representing

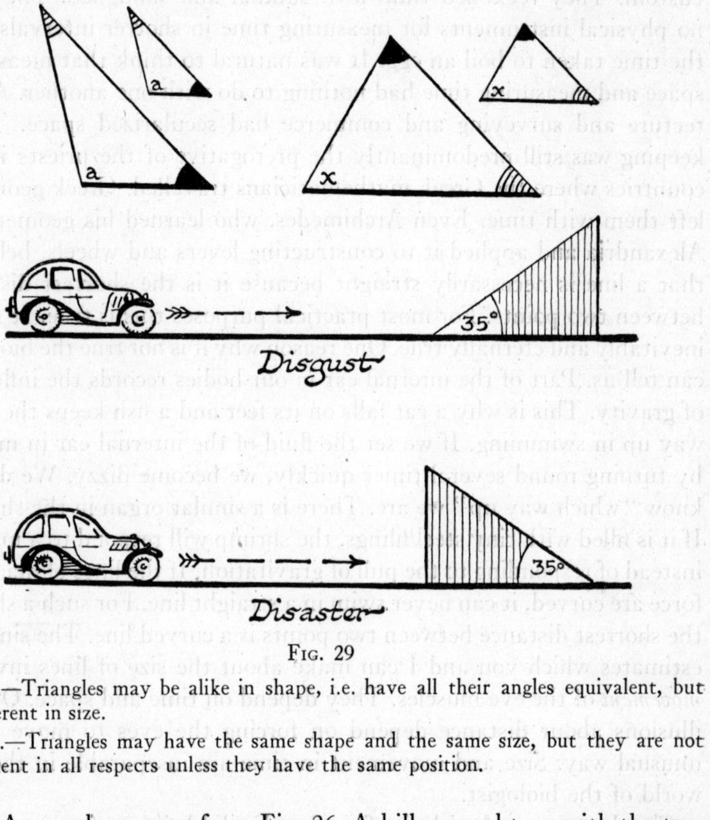

FIG. 29

ABOVE.—Triangles may be alike in shape, i.e. have all their angles equivalent, but be different in size.

BELOW.—Triangles may have the same shape and the same size, but they are not equivalent in all respects unless they have the same position.

time. As you have seen from Fig. 26, Achilles caught up with the tortoise at the Reformation, which took time away from the priests by taking the saints out of the calendar.

This limitation leads us to the first three definitions which we shall use in starting the dissection of flat figures, i.e. our first three directions to guide us in laying out the cadaver and applying the scalpel. In the geometry of Euclid figures are said to be alike with respect to shape, with respect to size, and with respect to both. When they are alike in both respects, Euclid calls them equal in all respects. Figures bounded by straight lines are alike in shape alone, or "similar" (remember how this word is used) when their angles are equivalent. They are alike in size when their sides as well as their angles are equivalent, and when they enclose equivalent surfaces. Two triangles may enclose equivalent areas without having equivalent sides and angles. You have only to

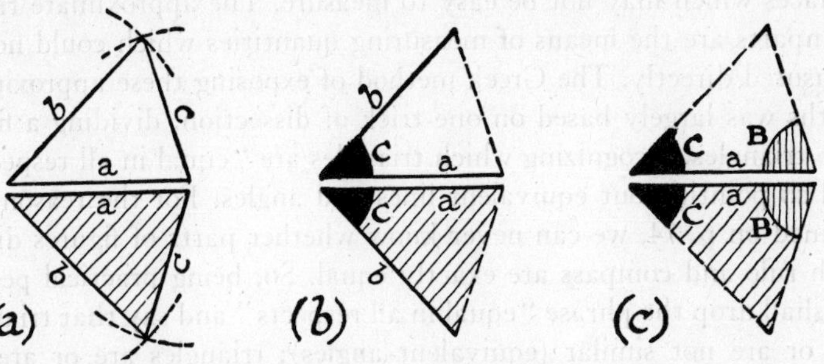

HOW TO DRAW A TRIANGLE

(*a*) Length of three sides known.
(*b*) Length of two sides and size of the angle enclosed.
(*c*) Length of one line and the two angles which the other two sides make with it known.

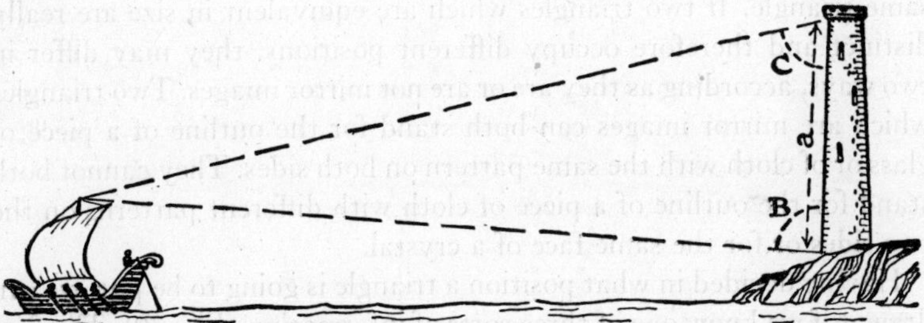

AN EARLY USE WHICH WAS MADE OF (*c*). ATTRIBUTED TO THALES

FIG. 30

look at Fig. 29 to see that we have to reckon with another important characteristic besides size and shape when we use figures as models of the real world.

We need not bother ourselves with the use of Euclid's attempts to demonstrate when triangles have the same size. He started dissecting in the most difficult place. The sensible way to proceed is to ask what facts we need in order to draw a triangle when we have decided what its position is going to be. Even when we have fixed one line (Fig. 30) there are always four triangles we can draw unless we say something more about the position in which the triangle is to be drawn. Two, one above the other, are given in Fig. 30, the other two corresponding with inversions of these from left to right. The Greek anatomy of flat figures is useful as a model of the real world because it exposes easily measured distances, angles, or surfaces equivalent to other distances, angles, or surfaces which may not be easy to measure. The approximate truths it imparts are the means of measuring quantities which could not be measured directly. The Greek method of exposing these approximate truths was largely based on one trick of dissection, dividing a figure into triangles, recognizing which triangles are "equal in all respects," and so pointing out equivalent lines and angles. For the reasons explained on p. 74, we can never know whether parts of figures drawn with rule and compass are exactly equal. So, being practical people, we shall drop the phrase "equal in all respects" and say that triangles are or are not similar (equivalent angles); triangles are or are not equivalent in area; and triangles are or are not equivalent in size (equivalent sides, equivalent angles, and equivalent areas). To be equivalent in all respects two triangles must have a fourth characteristic, equivalent position, in which case they are really one and the same triangle. If two triangles which are equivalent in size are really distinct and therefore occupy different positions, they may differ in two ways, according as they are or are not mirror images. Two triangles which are mirror images can both stand for the outline of a piece of glass or of cloth with the same pattern on both sides. They cannot both stand for the outline of a piece of cloth with different patterns on the two sides or for the same face of a crystal.

Having decided in what position a triangle is going to be put, we can draw it if we know one of three sorts of information (Fig. 30). The first is the lengths of all three sides. Having drawn one of them, we trace a circle of which the centre is at the end of the line already drawn, and the radius (or spoke) is of the same length as one of the other two sides. We then trace another circle with its centre at the opposite extremity of the first line, the radius being of length equivalent to the length of the third side. Where the circles cut is the only place where two lines of the sizes given can meet. If their sum is less than the first, they do not meet, and no triangle can be drawn. This recipe depends on the fact that the distance of the centre from any spot on the boundary of a circle is equivalent to the distance of the centre from any other spot on the boundary. This definition of a circle is merely a description of how circles were first drawn with a stretched cord tied to two sticks, one of which is fixed in the sand (Fig. 18). The second recipe is to be told the lengths of two lines and the angle enclosed between them. This is good enough, because we have only to connect the ends of the two lines. If the angle is greater than two right angles, we cannot draw a triangle which includes it as one of its angles. The third is to know the size of one side and the two angles which the other two sides make with it. We can make a triangle like this so long as the sum of the two angles given is less than two right angles. When we have laid out the angles we have only to continue the lines bounding them till they meet. Fig. 30 shows how this recipe was used at a very early date to make a scale diagram to find the distance of a ship at sea.

We can now state three rules for exposing the connexions between the parts of figures when we have dissected them into triangles:

TRIANGLE RULE ONE.—The sizes of two triangles are equivalent if they have equivalent sides.

TRIANGLE RULE TWO.—The sizes of two triangles are equivalent if in one of the triangles two sides and the angle enclosed by them are equivalent to two sides and the angle enclosed by them in the other triangle.

TRIANGLE RULE THREE.—The sizes of two triangles are equivalent if one side and the angles the other two sides make with it in one triangle are equivalent to one side and the angles the other two make with it in the other triangle.

A third limitation of Euclid's geometry makes it very much more difficult than it need be. The Ionian geometer Thales demonstrated a very fundamental truth about triangles. This is that the ratio of the lengths of any two corresponding sides in similar triangles (i.e. triangles which are equiangular), is always the same whatever their actual size. We shall see later how he used it to find the height of the Great Pyramid. It is not surprising that this truth was grasped at an early date. The fact is that we assume it in most cases when we make any use of geometry by drawing a scale diagram involving triangles. Once we recognize the truth of it, we can go ahead very quickly to the discovery of other useful conclusions. The chief reason why Euclid is so long-winded is because he put everything about ratios at the end instead of at the beginning of his course. There is a quite simple reason for this. He was limited by the social culture in which he lived. The Greeks did not live in a world of interest and petrol consumption and bowling analysis. Ratios were not familiar quantities. They represented a process of division which was carried out with a very stiff instrument, the abacus. Proportion did not sit lightly on Euclid's pupils.

You can easily see the difficulty of Euclid's pupils. Suppose I know that the petrol consumption of a car is 35 miles to the gallon. I can get the number of miles I can run before filling up by multiplying the number of gallons in the tank by 35. I can get the number of gallons I require by dividing the number of miles I intend to run by 35. The two processes are equally easy in our arithmetic. The arithmetic of

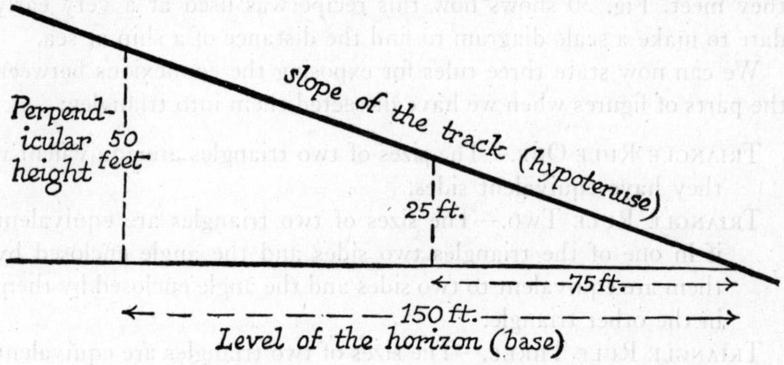

FIG. 31.—A GRADIENT OF ONE IN THREE

If the angle between the track and the horizon level is A, tan A = $\frac{1}{3}$

This figure is also a hieroglyph of division by three. To use it mark off the number of units to be divided along the base line and measure the perpendicular.

the counting frame is different. Multiplying one proper number by another always gives you an exact result which you get by repeated addition (Fig. 6). Dividing one proper number by another means finding how many times you can take one away from the other. Usually you have some beads left over on the counting frame. You rarely get an exact answer. So division was a much more difficult process to grasp when people thought that all real numbers were proper numbers. Euclid had to devote a whole book (Book V) to illustrate the very simple rules of proportion which are all summed up in the diagonal rule given in the last chapter. Draw two right-angled triangles, one with the two shorter sides 3 and 4 centimetres long, the other with the two shorter sides of $1\frac{1}{2}$ and 2 inches; compare them, and you will see without difficulty that two triangles having corresponding sides whose lengths are in the same ratio is a situation no more difficult to grasp than the fact that a motor-cycle has the same petrol consumption on Good Friday and All Fools' Day.

One ratio of the sides of a triangle is a familiar quantity of modern life. It is inscribed along railway tracks and near dangerous hills. A gradient of 1 in 10 means that if you make a scale drawing of a right-angled triangle, one side being part of the slope of the track or hill (hypotenuse), one side being level with the horizon (base), and one side being the perpendicular height to it, the base is always ten times the perpendicular, and the perpendicular is always one-tenth of the base, i.e.

$$\frac{\text{perpendicular}}{\text{base}} = \frac{1}{10}$$

In mathematics this ratio is often called the *tangent* of the angle (A) which the slope makes with the horizon, and is then written tan A, which means "Look up the number corresponding to A in the table of tangents."* Two branches of later mathematics (Chapters 6 and 11) are mainly about gradients. Trigonometry tabulates them, so that we can get a distance which is difficult or impossible to measure exactly (like our distance from the moon) if we can measure an angle (A) and some other distance (e.g. the distance between two different places on the earth). This is like using petrol consumption to tell us how many miles we can go if we have so many gallons in the tank, or how many gallons we need if we are going so many miles. The branch of mathematics called the differential calculus measures slopes which bend, like calculating a distance from the petrol consumption when the tank leaks. Had Euclid known how important these ratios would become, he might have tried harder to introduce them, as we are doing, at an early stage in his course.

EUCLID'S METHOD

When Sherlock Holmes used to say, "You know my methods, Watson," Dr. Watson ought to have said, "No, I don't. Please explain them." We have already noticed the chief trick which Euclid used to detect connexions between the organs (lines, angles, or surfaces) of dead figures. He dissected them into triangles. If we only know the size of one or two of the sides of each, we need to know whether any of their angles are equivalent before we can tell whether two triangles are equivalent. The pastoral degree, based on the calendar of the seasons, does not help us to recognize when angles are equivalent.

* If you look up the table, you will see that tan 5·7° is almost exactly 0·1. So a gradient of 1 in 10 corresponds with a slope of 5·7°.

The geometers of the city-states used the urban angle of the builder for comparing the size of angles (Fig. 32). Euclid's definition of the right angle (= 90°) amounts to saying that the gap between the plumb-line and the horizon is the same on all sides. This is obvious without spending five full years in Egypt. Two angles make up a right angle if one stands for the inclination of a straight edge to the horizon and the other represents the inclination of the same straight edge to the plumb-line. If you study the text attached to Fig. 33, you will have

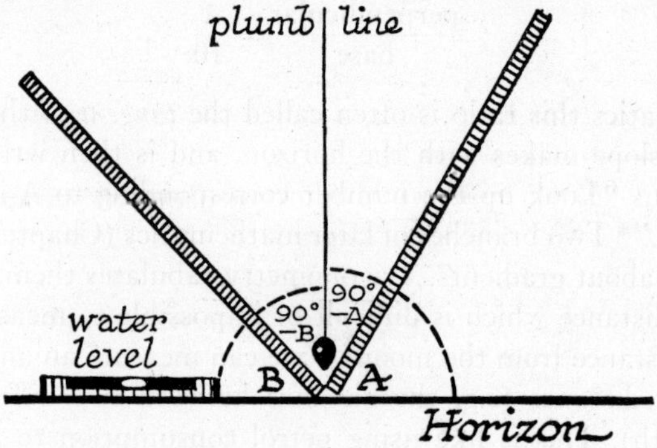

FIG. 32.—LEARNING TO ADD WITH ANGLES

very little difficulty in seeing two rules which were used by the Greek geometers to recognize when angles are equivalent. The rules are:

ANGLE RULE ONE.—When two straight lines meet at one spot on a third, the three angles so made add up to two right angles, or 180°.

ANGLE RULE TWO.—When two lines cross, the vertically opposite angles are equal.

Two other rules which help us to see when angles are equivalent recall a fourth limitation of Euclid's geometry. Euclid defined parallel lines as straight lines which do not meet, however far we go on drawing them. This definition takes us up into the skies, and leaves us in the air like Plato. We simply do not know of any surface so flat that it allows us to go on drawing lines as far as we like, and still keep them straight. We make drawings on a bit of the earth small enough in comparison with the rest of it to make it look as if it were really flat. Modern astronomy has taught us that lines which are parallel in Euclid's sense are not the sort of lines which would reach out to the furthest stars, if we could get to them. It is more sensible to ask how we recognize when lines are parallel. One way is to notice that two straight edges are parallel when we make one of them gape as widely

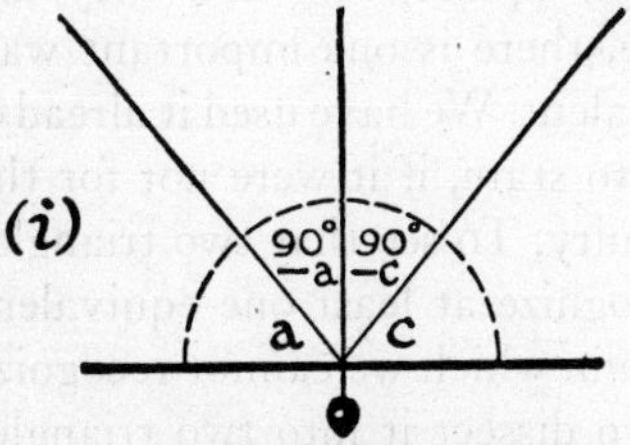

(i) ANGLE RULE ONE

The middle angle is $90° - a + 90° - c$

or $180° - a - c$

All three together make

$(180° - a - c) + a + c = 180°$

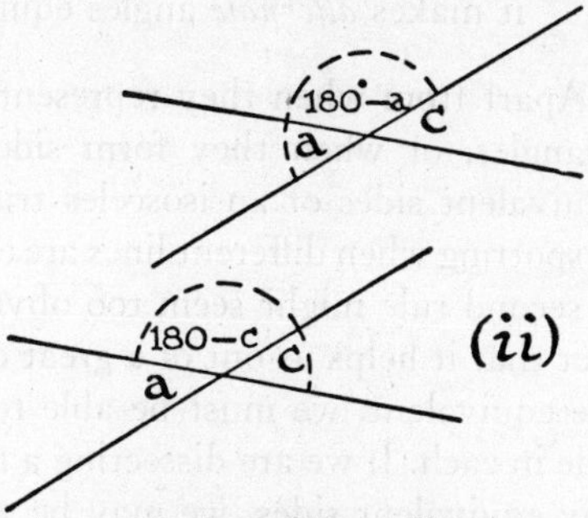

(ii) ANGLE RULE TWO

The figure is drawn twice: comparing the two we see that

$180 - a = 180 - c$

$\therefore \quad a = c$

The two angles *a* and *c* are called vertically opposite angles.

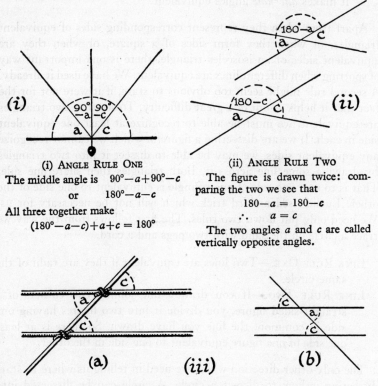

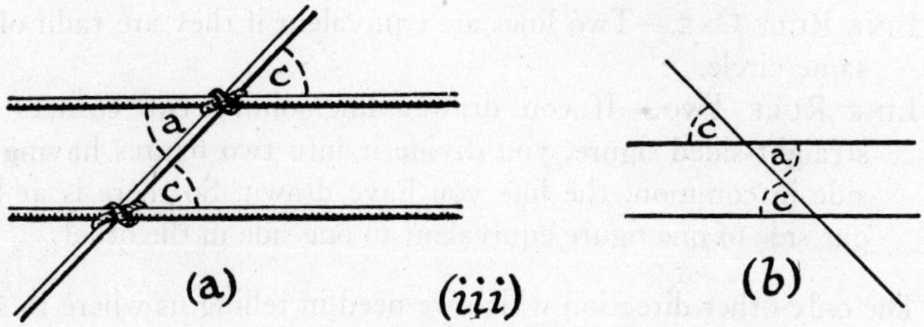

(iii) THE TWO PARALLEL RULES

(*a*) Seeing when two poles are parallel.

(*b*) Learn to recognize the angles which are equivalent drawn either way.

FIG. 33

as the other from a straight edge against which they are placed, or in technical language, when the *corresponding* angles are equivalent (Fig. 33). Looking back to Fig. 12 and comparing it with Fig. 33, you will see that this is the principle by which the astrolabe is used to measure the angle which a hill or a star makes with the horizon. ANGLE RULE Two then tells us that the *alternate* angles (*a* and *c* in Fig. 33) are also equivalent. This gives us two new rules about equivalent angles:

PARALLEL RULE ONE.—When a third line crosses two parallel lines, the *corresponding* angles which it makes with them are equivalent.

PARALLEL RULE TWO.—When a third line crosses two parallel lines, it makes *alternate* angles equivalent.

Apart from when they represent corresponding sides of equivalent triangles, or when they form sides of a square, or when they are equivalent sides of an isosceles triangle, there is one important way of spotting when different lines are equivalent. We have used it already. A second rule might seem too obvious to state, if it were not for the fact that it helps us out of a great difficulty. To see that two triangles are equivalent, we must be able to recognize at least one equivalent side in each. If we are dissecting a figure in which we cannot recognize any equivalent sides, we may be able to dissect it into two triangles by drawing some line across it. Both triangles then share one side. That is to say, one side of one triangle is equivalent to one side of the other. Euclid used a third trick which will not be necessary for us. We need only put down two rules. The first follows from the way we trace a circle on the sand with two pegs and a cord.

LINE RULE ONE.—Two lines are equivalent if they are radii of the same circle.

LINE RULE TWO.—If you draw a line joining two corners of a straight-sided figure, you divide it into two figures having one side in common, the line you have drawn. So there is at least one side of one figure equivalent to one side in the other.

The only other direction which we need in telling us where to start dissecting is how to dissect a circle. A circle can be dissected into separate strips or sectors by drawing two or more radii, or into *segments* by drawing a line from one spot on the boundary to another. The curved side of a segment or sector is called an *arc*. The line drawn from one spot on the boundary through the centre to the opposite spot on the boundary, called the *diameter*, divides the circle into two equivalent parts, called *semicircles*. So far nothing has been said about a rectangle. Before we can dissect a body we must be able to find it. To draw a rectangle, all we need to know is that it is a closed figure bounded by four straight sides, the opposite sides being parallel, and *one of the angles* being a right angle. It follows from the way in which you use PARALLEL RULE ONE to draw a rectangle that if one angle is a right angle, all the angles of a rectangle are right angles (Fig. 34, (*f*)).

The geometrical rules which made it possible for those who came after the Greeks to devise more useful and less laborious size languages

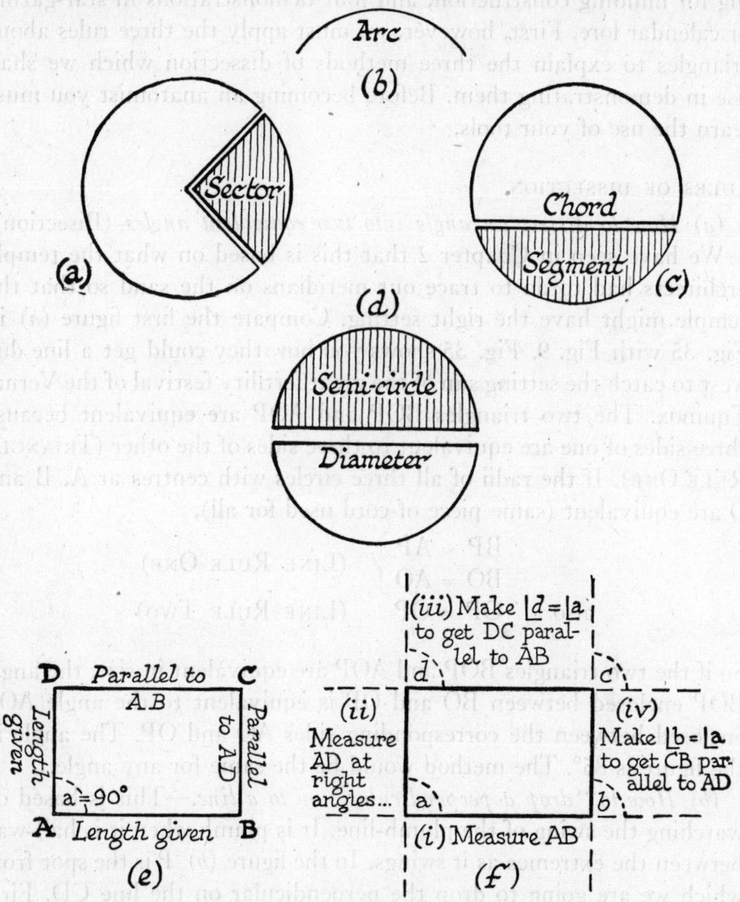

FIG. 34.—THE ANATOMY OF CIRCLE AND RECTANGLE

NOTE.—To draw the sides parallel use PARALLEL RULE ONE, start by making $a = 90°$. From this you see that all the angles are right angles.

like trigonometry and algebra are very few. Twelve will be sufficient for us. We shall arrange them under three headings which signify the social context in which they arose. Euclid called the exposure of a rule about figures a theorem. Following the materialist Democritus, we shall call them demonstrations. According to the way in which they were first used or recognized we shall group them as: four demonstrations in surveying, four demonstrations in shadow-reckoning for building construction, and four demonstrations in star-gazing or calendar lore. First, however, we must apply the three rules about triangles to explain the three methods of dissection which we shall use in demonstrating them. Before becoming an anatomist you must learn the use of your tools.

RULES OF DISSECTION

(*a*) *How to dissect an angle into two equivalent angles* (Bisection).—We have seen in Chapter 2 that this is based on what the temple architects had to do to trace out meridians on the sand so that the temple might have the right setting. Compare the first figure (*a*) in Fig. 35 with Fig. 9. Fig. 35 shows you how they could get a line due west to catch the setting sun of the great fertility festival of the Vernal Equinox. The two triangles BOP and AOP are equivalent because three sides of one are equivalent to three sides of the other (TRIANGLE RULE ONE). If the radii of all three circles with centres at A, B and O are equivalent (same piece of cord used for all),

$$\left.\begin{array}{l} BP = AP \\ BO = AO \end{array}\right\} \quad \text{(LINE RULE ONE)}$$

$$\text{also} \quad OP = OP \quad \text{(LINE RULE TWO)}$$

So if the two triangles BOP and AOP are equivalent in size, the angle BOP enclosed between BO and OP is equivalent to the angle AOP enclosed between the corresponding sides AO and OP. The angle in the figure is 85°. The method would be the same for any angle.

(*b*) *How to "drop a perpendicular" on to a line.*—This is based on watching the swing of the plumb-line. It is plumb when it is half-way between the extremes as it swings. In the figure (*b*) P is the spot from which we are going to drop the perpendicular on the line CD. First trace any circle with centre at P cutting the line at A and B. We bisect the angle of swing by the line PO, using the first method of dissection. This makes the angles OPB and OPA equivalent. Comparing the two triangles BOP and AOP we see:

$$PA = PB \quad \text{(LINE RULE ONE)}$$

$$PO = PO \quad \text{(LINE RULE TWO)}$$

$$\text{enclosed} \ \angle APO = \angle OPB$$

By TRIANGLE RULE Two the two triangles are equivalent in size.

Hence the angle POB enclosed between PO and OB is equivalent to the angle POA enclosed between the corresponding sides PO and OA. When a straight line meets another making the angles on either

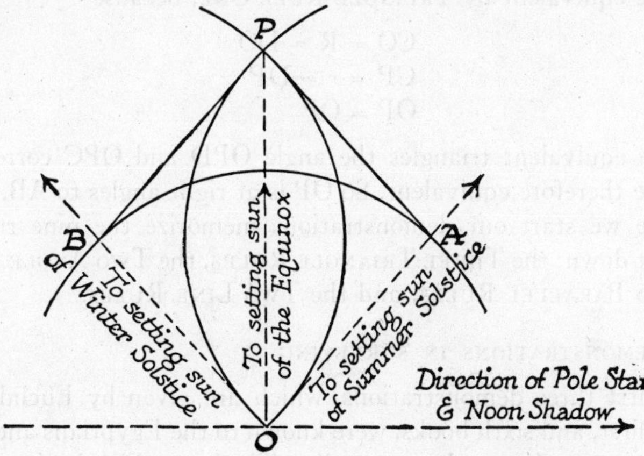

(*a*) Bisecting an angle (AOB) to get the west (and east) point on the horizon.

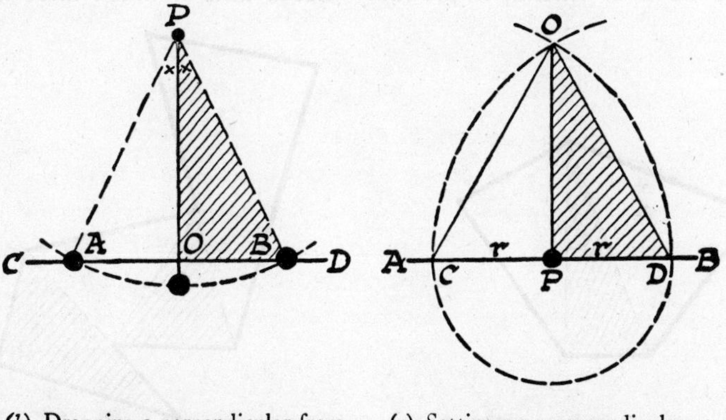

(*b*) Dropping a perpendicular from P above.

(*c*) Setting up a perpendicular at a particular spot P on a line.

FIG. 35.—RULES FOR DISSECTION

side equivalent, they are right angles. So PO is perpendicular, i.e. at right angles to CD.

(*c*) *How to erect a perpendicular to a line at a particular spot.*—We have to find the spot from which the plumb-line would be suspended. In the figure (*c*) P is the spot on the line AB where we are going to erect the perpendicular, i.e. put up a line at right angles to AB. Trace any circle of radius *r* with its centre at P, cutting AB at C and D. Then with centre at C trace a larger circle of radius R, and a circle with the same radius R having its centre at D. The triangles COP and DOP are equivalent by TRIANGLE RULE ONE, because

$$CO = R = DO$$
$$CP = r = DP$$
$$OP = OP$$

In these equivalent triangles the angle OPD and OPC correspond. They are therefore equivalent. So OP is at right angles to AB.

Before we start our demonstrations memorize the nine rules we have put down: the THREE TRIANGLE RULES, the TWO ANGLE RULES, the TWO PARALLEL RULES, and the TWO LINE RULES.

FOUR DEMONSTRATIONS IN SURVEYING

The first three demonstrations, which are given by Euclid in his second, first, and sixth books, were known to the Egyptians and to the Sumerians two thousand years earlier. The last, which is given in the second book of Euclid, is probably Greek and of much later date.

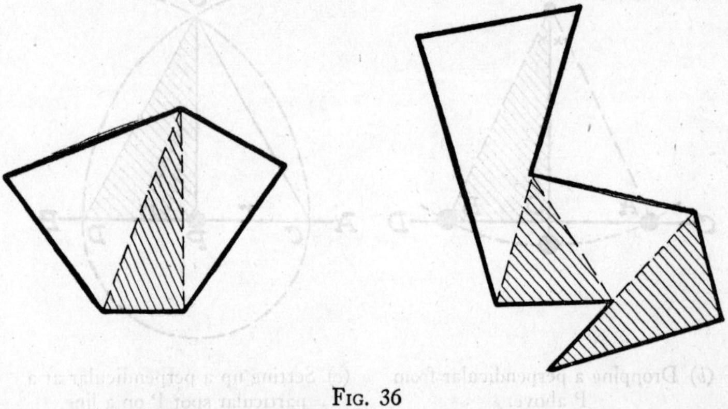

FIG. 36

If we can find the area of any triangle, we can measure the surface of a plot of land of any shape, provided that the walls run straight.

They are about measuring area, and originated in connexion with land measurement. Starting with the flat space enclosed by a square as our measure, we can show how to get the area of a rectangle as the sum of a patchwork of squares. We also see how to make a rectangle twice the size of any right-angled triangle. We can thus get the area of a right-angled triangle. Next we show that any triangle can be split into two right-angled triangles. So we can get the area of any kind of a triangle. Any figure which is bounded by straight sides can be split into triangles (Fig. 36). With this knowledge we can measure the surface of any piece of land, whatever its shape, provided it has straight sides. So Euclid's trick is the method of the practical surveyor.

Besides being models of land measurement, these demonstrations are models of how to carry out calculations. The second, and last, suggest some simple recipes to shorten work on the abacus. At a later date they led the Arabs to set down the rules of calculation we use. These rules are called algebra. It might seem more straightforward to start from the connexion between a rectangle and a square; but we have to use something which depends upon the relation of a rectangle to a right-angled triangle to demonstrate how to get the area of a rectangle. So we start with the right-angled triangle and the rectangle.

Demonstration 1

"The diagonal of a rectangle divides it into two equivalent right-angled triangles."

In Fig. 37, AC is the diagonal of the rectangle ABCD. We have seen that all the angles of a rectangle are right angles (Fig. 34). So the triangles ABC and ADC are right-angled triangles in which:

(i) AC = *d* = AC LINE RULE TWO
(ii) CAB = ACD PARALLEL RULE TWO see Fig. 33 (iii)
(iii) BCA = CAD PARALLEL RULE TWO ditto

Comparing (v) in Fig. 37 with (*c*) in Fig. 30, we see from TRIANGLE RULE THREE that the triangles ABC and ADC are equivalent. Another way of putting this conclusion is to say that *we can find the area of a right-angled triangle if we can find the area of a rectangle by making the rectangle whose length and breadth are equivalent to the two sides at right angles*. Two important results arise out of this demonstration:

(*a*) *Opposite sides of a rectangle are equivalent.*—Since the two triangles are equivalent in size, the corresponding sides AB, AC, and DC, AC enclosing the equivalent angles CAB and ACD, are equivalent. Also the corresponding sides AD and BC are equal.

(*b*) *Perpendiculars joining two parallel lines are equivalent.*—You will see from (vi) in Fig. 37 why this is. AB and DE are parallel. If AD and BC are perpendiculars they make equivalent corresponding angles (PARALLEL RULE ONE), and are therefore parallel. So ABCD has opposite sides parallel. Having also a right angle, it is a rectangle. Therefore the opposite sides AD and BC are equivalent.

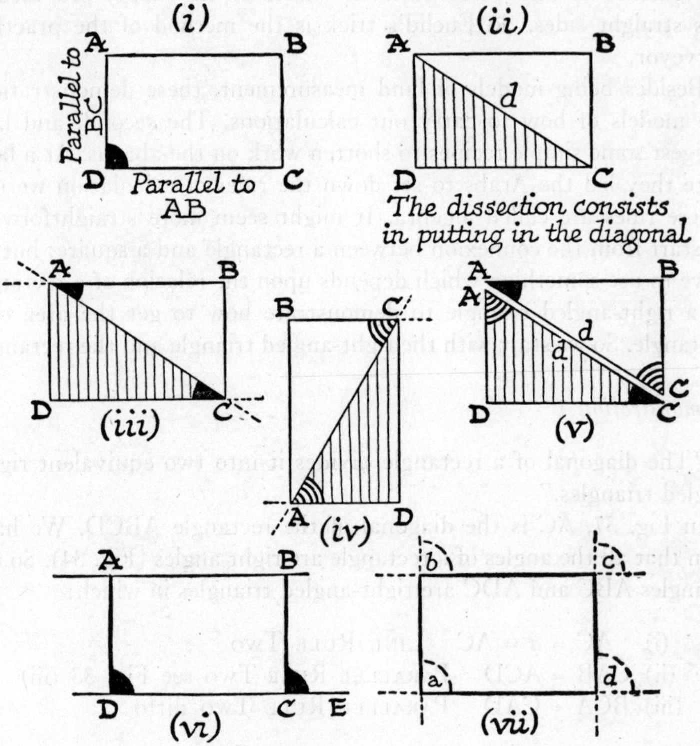

FIG. 37.—DEMONSTRATION 1

Demonstration 2

"If one side of a rectangle is divided into separate segments of any length, its whole area is equivalent to the sum of the areas of the rectangles formed by the undivided side and each segment of the divided side."

A side AB of length B in Fig. 38 (i) is divided at P and Q into three segments AP, PQ, and QB, respectively, *l*, *m*, and *n* units long. The dissection is shown in (ii), two perpendiculars being drawn from P and Q to the opposite side. This divides the figure into three rectangles. Since opposite sides of a rectangle are equivalent (Dem. 1 (*a*)), the perpendiculars are equivalent to H, the other side of the whole rectangle. We can now see:

Area of whole rect. H by B = Sum of areas of rect. H by *l*,
H by *m*, and H by *n*

Try to imagine that we are ancient Egyptians or Sumerians. We

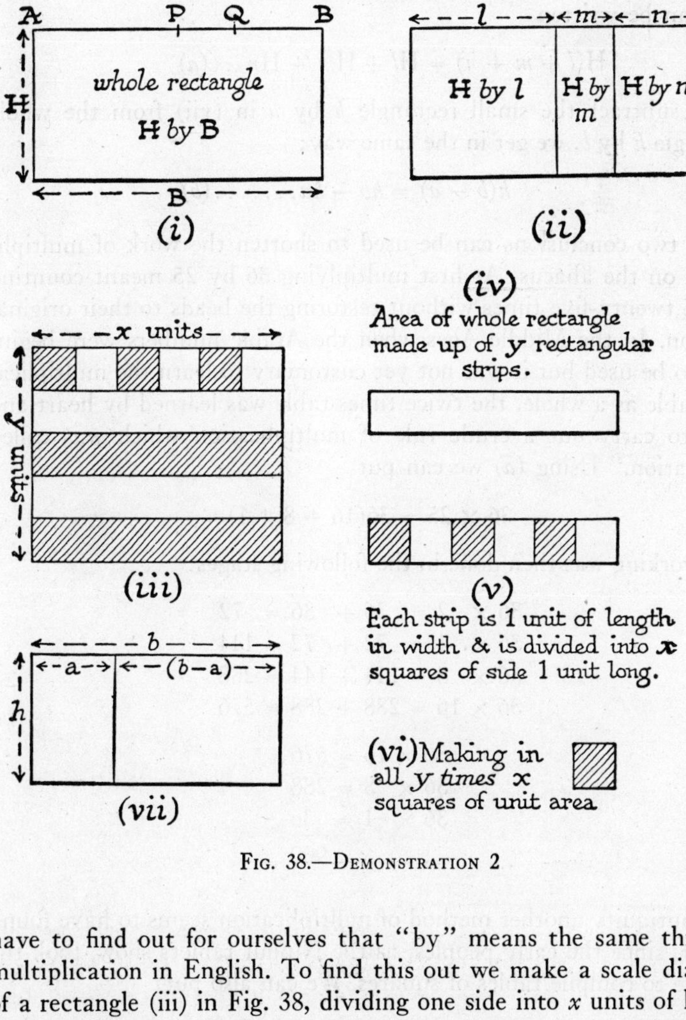

FIG. 38.—DEMONSTRATION 2

have to find out for ourselves that "by" means the same thing as multiplication in English. To find this out we make a scale diagram of a rectangle (iii) in Fig. 38, dividing one side into *x* units of length and the other into *y* units of length (compare Fig. 24, in which $x = 4$

and $y = 3$). If you look at (iv), (v), and (vi), you will see that we can write:

$$\text{HB units of area} = (\text{H}l + \text{H}m + \text{H}n) \text{ units of area}$$

And since

$$\text{B} = l + m + n$$

this can be written

$$\text{H}(l + m + n) = \text{H}l + \text{H}m + \text{H}n \ldots (a)$$

If we subtract the small rectangle h by a in (vii) from the whole rectangle h by b, we get in the same way:

$$h(b - a) = hb - ha \ldots\ldots (b)$$

These two conclusions can be used to shorten the work of multiplication on the abacus. At first multiplying 36 by 25 meant counting out 36 twenty-five times without restoring the beads to their original position. In the Middle Ages when the Arabic numbers were beginning to be used but it was not yet customary to learn the multiplication table as a whole, the twice times table was learned by heart and used to carry out a crude rule of multiplication which was called "duplation." Using (a) we can put

$$36 \times 25 = 36(16 + 8 + 1)$$

The working was then done in the following stages:

$$\begin{aligned} 36 \times 2 &= 36 + 36 = 72 \\ 36 \times 4 &= 72 + 72 = 144 \\ 36 \times 8 &= 144 + 144 = 288 \\ 36 \times 16 &= 288 + 288 = 576 \end{aligned}$$

$$\begin{aligned} 36 \times 16 &= 576 \\ 36 \times 8 &= 288 \\ 36 \times 1 &= \underline{36} \\ & 900 \end{aligned}$$

In antiquity another method of multiplication seems to have found favour, since the early peoples, as the Nippur tablets show, took the trouble to compile tables of squares. We can also put:

$$25 \times 36 = 25\ (25 + 11)$$

Continuing in this way:

$$\begin{aligned} 25 \times 36 &= 25^2 + 11.(25) = 25^2 + 11.(11 + 14) \\ &= 25^2 + 11^2 + 11.(14) = 25^2 + 11^2 + 11.(11 + 3) \\ &= 25^2 + 11^2 + 11^2 + 3.(11) \\ &= 25^2 + 11^2 + 11^2 + 3.(3 + 3 + 3 + 2) \\ &= 25^2 + 11^2 + 11^2 + 3^2 + 3^2 + 3^2 + 3.(2) \end{aligned}$$

The tables of squares would give this as

$$625 + 121 + 121 + 9 + 9 + 9 + 6$$

the last product being performed by memory.

The final addition then carried out on the abacus would give the correct result, 900.

Demonstration 3

"The area of a triangle is half the product of one side and the perpendicular height to the opposite corner."

Starting with the flat space enclosed by a square as a measure of area, we have now learned how to get the area of a rectangle, and how to get the area of a right-angled triangle, if we know how to get the area of a rectangle. For the next step, getting the area (A) of any triangle, the dissection is very simple (Fig. 39).

(i) If none of the angles are greater than a right angle, drop a perpendicular from the top corner to the base. This splits the triangle into two triangles which are right-angled. Each by Dem. 1 is equivalent to half a rectangle. From Dem. 2 for the area of a rectangle:

$$A = \tfrac{1}{2}px + \tfrac{1}{2}py$$

But we have seen that

$$\tfrac{1}{2}px + \tfrac{1}{2}py = \tfrac{1}{2}p(x + y) \quad \text{Dem. 2 } (a)$$

$$\therefore \quad A = \tfrac{1}{2}p(x + y)$$

$$\therefore \quad A = \tfrac{1}{2}pb$$

(ii) If one angle is larger than a right angle, drop a perpendicular on to the continuation of the side shown in Fig. 39 (ii). Then

$$\begin{aligned} A &= \tfrac{1}{2}p(b + x) - \tfrac{1}{2}px \\ &= \tfrac{1}{2}pb + \tfrac{1}{2}px - \tfrac{1}{2}px \\ &= \tfrac{1}{2}pb \end{aligned}$$

(*a*) Besides telling us how to measure the area of a triangle, this demonstration also helps us to expose a most important principle in shadow-reckoning (Dem. 7). If one triangle (Area A) has a base B units long, and perpendicular height p, and another triangle (Area a)

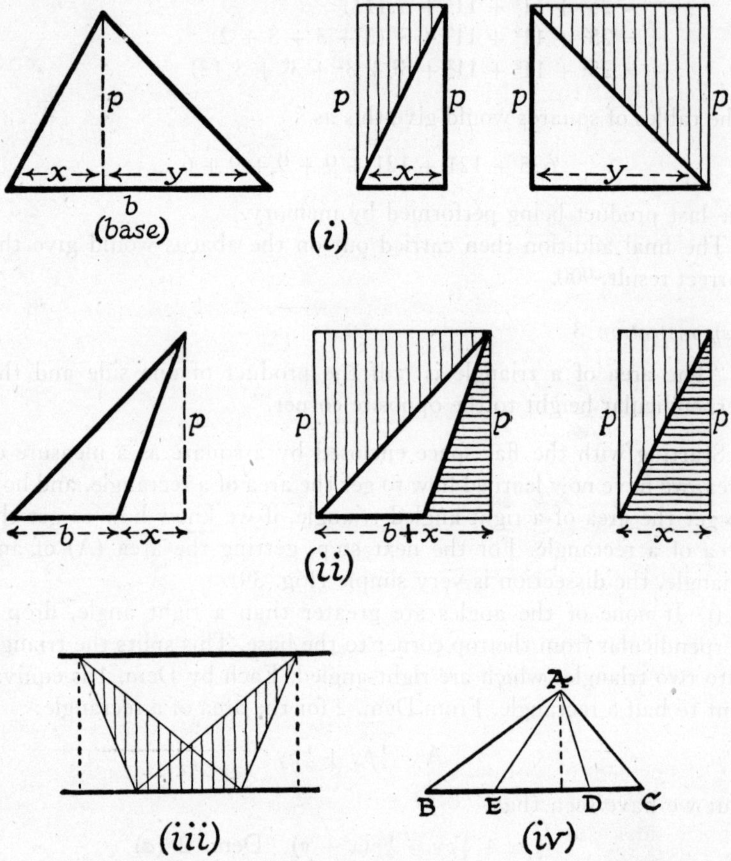

FIG. 39.—DEMONSTRATION 3

has a base b units long and the same perpendicular height, the ratio of their areas can be written:

$$\frac{A}{a} = \frac{\frac{1}{2}p \cdot B}{\frac{1}{2}p \cdot b} = \frac{B}{b}$$

That is to say, *the ratio of the areas of triangles having the same perpendicular height is the ratio of their bases.* For the very important demonstration which we have mentioned we need to be able to detect when two triangles have the same perpendicular height. Two clues are these:

(*b*) *Triangles having bases in line with one another and the opposite corners touching have the same perpendicular height.*

You can see this from Fig. 39 (iv). The triangles ABC, ABE, AED, ADC, AEC, ABD all have the same perpendicular height.

(*c*) *Triangles on the same base have the same perpendicular height if their opposite corners touch a line parallel to the base.*

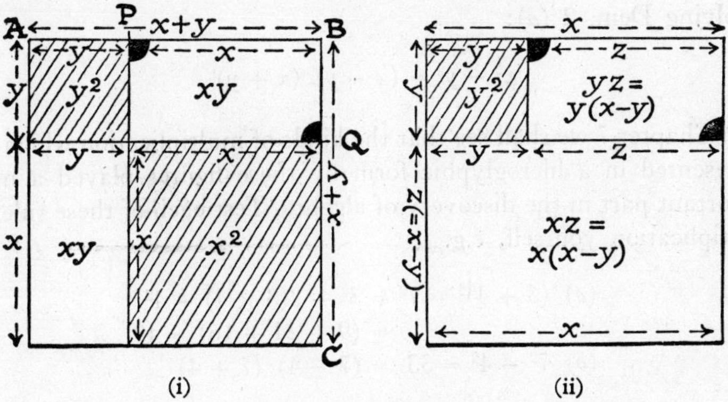

FIG. 40.—DEMONSTRATION 4

This is represented in Fig. 39 (iii). We learned in Dem. 1 (*b*) that perpendiculars connecting two parallel lines are equivalent.

Demonstration 4 (How to dissect a square)

"If one side of a square is divided into two segments, the area of the whole square is equivalent to the sum of the areas of the squares whose sides are the two segments, together with twice the area of the rectangle whose adjoining sides are equivalent to the two segments."

A square is a rectangle of which all the sides are equivalent. The only difficulty in seeing this is the meaning of the words. In Fig. 40 (i) the side AB of the large square is divided at P into two segments y units and x units long. So the length of AB is $(x + y)$. The adjacent side BC is divided in the same way at Q. Perpendiculars to the opposite sides are drawn from P and Q. Each of these divides the square into two rectangles. The size of all the sides in the four figures formed follows from the fact that opposite sides of a rectangle are equivalent.

The area of the large square is AB × AB or $(x + y)^2$. The figure thus shows that:

$$(x + y)^2 \text{ units of area} = (x^2 + 2xy + y^2) \text{ of the same units of area}$$

$$\text{i.e.} \qquad (x + y)^2 = x^2 + 2xy + y^2$$

A very similar demonstration shown in Fig. 40 (ii) gives

$$x^2 - y^2 = (x - y)x + (x - y)y$$

Applying Dem. 2 (*a*):

$$x^2 - y^2 = (x - y)\ (x + y)$$

In Chapter 7 we shall see that the kinds of multiplication which are represented in a hieroglyphic form by these figures played a most important part in the discovery of algebra. Test each of these rules of multiplication yourself, e.g.

(*a*) $(3 + 4)^2 = 7^2 = 3^2 + 2(3 \times 4) + 4^2$
$= (9 + 24 + 16) = 49$

(*b*) $7^2 - 4^2 = 33 = (7 - 4)\ (7 + 4)$

This demonstration is simply an application of the rule for finding the area of a rectangle. It is doubtful whether it was ever used for surveying. Its practical application in ancient times was to shorten the work of multiplication on the abacus, before people had a number script with which direct calculation, such as we do, could be carried out. Nicomachus of Alexandria (A.D. 100) gives examples of the way in which it was used before mathematicians—let alone ordinary people—used the multiplication table to work sums on paper. Here are two examples.

(*a*) To multiply 37 by 25, first find the number midway between, i.e. 31, then

$$37 \times 25 = (31 - 6)\ (31 + 6)$$
$$= 31^2 - 6^2 = 925 \quad \text{(Check this yourself)}$$

All you have now to do is to look up the squares of 31 and 6 in the ancient tables of squares, such as those found at Nippur (2000 B.C.), and subtract. This is much shorter than the methods given to illustrate the use of Demonstration 2. The previous example there given was

36×25. There is no whole number midway between these. So you use the next number above or below 36, e.g.

$$36 \times 25 = (37 - 1) . 25 = (37 \times 25) - 25 \text{ (Dem. 2 } (b))$$
$$= 31^2 - 6^2 - 25 = 900$$

The mid-number between two numbers is called the *arithmetic mean*, or common average. It is more misused, by politicians and others, than any quantity in size language. If a and b are numbers, the arithmetic mean is $\frac{1}{2}(a + b)$, e.g. for the two numbers 37 and 25 the A.M. is $\frac{1}{2}(37 + 25) = \frac{1}{2}(62) = 31$. For 36 and 25 the A.M. is $30\frac{1}{2}$.

(*b*) This trick to shorten work on the abacus made it very important to have good tables of squares. The same formula can be used to simplify making them. Suppose we have squares up to 100, and wish to continue them further. This is what Nicomachus recommended. To get the square of a higher number, e.g. 118, we proceed like this:

$$(118)^2 - (18)^2 = (118 - 18) \ (118 + 18)$$
$$\therefore \quad (118)^2 = (100) \ (136) + (18)^2 = 13{,}924$$

Multiplying by ten, a hundred, etc., on the counting frame for any script based on multiples of ten, as nearly all are, is very much more simple than multiplying by another number. So the result is obtained fairly quickly.

FOUR DEMONSTRATIONS IN SHADOW-RECKONING

For those of us who are urban products of a northern civilization, accustomed to dwell in houses with spacious glass windows, equipped with gas or electric light, with clocks, and, if we can afford them, with refrigerators and vacuum cleaners, it requires some effort of the imagination to realize the significance of light and shadow in the cradles of civilization where the first stone cities were built. Today we have to devise experiments to teach the schoolboy or schoolgirl that light coming through a slit follows a clear-cut path, and that the beams of the sun are parallel. The first city dwellers, whose only windows were narrow crevices through which sunrays and moonlight played upon the dusty air, lived in abundant sunshine casting high clean shadows with sharp edges on the sand. They did not need to be told that light "travels in straight lines," or that light rays coming from a very distant object slope so little that we can treat them as if they were *parallel*. They could see it for themselves all day and every day (Fig. 41).

When Thales visited Egypt and used the method of shadow-reckoning to find the height of the Great Pyramid, the older civilization of the Nile had already succumbed successively to the Assyrians and to the Hittites. Though we are told that he astonished the Egyptians, there is very little doubt that he employed the same simple principle of

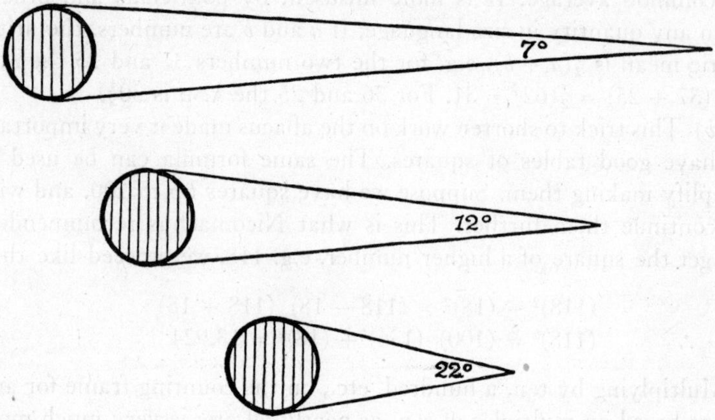

FIG. 41

The further away a heavenly body is situated, the smaller is the angle between the light rays which come from its extreme edges. So if it is very far away the beam appears to be parallel. The angle between the two furthermost points on the rim of the sun or moon, as seen from the earth, is only about half a degree. The approximately parallel rays of the sunbeam or moonbeam were a familiar feature of everyday life when there was no glass, and windows were narrow and high.

architectural measurement used by the pyramid builders themselves. The art of shadow-reckoning was one of the great arts of antiquity. The geometry of the triangle discloses the use of shadow-reckoning in building, just as the geometry of the rectangle arises in connexion with the measurement of land for taxation of the small cultivator. Geometry was flourishing in Egypt and Mesopotamia when northern peoples put up stone circles and stone avenues, which still abound on the moors of Devon and Cornwall, where Phoenician ships came for tin. The wreckage of innumerable villages of crude stone huts is still strewn where tin was abundant. Like the Bantu, they never built cities or temples on their own initiative. The backwardness of man in Northern Europe was not due to his stupidity, as Aristotle, the apostle of slavery, believed, or as the cultivated Said of Toledo taught, when the Moors were building baths which were destroyed by their Nordic conquerors who expelled the Jews and introduced the odour of sanctity. Aristotle and Said had just as good reason to support their own prejudices as those who point to the backwardness of the Bantu in our own generation. What such people leave out of account is the material conditions which made it possible for civilization to begin. Northern man had to learn the art of building from the earlier civilizations. Before he could progress far, he had also to learn the art of time-keeping. In countries where the sundial could never be more than a garden ornament, settled city life and stable cultivation progressed very little before a foreign priesthood introduced the candle clock to toll the bell for matins and vespers.

The next four demonstrations are given respectively in the first (5, 6, 8) and sixth (7) books of Euclid. The first three were known to the Phoenician Thales. The last still bears the name of the Phoenician Pythagoras, though we have good reasons to believe that he got it from the Chinese. In explaining them we shall give examples of their use in architecture and surveying, anticipating the next step made by the Alexandrians, who applied them to the survey of the heavens. The first, which you will find very simple, is not directly useful. Its importance lies in the fact that it helps us to recognize the truth of the other three.

Demonstration 5

"The three angles of a triangle together add up to two right angles."

All you have to do is to tilt one corner of a triangle on a straight edge till the opposite side is parallel to the straight edge. In Fig. 42 (i), (ii), and (iii) the text explains the steps which can be summarized as follows:

$A + B + C = D + C + E$ (PARALLEL RULE TWO)
$D + C + E = 180°$ (ANGLE RULE ONE—Fig. 33(i))

This is so simple that we shall take the opportunity of explaining the ways in which it is used to expose the principles of shadow-reckoning given in the next three demonstrations. Note the following.

(*a*) *Two triangles are equivalent if one side in each is equivalent and two angles of one are equivalent to the two corresponding angles of the other.*

This combines what we have just learned with TRIANGLE RULE THREE (Fig. 30 (*c*)), which tells us that we can draw a triangle if we know one side *a* and the angles B and C. If we happen to be given the angles A (opposite the side *a*) and B, we can at once get the third angle C as follows:

$$A + B + C = 180°$$

$$\therefore \quad C = 180° - (A + B)$$

e.g. if A is 60° and B is 60°, C is 180° – (60° + 60°), i.e. C is 60°.

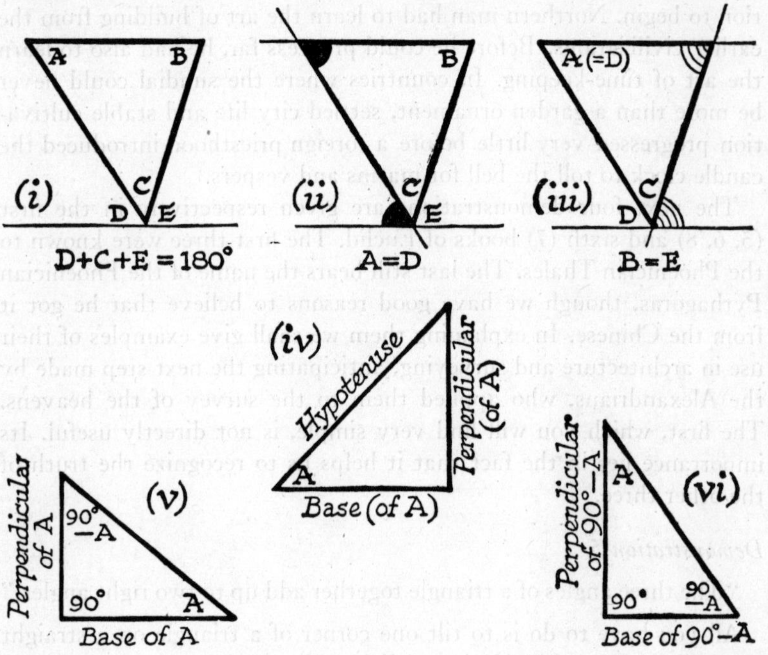

Fig. 42.—Demonstration 5

If A is 45° and B is 90°, C is 180° – (45° + 90°), i.e. 45°. If A is 30° and B is 90°, C is 60°. Similarly, if we know A and C, we can find B, e.g. if A is 60° and C is 90°, B = 180° – (A + C), i.e. 30°.

(*b*) *If we know one angle* (*A*) *of a right-angled triangle other than the right angle, we know the third* (90° – *A*).

This you have already seen. If the three angles are A, 90°, and 90° – A, they all add up to 180°, i.e.

$$A + 90° + 90° - A = 180°$$

There are three terms which are used for the sides of a right-angled triangle. The longest side opposite the right angle is called the hypotenuse. If A is an angle other than the right angle, the side opposite it is called the perpendicular of A. The third side is called the base of A. You will notice that the perpendicular of 90° – A is the base of A and *vice versa* (Fig. 42, (iv), (v), (vi)).

(*c*) *All right-angled triangles with the same corner angle are similar, i.e. equiangular* (Fig. 43 (i)).

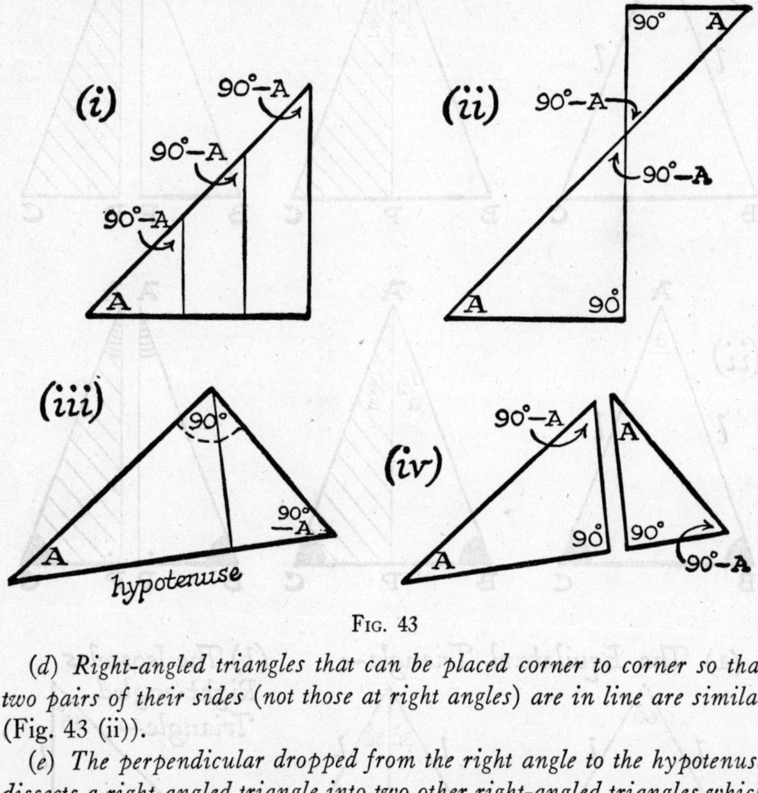

FIG. 43

(*d*) *Right-angled triangles that can be placed corner to corner so that two pairs of their sides (not those at right angles) are in line are similar* (Fig. 43 (ii)).

(*e*) *The perpendicular dropped from the right angle to the hypotenuse dissects a right-angled triangle into two other right-angled triangles which are similar to it, and therefore also to one another.*

This is shown in Fig. 43 (iii) and (iv). It is one of the most important tricks for the dissection of triangles.

Demonstration 6

"If two sides of a triangle are equivalent the angles opposite to them are equivalent, and if two angles are equivalent the sides opposite to them are equivalent."

There are two things to show. The dissection is the same for both.

We split the triangle into two by dividing the angle between the equivalent sides or the angle other than the two equivalent ones into two, using the first rule of dissection.

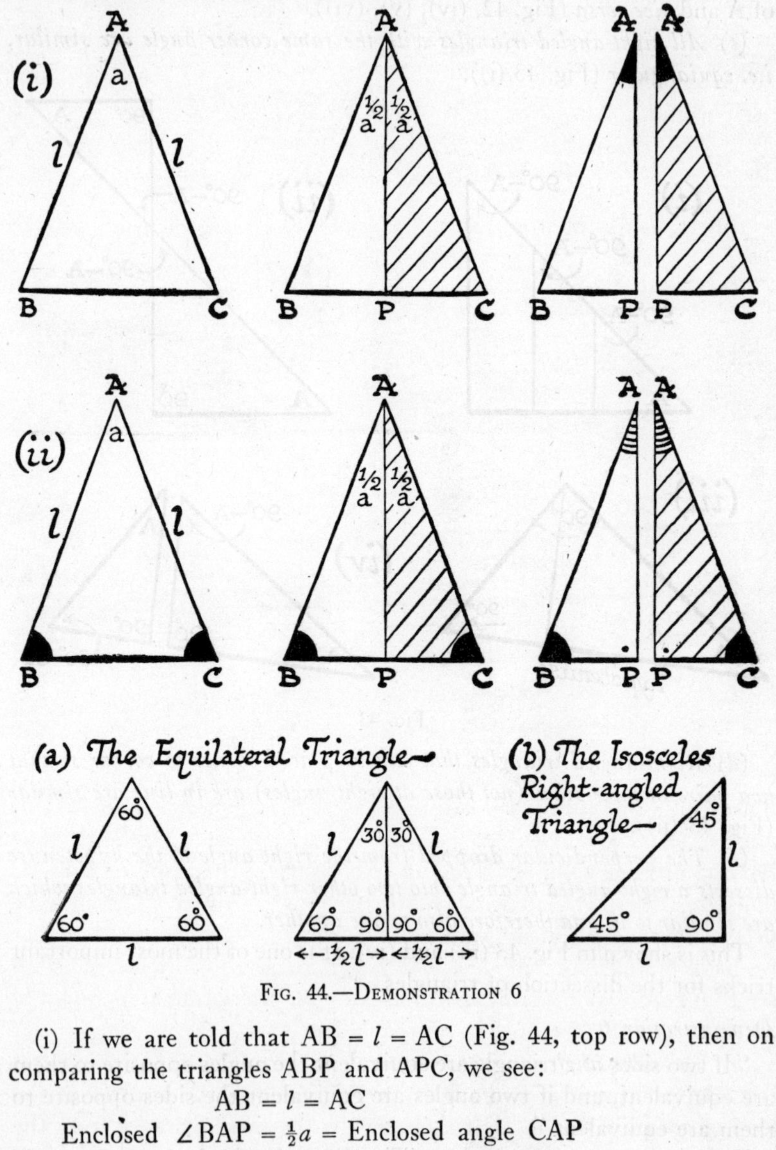

FIG. 44.—DEMONSTRATION 6

(i) If we are told that AB = l = AC (Fig. 44, top row), then on comparing the triangles ABP and APC, we see:

$$AB = l = AC$$

$$\text{Enclosed } \angle BAP = \tfrac{1}{2}a = \text{Enclosed angle } CAP$$

$$AP = AP \quad \text{(common to both)}$$

TRIANGLE RULE Two therefore tells us that the triangles are equivalent. This means that all their corresponding sides and all their corresponding angles are equivalent. So the angle ACB opposite AB is equivalent to the angle ABC opposite the equivalent side AC.

(ii) If we are told (Fig. 44, second row) that the two angles B (ABC) and C (ACB) are equivalent, we see:

$$\angle ABC = \angle ACB \quad \text{(as we are told)}$$
$$\angle BAP = \tfrac{1}{2}a = \angle CAP$$
$$AP = AP \quad \text{(common to both triangles)}$$

But we have seen from Dem. 5 (*a*) that two triangles are equivalent

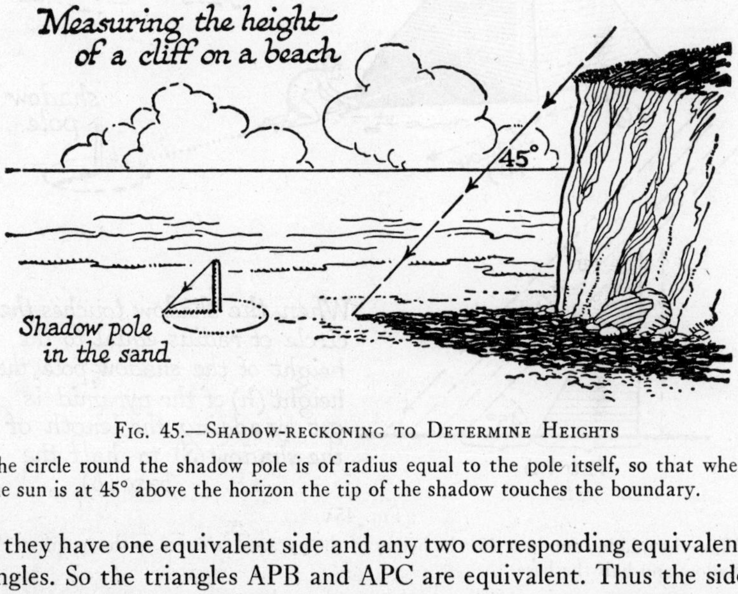

FIG. 45.—SHADOW-RECKONING TO DETERMINE HEIGHTS

The circle round the shadow pole is of radius equal to the pole itself, so that when the sun is at 45° above the horizon the tip of the shadow touches the boundary.

if they have one equivalent side and any two corresponding equivalent angles. So the triangles APB and APC are equivalent. Thus the side AB opposite the angle ACB is equivalent to the corresponding side AC opposite the equivalent angle ABC. Before showing how this may be used to measure the height of a cliff from its shadow, or to see whether we have built a high edifice to the height required, we must pause to see that this demonstration gives us a simple way of making angles of 30°, 60°, and 45° (see Fig. 44, bottom row).

(*a*) *To make angles of* 30° *and* 60°.—We can make an equilateral triangle (all three sides equal) by pegging out at the knots a closed loop of cord knotted so that each knot is the same distance from the next. From what we have just learned, if all three sides are equivalent (length, l), all three angles are equivalent. Since all three make up 180°, each is one-third of 180°, or 60°. If you look back at the top row of Fig. 44, you will see that if the triangles ABP and ACP are equivalent, the side BP is equivalent to the corresponding side PC, i.e. P divides BC into two equivalent parts. In the equilateral triangle dis-

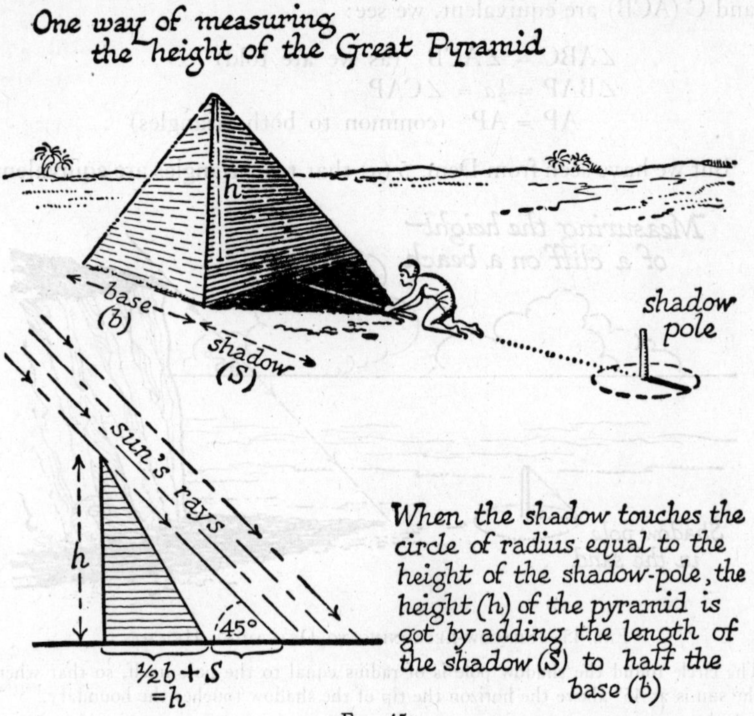
One way of measuring the height of the Great Pyramid
h
base (b)
shadow (S)
shadow pole
sun's rays
h
45°
½b + S = h
When the shadow touches the circle of radius equal to the height of the shadow-pole, the height (h) of the pyramid is got by adding the length of the shadow (S) to half the base (b)

FIG. 45A

When the midday sun is at 45° the height of the pyramid is equal to the length of the shadow and half the base.

sected in the same way below we see that the sides opposite to the angles 30° ($\frac{1}{2}$ of 60°) are therefore $\frac{1}{2}l$. By joining the corner of an equilateral triangle to the middle of the opposite side we thus get an angle of 30°, the other angle (Dem. 5) is a right angle.

(*b*) *To make angles of* 45°.—Dem. 5 (*b*) showed us that if one angle of a right-angled triangle is 45° the third angle is 45°. So a right-angled triangle of 45° has two equivalent angles and therefore two equivalent sides. Having laid out a right angle, we can make an angle of 45° by measuring equivalent distances (l) along the perpendicular and the base and joining the ends. The Egyptian geometers and architects would do this with rope and peg on sand. You can do it with drawing-pins and string on the table.

The use of this demonstration, which used to be called the *Pons Asinorum*, or bridge of asses (because the asses who taught it took the greatest trouble to destroy the bridge which connects it with the real world), is seen in Fig. 45. When the sun is at 45° above the horizon (or 45° from the zenith), sunbeam, cliff, and shadow, or sunbeam, shadow, and any *upright* object form an isosceles right-angled triangle.

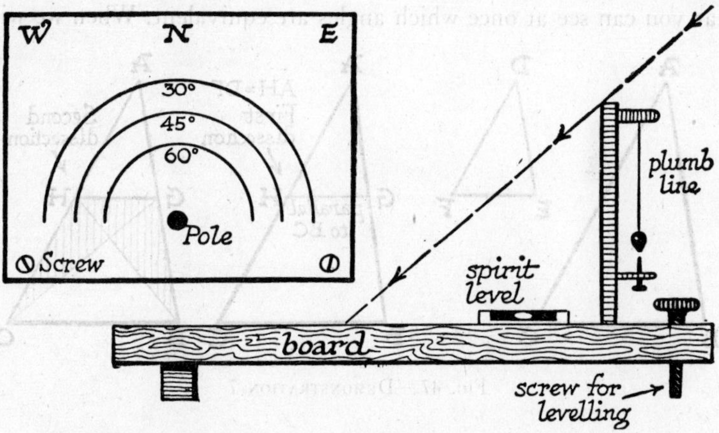

FIG. 46.—DESIGN FOR HOME-MADE SHADOW POLE

This means that the length of the shadow is then equivalent to the height of the cliff. To use it, you put a stick in the sand and sit around till the length of the shadow is the same as the stick. You then measure the shadow of the cliff, and this gives you its height. How it could be used for building up a pyramid is shown in the next figure, where the rule stated is only true at noon on two days of the year. Waiting for noon on these two days is a mug's game. It takes far more time to sit around to catch the shadow of the pyramid at the moment when it is the same as the height than to learn the next demonstration, which shows you how to do the same thing when the sun's rays are at any angle. So if you find it is a little long-winded, you will have the satisfaction of knowing that it saves time in the long run.

If you have access to a roof, back garden, or yard, Fig. 46 is a design for a shadow pole with which, as you will see later, you can find the height of your house, your latitude and longitude, the time of the day, and how much the earth appears to tilt on its axis throughout the year (i.e. the inclination of the orbit to the poles, called by astronomers the obliquity of the ecliptic).

Demonstration 7

"In similar triangles the ratio of corresponding sides is the same."

The dissection for this is tricky; we shall do it in three stages. Two similar triangles ABC and DEF are drawn on the left of Fig. 47 so that you can see at once which angles are equivalent. When we wish

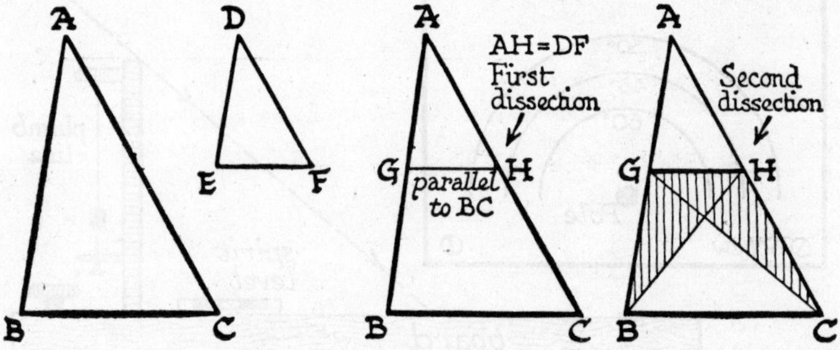

Fig. 47.—Demonstration 7

to demonstrate something new, the first thing we have to ask is what we already know about the sort of thing we are looking for. Here we are looking for ratios. The only thing we have yet learned about ratios is that the areas of triangles with the same height have the same ratio as their bases (Dem. 3). So we have got to find triangles of which the bases are corresponding sides in the two triangles we are comparing. To do this we have first to put both the triangles in the same figure.

(i) Figure on the right: AH is measured off along AC equivalent to DF, and GH is drawn parallel to BC. Comparing the triangles AGH and ABC we first see that

$\angle GAH = \angle BAC$

$\therefore \angle GAH = \angle EDF$ ($\because$ the triangles ABC and DEF are similar)

$\left.\begin{array}{l}\angle AHG = \angle ACB \\ \angle AGH = \angle ABC\end{array}\right\}$ (Parallel Rule One)

$\therefore \angle AHG = \angle DFE$; and $\angle AGH =$ DEF ($\because$ the triangles ABC and DEF are similar)

So comparing the triangles DEF and AGH

$$\angle EDF = \angle GAH$$
$$DF = AH \quad \text{(as we drew it so)}$$
$$\angle DFE = \angle AHG$$

By TRIANGLE RULE THREE the triangles DEF and AGH are equivalent

$$\therefore \quad GH = EF \quad \text{and} \quad AG = DE \quad . \; . \; . \; . \; . \; . \; (a)$$

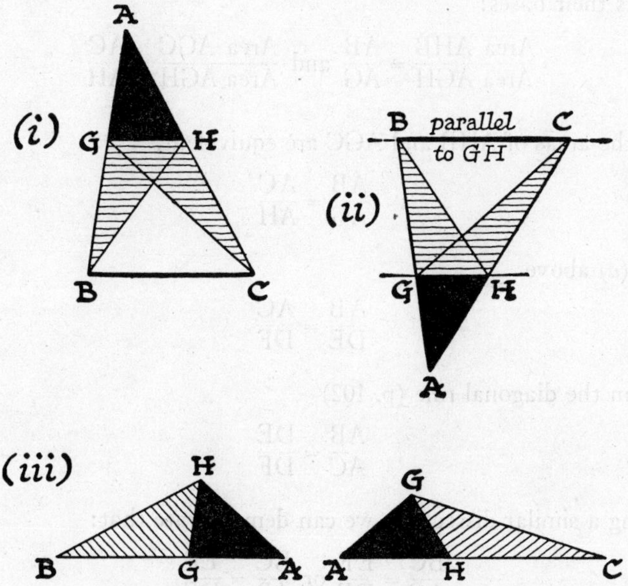

FIG. 48.—DEMONSTRATION 7 (*continued*)

(ii) In Dem. 3 we have learned that triangles have the same height when they have their bases on one line and the opposite corners on a line parallel to it. This suggests the next step. Draw lines joining GC and HB (right hand Fig. 47), and to get the figure in a more familiar position for what we do next, look at it upside down (as in Fig. 48 (ii). You can now see (Dem. 3 (*c*), Fig. 39 (iii)):

$$\text{Area } \triangle \text{ BGH} = \text{Area } \triangle \text{ GCH} \quad . \; . \; . \; . \; . \; . \; (b)$$

(iii) In Dem. 3 we also learned that triangles have the same height if their bases are in the same straight line and their opposite corners touch. We can get two such pairs of triangles by adding the triangle AGH both to the triangle GHB and to the triangle GCH, i.e.

$$\text{Area } \triangle\text{s AGH} + \text{BGH} = \text{Area } \triangle\text{s AGH} + \text{GCH}$$
$$\text{or} \quad \text{Area } \triangle \text{ AHB} = \text{Area } \triangle \text{ AGC} \quad . \; . \; . \; . \; . \; (c)$$

The triangles AHB and AGH have the same perpendicular height, as have also AGH and AGC (Dem. 3 (*b*)). So, from Dem. 3 (*a*), which tells us that the areas of triangles with the same height have the same ratio as their bases:

$$\frac{\text{Area AHB}}{\text{Area AGH}} = \frac{\text{AB}}{\text{AG}} \text{ and } \frac{\text{Area AGC}}{\text{Area AGH}} = \frac{\text{AC}}{\text{AH}}$$

Since the areas of AHB and AGC are equivalent,

$$\frac{\text{AB}}{\text{AG}} = \frac{\text{AC}}{\text{AH}}$$

From (*a*) above

$$\frac{\text{AB}}{\text{DE}} = \frac{\text{AC}}{\text{DF}}$$

Or from the diagonal rule (p. 102)

$$\frac{\text{AB}}{\text{AC}} = \frac{\text{DE}}{\text{DF}}$$

Using a similar dissection, we can demonstrate that:

$$\frac{\text{BC}}{\text{AC}} = \frac{\text{EF}}{\text{DF}} \text{ or } \frac{\text{BC}}{\text{AB}} = \frac{\text{EF}}{\text{DE}}$$

How Thales used this to measure the height of the Great Pyramid of Cheops without waiting for the two days when the midday sun was at 45° is seen in Fig. 49. He put his stick in the ground upright at the tip of the shadow of the pyramid. Pole, sunbeam, and shadow give you a triangle with angles 90°, A, and 90° – A. The height of the pyramid, the sunbeam, and its shadow added to half its base give you another with the same angle. Since these triangles are similar the ratios of corresponding sides are the same, i.e.

$$\frac{\text{H}}{\frac{1}{2}b + \text{S}} = \frac{p}{s}$$

Using the diagonal rule, we get for the height of the pyramid:

$$H = \frac{p}{s}(\tfrac{1}{2}b + S)$$

The height of pole (p), the base (b), and the two shadows (s and S) can all be measured easily at noon on any day.

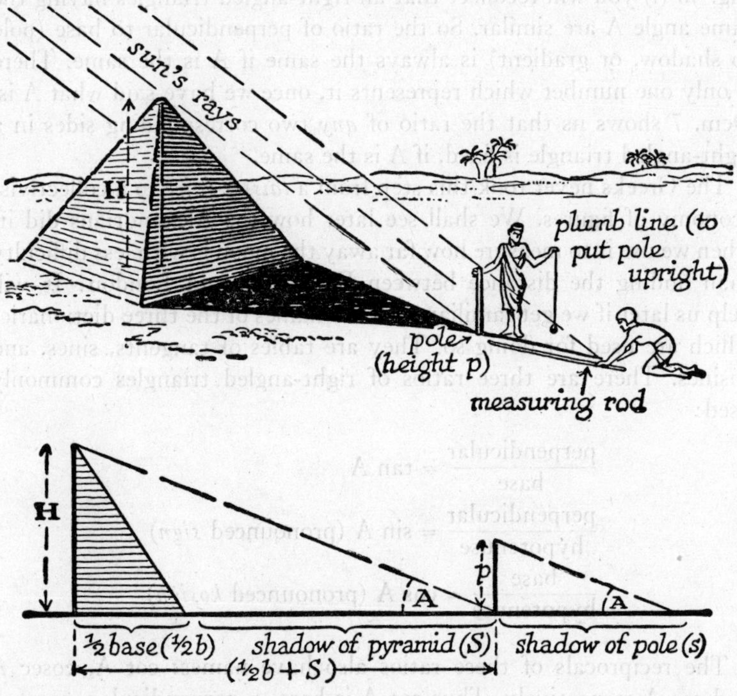

FIG. 49.—HOW THALES MEASURED THE HEIGHT OF THE GREAT PYRAMID

The angle A is the midday sun's inclination to the horizon, and is therefore the same for both triangles.

In essentials the same method could be used to determine the height of any inaccessible object. We can find how far it is away, provided we can measure the angle which the top makes with the horizon by some sort of theodolite, like the one shown in Fig. 12. The crudest way is to make a scale diagram. That is the *laissez-faire* method of Greek geometry. There is a better method, the socialized geometry, or trigonometry, as we usually call it, of the Alexandrians. This is to make a table once and for all of ratios of pole and shadow for any angle of inclination. If you look back at Fig. 31, you will see that the ratio of pole to shadow for an angle of inclination A is what is called tan A in the dictionary language of trigonometry. This means, "Look up a number in a dictionary (table of tangents) which has been made once and for all, instead of going to the trouble of drawing a diagram to scale, every time you make an estimate." If you look back at Fig. 43 (i) you will recollect that all right-angled triangles having the same angle A are similar. So the ratio of perpendicular to base (pole to shadow, or gradient) is always the same if A is the same. There is only one number which represents it, once we have said what A is. Dem. 7 shows us that the ratio of *any* two corresponding sides in a right-angled triangle is fixed, if A is the same.

The Greeks never took this step from a *laissez-faire* to a collectivist economy of figures. We shall see later how the Alexandrians did it, when we use it to measure how far away the moon is with less difficulty than finding the distance between Edinburgh and London. It will help us later if we get familiar with the names of the three dictionaries which are used for doing so. They are tables of tangents, sines, and cosines. There are three ratios of right-angled triangles commonly used:

$$\frac{\text{perpendicular}}{\text{base}} = \tan A$$

$$\frac{\text{perpendicular}}{\text{hypotenuse}} = \sin A \text{ (pronounced } \textit{sign}\text{)}$$

$$\frac{\text{base}}{\text{hypotenuse}} = \cos A \text{ (pronounced } \textit{kosign}\text{)}$$

The reciprocals of these ratios also have names: cot A, cosec A and sec A respectively. Thus cot A is base ÷ perpendicular, cosec A $= h \div p$ and sec A $= h \div b$.

There are tables for all six of these sets of ratios. They are no more difficult to use than a railway time-table. In the Table of SINES one column like the departure column from Waverley station in Edinburgh gives the angle A. The other column, like the arrival column at London (or other place to which you may wish to escape), gives you the number you want (sin A). How these tables were constructed belongs to another chapter. Perhaps you will be sufficiently interested to want a clue already. One way of dealing with the problem would be to draw large numbers of very accurate scale diagrams of right-angled triangles with different corner angles (A), and measure the sides very accurately, writing down all the results. This would take a long time. It would not be efficient, because we want the most accurate values it is possible to get in an imperfect world, where first attempts are not necessarily the best. As a matter of fact, we have already picked up some information which could get results more quickly and correctly. Without noticing it we have collectivized the ratios of a few angles, but have not yet enough to make a complete table.

How far we have got can be seen by first looking at a more familiar sort of table, such as this one, which shows the progress of travellers leaving Edinburgh:

Departure, Waverley Station, Edinburgh (p.m.)	Arrival at		
	Newcastle	York	King's Cross, London
3.0	—	6.45	—
4.30	6.30	—	—
5.15	—	—	11.58

If you compare the figures in Fig. 50 with those at the bottom of Fig. 44, you will be able to draw up a similar table like this:

Angle (A) (degrees)	Tan A	Sin A	Cos A
30	—	$\frac{1}{2}$	—
45	1	—	—
60	—	—	$\frac{1}{2}$

You will also notice two things which make preparing tables easy:

(i) $\sin A = \cos (90° - A)$ (see Dem. 5(*b*))
$\cos A = \sin (90° - A)$

(ii) $\tan A = \dfrac{\sin A}{\cos A} \quad \left(\dfrac{p}{b} = \dfrac{p}{h} \div \dfrac{b}{h} = \dfrac{p}{h} \times \dfrac{h}{b}\right)$

Demonstration 8

"The square of the hypotenuse of a right-angled triangle is equivalent to the sum of the squares of the perpendicular and the base."

The dissection for this demonstration has been explained already in Dem. 5 (*e*) and Fig. 43. The perpendicular from the right angle to the hypotenuse cuts up a right-angled triangle into two triangles similar to one another and to the parent triangle. All we have done

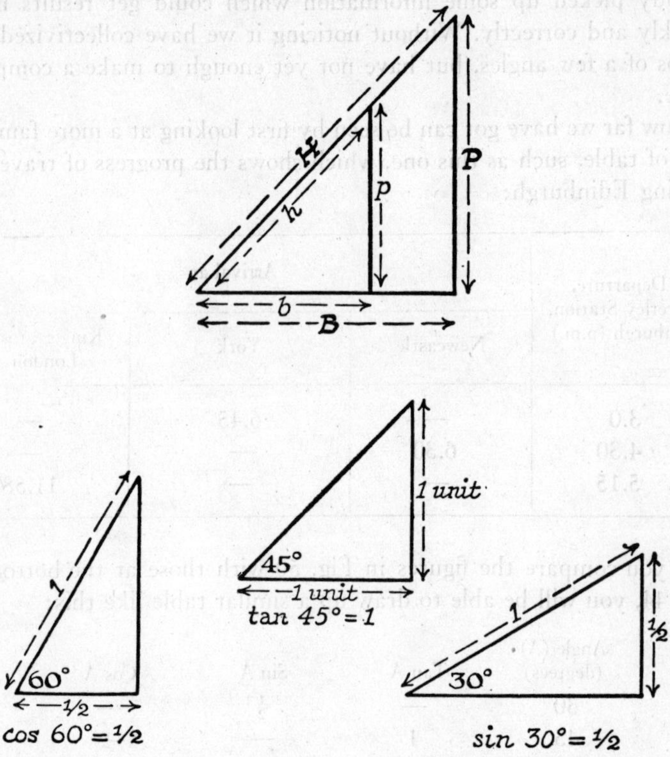

FIG. 50

in Fig. 51 is to arrange them so that the corresponding angles and sides are seen at a glance. From (iii) in Fig. 51:

$$\frac{a}{c} = \frac{x}{a} \quad \text{(Dem. 7)}$$

$$a^2 = cx \quad \text{(Diagonal rule p. 97)}$$

From (iv) for similar reasons:

$$\frac{b}{c} = \frac{y}{b}$$

$$b^2 = cy$$

Combining both results and remembering $c = x + y$, we see that

$$a^2 + b^2 = cx + cy$$
$$\therefore \quad a^2 + b^2 = c\,(x + y) \quad \text{(Dem. 2)}$$
$$\therefore \quad a^2 + b^2 = c^2$$

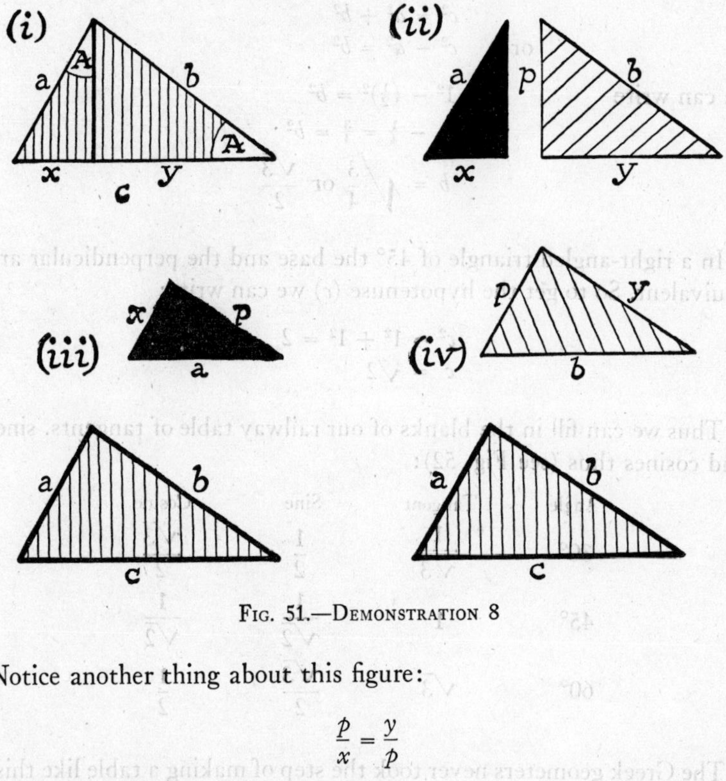

FIG. 51.—DEMONSTRATION 8

Notice another thing about this figure:

$$\frac{p}{x} = \frac{y}{p}$$

So that $\quad p^2 = xy \quad$ or $\quad p = \sqrt{xy}$

In the last expression p is called the *geometric mean*, or geometric average of x and y. The geometric mean of 3 and 27 is $\sqrt{3 \times 27}$, i.e. $\sqrt{81}$, or 9. The arithmetic mean or common average is $\frac{1}{2}(3 + 27) = 15$. In ninety-nine cases out of a hundred when politicians talk about an average, there is just as little reason for taking one as the other. There are many kinds of averages. Which you should use depends on what you are going to make it do.

This demonstration is of the greatest importance in determining the ratios of angles. You will recollect (if you do not, you will recall on looking back to Fig. 44) that if the angles of a right-angled triangle are 30°, 60°, and 90°, the hypotenuse (c) is twice the side (a) opposite the angle of 30°. To get the third side (b), taking the hypotenuse as 1, instead of

$$c^2 = a^2 + b^2$$

or

$$c^2 - a^2 = b^2$$

we can write

$$1^2 - (\tfrac{1}{2})^2 = b^2$$

$$1 - \tfrac{1}{4} = \tfrac{3}{4} = b^2$$

$$b = \sqrt{\frac{3}{4}} \text{ or } \frac{\sqrt{3}}{2}$$

In a right-angled triangle of 45° the base and the perpendicular are equivalent. So to get the hypotenuse (c) we can write:

$$c^2 = 1^2 + 1^2 = 2$$

$$c = \sqrt{2}$$

Thus we can fill in the blanks of our railway table of tangents, sines and cosines thus (see Fig. 52):

Angle	Tangent	Sine	Cosine
30°	$\frac{1}{\sqrt{3}}$	$\frac{1}{2}$	$\frac{\sqrt{3}}{2}$
45°	1	$\frac{1}{\sqrt{2}}$	$\frac{1}{\sqrt{2}}$
60°	$\sqrt{3}$	$\frac{\sqrt{3}}{2}$	$\frac{1}{2}$

The Greek geometers never took the step of making a table like this, or of extending it into a Bradshaw for every degree. So we shall leave how this can be done till a later stage. In the meantime, you will notice that we are no longer tied down to the shadow pole. Greek geometers had the means of making measurements of height without the shadow pole. If you have a simple theodolite (see Fig. 12), you can walk away from the cliff in Fig. 45 x yards till you sight the edge of the cliff at 30°. If h is the height of the cliff,

$$\frac{h}{x} = \frac{1}{\sqrt{3}} \text{ or } h = \frac{x}{\sqrt{3}}$$

If you walk back from it till you are y yards away, when the sighting-angle is 60°,

$$\frac{h}{y} = \sqrt{3} \quad \text{or} \quad h = y.\sqrt{3}$$

You can do a great deal more than this. Suppose you cannot get right up to the cliff, then you only need the distance d between two spots

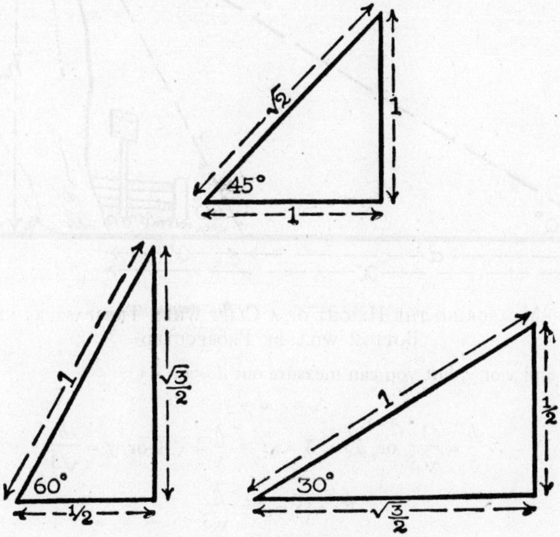

FIG. 52

$\tan 45° = 1 \quad \sin 45° = 1/\sqrt{2} \quad \cos 45° = 1/\sqrt{2}$
$\tan 60° = \sqrt{3} \quad \sin 60° = \sqrt{3}/2 \quad \cos 60° = \frac{1}{2}$
$\tan 30° = 1/\sqrt{3} \quad \sin 30° = \frac{1}{2} \quad \cos 30° = \sqrt{3}/2$

in the line directly away from the cliff where the sighting angles are 30° and 60° respectively (see Fig. 53).

At the end of this chapter we shall ask why the Greeks got so near to having a dictionary of angles without actually doing so. The point to notice here is that the mathematician came up against quantities like $\sqrt{2}$ and $\sqrt{3}$ (approx. 1·414 and 1·732), which could not be expressed with the numbers at his disposal. The practical man could only solve the problem as best he could by a sand-tracing like the one shown in Fig. 55, or by a sand-tracing based on the geometric mean. This we shall give later.

FOUR DEMONSTRATIONS IN STAR GAZING

To carry on with the method of measuring inaccessible distances by means of known distances and angles, as when we get the height

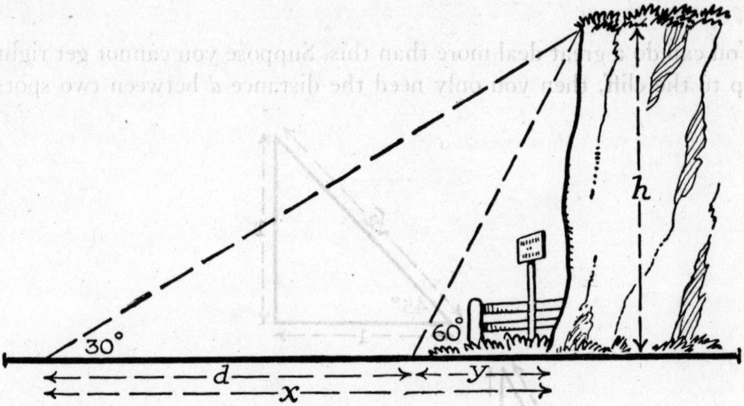

FIG. 53.—MEASURING THE HEIGHT OF A CLIFF WHEN TRESPASSERS NEAR THE BOTTOM WILL BE PROSECUTED

You cannot find x or y, but you can measure out $d = (x - y)$.

$$\therefore\ x - d = y$$

$$\therefore\ \frac{h}{x} = \frac{1}{\sqrt{3}} \text{ or } h \cdot \sqrt{3} = x: \qquad \frac{h}{y} = \sqrt{3} \text{ or } y = \frac{h}{\sqrt{3}}$$

$$h \cdot \sqrt{3} - d = \frac{h}{\sqrt{3}}$$

Multiplying both sides by $\sqrt{3}$, we get

$$3h - d\sqrt{3} = h$$

$$2h = d\sqrt{3}$$

$$h = \frac{\sqrt{3}}{2} \cdot d$$

Measuring the distance of the moon from the earth is essentially like this.

of a cliff, it is necessary to know something about the circle. The geometry of the circle was started by the calendar makers. Precisely how much the Greeks got from them we do not know. The second demonstration which follows is attributed to Thales. The first three are given in the third book of Euclid, and the last in the twelfth book of Euclid. The principle involved in the last was certainly known from the earliest times, when men began to make wheels for ox wagons or chariots. The Egyptian priests and artificers knew it as early as 1500 B.C.

When the Phoenician Thales discovered how to inscribe a right-angled triangle with its corners in a semicircle, he sacrificed an ox to the gods. It was a bad business for the ox. In the end it was a bad business for the gods. Navigation beyond sight of land became possible when men began to use the courses of the stars to steer the courses of their ships. The Phoenicians made the pole star of the priests the pole star of the

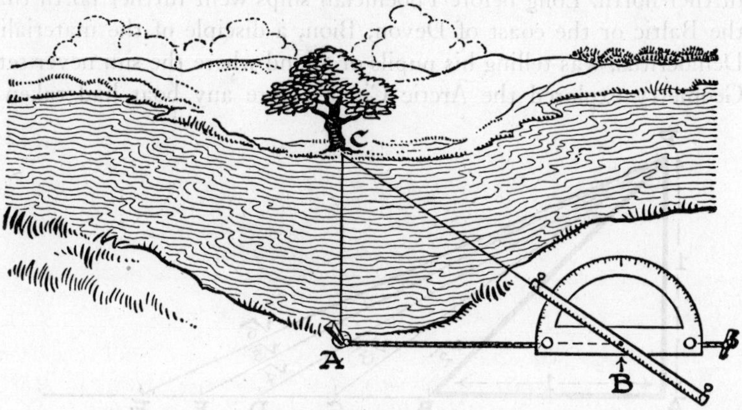

FIG. 54.—MEASURING THE WIDTH OF A RIVER

A simple instrument may be made by nailing a strip of wood to the centre of a protractor so that it can revolve freely. Screw into the two ends of this strip and into the two ends of the base line of the protractor screws with eyes (such as are used for holding extensible curtain rods) to use for sighting. Standing on one bank at A select an object, e.g. a tree, on the bank exactly opposite at C. Setting the movable arm at 90° on the scale, make a base line at 90° to AC by pegging down a piece of cord in line with the base of the protractor. Walk along this line to B, where C is seen to be exactly at 30° to AB. Measure AB. Then ABC is a right-angled triangle in which AC = $\frac{1}{2}$BC and AB = $(\sqrt{3}/2)$BC. So AC, the width of the stream, is AB $\div \sqrt{3}$.

mariner. They began the secularization of the calendar. Men measured the latitude and longitude of the celestial sphere of stars before they made proper maps of the spherical earth. In systematizing the measurement of the circle the Ionian Greeks laid the foundations of Alexandrian geography and drew a dividing line between astrology and astronomy.

The belief that the earth is spherical is of great antiquity among these seafaring peoples. It was a cardinal point in the teaching of the Phoenician Pythagoras. The calendar makers knew it, because they were accustomed to look at the circular rim of the earth's shadow in a lunar eclipse. The seafaring people did not take long to see that it gives a simple explanation of something which every traveller sees as he strains for sight of land, or watches the shore recede. They saw mountains rise out of the water as they approached haven. They saw the tops of buildings sink into the water as they put out to sea (Fig. 59). When artificial light was a luxury, a voyage across the Mediterranean was sufficient to impress upon the imagination of the traveller the lengthening of days in summer and of nights in winter, as ships go further north. Long before Phoenician ships went further north than the Baltic or the coast of Devon, Bion, a disciple of the materialist Democritus, was telling his pupils of a land where the sun never sets. Geometry explored the Arctic Circle before any boat had taken a

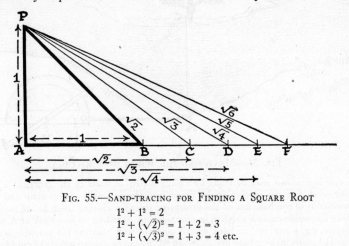

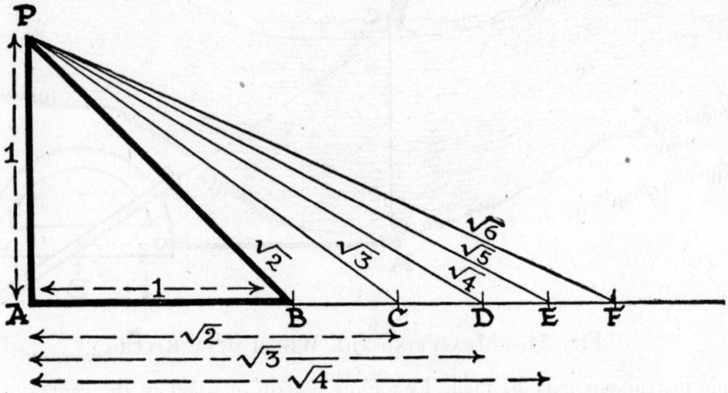

FIG. 55.—SAND-TRACING FOR FINDING A SQUARE ROOT

$$1^2 + 1^2 = 2$$
$$1^2 + (\sqrt{2})^2 = 1 + 2 = 3$$
$$1^2 + (\sqrt{3})^2 = 1 + 3 = 4 \text{ etc.}$$

civilized man to watch the midnight sun within the Polar region. By then Greek geometry had already become the plaything of a prosperous class with slaves to do its work. Brainwork and handwork reflected the stratification of social classes. At the very point when it had created a new instrument for man's conquest of the world in which he lives, geometry degenerated into a mere toy. Only when Greek civilization was destroyed were the fruits of Greek geometry harvested.

Demonstration 9

"The line (tangent) just grazing a circle is at right angles to the line which joins the centre to the spot where it touches the boundary."

The informal way of showing this is illustrated in Fig. 56. When the plumb-line just grazes the horizon at rest it is at right angles to it.

If we swing it (or swing a pendulum of equivalent length suspended from the same spot), it describes the arc of a circle just grazing the horizon. The spoke of a wheel in line with the spot where the rim touches the surface on which it runs passes through a right angle in reaching the position when it is parallel to it. A formal demonstration given in some textbooks of elementary geometry is illustrated in Fig. 57. It is given here for what it is worth. If it worries you, do not go on worrying. The fact is that the demonstration is less convincing than the experience of everyday life.

(i) First look at (*a*) in Fig. 57. OP is a perpendicular dropped from

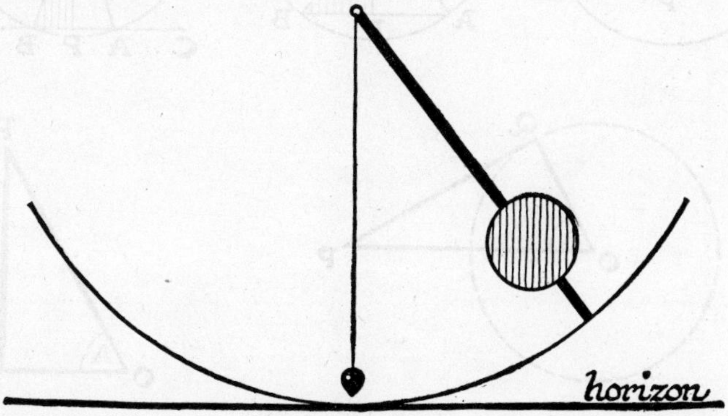

FIG. 56.—THE PRINCIPLE OF TANGENCY ILLUSTRATED BY PLUMB-LINE AND PENDULUM

the centre on the chord AB. In the triangles AOP and BOP, AO = r = BO. By Dem. 6 the angle OAP = x = the angle OBP. Comparing the two triangles, we have

$$\angle OPA = 90° = \angle OPB$$
$$OP = OP$$
$$\angle BOP = (90° - x) = \angle AOP$$

By TRIANGLE RULE THREE the two triangles are equivalent and AP = PB.

(ii) Look at the second figure (*b*). You now see that AB is nearer the boundary and shorter, OA and OB are still equivalent, but OP is not much smaller than OA or OB. Also the angles OAP and OBP are still equivalent and nearer to a right angle.

(iii) In (*c*) A and B are much closer. It is getting difficult to distinguish A, P, and B. The line nearly grazes the circle. When it just grazes, OP will be indistinguishable from OA and OB. So ∠OAP will be indistinguishable from a right angle, fusing with ∠OPB, and the angle OAC will, therefore, be a right angle. Also ∠OBP, which is

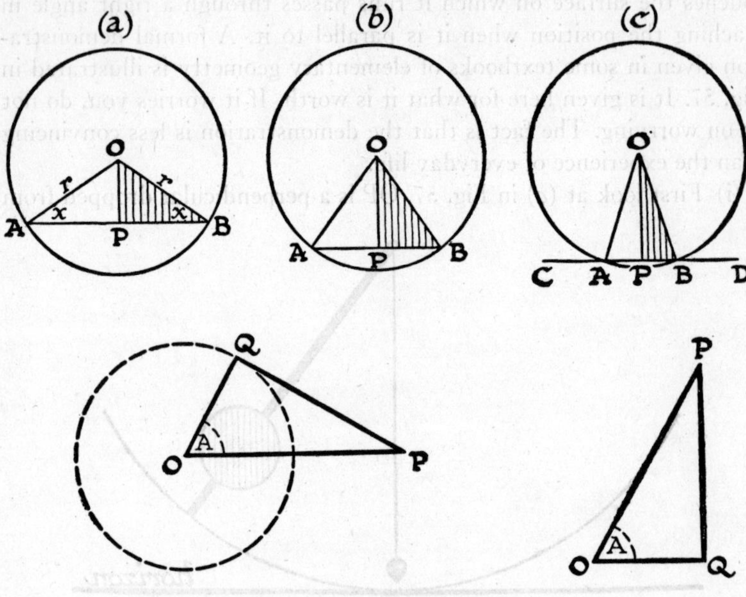

FIG. 57.—DEMONSTRATION 9

WHY THE TANGENT OF AN ANGLE IS SO-CALLED

Tangent comes from the Latin verb *tangere*, to touch. This shows why the word is used for an angle ratio as well as for the line touching the circle.

$$\tan A = \frac{PQ}{OQ}$$

If the circle is of unit radius (OQ = 1 unit of length)

$$\tan A = PQ$$

approaching ∠OPA in the same way, will become indistinguishable from a right angle. So also will ∠OBD.

The applications of this demonstration are innumerable. Two are specially worth noticing. The first, which depends on the fact that light travels in straight lines, is that, if the observer's eye is at sea level, *the line joining the observer to a point on the horizon is at right angles to the line which joins the observer to the earth's centre.* Hence zenith, observer, and earth centre are all in line (Fig. 58). For the same reason the plumb-line at all points on the earth's surface is directed towards the earth's centre.

This demonstration can be used to calculate the distance at which a body of known height is just visible on the horizon, and hence among other things to form an estimate of how far a ship is from the shore.

Distance of the horizon

In Fig. 59 the observer is at A and BC is the distant object (e.g.

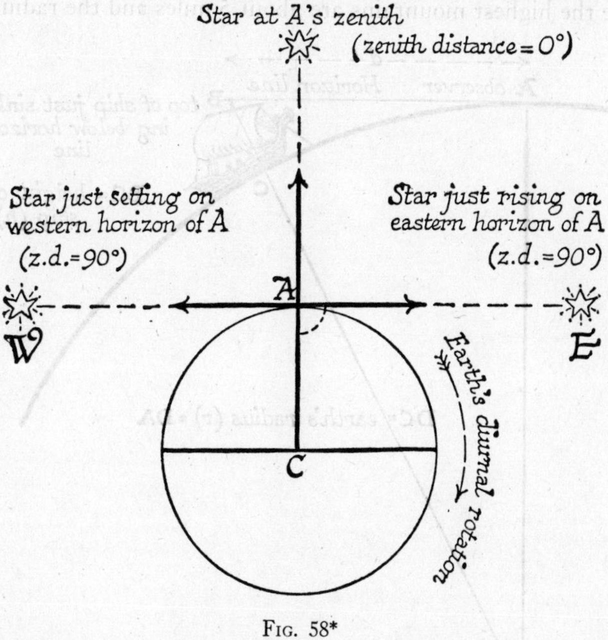

FIG. 58*

mountain or ship), of which he can only just see the topmost point B, the rest being below his horizon line AB. Since light travels in straight lines, this is the line which goes through B and just grazes the circumference of the earth at A. So ∠BAD is a right angle. Applying Dem. 8,

$$\begin{aligned} AB^2 + AD^2 &= DB^2 \\ &= (DC + CB)^2 \\ &= DC^2 + 2DC.CB + CB^2 \end{aligned}$$

Since AD and DC are both earth radii, $AD = r = DC$

$$\therefore \quad AB^2 + AD^2 = AD^2 + 2DC.CB + CB^2$$

$$\therefore \quad AB^2 = 2DC.CB + CB^2$$

* On entering the earth's atmosphere light rays are somewhat bent (refracted). So the true z.d. of a star setting or rising is not exactly 90°.

Calling AB (the distance of the object as it vanishes below the horizon) d, and BC (its height if it were fully visible) h, we have

$$\begin{aligned} d^2 &= 2rh + h^2 \\ &= h(2r + h) \end{aligned}$$

Since the highest mountains are about 5 miles and the radius of the

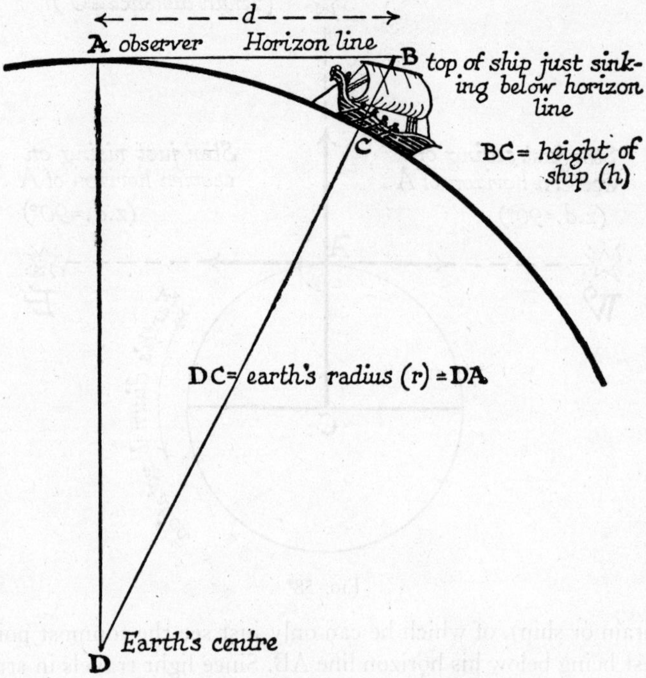

FIG. 59.—THE TANGENT OF THE HORIZON LINE

earth's circumference is roughly 4,000, $(r + h)$ cannot differ from r by more than about one in a thousand. The height h of a ship is of course extremely small compared with r. Hence we may put $(2r + h) = 2r$, so that

$$d^2 = 2hr$$

This shows how far away a mountain 2,000 feet high must be when it just dips below the sea line, if the observer's eye is level with the sea.

$$d^2 = 2 \times \frac{2000}{5280} \times 4{,}000 \text{ (square miles)}$$
$$= \frac{100000}{33}$$
$$\therefore \quad d = \sqrt{100{,}000 \div 33}$$
$$= 55 \text{ miles (approximately)}$$

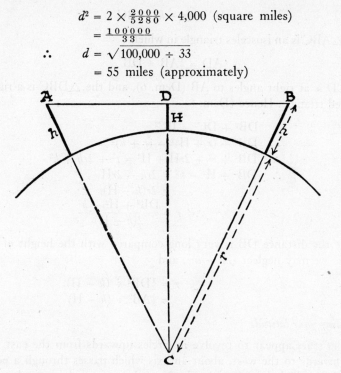

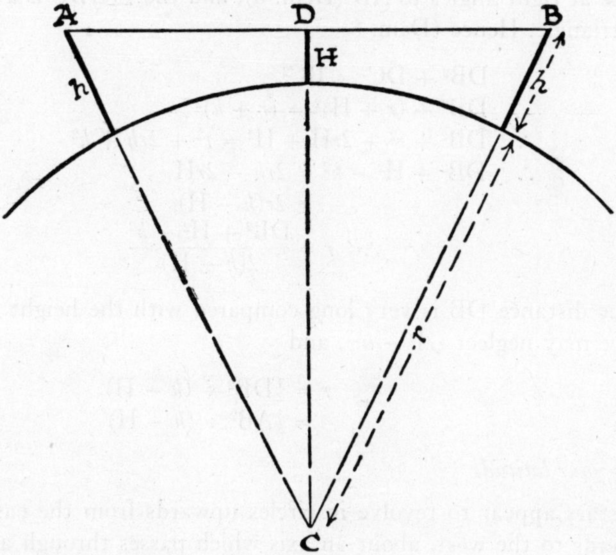

FIG. 60.—CANAL METHOD OF MEASURING THE EARTH'S CIRCUMFERENCE

Earth's circumference

A. R. Wallace, associated with Darwin in the great evolutionary controversy, started life as a surveyor, and suggested a very simple method of measuring the radius of the earth's circumference. Two sticks (Fig. 60), the upper ends (A and B) of which are separated by a measured distance AB in a *straight* canal, are driven in so that they stand upright at the same height h above the level of the water. Exactly midway between them a third stick is driven in so that its upper end D is in the line of sight with A and B. Since the earth's surface and, therefore, that of the water in the canal, is really curved, the height H of D above the water level of the water will be a little less than h. If we measure h, H, and BD accurately we can find the radius of the earth's circumference by applying Dems. 6 and 8. Since

$$AC = (r + h) = BC$$

the $\triangle ABC$ is an isosceles triangle in which

$$AD = \tfrac{1}{2}AB = DB$$

So CD is at right angles to AB (Dem. 6), and the $\triangle DBC$ is a right-angled triangle. Hence (Dem. 8)

$$\begin{aligned}
& DB^2 + DC^2 = BC^2 \\
& DB^2 + (r + H)^2 = (r + h)^2 \\
\therefore\quad & DB^2 + r^2 + 2rH + H^2 = r^2 + 2rh + h^2 \\
\therefore\quad & DB^2 + H^2 - h^2 = 2rh - 2rH \\
& \qquad\qquad\qquad = 2r(h - H) \\
\therefore\quad & r = \frac{DB^2 + H^2 - h^2}{2(h - H)}
\end{aligned}$$

Since the distance DB is very long compared with the height of the sticks we may neglect $(H^2 - h^2)$, and

$$\begin{aligned}
r &= \tfrac{1}{2}DB^2 \div (h - H) \\
&= \tfrac{1}{8}AB^2 \div (h - H)
\end{aligned}$$

Finding your latitude

The stars appear to revolve in circles upwards from the east and downwards to the west, about an axis which passes through a point which is called the celestial pole. Nowadays we explain this by saying that the earth revolves around an axis which passes through its centre, its poles, and the celestial pole, in the opposite direction to the apparent motion of the heavenly bodies. Most stars set below the horizon and are only visible at night during part of the year, but the stars very near the pole, like those in the constellation of the Great Bear, the Little Bear, Lyra, Draco, and Cassiopeia, in our latitude never sink below the horizon, being seen most of the night below the pole at some seasons and above it at others. One star, the *pole star*, is so near the celestial pole that it always seems to be in the same place. It lies almost exactly in line with the earth's north pole and the earth's centre. As star beams are parallel, the rays which reach us from the pole star are parallel to the earth's axis. You will see from Fig. 61 that the latitude of a place is the angle ("altitude") which the celestial pole makes with the horizon. So you can get the latitude of your house on any clear night by going into the garden and sighting the altitude of the pole star with a home-made astrolabe (Fig. 12). The pole star at present revolves in a circle one degree from the

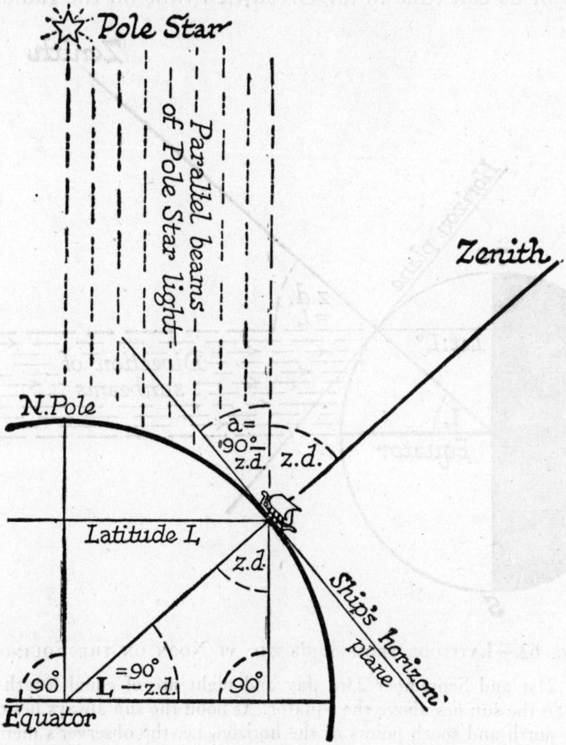

Fig. 61.—Latitude from Pole Star

The altitude (horizon angle) of the pole star is the observer's latitude, both being equivalent to 90° — zenith distance of pole star.

celestial pole. So its altitude will not be more than a degree greater or less than your latitude, even if you are unlucky enough to sight it at its upper or lower transit across the meridian. Since the earth's circumference is 25,000 miles, this gives you your distance from the equator with an error of not more than 25,000 ÷ 360, or approximately 70 miles. If you want to be really accurate, take the mean of two observations made at the same time of night, one six months after the other, when the pole star will be just as much above the celestial pole as it was previously below it, or *vice versa*.

At the same time you may like to know how to find your longitude (Fig. 63). Nowadays this is a very simple matter because ships have accurate clocks which can keep Greenwich time over a long voyage, and most of us can tune in for Greenwich time on the radio. Noon is

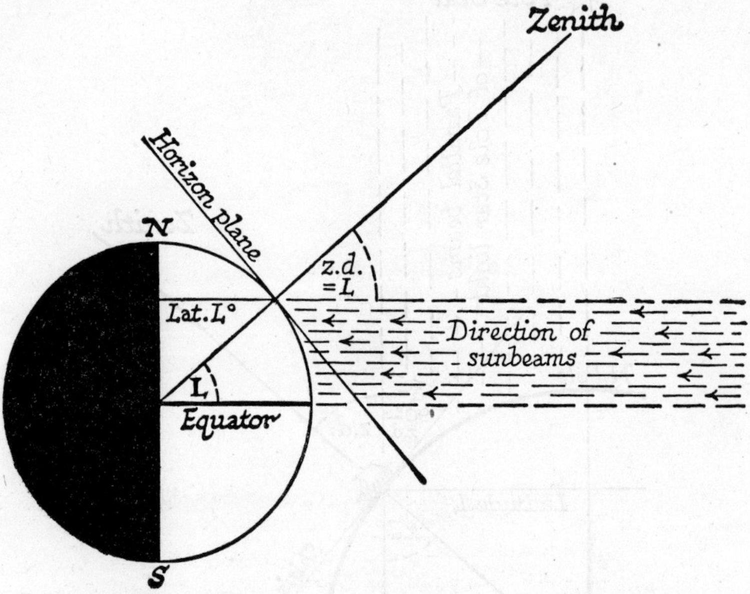

FIG. 62.—LATITUDE FROM SUN'S Z.D. AT NOON ON THE EQUINOXES

On March 21st and September 23rd day and night are of equal length throughout the world. So the sun lies above the equator. At noon the sun always lies over the line joining the north and south points of the horizon, i.e. the observer's meridian of longitude. So the sun, the poles, observer, zenith, and earth centre are all in the same flat slab (or "plane") of space. Since the edges of a sunbeam are parallel, the sun's z.d. at noon on the equinoxes is the observer's latitude.

the time when the sun is exactly above the meridian at its highest point in the heavens. If our sundial registers noon an hour after it is noon at Greenwich, the sun has to travel, as the ancients would say, 15° further west, or our earth has to rotate eastwards through 15° on its axis, between the times of the two noons. We are therefore 15° West of Greenwich. The peoples of antiquity discovered that time recorded by the shadow clock does not synchronize in different places through observing when an eclipse occurred, or when a planet passed behind the moon's disc. The Babylonians had hour-glasses of sand, and could observe the time which elapsed between noon on a particular day and the beginning or end of an eclipse or occultation. Before chronometers were invented this was the chief way of finding longitude. If at one place a lunar eclipse was seen to begin at 8 hours after local noon and at another $9\frac{1}{2}$ hours after local noon, noon in the second

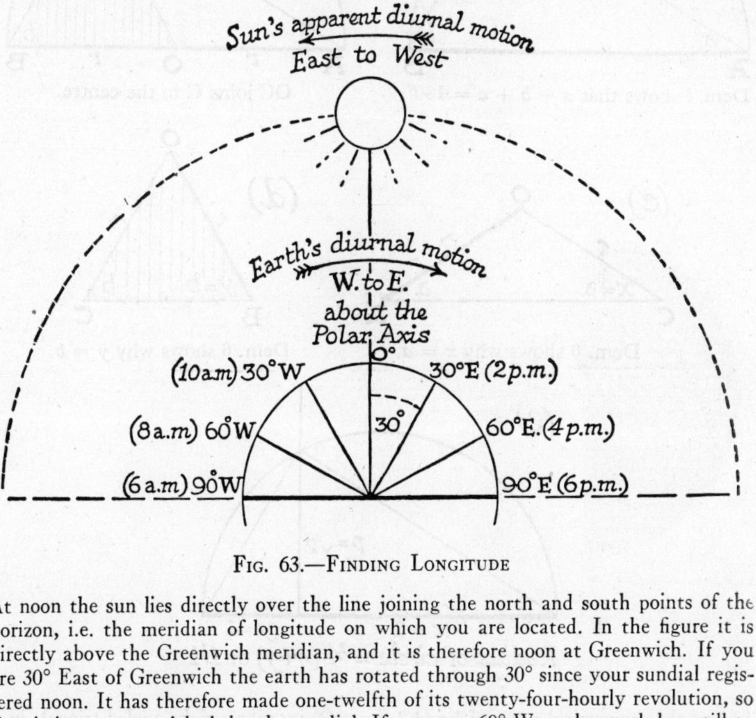

FIG. 63.—FINDING LONGITUDE

At noon the sun lies directly over the line joining the north and south points of the horizon, i.e. the meridian of longitude on which you are located. In the figure it is directly above the Greenwich meridian, and it is therefore noon at Greenwich. If you are 30° East of Greenwich the earth has rotated through 30° since your sundial registered noon. It has therefore made one-twelfth of its twenty-four-hourly revolution, so that it is now two o'clock by the sundial. If you are 60° West the earth has still to rotate 60° before the sun will be over your meridian, i.e. one-sixth of its twenty-four-hourly rotation; so your sundial will register 8 a.m.

place occurred $1\frac{1}{2}$ hours earlier than noon at the first (see Fig. 116A). So the second was $1\frac{1}{2} \times 15° = 22\frac{1}{2}°$ East of the first. The construction of maps based on latitude and longitude was never achieved by the Greeks. It was done when Greek geometry was transferred to the great shipping centre of the classical world, Alexandria.

Demonstration 10

"The lines joining the ends of the diameter to any spot on the boundary of a semicircle enclose a right angle."

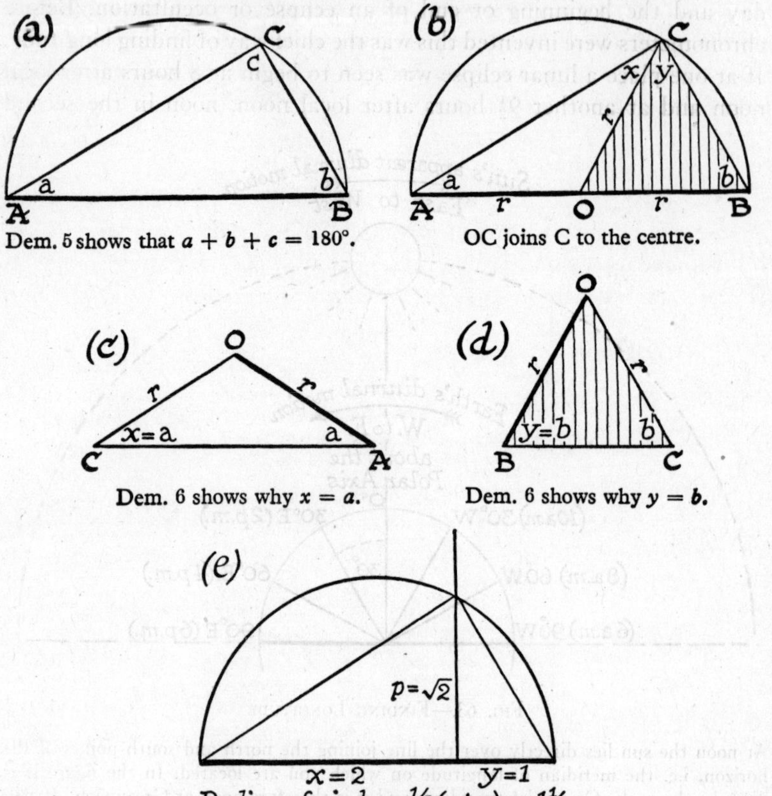

Dem. 5 shows that $a + b + c = 180°$.

OC joins C to the centre.

Dem. 6 shows why $x = a$.

Dem. 6 shows why $y = b$.

To find the geometrical mean of 1 and 2 (i.e. $\sqrt{2}$) inscribe a right-angled triangle in a semicircle of which the radius is the arithmetic mean (i.e. $1\frac{1}{2}$).
To find $\sqrt{6}$ by this method make $x = 3$ $y = 2$ $r = 2\frac{1}{2}$

FIG. 64.—DEMONSTRATION 10

The steps in the dissection are all given in (*b*), (*c*), and (*d*) of the same figure. The radius of the semicircle in Fig. 64 is *r* units of length. They may be tabulated thus:

$$
\begin{aligned}
a + b + c &= 180° \\
a + b + (x + y) &= 180° \\
(x + y) + (x + y) &= 180° \\
2c &= 180° \\
c &= 90°
\end{aligned}
$$

This demonstration shows us how to make a sand-tracing for the geometric mean of two numbers (Fig. 64 (*e*)). So it can be used as a hieroglyph to get square roots with greater accuracy than the method of Fig. 55. In Dem. 8 (see Fig. 51) we found that

$$p = \sqrt{xy}$$

To find $\sqrt{xy}$ (see Fig. 51) we need to construct a right angle, of which the perpendicular (p units of length) from the right angle divides the hypotenuse into x and y units of length. Suppose I want to get $\sqrt{7}$. If $x = 7$ and $y = 1$, $xy = 7$. So I make a line 8 units long, and put

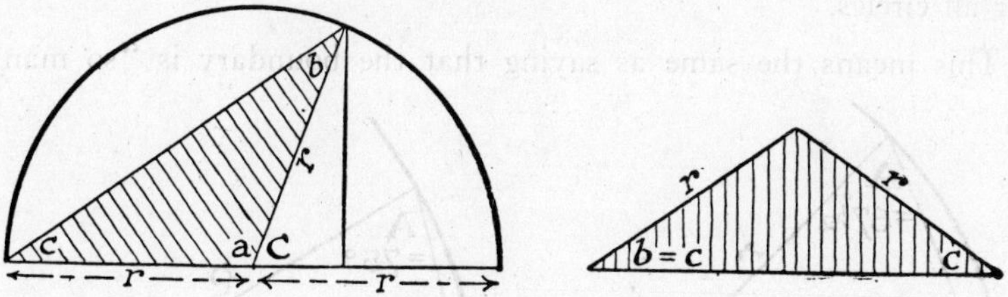

FIG. 65.—DEMONSTRATION 11

$C = 180° - a$ (Fig. 33)
$b = c$ (Dem. 6)
$\therefore \quad b + c = 2c$

up a perpendicular 1 unit from one end (or 7 from the other). At the spot halfway along the line I draw a semicircle of radius 4 units. Join the ends of the line to the point where the circle cuts the perpendicular. You have here a right angle, and this gives you the length of p.

Demonstration 11

"If two right-angled triangles are formed on the same side of a perpendicular to the diameter of a semicircle by joining where it meets the boundary to the centre and to the end of the diameter, the angle at the centre is twice the angle at the end of the diameter."

The steps in the demonstration of this are fully explained in Fig. 65. First notice that $C = 180° - a$, also

$$\begin{aligned} a + b + c &= 180° \\ \therefore \quad b + c &= 180° - a \\ \therefore \quad 2c &= 180° - a \\ 2c &= C \\ c &= \tfrac{1}{2}C \end{aligned}$$

This demonstration is of very great importance, because it is used, as we shall see later, to get the first Alexandrian dictionary of SINES. Fig. 66 shows you how you can make circles on the board of the shadow pole (Fig. 46) for a large series of angles, starting with any angle (e.g. 60°, 30°, 45°) which you know how to get. Other angles from which you might start to get a fresh series of circles for measuring the sun's angle by the shadow pole are given in Fig. 65A.

Demonstration 12

"The ratio of the boundary of a circle to its diameter is the same for all circles."

This means the same as saying that the boundary is "so many

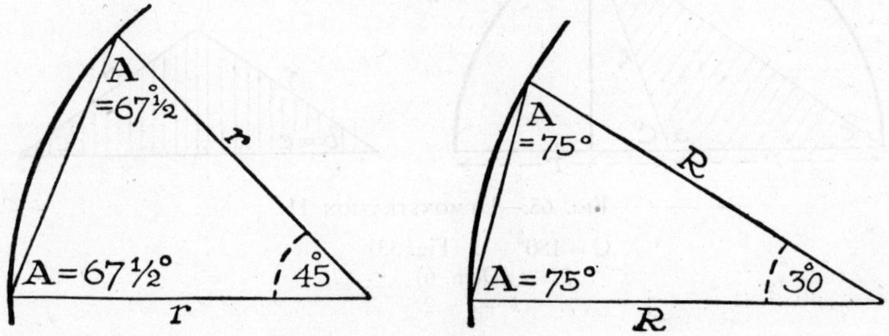

FIG. 65A.—HOW TO GET ANGLES OF $67\frac{1}{2}°$ AND 75°

The two angles A are equivalent in both figures (Dem. 6). Their values are shown by Dem. 5.

times" the diameter, whatever the size of the circle. The number is a number which stretches like $\sqrt{2}$, as it stands for a measurement. It cannot be represented in a short form like a recurring decimal, so it is represented by the pronoun π. Later we shall see that its value lies in the neighbourhood of $3\frac{1}{7}$. The demonstration which leads us to it links up the measurement of the triangle with the measurement of the circle. It shows how to find the rim of a wheel if we know the spoke, or what size of spoke we need to make a rim which turns so many times in a mile. It is the basis of the cyclometer (the first model of which was made in Alexandria about 100 B.C.) and the speed indicator. It is the basis of all large earth measurements and estimates of the size of the sun and moon. As we know the circumference of the earth (calculated very simply on p. 238), it gives us the earth's radius and the circumference of any circle of latitude. Without π there would have been no Columbus and no George Stephenson.

It is a tempting speculation to suppose that the measurement of the circle was suggested by polygonal figures and circles drawn, as they are so easily drawn, on the yielding convex surface of the clay

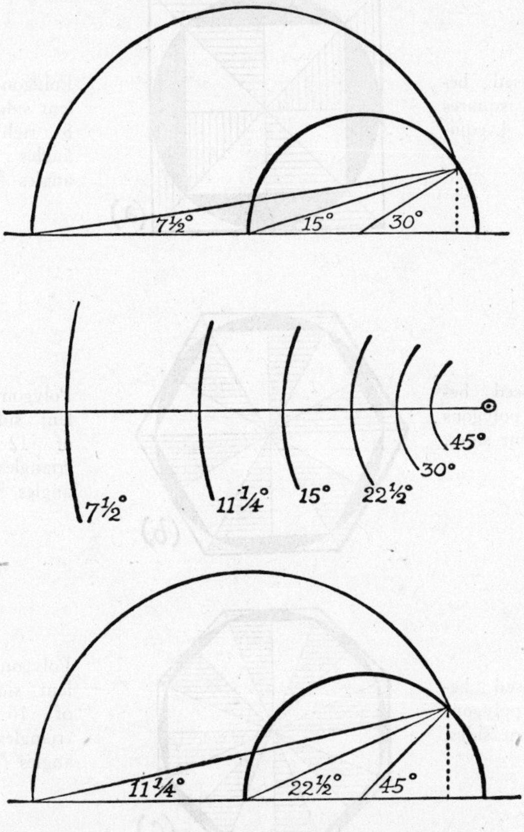

FIG. 66.—CALIBRATING THE SHADOW POLE

Starting with $67\frac{1}{2}°$ and 75° as in Fig. 65A we can also get:
$67\frac{1}{2}°$ $33\frac{3}{4}°$ . . . 75° $37\frac{1}{2}°$ $18\frac{3}{4}°$ . .

on the potter's wheel. Figures like those in Fig. 67 suggesting sunlight and shadow, sun and moon, eclipse and noon, ever-present realities of work and worship in the ancient world, are reminiscent of the geometrical patterns which adorned ancient vessels like Cyprian vases (*circa* 1000 B.C.). Or it may have been discovered through the way a hexagon was inscribed in a circle by the Babylonians, possibly to divide the ecliptic belt into the six primitive constellations of the zodiac.

Looking at Fig. 67 you see at once three things: (*a*) the boundary

Circle enclosed between two squares (polygons of 4 equivalent sides).

Polygon of 4 equivalent sides made up of 8 right-angled triangles with centre angles $\frac{360°}{8} = 45°$.

Circle enclosed between two polygons of 6 equivalent sides.

Polygon of 6 equivalent sides made up of 12 right-angled triangles with centre angles $\frac{360°}{12} = 30°$.

Circle enclosed between two polygons of 8 equivalent sides.

Polygon of 8 equivalent sides made up of 16 right-angled triangles with centre angles $\frac{360°}{16} = 22\frac{1}{2}°$.

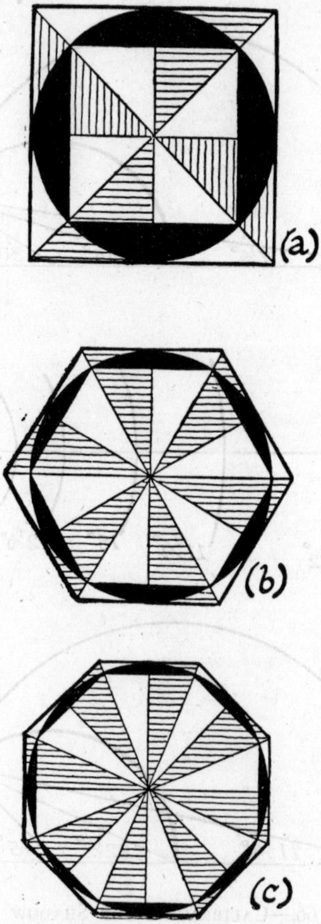

FIG. 67.—FROM THE POTTER'S WHEEL TO π

and area of a circle are less than the boundary and area of a polygon enclosing it, and greater than that of the polygon it encloses; (*b*) a polygon enclosing (sides tangent to) a circle or a polygon enclosed by (corners touching) a circle can be built up to twice as many right-angled triangles as the number of sides which the polygon has; (*c*) the centre angles of these triangles together make up 360°.

Looking next at Fig. 68, you see how to make a polygon of any number (n) of equivalent sides enclosed by a circle of radius r units of length, or enclosing a circle of radius R units. Placing the angle A at the centre, we can go on putting $2n$ equivalent right-angled triangles

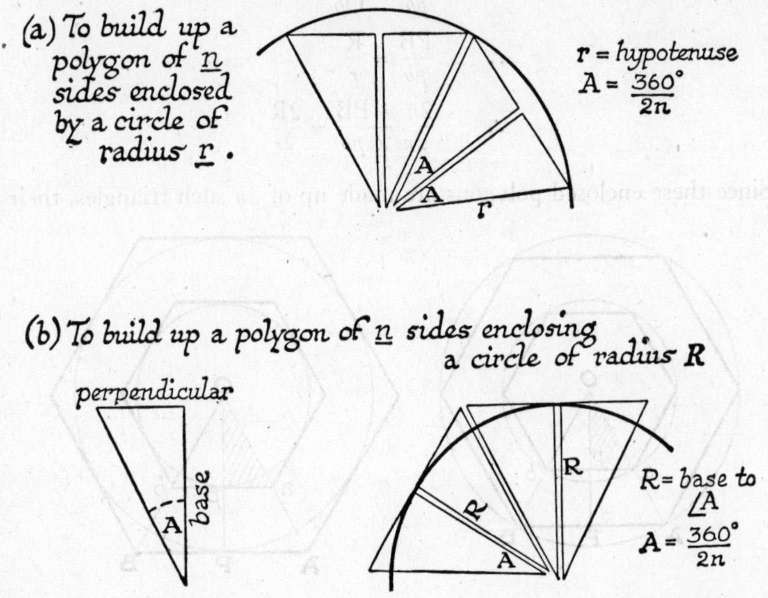

FIG. 68

alternately with their hypotenuses together and with their bases (i.e. base to A) together, until we get back to where we started. If all the centre angles add up to 360°, and they are all equivalent:

$$A = \frac{360^\circ}{2n}$$

Now look at Fig. 69. On the left are two circles enclosing two polygons with equivalent sides. On the right are two polygons with equivalent sides enclosing two circles drawn with the same centre. In the figure n is 6. In each figure the larger and smaller polygons are drawn so that the 12 right-angled triangles into which they can be dissected lie with their corner angles in common. Since all right-angled triangles with the same corner angle are similar (Dem. 5 (c)), the ratio of corresponding sides of the larger and smaller triangles is the same (Dem. 7).

If we call r the radius of the small circle and R the radius of the larger circle, the figure on the left shows us that:

$$\frac{PB}{pb} = \frac{OB}{Ob}$$

$$\therefore \quad \frac{PB}{pb} = \frac{R}{r}$$

$$\therefore \quad \frac{2n \times PB}{2n \times pb} = \frac{2R}{2r}$$

Since these enclosed polygons are made up of $2n$ such triangles, their

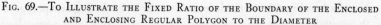

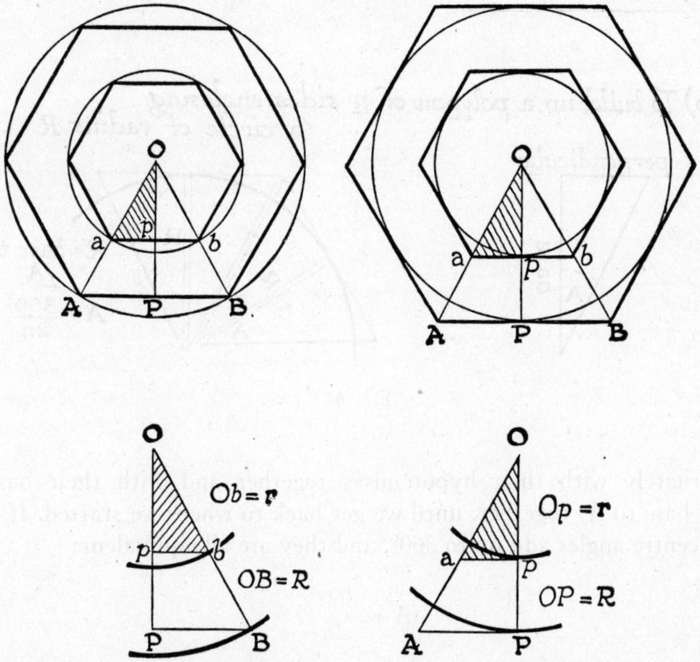

FIG. 69.—TO ILLUSTRATE THE FIXED RATIO OF THE BOUNDARY OF THE ENCLOSED AND ENCLOSING REGULAR POLYGON TO THE DIAMETER

boundaries are $2n$ times pb or PB. So if C'' is the boundary of the larger and c'' the boundary of the smaller polygon, D being the diameter of the larger circle and d the diameter of the smaller circle:

$$\frac{C''}{c''} = \frac{D}{d} \text{ or } \frac{C''}{D} = \frac{c''}{d}$$

i.e. the ratio of the diameter of the enclosing circle to the boundaries of polygons with n equivalent sides is always the same if n is the same.

From the figure on the right we get:

$$\frac{pa}{pO} = \frac{PA}{PO} \text{ or } \frac{PO}{pO} = \frac{PA}{pa}$$

$$\therefore \quad \frac{2n \times (PA)}{2n \times (pa)} = \frac{2R}{2r} = \frac{D}{d}$$

So if we put C′ and c' for the boundaries of the larger and smaller enclosing polygons

$$\frac{C'}{D} = \frac{c'}{d}$$

So it is also true that the ratio of the boundary of a polygon of n equal sides to the diameter of the circle it encloses is the same for all circles which we can draw.

Looking again at Fig. 67 you will see that if the number of sides is greater, the boundary (and area) of the inner polygon is nearer to the boundary (and area) of the outer polygon, and both differ less from the boundary (and area) of the circle which lies somewhere between these two limits. By going on making enclosed and enclosing polygons with a greater and greater number of equivalent sides, we can get nearer and nearer to a figure which is indistinguishable from the circle lying between them. As the ratio of the boundary of similar enclosing polygons to the diameter is the same for all circles which we can draw, and the ratio of the boundary of similar enclosed polygons to the diameter is the same for all circles which we can draw, the ratio of the boundary (c) of the circle itself to its diameter is the same for all circles. We call this ratio π, i.e.

$$\frac{c}{d} = \pi \text{ or } c = \pi d = 2\pi r$$

We shall work out how to get a good value for π later, when we have seen how it is used. As you will probably want to have some idea, after going to so much trouble, we shall give a first estimate. Euclid did not proceed to use this demonstration, though in fact the Egyptians had arrived by 1500 B.C. at a value (3·16), which is good enough for working to an accuracy of 1 per cent. If you had asked him what is the good of knowing it, he would have offered you a small coin for your trouble. Here is the small coin. The boundary of the square which encloses a circle of diameter d is $4d$. Draw it and you will see why. So the boundary of the circle is less than $4d$. The polygon of 6 equivalent sides is made up of 12 right-angled triangles of 30°. We have seen that the perpendicular to 30° is half the hypotenuse (Dem. 6). For the polygon enclosed by a circle of radius $\frac{1}{2}d$ the hypotenuse (see top of Fig. 68) is equivalent to the radius. So the perpendicular to the centre angle is $\frac{1}{4}d$. The boundary of the polygon with 6 equivalent sides is 12 times this, i.e. $3d$. So the boundary of the circle is less than $4d$ and more than $3d$. That is to say, π lies between 3 and 4 ($\pi = 3{\cdot}5 \pm 0{\cdot}5$). A glance shows that the boundary of the circle is closer to that of the 6-sided polygon it encloses than to that of the square which encloses it. So π is more than 3 and nearer to 3 than to 4. In other words, it lies between 3 and 3·5 ($\pi = 3{\cdot}25 \pm 0{\cdot}25$).

Having a value for π, we can get the area of a circle without difficulty. Looking at the lower figure in Fig. 68 you see that the area of the enclosing polygon of n sides is:

$$2n \text{ times } \tfrac{1}{2}\text{R}.(\text{perp.}) \quad (\text{Dem. } 3)$$
$$\text{or} \quad \tfrac{1}{2}\text{R times the boundary}$$

When n is so large that we cannot distinguish the boundary of the polygon from that of the circle,

$$A = \tfrac{1}{2}R.\pi D$$

Since $D = 2R$, $\quad A = \pi R^2$

If we know the radius of the earth, π helps us to find its bulk. Euclid gives a demonstration which enables us to do so. We have omitted any reference to the Greek geometry of solid figures in the present chapter for a simple reason. The results can be obtained with much less labour by other kinds of mathematics which superseded Greek geometry. What we have learned is sufficient to show us the beginnings of these later developments. If we can find the distance of the moon, by the method at which we have hinted and shall later on examine more fully, we can find its radius by the same method. So we can get the bulk of the moon. We shall have π in the sky by and by (Chapter VI).

THE CLIMAX OF GREEK GEOMETRY

The Greek geometry which Euclid brought to Alexandria about 300 B.C. had already reached its climax. It embodied all the necessary principles from which the Alexandrians and Arabs derived simple rules of calculation, and a more economical method of surveying, astronomical and geographical as well as architectural and domestic. The failure of the Greeks to make any noteworthy discoveries by following up the daring and brilliant surmise of Anaxagoras with actual measurements like those of Aristarchus and Eratosthenes (Chapter 6) was due to the fact that geometry had become a hobby of intellectuals who had lost interest in the social achievements of the craftsman and the mariner. When they encountered quantities like $\sqrt{3}$ or π, which cannot be represented by the sheep and cow numbers of their social heritage, they were confronted with two alternatives. One was to improve their vocabulary of numbers as Archimedes attempted to do at a later date, making it more suitable to the practical task of representing the imperfection of human knowledge. The other was to take shelter in an abstract perfection, which banished measurement from geometry. They chose the latter. Euclid does not speak, as we have done, of sides and areas, or the squares of numbers which stand (approximately) for lengths. He speaks of sides and lines and figures. He does not use abstract numbers, as we have done, to stand for so many units of measurements. He only used letters as labels for lines and figures, just as he could only use numbers for calculations which were done on a counting frame.

Plato's doctrine that the rule and the compass were the only instruments which a geometer should use for drawing figures is entirely consistent with his other views about mathematics. Geometry was an aid to spiritual perfection. We are not expected to attain spiritual perfection and enjoy ourselves at the same time. So it was natural for those who held this belief to make geometry as difficult and unpalatable as generations of schoolchildren have found it. Geometry was the highest exercise for cultivated leisure. The fun of the game lay in making the rules more complicated. Draughts and auction bridge were too tame for the unemployed intellectuals with whom Platonism found favour. They wanted chess and contract. Men who made mechanical devices for drawing new sorts of curves, like the early Athenian Archytas, found no favour, and a path to new discovery was blocked.

All the while an essential contradiction lay concealed from view. Figures are after all things which have to be drawn by imperfect human beings with imperfect instruments, even if only two of them are permitted, and Euclid himself laid down the doctrine that no construction (what we have called dissection) may be used, unless the possibility of carrying it out with these imperfect instruments has been demonstrated. We have done this in our preliminary rules of dissection. It is quite true to say that a line cannot be divided into any *whole* number of exactly equal units. It is equally true (pp. 76–82) that the experimental materials of Greek geometry, marks on paper or

1	15	14	4
12	6	7	9
8	10	11	5
13	3	2	16

FIG. 70.—THE MAGIC SQUARE

You will find that any column or row or diagonal adds up to 34. Inscribed on a silver plate in the sixteenth century this square protected its owner from plague. This method of therapeutics was not limited to diseases of bacterial origin. It also made the same claims as psycho-analysis. There is a magic square on the wall of one of Albrecht Dürer's most famous engravings.

scratches on wax and sand, were not the sort of things which could ever be used to represent something which is exactly equal to another thing.

After the foundation of the University of Alexandria about 320 B.C. mathematics in Greece made little more progress. Our last glimpse of mathematics on the mainland of Greece, before Constantinople fell to the Turks, discloses the cult of the magic square (Fig. 70), which the Byzantine Moschopoulos brought to Italy in the fifteenth century A.D. The grammar of numbers ended, where it had begun, in a medley of superstition and crossword puzzles. In the next chapter we shall see that the Greek intellectual, when faced with a crisis in his social culture, had already taken to the crossword puzzle before he banished numbers from geometry.

Discoveries and Tests on Chapter 4

1. Two straight lines cross one another making the four angles A, B, C, D. Make diagrams putting in the other three angles when A is (i) 30°, (ii) 60°, (iii) 45°.

2. A triangle has three sides, lengths *a*, *b*, *c*, opposite the angles A, B, C respectively. Continue *a* beyond C to E, draw the figure and find what ∠ACE is when (i) A = 30°, B = 45°; (ii) A = 45°, B = 75°. If ∠ACE, is called the "exterior angle" at C, what is the general rule connecting an exterior angle of a triangle with the two opposite interior angles?

3. Draw an equilateral triangle with sides 1 unit in length. Draw a perpendicular from one corner to the opposite side. Express the area of the triangle in terms of (*a*) sin 60°, (*b*) cos 30°. If the length of a side is *a* units, what will the area be?

4. Draw an isosceles triangle with one angle of 120°. If the equal sides are of unit length, find an expression for the area of the triangle. What is the area if the equal sides are *a* units in length?

5. Draw diagrams to illustrate the following statements:

$$(2a + 3b)^2 = 4a^2 + 12ab + 9b^2$$
$$(3a - 2b)^2 = 9a^2 - 12ab + 4b^2$$
$$(2a + 3b)\ (3a - 2b) = 6a^2 + 5ab - 6b^2$$
$$(2a + 3b)\ (2a - 3b) = 4a^2 - 9b^2$$

6. In the last chapter you found out how to write down $(a + b)^2$, $(a - b)^2$. These identities can be used for squaring many different types of expressions. For example:

$$\left(\boxed{x + y} + 1\right)^2 = \boxed{x + y}^2 + 2.1.\boxed{x + y} + 1^2$$
$$= x^2 + 2xy + y^2 + 2x + 2y + 1$$

This is more usually written:

$$\{\ (x + y) + 1\ \}^2 = x^2 + 2xy + y^2 + 2x + 2y + 1$$

Notice that when two sets of brackets are used, one inside the other, they are of different shapes to avoid confusion. In this way write down the values of the following:

$$(x + y + 2)^2 \qquad (x + 1)^2$$
$$(x + y - 2)^2 \qquad (x - 1)^2$$
$$(2a^2 + 3y^2)^2 \qquad (4a - 5b)^2$$
$$(x^2 + y^2)^2 \qquad (xy - 1)^2$$
$$(x^2 - y^2)^2$$

7. By reversing the process you can write down the square roots of any expression of the form

$$a^2 \pm 2ab + b^2$$

Write down the square roots of the following:

$$9x^2 + 42xy + 49y^2 \qquad a^2 + 6a + 9$$
$$4a^2 - 20ab + 25b^2 \qquad x^2 - 2x + 1$$
$$16a^2 - 72ab + 81b^2 \qquad x^2 + 2x + 1$$
$$x^2 + 24xy + 144y^2$$

8. Using the identity $(a + b)\ (a - b) = a^2 - b^2$, find the values of the following:

$$(x + 1)\ (x - 1) \qquad (x + 3)\ (x - 3)$$
$$(ab + 1)\ (ab - 1) \qquad (a^2 - b^2)\ (a^2 + b^2)$$
$$(x + y - 2)\ (x + y + 2)$$

9. It is very useful to be able to split up a complicated expression into factors. You have already seen how to find the factors of expressions like $a^2 + 2ab + b^2$. The identity $a^2 - b^2 = (a - b)\ (a + b)$ can be used to find the factors of any expression which is the difference of two squares.

e.g. $$64x^4 - 81y^2 = (8x^2)^2 - (9y)^2 = (8x^2 - 9y)\ (8x^2 + 9y)$$

In this way write down the factors of:

$$x^2 - 1 \qquad a^2 - (b + c)^2$$
$$(a + b)^2 - c^2 \qquad (x + y)^2 - 1$$
$$a^2 - (b - c)^2 \qquad x^8 - y^8$$
$$a^4 - b^4 \qquad a^2 + 2ab + b^2 - 1$$
$$81 - x^2 \qquad x^2 + 2xy + y^2 - 2^2$$
$$(x + 2)^2 - (x - 1)^2$$

10. Write down the value of the third angle of a triangle when the other two angles have the following values:

(i) $15°, 75°$ (ii) $30°, 90°$
(iii) $49°, 81°$ (iv) $110°, 60°$
(v) $90°, 12°$

11. If you refer to Fig. 13 you will see what is meant by the zenith distance (z.d.) and altitude (a) of a heavenly body. Explain why $a = 90° - \text{z.d.}$ and $\text{z.d.} = 90° - a$.

12. If the altitude of the pole star is 30° at Memphis, 41° at New York, and $51\frac{1}{2}°$ at London, what is its zenith distance at these places?

13. The star Sirius is $106\frac{1}{2}°$ measured along the meridian from the pole star. Draw diagrams to show its position relative to the pole star when on the meridian at each of the three places mentioned in the last paragraph. What is its zenith distance and altitude in each case?

14. Draw four right-angled triangles in which one angle is 10°, 30°, 45°, 75° respectively. In each triangle drop a perpendicular from the right-angled corner to the hypotenuse. Into what angles does the perpendicular divide the right angle in each case?

15. A ladder leaning against a vertical wall makes an angle of 30° with the wall. The foot of the ladder is 3 feet from the wall. How high up the wall does the ladder reach and how long is the ladder?

16. A wardrobe 5 feet high stands in an attic in which the roof slopes down to the floor. If the wardrobe cannot be put nearer the wall than 2 feet, what is the slope of the roof?

17. A thatched roof has a slope of 60°. It ends 15 feet above the ground. In building an extension the roof can be continued until it is 6 feet from the ground. How wide can the extension be?

18. At noon a telegraph pole known to be 17 feet high cast a shadow 205 inches long. What was the sun's approximate zenith distance? (Use the table of tangents.)

19. At noon, when the sun's zenith distance was 45°, the shadow of a lamp-post just reached to the base of a 12-foot ladder whose top touched the top of the lamp-post. How much longer was the shadow of the lamp-post later in the day when the sun's zenith distance was 60°? (Draw a figure. No calculation needed.)

20. The shadow of a pole 3 feet 6 inches long was found to be 5 feet at four o'clock in the afternoon. At the same time the shadow of a cliff with the sun directly behind it was 60 yards. How high was the cliff?

21. A surveyor wants to measure the width of a river he cannot cross. There is a conspicuous object P on the opposite bank. From a point A on his own side to the left of P, he finds that the angle between his bank and the direction of P is 30°. From another point B to the right on the surveyor's side, the direction of P is 45°. He then measures AB and finds it to be 60 feet. Draw a diagram of this, and find the width of the river. (Hint. Find the relations between the perpendicular from P to AB in terms of the segments of AB and add the segments.)

22. A halfpenny (diameter 1 inch) placed at a distance of 3 yards from the eye will just obscure the disc of the sun or moon. Taking the distance of the sun as 93 million miles, find its diameter. Taking the diameter of the moon as 2,160 miles, find its distance.

23. If $\sin A = \cos 60°$, what is A?
If $\sin A = \cos 45°$, what is A?
If $\cos A = \sin 15°$, what is A?
If $\cos A = \sin 8°$, what is A?

24. If $\sin x = \frac{\sqrt{3}}{2}$ and $\cos x = \frac{1}{2}$, what is $\tan x$?
If $\sin x = 0{\cdot}4$ and $\cos x = 0{\cdot}9$, what is $\tan x$?
If $\cos x = 0{\cdot}8$ and $\sin x = 0{\cdot}6$, what is $\tan x$?
If $\sin x = 0{\cdot}8$ and $\cos x = 0{\cdot}6$, what is $\tan x$?

25. Use tables of squares or square roots to find the third side in the right-angled triangles whose other sides are:

(*a*) 17 feet, 5 feet.
(*b*) 3 inches, 4 inches.
(*c*) 1 centimetre, 12 centimetres.

How many different possible values are there for the third side in each triangle?

26. Make two different geometrical constructions with careful scale diagrams to tabulate the squares of the whole numbers from 1 to 7.

27. Make geometrical constructions to find the arithmetic mean and geometrical mean of 2 and 8, 1 and 9, 4 and 16.

28. What is a star's zenith distance when it is just grazing the horizon? When it is directly over the meridian, Canopus, next to Sirius the brightest star, is $7\frac{1}{2}°$ above the south point of the horizon in the neighbourhood of the Great Pyramid (Lat. 30°). What is the angle between Canopus and the pole star? On the assumption that the angle between any two stars when they lie over the meridian is fixed, what is the most northerly latitude at which Canopus can be seen at all?

29. If the sun is directly over the Tropic of Cancer (Lat. $23\frac{1}{2}°$ N.) on June 21st, show by the aid of a diagram like that of Figs. 61 and 62 what are its altitude and zenith distance at New York (Lat. 41° N.) when it is over the meridian (i.e. at noon). What is the most southerly latitude at which the sun can be seen at midnight on that day?

30. What is the zenith distance of the pole star at New York (Lat. 41° N.) and London ($51\frac{1}{2}°$ N.), and the altitude of the noon sun on September 23rd?

31. In a Devonshire village the shadow of a telegraph pole was shortest at the time when the radio programme gave Greenwich time as 12.14 p.m. on December 25th. What was its longitude?

32. By dividing a polygon of x equivalent sides into x equivalent triangles, show that the angle between any two sides is the fraction $\frac{2x-4}{x}$ of a right angle.

33. What is the height of a lighthouse if its light can be seen at a distance of 12 miles?

34. From a ship's mast-head 60 feet above sea-level it is just possible to see the top of a cliff 100 feet high. How far is the ship from the cliff?

35. At noon on a certain day the shadows of two vertical poles A, B, each 5 feet high, are 3 feet 3 inches and 3 feet $1\frac{1}{2}$ inches respectively. If A is 69 miles north of B, what is the radius of the earth?

36. If a square is drawn outside a circle of 1 inch radius so that its sides just touch the circle, show that the length of its boundary is

8 tan 45°. If it is drawn inside the circle so that the corners of the square lie on the circumference, show that the length of the boundary is 8 sin 45°. Similarly show that the boundary of a circumscribed hexagon is 12 tan 30°, and of an inscribed hexagon 12 sin 30°. What would you expect the boundaries to be of a circumscribed and inscribed octagon (8 sides) and dodecagon (12 sides)?

37. Calculate the numerical values of the boundaries of a square, hexagon, octagon, and dodecagon, both circumscribed and inscribed. Tabulate your results to show between what values π lies, using the tables of sines and tangents.

38. Show that the area of the circumscribed square is 4 tan 45°, and of the inscribed square 4 sin 45° cos 45°. What are the areas of the circumscribed and inscribed hexagon? Give a general expression for the area of circumscribed and inscribed figures with n equivalent sides, noticing that in the case of a square the area is 4 tan $\frac{360°}{8}$.

39. Since the area of a circle of unit radius is π ($\pi r^2 = \pi$ when $r = 1$), use the general expressions you have just obtained to find the limits between which π lies, taking π to lie between the areas of circumscribed and inscribed figures with 180 equal sides.

40. If the radius of the earth is taken to be 3,960 miles, what is the distance between two places with the same longitude, separated by one degree of latitude?

41. What is the distance apart of two places on the equator separated by one degree of longitude?

42. A ship after sailing 200 miles due west finds that her longitude has altered by 5°. What is her latitude? Use the table on p. 663.

43. On Midsummer Day the sun is directly above the Tropic of Cancer (Lat. 23½° N.). On Midwinter Day it is directly above the Tropic of Capricorn (Lat. 23½° S.). Make a diagram to show at what angles the noon's sun is inclined to the horizon at London (Lat. 51½° N.) on June 21st and December 21st.

44. Show by diagrams that the noon shadow always points north at New York (Lat. 41° N.).

45. How would you know by watching the noon shadow throughout the year whether you were:

(*a*) North of Latitude $66\frac{1}{2}°$ N.?
(*b*) Between Latitude $66\frac{1}{2}°$ N. and $23\frac{1}{2}°$ N.?
(*c*) Between Latitude $23\frac{1}{2}°$ N. and the equator?
(*d*) Exactly at the North Pole?
(*e*) Exactly on the Arctic Circle?
(*f*) Exactly on the Tropic of Cancer?
(*g*) Exactly on the equator?

46. At what latitude will the sun's noon shadow be equal to the height of the shadow pole on (*a*) June 21st, (*b*) March 21st, (*c*) December 21st?

47. A ship's chronometer on September 23rd recorded Greenwich time as 10.44 a.m. when the sun crossed the meridian at an angle of 56° above the *northern* horizon. What port was it approaching? (Use a map.)

48. If New York is on the meridian of Longitude 74° W. and Moscow on $37\frac{2}{3}°$ E., what will be the local time in New York and Moscow when Greenwich time is 9.0 p.m.?

49. Using Dem. 9 and the definition of a circle as a figure in which every point on the boundary is equidistant from a fixed point called the centre, show that the centre is also the point where lines drawn at right angles to the mid-point of any two chords of a circle cross one another.

50. How would you use this, if you wished to make the base of a home-made theodolite like the one in Fig. 12 from the circular top of a second-hand three-legged stool, or to pierce the centre of a circular tin?

51. If one side BC of a triangle ABC is extended to a point D, show that $\angle$ ACD = $\angle$ CAB + $\angle$ ABC. When two observers at B and C sight an object at A, $\angle$CAB is called its *parallax* with reference to the two observers. Explain by Dem. 5 why the parallax of an object is the difference between its elevations at B and C, if A has the same aximuth for both observers.

THINGS TO MEMORIZE

1. In a triangle which has a base b opposite $\angle$ B, a side a opposite $\angle$A, a side c opposite $\angle$C, and a perpendicular height h from B to b:

(i) Area $= \frac{1}{2}hb$ (ii) $A + B + C = 180°$

If $B = 90°$

(i) $C = 90° - A$

$A = 90° - C$

(ii) $b^2 = c^2 + a^2$

(iii) $\sin A = \dfrac{a}{b} = \cos C$

$\cos A = \dfrac{c}{b} = \sin C$

$\tan A = \dfrac{a}{c} = \dfrac{1}{\tan C}$

2. In a circle of radius r (diameter d):

Boundary $= 2\pi r$ (or πd)

Area $= \pi r^2$

3. Two triangles are equivalent:

(i) If all three sides are equivalent.

(ii) If two sides and the enclosed angle of one triangle are equivalent to two sides and the enclosed angle of the other.

(iii) If one side and the angles the other two sides make with it in one triangle are equivalent to one side and the two corresponding angles in the other.

CHAPTER V

From Crisis to Crossword Puzzles

OR

THE BEGINNINGS OF ARITHMETIC

PLANNING education for the Age of Plenty is quite a different thing from letting middle-class children of parents with "advanced" views do nothing at all. Generations of schoolboys have been brought to the Bridge of Asses by the system of education which arose from the cultural needs of the middle classes. They stood in front of it, "groaning and travailing in pain together," as the apostle says. The old sort of educationist offered them the small coin of a secure appointment for their pains, when the examinations were passed. The "new educationist" offers them a holiday. Rational education would show them that knowledge of geometry is something which it is our privilege to share, because it has helped to make us able to plan the society in which everyone can share the satisfaction of common needs. Having made some acquaintance with the mathematical achievements of the Greeks, we may recall Cobbett's words. We can begin to see how mathematics might be taught so as to advance the liberties of the people.

When you come to think about it, what could be a more fitting text for such a lesson than the Bridge of Asses? In the fifth proposition of the first book of Euclid the most dramatic dichotomy in human history lies buried. The priestly superstitions which had grown up with the calendar demanded that temple sites should greet the vision of their august and celestial patrons. To make hotels comfortable and luxurious enough for star gods to visit, slaves toiled on burning sand. This brought into being a craft which possessed the secret of making houses fit for men to live in. Greek literature made their knowledge the articulate possession of mankind. The whole after-history of human thought may be viewed as a struggle between these two ways of dealing with the world. One is the way of the practical man who uses knowledge to change the world. The other is the culture of a caste with leisure to contemplate the world.

Among the Ionian Greeks there were men like Democritus, who realized, as we do, that knowledge is something we have the privilege of sharing with others. Maybe that is why they spoke of *demonstrations* instead of *proofs*. The first mathematicians wanted to distribute their knowledge. Pythagoras, who came after Thales, went about giving lectures on figures and numbers to large audiences in the fifth century B.C., and eventually married one of his lady students, Theono. We soon see the beginnings of another attitude. There were others more like our eugenists and South Africans, for whom knowledge is something which you keep from men who have a black skin or very little money. The pupils of Pythagoras formed themselves into secret societies and invested mathematics with the august and awful mystery which it has had ever since. Mathematical discoveries were communicated under oath. In the fourth century B.C., Hippasus, a member of one of these societies, is said to have been drowned in his bath for giving away mathematical truths for nothing. He announced in public that he had added a regular solid of twelve faces to the list enumerated by the founder. There is much to suggest that the whole arrangement of Euclid's elements was made to lead up to this proposition. When the Pythagorean brotherhoods slackened their vows sufficiently to allow books to be written, geometry and the study of number had lost touch with the work of the world. Plato, who transmitted their tradition, learned his geometry from the Pythagorean Philolaus.

Although Pythagoras himself seems to have liked sharing his knowledge with others, the fate of his doctrine was a very natural result of the way he taught. Men like Thales and Democritus went to Egypt, saw what the priests were doing, rejected the magic and used the arts, as the U.S.S.R. rejects American economics and uses American engineers. One of the reassuring facts about human history is that we can all be rationalists about the superstitions of other people. Jews are notoriously secularist when there are Christians around. There are rarely more than a few of the unusual people who can carry through a radical re-examination of their own beliefs. The Greeks were no exception to the rule. The merchants of the city-states were acquiring land and becoming slave-owners. They had not outgrown the need for social superstition. They had taken over the Phoenician culture of number, which seems to have collected a vast amount of superstitious rubbish from the eastern caravan routes. This rubbish was highly intriguing to the prospering townspeople who had an itch for change, characteristic of a rapidly expanding society. The audiences of Pythagoras wanted charades. He gave them brighter and better charades. It was a short step to the queer ceremonial of prayers which his pupils offered to magic numbers. "Bless us, divine number, who generatest

Gods and men, O holy *tetraktys*, that containest the root and source of the eternally flowing creation." Such was the incantation of his pupils to the number four.

The idealistic teaching which brought large audiences to hear Pythagoras is illustrated by the way he invested numbers and figures with moral qualities. One, being regarded as the source of all numbers rather than a number itself, stood for reason, two for opinion, four for justice, five for marriage, because it is formed by the union of the first male number 3 and the first female number 2. In the properties of five lay the secret of colour, in six the secret of cold, in seven the secret of health, in eight the secret of love, i.e. three (potency) added to five (marriage). The six-faced solid figure held the secret of the earth. The pyramid held the secret of fire (later the *logos spermatikos* of the Stoics, the light which lighteth every man). The twelve-faced solid held the secret of the heavens. The sphere was the most *perfect* figure. The distances of the stars were supposed to form a harmonic number series like the lengths of the wires of early stringed instruments, whence the "harmony of the spheres." Numbers were put into classes of bright and obliging or dull and discontented boys and girls. There were *perfect* numbers of which all the whole-number factors add up to the number itself. The first of these is 6, of which all the devisors are 1, 2, and 3 ($1 + 2 + 3 = 6$). The second is 28, of which all the factors are 1, 2, 4, 7, and 14 ($1 + 2 + 4 + 7 + 14 = 28$). The neo-Pythagorean Nichomachus of Alexandria spent a great deal of time hunting for the next two, which are 496 and 8,128. There is not another till we get to 33,550,336. In a fruitless effort to get so far Nichomachus discovered that "the good and the beautiful are rare and easily counted, but the ugly and bad are prolific." There were also *amicable* numbers. Asked what a friend was, Pythagoras replied, "One who is the other I. Such are 220 and 284." Being interpreted, this means that all the divisors of 284 (1, 2, 4, 71, and 142) add up to 220, and all the divisors of 220 (1, 2, 4, 5, 10, 11, 20, 22, 44, 55, and 110) add up to 284. You can amuse yourself like the audiences of Pythagoras by trying to find others. Another class of good omen was the class of triangular numbers (Fig. 76). Centuries later, as we shall see, these turned out to have a use. They are formed by adding a number to all the numbers which go before. For instance, the first four simple triangular numbers are 1, $3 = (1 + 2)$, $6 = (1 + 2 + 3)$, and $10 = (1 + 2 + 3 + 4)$. A story about these shows you how mathematics was ceasing to be an instrument which the Greek merchants and craftsman could use as Thales used his knowledge. In Lucian's dialogue a merchant asks Pythagoras what he can teach him. "I will teach you to count," says Pythagoras. "I know that already," replies the merchant. "How do you count?" asks the philosopher. The merchant begins, "One, two, three, four. . . ." "Stop," cries Pythagoras, "what you take to be four is ten, or a perfect triangle, and our symbol."

From great antiquity this cult of magic number can be traced far afield along the inland trade routes which radiate from the ancient Sumerian civilization. The Hindus and the Hebrews had their perfect numbers and amicable numbers before Pythagoras taught. The six days of creation and the twenty-eight days of the lunar month illustrate the perfection of the Providential Plan. St. Augustine understood the early preference of the Hittites for perfection when he said that "God created all things in six days, because this number is perfect." The Eastern influence on the teaching of Pythagoras has long been detected in his doctrine of metempsychosis, i.e. that every soul has a season ticket for travelling in bodies. There is reason to suspect that some of his geometry, and with it number phallicism, came from Chinese sources of a much earlier date. The number lore of ancient China gives us a clue to the first magical beginnings of a size language which forms the basis of modern statistics. We shall now go back five hundred years or more and see how men first began to classify the properties of numbers.

The distinctive feature of early Chinese number lore is that the numbers are *figurate*. They are represented by simple patterns of lines or circles or dots. This characteristic throws some light on the way in which the Hindus were able to replace the ancient letter numbers by a rational script. For our present purpose it is important because it helps us to reconstruct the beginnings of a very useful branch of mathematics, the study of "series." In the Chinese *Book of the Permutations*, written about five hundred years before Pythagoras, the first eight numbers are represented by combinations of horizontal bars, either whole—or broken—to signify the male principle (–) of the odd numbers and the female principle (– –) of the even numbers. Each number contains the secret of some object—sky, earth, fire (three, of course), water, air, wind, and mountain. These horizontal bars reappeared later in the matchstick notation, which suggested the Hindu number symbols (= becomes 2 and ≡ becomes 3). The Maya calendar script, which is the only number language based on the same principle as the Hindu notation, also uses horizontal bars placed one above another. An alternative, and for our present purpose more significant, way of writing numbers was to represent them by patterns of dots and circles (white circles for male numbers and black ones for female numbers). This is used in the first magic square which we meet in history. The one shown in our own notation in Fig. 71 is dated at least as early as 1000 B.C. As it was actually represented in the old Chinese text it was essentially like that given in Fig. 72, where

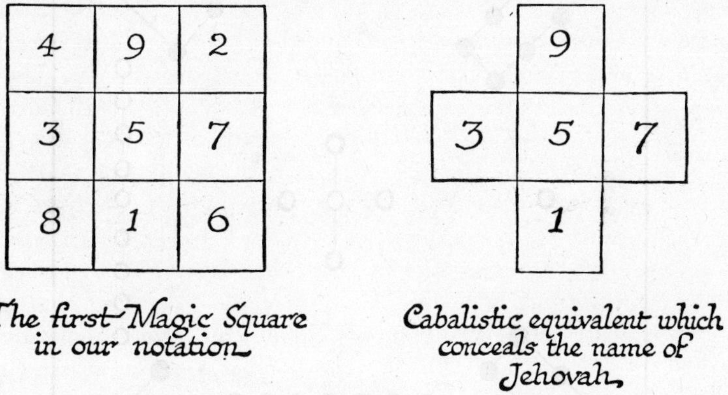

FIG. 71

the odd or male numbers are represented by white circles, and the even or female numbers by black ones.

The cult of the magic square drifted all round the ancient world. At a later date its vogue may have had something to do with the magic called "gematria." This is certainly the basis of the comparatively late cabalistic cross formed of the middle row and column of the square in Fig. 71. Gematria is the name for the quaint superstitions which arose in connexion with the use of alphabet letters for numbers of the Hebrews and Greeks. In those days, when men were first learning to use signs for numbers, they found themselves entangled in a bog of confusion by first attempts to invent symbols which took up less space than the earlier hieroglyphic forms. When each letter came to represent a number, each word had its characteristic number formed by adding all the separate numbers alternatively represented by its letters. When the numbers of two words were the same there were dark forebodings of hidden mysteries for hosts of commentators. The superiority of Achilles over Hector was due to the fact that the letters of Achilles add up to 1,276, whereas the name of Hector was only equivalent to

1,225. In Hebrew *Eliasar* adds up to 318. The Hebrew saga tells us that Abraham drove out 318 slaves when he rescued Eliasar. Gematria linked up stars and planets and portents in the astrological writings of the theosophists and the astrologers of the middle ages. A latin

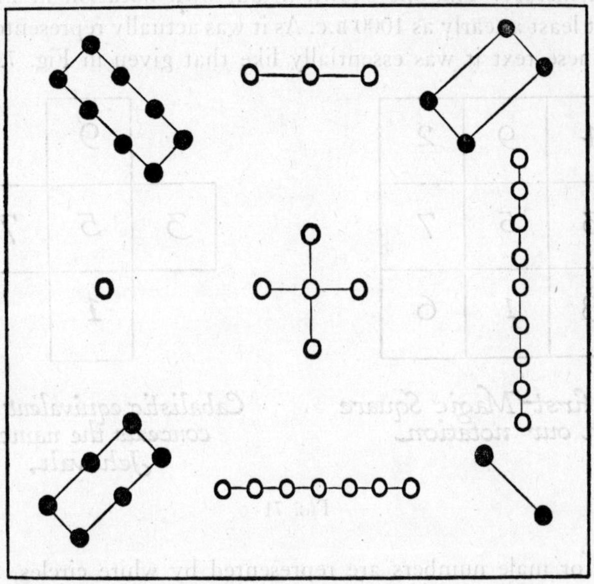

FIG. 72.—THE LO SHU IN THE "BOOK OF THE PERMUTATIONS"
This figure, which represents the first magic square in history, was first constructed about 1000 B.C.

proverb (given in the *Week-End Book*) shown in Fig. 73 illustrates an analogous game.

Plato's obscure number, which was "lord of better and worse births," stimulated a great deal of useless intellectual effort among the Platonists. The number of the beast in the book of Revelation gave later investigators prolific opportunities for practice in this branch of arithmetic. So did the book of Daniel to which Newton devoted the intellectual efforts of his declining years. Peter Bungus, a Catholic theologian, wrote a book of 700 pages to show that the number 666 of the beast was a cryptogram for the name of Martin Luther. Luther replied by interpreting it as a prophecy of the duration of the papal regime, which was happily approaching its predestined end. The Protestants, who sponsored the new mercantile arithmetic, were much better at this method of propaganda. Stifel, a convert of Luther, and the first European mathematician to use the signs +, −, and √ in a book on algebra, traced his conversion to the discovery that 666 refers to Pope Leo X. When written in full Leo X is LEO DECIMVS.

S	A	T	O	R
A	R	E	P	O
T	E	N	E	T
O	P	E	R	A
R	O	T	A	S

Sator arepo tenet opera rotas

FIG. 73.—WORD SQUARE BASED ON THE LATIN SENTENCE—
Sator arepo tenet opera rotas
(Arepo, the sower, delays the wheels by his works—inscription at Cirencester, Glos.)

The simplicity of the proof merits repetition. Stifel first saw that E, O and S are not numbers in Roman script. So their inclusion is merely an oversight. The number letters arrange themselves with little help to give MDCLVI, i.e. 1,656. This is 666 + 990. It is only fair, argued Stifel, to add in X the alternative way of writing DECIMVS. This gives us 666 + 1,000. The latin equivalent of 1,000 is M, the initial letter of *mysterium*. Hence the apocalyptic reference to the "mystery" of the beast. The interviews which contemporary mathematicians of some eminence give to Sunday newspapers need not surprise us greatly when we recollect that Napier, who is now famous for his logarithms, attached equal importance to his own method of identifying the Pope as antichrist.

The separation of odd and even numbers as male and female in this primitive number lore of the Chinese recalls the preoccupation of primitive man with the fertility of flock and field, and with the patriarchal family-group. Animism of number has a strict parallel in ordinary speech. While we laugh at the English Podsnap, who invariably associates the continent with the incontinent, it is only fair to admit that there is a legitimate excuse for the confusion. If an Englishman learns a living language at all, he learns French, in which every noun has to have a sex. English is a peculiarly sophisticated language in so far as it has eliminated *gender* in the grammatical sense. The animistic treatment of number (Fig. 74) in the earliest Chinese books on mathematics was apparently mixed up with the recognition of a special class of odd numbers, which are now called PRIMES. Prime numbers cannot be divided into an exact (whole) number of equal whole numbers.

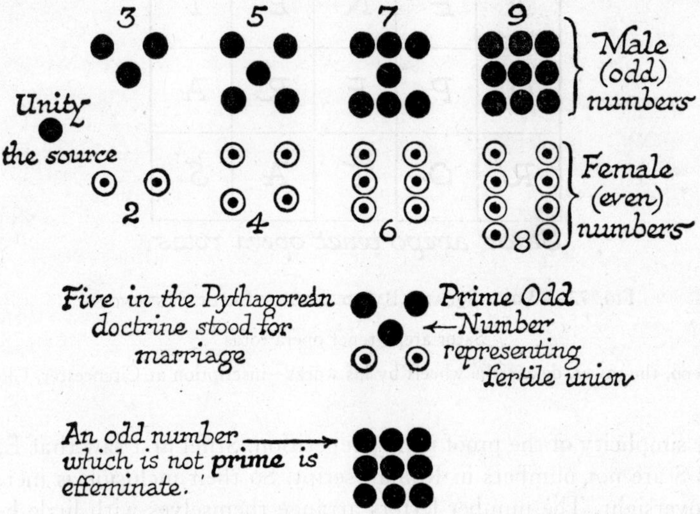

FIG. 74.—ANIMISM AND GENDER IN CHINESE AND PYTHAGOREAN NUMBER LORE

Figuratively (Fig. 74) they cannot be represented by equivalent rows of dots or circles. Thus 3, 5, 7, 11, and 13 are primes. The odd numbers 9, 15, 21, and 25 are not prime numbers. The recognition of this class of numbers was not a very useful discovery except in so far as it simplified finding square roots before modern methods were discovered.

To get all the primes between 1 and 100 you first leave out all the even numbers (which are divisible by 2) and all numbers ending in 5 or 0 in our notation (because these are divisible by 5), except, of course, 2 and 5 themselves. This leaves:

1	2	3	5	7	9	11	13	17	19
21	23	27	29	31	33	37	39		
41	43	47	49	51	53	57	59		
61	63	67	69	71	73	77	79		
81	83	87	89	91	93	97	99		

Now you must throw out all the numbers (other than 3 or 7) which are exactly divisible by 3 or 7. This leaves:

1	2	3	5	7	11	13	17	19
23	29	31	37	41	43	47		
53	59	61	67	71	73	79		
83	89	97						

We have already rejected all numbers divisible by 9, since these are all divisible by 3, and all numbers divisible by 6, 8, and 10, since these are all divisible by 2. Any number which is divisible by 11 or a higher number is also divisible by one of the first ten numbers, since higher multiples of 11 are greater than 100. So all those left are prime.

The use of primes for finding square roots depends upon an important rule which you will meet again and again. It is illustrated by the following examples:

$$\begin{aligned}
\sqrt{4\times 9} &= \sqrt{36} = 6 = 2\times 3 = \sqrt{4}\times\sqrt{9}\\
\sqrt{4\times 16} &= \sqrt{64} = 8 = 2\times 4 = \sqrt{4}\times\sqrt{16}\\
\sqrt{4\times 25} &= \sqrt{100} = 10 = 2\times 5 = \sqrt{4}\times\sqrt{25}\\
\sqrt{9\times 16} &= \sqrt{144} = 12 = 3\times 4 = \sqrt{9}\times\sqrt{16}\\
\sqrt{4\times 49} &= \sqrt{196} = 14 = 2\times 7 = \sqrt{4}\times\sqrt{49}\\
\sqrt{9\times 25} &= \sqrt{225} = 15 = 3\times 5 = \sqrt{9}\times\sqrt{25}\\
\sqrt{9\times 49} &= \sqrt{441} = 21 = 3\times 7 = \sqrt{9}\times\sqrt{49}
\end{aligned}$$

These examples illustrate the rule:

$$\sqrt{ab} = \sqrt{a}\times\sqrt{b}$$

So we may put:

$$\begin{aligned}
\sqrt{6} &= \sqrt{2}\,.\,\sqrt{3}\\
\sqrt{8} &= \sqrt{4}\,.\,\sqrt{2} = 2\sqrt{2}\\
\sqrt{12} &= \sqrt{4}\,.\,\sqrt{3} = 2\sqrt{3}\\
\sqrt{18} &= \sqrt{9}\,.\,\sqrt{2} = 3\sqrt{2}\\
\sqrt{24} &= \sqrt{4}\,.\,\sqrt{6} = 2\sqrt{2}\,.\,\sqrt{3}
\end{aligned}$$

In other words, if we know $\sqrt{2}$ and $\sqrt{3}$, we can get the square root of any number formed by multiplying twos and threes, such as 32, 48,

72, 96. If we also know $\sqrt{5}$, we can get all square roots of numbers formed by multiplying fives with twos and threes, e.g. 10, 15, 30, 40, 45, 50, 60. You can test this as follows:

If we take $\sqrt{2} = 1\cdot414$ and $\sqrt{3} = 1\cdot732$, then $\sqrt{6} = 1\cdot414 \times 1\cdot732 = 2\cdot449$ correct to three decimal places. Multiplying out, we get:

1·414	1·732	2·449
1·414	1·732	2·449
1·414	1·732	4·898
0·5656	1·2124	0·9796
0·01414	0·05196	0·09796
0·005656	0·003464	0·022041
1·999396	2·999824	5·997601

The error, as we should expect, is greater in the third product, because we have only taken the result of multiplying $\sqrt{2}$ and $\sqrt{3}$ correct to three decimals, and are multiplying the errors in the values we gave to them. The final result is less than one in two thousand (0·0024 in 6·0) out.

This rule is one which we shall use often in later chapters. You must be able to recognize it when it is used with fractions, e.g.

$$\sqrt{\frac{a}{b}} = \sqrt{a \times \frac{1}{b}} = \sqrt{a} \times \sqrt{\frac{1}{b}} = \frac{\sqrt{a}}{\sqrt{b}}.$$

$$\text{e.g.}\ \sqrt{\frac{3}{4}} = \frac{\sqrt{3}}{2}$$

Notice how it can be used in cancelling expressions, e.g.

$$\frac{3}{\sqrt{3}} = \frac{\sqrt{3} \times \sqrt{3}}{\sqrt{3}} = \sqrt{3} \text{ or } \frac{1}{\sqrt{2}} = \frac{\sqrt{2}}{2}.$$

Also notice its use in the following sentences, which we shall meet when we come to find a value for π:

$$\sqrt{1 - \left(\frac{2}{3}\right)^2} = \sqrt{1 - \frac{2^2}{3^2}}$$

$$= \sqrt{\frac{3^2 - 2^2}{3^2}} = \tfrac{1}{3}\sqrt{3^2 - 2^2}$$

$$= \frac{\sqrt{5}}{3}$$

The animistic belief that a real number must have sex like a sheep or a cow recalls a proof given by Euclid in the tenth book of his *Elements* to show that the diagonal of a square whose sides are represented by whole numbers cannot itself be represented by a whole number. It is probably of Pythagorean origin. To follow it you need to remember three assumptions which you will not find difficult:

(*a*) Squares of even numbers are even (e.g. $6^2 = 36$), and squares of odd numbers are odd (e.g. $7^2 = 49$).

(*b*) Twice any number is even (e.g. $2 \times 5 = 10$), and any even number is twice some other whole number ($2 = 2 \times 1$, $4 = 2 \times 2$).

(*c*) If two numbers are even, they have a common factor 2, so that if two numbers have no common factor but 1, like a fraction in its simplest form, they cannot both be even. If one is even the other is odd. Starting with these assumptions, and using a number language in which the simplest form of a fraction must be the ratio of an odd to an even or of two odd numbers, the Greek argument runs like this. Suppose we make a square with two sides, 1 unit and 1 unit. Then from Dem. 8

$$1^2 + 1^2 = 2$$

i.e. the diagonal is $\sqrt{2}$. This is a fraction greater than 1 and less than 2 (p. 94). Let us call it $\frac{a}{b}$ when all its divisors have been cancelled out. Then if

$$\frac{a}{b} = \sqrt{2}$$

$$\frac{a^2}{b^2} = 2$$

$$a^2 = 2b^2 \quad . \quad . \quad . \quad . \quad . \quad \text{(i)}$$

So as a^2 is twice another whole number it is even. Hence a is even. If $\sqrt{2}$ is a fraction in its simplest form, b must be odd if a is even. If a is even, it is twice some whole number, which we will call n, i.e.

$$a = 2n$$

$$a^2 = (2n)^2 = 4n^2 \quad . \quad . \quad . \quad \text{(ii)}$$

But combining (i) and (ii), we find

$$4n^2 = 2b^2$$

$$2n^2 = b^2$$

According to this b is even. Since we have already assumed that it is odd, there is a catch somewhere. That is to say, we have made a wrong assumption. If, like the Pythagoreans, we assume that all numbers must be male or female, we conclude that $\sqrt{2}$ is not a number at all. So we give up hope of making geometry useful, and banish number and measurement from it.

The disciples of Plato, who enjoyed an independent income and held up to ridicule teachers who had to earn a livelihood by instruction, set great store by this ingenious argument. It will not worry us as much as it impressed them, nor force us, like Plato, to regard geometry as a useless and therefore exalted ornament of leisure. Being good citizens, we are interested in the profitable sort of brainwork which tells you how to do something in contradistinction to the ornamental culture which concerns itself with showing what it is impossible to do. You will notice that Euclid (or more probably Eudoxus) made the initial assumption that the side of a square can be represented by the whole numbers which correspond to beads on the counting frame. As practical people, we have already come to the conclusion (p. 78) that the whole numbers which correspond to the beads are all very well for *enumerating* the sheep in each compartment of the fold but are not the right sort of numbers for representing *estimates* of the wall, or, for that matter, the sides of a sand tracing or ink and paper model of the wall drawn with Euclid's rule and compass (Fig. 75).

The trouble began because the Pythagoreans had pictured the line as a row of points pressed together like the beads in the column of the abacus. From that they went on to consider a figure as a set of such lines pressed close together sideways. The physical model was imperfect, because the Pythagorean point had no shape to discuss.

To fit physical objects together we must make them with a particular shape. We can make a right-angled triangle by fitting together as many similar right-angled triangles as we can cut out, and we can make a rectangle by fitting together many little rectangles with sides of the same ratio or right-angled triangles similar to the two into which it is divided by its diagonal. When we have done so the ratio of the hypotenuse or diagonal to the sides of each element of the figure is the same as that of the corresponding sides of the composite one. The actual number of diagonal elements is the same as the number of either of the side elements, and it has nothing to do with the ratio of the two. The materialist critics of Pythagoras, like Leucippus and Democritus, did not get themselves into these difficulties. To represent space as a collection of separate atoms they saw that you have to have a void between them, and since you cannot make any figure you like by atoms spaced at equal distances from their neighbours, numbers of atoms counted in different directions refer to different scales of measurement.

The dilemma which came from confusing what we have called *flock*

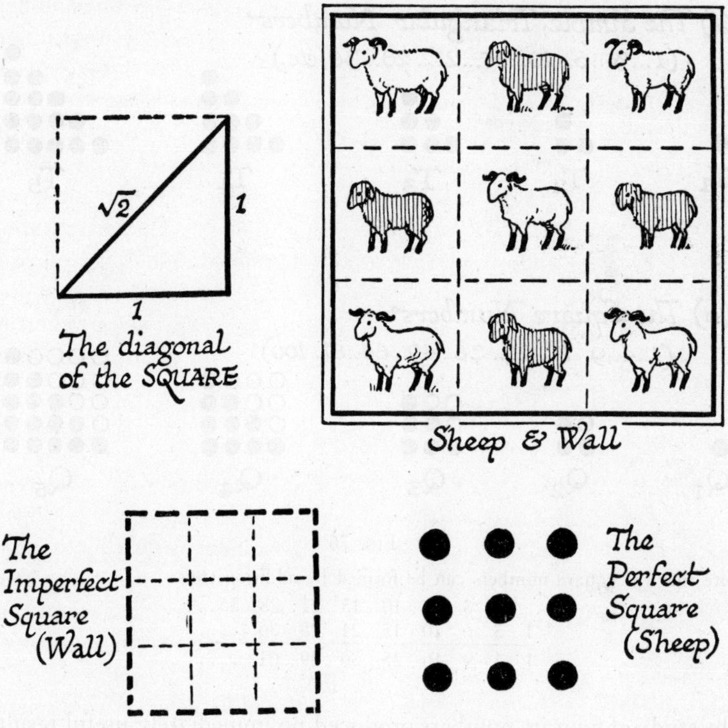

FIG. 75.—THE PYTHAGOREAN DILEMMA

numbers with *field* numbers had an interesting by-product. The Pythagoreans amused themselves with a class of figures made up of separate points like those of the Chinese magic square. The numbers of points in such figures were classified in families, and studying the family likeness of such figurate numbers, some of which are shown in Figs. 76 and 77, led to the discovery of *series*. In the course of time this led to the recognition that the right sort of numbers for representing measurements are built up like series which go on as far as you like. We shall come to them in Chapter x.

What is called Greek arithmetic was mainly occupied with studying these figurate numbers. It paid little attention to devising rules of calculation such as we possess to-day. That was left to the counting frame. The art of calculation, without which we could have no modern mathematics, was despised by the Greek intellectual of Plato's time.

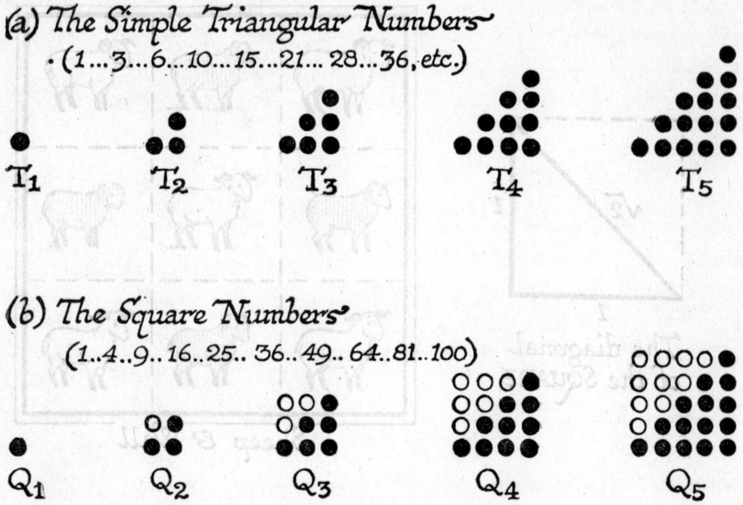

FIG. 76

Note that the square numbers can be formed by addition thus:

	1	3	6	10	15	21	28	36 . . .
1	3	6	10	15	21	28	36	. . . . .
1	4	9	16	25	36	49	64	. . . . .

The study of figurate numbers produced no immediately useful results. It is important because it led to the study of series, which ultimately provided the clue to an understanding of numbers which are not full grown. We shall devote the rest of this chapter to studying how the recognition of series began.

A series is a set of numbers arranged in a definite order so that each term is connected with the next according to a definite rule. The "natural" number series is the simplest example. When the whole numbers are arranged in the customary order

1 2 3 4 5 6 7 8 . . .

we recognize at once that each term is one more than the previous term or one less than its successor. The first two simple series to be added to the natural number series, as we have seen, were the series

$$3 \quad 5 \quad 7 \quad 9 \quad 11 \quad 13 \quad 15 \quad 17 \quad 19 \ldots$$

and $$2 \quad 4 \quad 6 \quad 8 \quad 10 \quad 12 \quad 14 \quad 16 \quad 18 \ldots$$

In either of these series each term differs by 2 from its successor or predecessor, being 2 more than the latter and 2 less than the former. Series of which successive numbers differ from one another by the same amount are called arithmetic series (or progressions). Another of this class is

$$3 \quad 10 \quad 17 \quad 24 \quad 31 \quad 38 \quad 45 \quad 52 \ldots$$

A different sort of connexion is seen in another series which we have met:

$$\frac{6}{10} \quad \frac{6}{100} \quad \frac{6}{1000} \quad \frac{6}{10000} \quad \frac{6}{100000} \text{ etc.}$$

Here every term is ten times its successor, or a tenth of its predecessor. Series in which every term is so many times (or such and such a fraction of) its predecessor whether the numbers are arranged in ascending or, like this one, in descending order of size are called *geometric series*. The rules for the connexion between the numbers in these two of the many different families of series can be stated thus. If m is any number in a series, the next number in an arithmetic series is $m + b$, and the next number in a geometric series is mb (m times b). For any particular series b is always the same number. It may be a whole number or a fraction. Thus b is $2\frac{1}{2}$ in the arithmetic series

$$3 \quad 5\tfrac{1}{2} \quad 8 \quad 10\tfrac{1}{2} \quad 13 \quad 15\tfrac{1}{2} \quad 18 \ldots$$

Describing a series in this way does not distinguish between two arithmetic series like

$$1 \quad 5 \quad 9 \quad 13 \quad 17 \quad 21 \quad 25 \quad 29 \ldots$$
$$3 \quad 7 \quad 11 \quad 15 \quad 19 \quad 23 \quad 27 \quad 31 \ldots$$

or between two geometric series like

$$0{\cdot}6 \quad 0{\cdot}06 \quad 0{\cdot}006 \quad 0{\cdot}0006 \quad 0{\cdot}00006 \ldots$$
$$0{\cdot}7 \quad 0{\cdot}07 \quad 0{\cdot}007 \quad 0{\cdot}0007 \quad 0{\cdot}00007 \ldots$$

Another way to bring out the connexion between the numbers in a series is to regard the latter as the offspring of the natural number series (marriage of male and female numbers in the ancient number lore). Thus, putting the parent series above, we may represent the even numbers as the daughter series:

Parent	1	2	3	4	5	6	7	8 ...
Daughter	2	4	6	8	10	12	14	16 ...

Or we may put down the son series:

Parent	1	2	3	4	5	6	7	8 ...
Son	3	5	7	9	11	13	15	17 ...

In this patriarchal family-group each daughter is two years younger than her next elder sister, and each boy is two years younger than his next elder brother. In other words, if m is any number in either series, the one which follows is $m + 2$. So our first way of describing a series does not distinguish between boys and girls. We can do this by dating their births from the beginning of the old-fashioned marriage in which a new addition to the family happens with annual regularity. Looking at the daughter series and the parent series, we see that any number in the daughter series is twice the corresponding number in the parent series. If we call any number (or *term*, as is more usual) in the parent series n, the corresponding number (or nth term) is $2n$. Similarly every term in the male series is formed by adding 1 to twice the corresponding term in the parent series. In other words, the nth term is $2n + 1$. If you do the same with the series

7 9 11 13 15 17 19 ...

you will find that the nth term is $5 + 2n$. This way of describing series lead to a very striking peculiarity of geometric series. We shall see later how it led to the discovery of logarithms. Here is a geometric series put below the generating (or parent) series of natural numbers:

1	2	3	4	5	6	7	8	9	10 ...
2	4	8	16	32	64	128	256	512	1,024 ...

We can also write this:

Parent	1	2	3	4	5	6	7	8	9	10
Offspring	2^1	2^2	2^3	2^4	2^5	2^6	2^7	2^8	2^9	2^{10}

In the same way we can write

Parent	1	2	3	4	5	6	...
Offspring	10	100	1,000	10,000	100,000	1,000,000	...

in the alternative form

Parent	1	2	3	4	5	6
Offspring	10^1	10^2	10^3	10^4	10^5	10^6

Geometric series were among those which the Pythagoreans studied. If they had been using numbers to describe the real world, they might have made a discovery which is the basis of our system of recurring decimals. This would have allowed Achilles to catch up with the tortoise. One of the things which they worked out was how to find the sum of all the numbers in a geometric series,* such as:

$$4 \quad 12 \quad 36 \quad 108 \quad 324 \quad 972 \quad 2{,}916$$

The seven terms of this series may be written:

Parent	1	2	3	4	5	6	7
Offspring	4	$4(3^1)$	$4(3^2)$	$4(3^3)$	$4(3^4)$	$4(3^5)$	$4(3^6)$

If we put the first term at the end, the sum, S, may be written:

$$S = 4(3^1) + 4(3^2) + 4(3^3) + 4(3^4) + 4(3^5) + 4(3^6) + 4$$

Now 3 times the sum of this series written in its original order of terms is

$$3S = 4(3^1) + 4(3^2) + 4(3^3) + 4(3^4) + 4(3^5) + 4(3^6) + 4(3^7)$$

Twice the sum can be got by taking away the sum of the series from 3 times the sum of the series, thus:

$$\begin{array}{r} 4(3^1) + 4(3^2) + 4(3^3) + 4(3^4) + 4(3^5) + 4(3^6) + 4(3^7) \\ \underline{4(3^1) + 4(3^2) + 4(3^3) + 4(3^4) + 4(3^5) + 4(3^6) \;\ldots + 4} \\ \text{Difference} = 2S = 4(3^7) - 4 \end{array}$$

So the sum is half this amount, or

$$S = \frac{4(3^7 - 1)}{2} = 4{,}372$$

Check this by addition, thus:

$$4 + 12 + 36 + 108 + 324 + 972 + 2{,}916 = 4{,}372$$

In modern number shorthand we should express the rule which is illustrated by this example, using letters or *abstract numbers*, like *n* for

* When the word "sum" is used by mathematicians in connexion with a series, they mean some short rule which saves the trouble of performing a laborious addition "sum."

the number of terms, b for the number by which succeeding terms are multiplied, and a for the first term, thus:

$$S = \frac{a(b^n - 1)}{b - 1}$$

The method used is essentially the same as that which we use for finding a fraction equivalent to a recurring decimal.

$$0\cdot\dot{1} = 0\cdot 1 + 0\cdot 01 + 0\cdot 001 + 0\cdot 0001 + 0\cdot 00001 + \text{and so on}$$

Similarly

$$\tfrac{1}{10} \times (0\cdot\dot{1}) = \ldots 0\cdot 01 + 0\cdot 001 + 0\cdot 0001 + 0\cdot 00001 + \text{and so on}$$

Subtracting the bottom from the top series, we get:

$$\frac{9}{10}(0\cdot\dot{1}) = 0\cdot 1 \text{ or } 0\cdot\dot{1} = \frac{10 \times 0\cdot 1}{9} = \frac{1}{9}$$

We have already referred to the simple triangular numbers

1 3 6 10 15 21 28 36 45 55 etc.

The figurate representation of these numbers is given at the top of Fig. 76. This series, to which the Pythagoreans attached magical properties like geometric series, led to no useful results in their own hands. If the Pythagoreans had been less interested in saying prayers to perfect numbers, and more concerned about making numbers which fit the imperfect observations of imperfect human beings, they would have seen the catch in Zeno's paradox. They might also have advanced towards the beginnings of a mathematical study of "probability." Triangular numbers did not become important till two thousand years later, when a decaying aristocracy was squandering its resources at the gaming tables and wealthy merchants were securing their gains with combination locks. In the earlier history of number lore, triangular numbers probably played an important part in suggesting rules for forming and adding the terms of series, which were much studied later, in particular by the Hindus. One of the things which helped to stimulate the need for a shorthand of number rules, or as we call it today *symbolic* algebra, was the cult of finding the sum of a series. The achievements of the Hindus in finding rules for doing so would be astonishing, if it were not for the fact that the Eastern peoples were familiar with a clue which is generally omitted from textbooks of elementary mathematics.

You will see from Figs. 76 and 77 that a variety of number series,

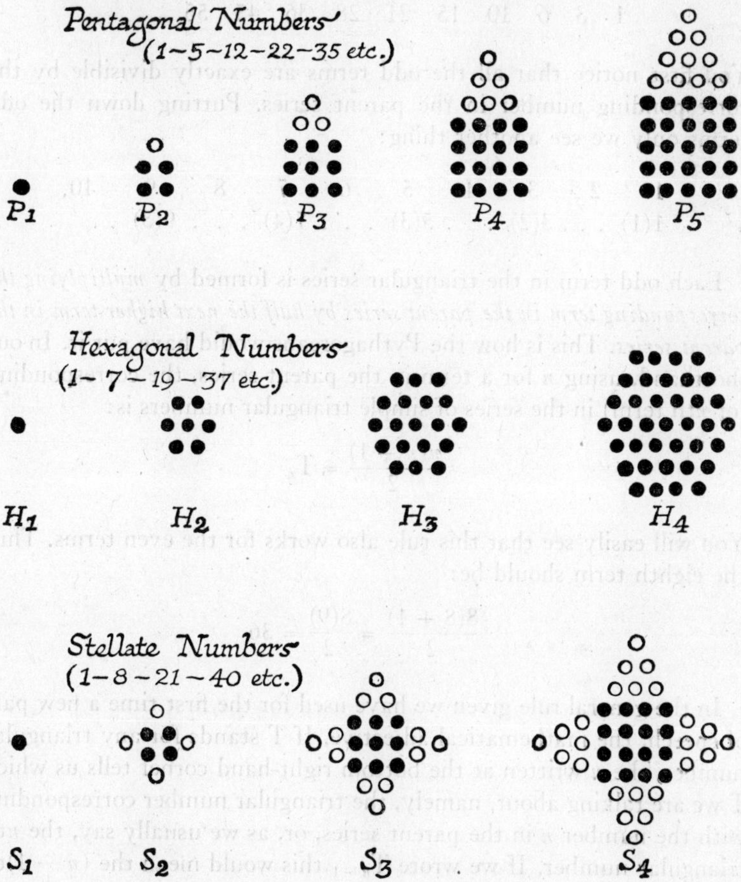

FIG. 77

e.g. the triangular number series, can be represented in a figurative form. Just as straight-line figures in Greek geometry can always be split up into triangles, figurate numbers can be split up into triangular numbers. This means that if we know how the triangular number series is formed, we can easily recognize the rule which connects the numbers in any series of figurate numbers. The rule for the formation of the simple triangular numbers is easy to see when they are arranged below the generating series of the natural numbers:

1	2	3	4	5	6	7	8	9	10	...
1	3	6	10	15	21	28	36	45	55	...

You first notice that all the odd terms are exactly divisible by the corresponding number in the parent series. Putting down the odd terms only we see another thing:

1	2	3	4	5	6	7	8	9	10
1(1)	...	3(2)	...	5(3)	...	7(4)	...	9(5)	..

Each odd term in the triangular series is formed by *multiplying the corresponding term in the parent series by half the next higher term in the parent series.* This is how the Pythagoreans would have put it. In our shorthand, using n for a term in the parent series, the corresponding (or nth term) in the series of simple triangular numbers is:

$$\frac{n(n+1)}{2} = T_n$$

You will easily see that this rule also works for the even terms. Thus the eighth term should be:

$$\frac{8(8+1)}{2} = \frac{8(9)}{2} = 36$$

In the general rule given we have used for the first time a new part of speech, the mathematical adjective. If T stands for any triangular number, the n written at the bottom right-hand corner tells us which T we are talking about, namely, the triangular number corresponding with the number n in the parent series, or, as we usually say, the nth triangular number. If we wrote T_{n-1} this would mean the $(n - 1)$th triangular number, i.e. the one immediately before the nth. This, of course, would be:

$$\frac{(n-1)([n-1]+1)}{2} \text{ or } \frac{(n-1)n}{2}$$

Thus the seventh or $(8 - 1)$th triangular number is $\frac{7(8)}{2} = \frac{8(7)}{2} = 28.$

How triangular numbers can be used to get the rule for making other series is seen in its most simple form in Fig. 76, which shows the series of square numbers, i.e.

Parent	1	2	3	4	5	6	7	8	9	10	etc.
Offspring	1	4	9	16	25	36	49	64	81	100	etc.

In this case we see at once that the rule for forming the son and daughter series from the generating series is simply that the *n*th term (Q_n) is n^2. If we had not recognized these numbers straight away, we could have seen the rule from the figurate form of the series. The square number is made up of the corresponding triangular number and the next one below, i.e.

$$Q_n = T_n + T_{n-1} = \frac{n(n+1)}{2} + \frac{n(n-1)}{2}$$

Using Dem. 2 we can write this:

$$\frac{n}{2}(n + 1 + n - 1) = \frac{n}{2}(2n) = n^2$$

The "pentagonal" numbers (Fig. 77) can be treated in the same way. The series is:

Parent	1	2	3	4	5	6	...
Offspring	1	5	12	22	35	51	...

Here the figure gives:

$$P_n = T_{n-1} + n^2$$
$$= \frac{n(n-1)}{2} + n^2 = \frac{n(n-1)}{2} + \frac{n(2n)}{2}$$
$$= \frac{n}{2}(3n - 1)$$

You can derive some amusement from getting similar rules for forming a series of "hexagonal" numbers (see also Ex. 22, p. 232):

1 7 19 37 61 91 ...

or the series of stellate numbers in Fig. 77:

1 8 21 40 65 96 ...

You can also get a good deal of fun, if you have some marbles or ball-bearings, by making up figurative number series which correspond to *solids* of which the faces are made up of points like atoms in the modern theory of crystal structure. Three general classes may be distinguished: (*a*) the pyramids, (*b*) the prisms, (*c*) regular polyhedra such as fit inside or enclose a sphere. The pyramid class is formed by adding successive layers of which the next above the nth is the $(n-1)$ th member of the same figurate number series, and have the general formula $(F_n + F_{n-1} \ldots + 1)$. Thus the pyramid with a three-sided base (tetrahedron) is formed by adding layers of successively lower triangular numbers. The fourth member of the series is numerically $20 = (10 + 6 + 3 + 1)$. With squares we get a pyramid with a 4-sided

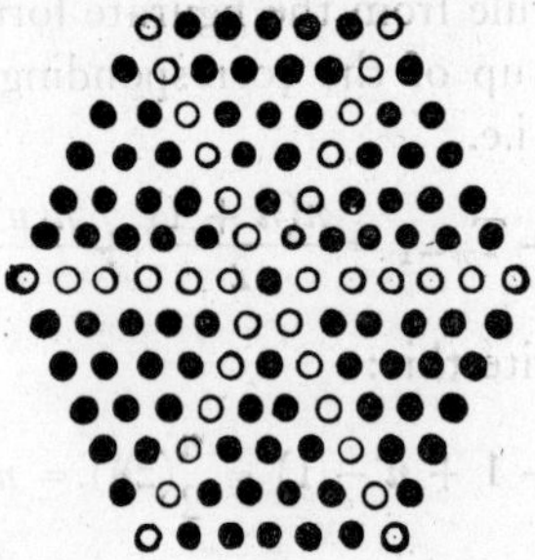

The 7th Hexagonal Number of the Series on p.211

FIG. 78

$6(T_5) + 6(6) + 1$ or $6(T_{n-2}) + 6(n-1) + 1$

base. The fourth pyramidal number of this type is 30 $(16 + 9 + 4 + 1)$. The prisms are made up of m layers of the same flat figurate number. This may be written $[m]. F_n$, in which [. .] means "go on adding . . . layers of." If the parent series is the square numbers, the solid is a cuboid, and, if $m = n$, it is a cube. If the series is the triangular numbers, the figure is a triangular prism. Polyhedra are built up by fitting together pyramids with superimposed faces just as higher figurative numbers can be built up by fitting together triangular numbers. You can try and build some of them yourself, if you have some wire and beads.

The Pythagoreans studied series of this essentially ornamental kind. They confined their attention mainly to whole numbers, and paid very little attention to series of fractional quantities which diminish as we go up the series, like:

Parent	1	2	3	4	5	6	7	8	9	10
Offspring	1	$\frac{1}{2}$	$\frac{1}{3}$	$\frac{1}{4}$	$\frac{1}{5}$	$\frac{1}{6}$	$\frac{1}{7}$	$\frac{1}{8}$	$\frac{1}{9}$	$\frac{1}{10}$

We have already seen that series like this sometimes choke off, though this particular one does not.* If they do, they can never exceed a certain quantity, however long we go on with them. Mathematicians say that the sum tends to a "limiting value" like the sum of the series represented by $0\cdot\dot{6}$, i.e.

$$\tfrac{6}{10} + \tfrac{6}{100} + \tfrac{6}{1000} + \tfrac{6}{10000} + \text{and so on.}$$

When this happens, it may be quite easy to see between what limits this *limiting* fraction lies, even if we cannot say what it is. In the second example the limiting fraction is, of course, $\frac{6}{9}$ or $\frac{2}{3}$. Even if we could not find a simple fraction corresponding with the limiting value, we could say where it lies. In this example it lies between 0·6 and 0·7, 0·66 and 0·67, 0·666 and 0·667, etc. We can stop short at any point suitable to the accuracy of our instruments. Series of this sort are thus the sort of numbers which we need for measuring things. They represent the way in which the modern mathematician represents quantities like π and $\sqrt{2}$ which puzzled and paralysed the Greek intellectuals. The Greek intellectuals who gave up hope of making sense out of these quantities had the intellectual equipment to tackle them. It was their social culture which prevented them from making further progress.

From what has been said so far, a careless reader might almost begin to wonder whether ordinary numbers, the "natural" numbers, have any use at all. Of course they have, provided they are used to deal with the sort of things to which they naturally refer. In nature they were first applied to the individual sheep of a flock or cattle in a herd and similar distinct things. They are the proper numbers to use in dealing with the statistics of a population. Some of the most controversial questions in modern mathematics arise in the study of statistics built up very largely on the sort of series which are most useful to describe measurements. Just as the Greeks could not see the wall for the sheep, some statisticians do not seem to see the sheep for the wall. It has already been hinted that the triangular numbers play an important part in the fundamental principles of this branch of mathematics. The Chinese seem to have had some notion of the special meaning which we attach to them in the modern theory of probability.

To see what they mean from this standpoint, an illustration from playing-cards will help. The illustration is not inappropriate, because the whole study of mathematical "probability" grew up in this atmos-

* See Note on p. 233.

phere of Chinese puzzles and playing-cards, and some of the mathematical tricks which are used in it have much in common with the magic square and the crossword puzzle. Perhaps our grandchildren will think that it has not yet outgrown the magic square. We are all familiar with a question such as: What are the odds that I shall select the Ace of Spades and the Ace of Hearts, if I take two cards from a set of all four aces? The mathematician interprets this in the following way. There are six ways of taking two cards from the set. These are:

(*a*) Spade, Heart.	(*c*) Spade, Club.	(*e*) Heart, Club.
(*b*) Spade, Diamond.	(*d*) Heart, Diamond.	(*f*) Diamond, Club.

One of these is the selection prescribed. The other five represent failure to get the result. The odds are five to one against getting it. For the present we will take this as a purely grammatical statement about how mathematicians talk to one another about odds. It does not necessarily mean the same thing as saying that if I do it often enough I select the right cards in about one-sixth and the wrong ones in about five-sixths of the attempts I make. Such an assertion implies knowing a number of other things about the real world: as, for instance, how the cards are shuffled, whether they are manufactured in such a way that one gets into the same position in the pack as often as another, or that a person drawing from the pack has no way of identifying individual cards by irregularities of printing, texture, and thickness, besides other experimental data with which mathematics is not directly concerned. When we come to talk about probability later, we shall have to draw a very clear distinction between *mathematical probability*, which is really concerned with stating something about all the possible ways in which something may happen if the right conditions are fulfilled, and *actual probability*, which has more to do with how we behave when we do not know whether all the conditions are fulfilled or not.

In stating the possibilities of selecting from a group of separate objects like playing-cards or populations, we meet two classes of numbers corresponding with two kinds of selection. The first, called *combinations*, are used when we are only interested in the qualities of the things selected, e.g. in this illustration whether the card is a heart or a spade. Combinations are numbers which tell us the number of different things which we can take from a set of *so many*, when we are allowed to select *so many* at a time. They are represented by the noun C with two adjectives, one written in the top left-hand corner telling us to what size of set it refers, the other written in the bottom right-hand corner telling us what number we are allowed to take from the set at a time. Thus $^5C_2$ means the number of different ways in which I can select two objects from a set of five different objects. If you look at Fig. 79 you will have no difficulty in continuing the series

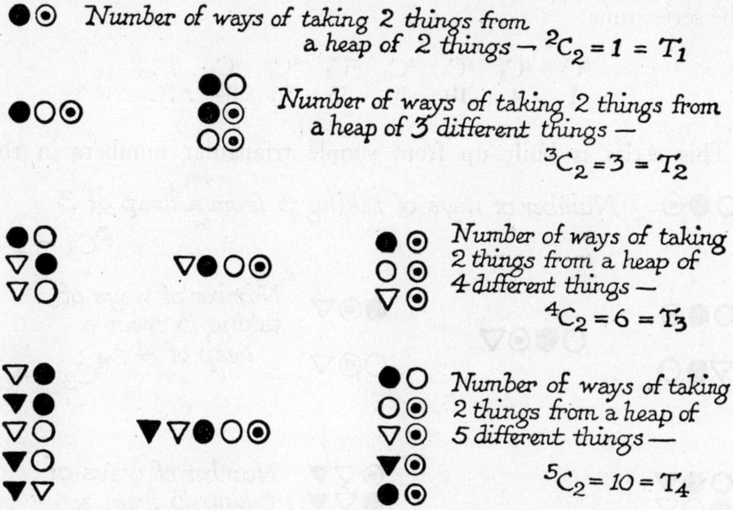

FIG. 79.—TRIANGULAR NUMBERS AS COMBINATIONS

of numbers representing the combinations of 2, 3, 4, 5, 6, 7, . . . different objects taken two at a time. You will get this result:

$^1C_2$	$^2C_2$	$^3C_2$	$^4C_2$	$^5C_2$	$^6C_2$	$^7C_2$	$^8C_2$	. . .
0	1	3	6	10	15	21	28	. . .

You will see at once that

$$^nC_2 = T_{n-1} = \tfrac{1}{2}n(n-1)$$

That is to say, the number of ways in which I can take two cards from the complete pack of 52 is $\frac{1}{2}(52)(51) = 1{,}326$. So the odds against picking two particular cards, e.g. the Queen of Spades and the Jack of Diamonds, are 1,325 to 1. If we are allowed to select three cards, we need to know the rule for the series:

$$^3C_3 \quad ^4C_3 \quad ^5C_3 \quad ^6C_3 \quad \text{etc.}$$

You will easily find the first few terms in this series by using a figurative device like that in Fig. 80, or, if you prefer it, letters, e.g. taking three from the five *abcde*, we have:

abc	*abd*	*abe*	*acd*	*ace*	*ade*
	bcd	*bce*	*bde*	*cde*	

The series runs:

$^3C_3$	$^4C_3$	$^5C_3$	$^6C_3$	$^7C_3$	$^8C_3$	$^9C_3$	. . .
1	4	10	20	35	56	84	. . .

This series is built up from simple triangular numbers in the

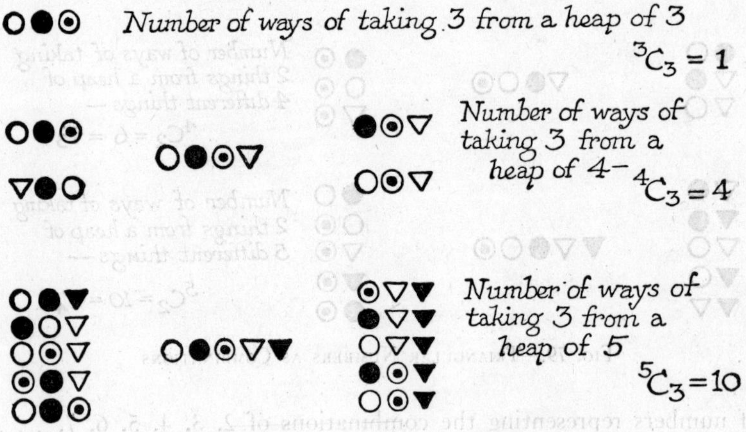

Fig. 80.—Higher Combinations and Triangular Numbers

same way as the simple triangular numbers are built up from natural numbers. Indeed, we can build up the natural numbers in the same way from unity (or Reason, as the Pythagoreans would say), "the source of all numbers":

1	1	1	1	1
1	(1 + 1)	(1 + 1 + 1)	(1 + 1 + 1 + 1)	(1 + 1 + 1 + 1 + 1)
1	2	3	4	5

Similarly we may build up the simple triangular numbers

1	2	3	4	5
1	(1 + 2)	(1 + 2 + 3)	(1 + 2 + 3 + 4)	(1 + 2 + 3 + 4 + 5)
1	3	6	10	15

The series for which we are looking is built up thus:

1	3	6	10	15
1	(1 + 3)	(1 + 3 + 6)	(1 + 3 + 6 + 10)	(1 + 3 + 6 + 10 + 15)
1	4	10	20	35

We shall call these the "second order triangular numbers" (^{2}T). As stated earlier, they represent solid figures, namely *tetrahedra* (pyramids with a three-sided base). The rule for forming them is seen when we write them like this:

1	2	3	4	5 . . .	(grandparent series)
1	4	10	20	35	
$\frac{3}{3}(1)$	$\frac{4}{3}(3)$	$\frac{5}{3}(6)$	$\frac{6}{3}(10)$	$\frac{7}{3}(15)$	

This gives us the simple rule:

$$^2T_n = \frac{(n+2)}{3} \cdot T_n = \frac{(n+2)\ (n+1).n}{3.2} \quad \text{(dot means multiply)}$$

Notice that the number n placed as an adjective in the bottom right-hand corner of T stands for the corresponding number in the *grandparent* series (1, 2, 3, 4 . . .)

Looking back at the series $^nC_3$, you will see that

$$^nC_3 = {}^2T_{n-2}$$

You get $^2T_{n-2}$ by putting $n - 2$ for n in the previous sentence, i.e.

$$^nC_3 = \frac{n(n-1)(n-2)}{3.2}$$

This means that if you are allowed to draw any three cards from a full pack, the number of possible ways is

$$\frac{52.51.50}{3.2} = 22{,}100$$

That is to say, the odds against picking the Ace of Spades, the Ace of Hearts, and the Ace of Diamonds together are 22,099 to 1.

You can go on making higher triangular numbers according to the same plan, as the following triangles show:

NATURAL NUMBERS

1 = 1
1 1 = 2
1 1 1 = 3
1 1 1 1 = 4
1 1 1 1 1 = 5
1 1 1 1 1 1 = 6
1 1 1 1 1 1 1 = 7

SIMPLE TRIANGULAR NUMBERS

1 = 1
1 2 = 3
1 2 3 = 6
1 2 3 4 = 10
1 2 3 4 5 = 15
1 2 3 4 5 6 = 21
1 2 3 4 5 6 7 = 28

SECOND ORDER TRIANGULAR NUMBERS

1 = 1
1 3 = 4
1 3 6 = 10
1 3 6 10 = 20
1 3 6 10 15 = 35
1 3 6 10 15 21 = 56
1 3 6 10 15 21 28 = 84

THIRD ORDER TRIANGULAR NUMBERS

1 = 1
1 4 = 5
1 4 10 = 15
1 4 10 20 = 35
1 4 10 20 35 = 70
1 4 10 20 35 56 = 126
1 4 10 20 35 56 84 = 210

FOURTH ORDER TRIANGULAR NUMBERS

1 = 1
1 5 = 6
1 5 15 = 21
1 5 15 35 = 56
1 5 15 35 70 = 126

FIFTH ORDER TRIANGULAR NUMBERS

1 = 1
1 6 = 7
1 6 21 = 28
1 6 21 56 = 84
1 6 21 56 126 = 210

From these triangles we can get the following rules:

$${}^nC_1 = n$$

$${}^nC_2 = \frac{n(n-1)}{2.1}$$

$${}^nC_3 = \frac{n(n-1)(n-2)}{3.2.1}$$

$${}^nC_4 = \frac{n(n-1)(n-2)(n-3)}{4.3.2.1}$$

$${}^nC_5 = \frac{n(n-1)(n-2)(n-3)(n-4)}{5.4.3.2.1}$$

We now meet another interesting series which plays an important part in statistics. This series was known to Euclid, who used it to arrive at some entirely useless conclusions about prime numbers. The series

1 2 6 24 120 720 5,040 . . .

is called the FACTORIAL series. It is born in this way:

Parent	1	2	3	4	5
	1	2.1	3.2.1	4.3.2.1	5.4.3.2.1
Offspring	1	2	6	24	120

Each term is formed by multiplying the corresponding number of the parent series by every number below it in the parent series. The nth term is often written $n!$ The exclamation mark is not an interjection. There are no interjections in mathematics. It is the verb which means, "Multiply the number by every whole number below it till you get to 1."

Factorial numbers represent another way of selection based on arrangement or order. The numbers of such selections are called simple permutations, written ${}^nP_n$, which means the number of arrangements of n things if all are taken. For instance, there are six permutations of all the letters ABC, namely, ABC, ACB, BAC, BCA, CAB, CBA. The rule for getting simple permutations is:

$${}^nP_n = n!$$

The rule is explained by the fact that, if there are, say, four different objects, any one of the four can be put first. This gives four different arrangements to begin with. When any one has been put first any of the remaining three can be put second. So each of the first four arrangements can be carried out in three ways, making in all 4×3 ways. When we have placed the first and second in any one of these 4×3 ways, we can fill the third from the two which are left in two ways. So each of these 4×3 arrangements of the first two places can be combined with either of two ways of selecting the third place, i.e. we have altogether $4 \times 3 \times 2$ ways of selecting the first three places. Each of these can only be combined with one way of filling the last place, since the other three objects have been used up in filling the previous ones, so

$${}^4P_4 = 4.3.2.1 \quad \text{or} \quad 4!$$

The following diagram may help you to construct others which illustrate the rule for numbers higher than 3.

	First Place	*Second Place*	*Third Place*
	a	*ab*	*abc*
		ac	*acb*
abc	*b*	*ba*	*bac*
		bc	*bca*
	c	*ca*	*cab*
		cb	*cba*
(Three ways)		(Two ways for each)	(One way for each)

All the different ways in which a complete pack of cards may be arranged are represented by 52!. This number is too big to put down here. It is 80 followed by sixty-six other figures. This is the number of miles which light travelling at 186,000 miles a second covers in about $13 \cdot 7 \times (1{,}000{,}000)^9$ years. If this tempts you to hope that you would ever commit to memory all the ways of arranging a pack of cards, you would be well advised to give up poker and take to biology. The number of nerve fibres in the human brain is only about three thousand million.

We call all the arrangements we can make by selecting all the numbers of a group *simple permutations*, and write the number for a group of n different things ${}^nP_n$, because we can combine both ways of selection by taking only a certain number r less than the whole set. Such permutations are written ${}^nP_r$. Thus ${}^4P_3$ means the possible number of different arrangements of four different things, when we can select any three of them at a time. To get the rule for finding these numbers, go back to the series for combinations. You will see that:

$$ {}^nC_5 = \frac{n(n-1)\,(n-2)\,(n-3)\,(n-4)}{5!} $$

This illustrates the more general rule

$$ {}^nC_r = \frac{n(n-1)\,(n-2)\,\ldots\,(n-r+1)}{r!} $$

If we are allowed to arrange each set of r different objects in every possible way, there will be $r!$ times as many arrangements as there are combinations, i.e.

$$ {}^nP_r = r! \times \frac{n(n-1)\,(n-2)\,\ldots\,(n-r+1)}{r!} $$

$$ = n(n-1)\,(n-2)\,\ldots\,(n-r+1) $$

As an illustration, if the key-word of a combination lock is RED, the number of possible ways in which the lock can be set is 26^3 or 17,576. If repetition of letters is not allowed, the number of ways is reduced to ${}^{26}P_3$, i.e. 26.25.24, or 15,600. But if you know the key-word is really a word, the number of possibilities is still further reduced; and you may save time by learning some elementary philology.

While making the acquaintance of these combination-lock numbers, notice that stating the odds against picking four aces from a pack is not the same thing as stating the odds against picking first the Ace of Spades, then the Ace of Diamonds, then the Ace of Hearts, and then the Ace of Clubs. For the first we need ${}^{52}C_4$, which is

$$\frac{52.51.50.49}{4.3.2.1} = 270{,}725$$

So the odds are 270,724 to 1 against. For the second we have a particular order of this combination, i.e. ${}^{52}P_4$, which is

$$52.51.50.49 = 6{,}497{,}400$$

So the odds are 6,497,399 to 1 against doing it.

Before leaving the magical stage in the evolution of the use of numbers there is another class of number triangles to which we may refer. These did not become important in mathematics till the time of Newton. It is quite probable that they were known to the Eastern peoples, who invented the number "0" about 100 B.C., at a much earlier date than that at which they became known in Europe. We have traced forwards the ancestry of certain series of numbers, starting with the succession of units or with the natural number series derived from it. All series which are built up in the same way as triangular series can be traced backwards to a triangle of which the apex is made of zeros. Such triangles are called vanishing triangles. Vanishing triangles of the simple triangular numbers may be represented thus:

0
0 0
0 0 0
1 1 1 1
2 3 4 5 6
1 3 6 10 15 21

or

0
1 1
2 3 4
1 3 6 10

Such triangles are formed by first putting down a certain number of terms of a series in succession on the base line. The line above is formed by *subtracting* terms next to one another. The next line is formed in a similar way from the one below it. This is continued till we get nothing but zeros. The reason why triangular series vanish is easy to see. The successive series of triangular numbers are based on adding adjoining terms of the parent series. They all have the same ancestry. Thus the parent series of the second order of triangular numbers is the series of simple triangular numbers of which the parent series is the natural number series. This can be looked on as the offspring of the succession of units. The difference between any pair of successive terms in a series of units is obviously zero. Here is a vanishing triangle of the second order of triangular numbers to illustrate the ancestry of such series more fully:

```
            0
         1     1
      3     4     5
   3     6    10    15
1     4    10    20    35
```

These triangular arrangements of numbers lead to a very simple trick which helps to find how some series are built up. We shall explain it more fully in a later chapter. The principle which underlies it is this. A large number of series, in fact all series which can be represented figuratively, can be looked upon as built up of the series of triangular numbers. Since we can always represent the ancestry of the latter by a vanishing triangle, we can form a vanishing triangle for any series of figurative numbers. You can try this for yourself with the series of figurate numbers like those given in Figs. 76 and 77. For instance the vanishing triangle of the series of squares of the natural numbers is:

```
         0
      2     2
   3     5     7
1     4     9    16
```

Here is a new series which betrays its ancestry very soon, though the numbers, as they stand, may not suggest anything to you:

```
1    2    3    4    5    6 . .
1    5   14   30   55   91 . . .
```

The vanishing triangle at once leads you to the series of squares of the natural numbers:

				0				
			2		2			
		5		7		9		
	4		9		16		25	
1		5		14		30		55

The nature of the series is:

$$1^2 \quad (1^2 + 2^2) \quad (1^2 + 2^2 + 3^2) \quad (1^2 + 2^2 + 3^2 + 4^2) \quad \text{etc.}$$

It is easy to see that the differences between successive terms of such a series is the series of squares, as the second line of the vanishing triangle tells you. The simple law which leads you from the vanishing triangle to the nature of a series will be explained when we have dealt with the discovery of the number "0." In referring to them here we have anticipated the solution of the next crisis in mathematics. They are included because their discovery arose naturally from the same social context as the figurative numbers of the Pythagorean cult. The representation of the pedigree of a series by a vanishing triangle was the culmination of experiments with numbers arising quite naturally from the ideology of a civilization still mainly made up of pastoral people living in patriarchal family-groups.

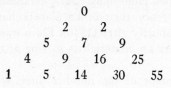

When we amuse ourselves at the expense of these early societies struggling to lisp the language of number in the childhood of civilization, it behoves us to ask whether we ourselves have completely grown out of magic. Caution is all the more pertinent when we recall the queer theosophical preoccupations of men like Pascal and Newton, who contributed so much to the sort of mathematics which is most useful in solving problems of measurement in the age of machinery. For European civilizations the numbers in which magical properties reside are more particularly seven and three. Theology bequeathed to us the seven golden candlesticks, the seven evil spirits cast out of Magdalen, the seven sorrows, the seven deadly sins, the seven (deadlier) virtues, and the sevenfold amen. The number seven has not been neglected by the unofficial theologians, more usually referred to as philosophers. In the year that Piazzi discovered Ceres seven planets were known: namely, Mercury, Venus, Earth, Mars, Jupiter, Saturn, Uranus. In the same year the Prussian philosopher Hegel wrote upbraiding scientists for the neglect of philosophy. He illustrated his disapproval by the amount of time astronomers wasted in looking for a new planet when philosophy clearly established the only possible number as seven. Since then other planets have been discovered. Neptune followed shortly after (1846), Pluto was discovered in 1930, because astronomers are materialists so long as they remain in their observatories.

The magical content of the number three, which has occupied a position of veneration in European culture, seems to be Semitic in origin. Probably the worship of triangular numbers, and the mystical attributes of the triangle itself in the Pythagorean culture, is traceable to the triangular symbol of the ancient Hittites, now the two triangles of Zionism. The phallic association of the threefold figure, as of the fleur-de-lys, and of the curious philological derivatives of the number itself, is widely accepted today. Besides the elementary triangles mentioned in the first chapter, Plato's *Timaeus* discloses the universal trinity of God, or the real world, our own or shadow world, and the *logos* or Word, which is God manifest in the world. The Stoics spoke of the *logos spermatikos* or seminal word, "the light that lighteth every man," the divine (pyramidal) fire. During the early years in which the scene of the Gospel narrative is set, Philo, the leader of the Alexandrian synagogue, imported Platonic doctrines into orthodox Judaism, identifying the Messiah with the *logos* of Plato. The mystery of the trinity was taking shape in Alexandria, the great factory of world religions, when Jewish national hopes were ready for the advent of the promised deliverer. Elaborate celestial arithmetic, which led to innumerable heresies and excommunications, and eventually to executions which possibly outnumbered the victims of the gladiatorial contests, was very largely the product of converts from Platonism and the later Pythagorean (or neo-Pythagorean) communities of the Roman world. When the Platonic logic of Aristotle came to occupy a place of honour beside the scriptural canon in Catholic theology, the doctors of the Sorbonne introduced the magical properties of three into psychology, beginning with the trinity of thought, will, and feeling, and subdividing each into threefold categories. This has not yet got out of contemporary textbooks of psychology.

The most bizarre excrescence of this cult came at a much later date. At the end of the eighteenth century deism had weakened public respect for the occult properties of three. It was high time for the unofficial theologians of philosophy to restore its magical pre-eminence.

The credit for this achievement must be awarded to Hegel. In Hegel's doctrine, as in the Pythagorean cult, Reason or unity was the source of all. So the secret of the universe lies in finding how the reason works. Hegel did not waste time, like astronomers, who make thousands of observations on stars, planets, and meteors, or like modern psychologists, who make thousands of observations on schoolchildren, lunatics, or the files of advertising firms. He found the truth in his own nature. According to Hegel this is how the reason works. Discourse is like the proceedings of an empanelled jury, fated to be locked up until they find a verdict in favour of the Absolute, unity, or the source of all. The weather is sultry. Tempers are jaded. Every statement which one juror makes is contradicted by somebody else. Eventually nothing is left but unity or the source of all. For philosophical purposes the apex of this vanishing triangle is spelt "the Absolute," for political use "the Prussian State" (now *der Führer*), in theology "God." Every argument which arises in the successive series leading to the Absolute consists of three parts. The first step, which Hegel never succeeded in taking, is a plain statement. Hegel calls it the thesis. The second step is usually translated in English as the "negation" or "contradiction." Unhappily, a defect of our own tongue makes it quite impossible to signify the rich content of the Hegelian equivalent with less circumlocution than the Shakespearian catalogue, which begins with the retort courteous and ends with the lie direct. Finally comes the negation of the negation. This combines the higher truth in both the preceding steps. The only single English word for it is "compromise." As is often the fate of compromise, it is only the beginning of a new argument.

Since the Absolute, alias the Deity, alias the orders of the leader, is also reason or unity, the source of all, history itself is nothing but a succession of triangular arguments. The hereditary properties of successive series explain what happens. So civilization naturally divides itself into the *Oriental* stage ("thesis"), the *Classical* ("antithesis"), leading up to the higher synthesis of the *Teutonic*, or, as we now say, Nordic, civilization. This last has all that is best and brightest in the other two. The cogency of the sequence has been amply confirmed by recent events, which have shown us how many virile characteristics of the earliest Oriental civilizations can be incorporated in the higher synthesis. Theologians and politicians who have reinforced their argumentative technique by a training in the intricate perversions of argument conducted on these lines are equal to most emergencies. The dialectic gathers into its own higher synthesis the principal advantage of every preceding variety of mysticism. Like the number magic of the Pythagoreans, it provides an excuse for shirking hard work instead of using the human reason to produce constructive results. Once you have convinced yourself that the universe is wound up by the Absolute, reason or unity, the source of all, you can enjoy the advantage of believing that your mistakes are inevitable, and that everything will turn out for the best in spite of all the ineptitudes avoided by painstaking study of the population of a particular planet.

Men of scientific training are not so easily attracted as theologians and politicians to number magic of this kind. They are prone to a more sophisticated form of the Pythagorean doctrine that looks for the secret of the universe in numbers. For instance, it is often said that mathematics is the grammar of science. This statement is profoundly misleading, the more so because the error is not expressed in a comparatively obvious form. To say that mathematics is the grammar of science implies that science is concerned with nothing more than enumeration and measurement. The plain fact is that the first task of science is to recognize what different sorts of things there are in the world. It is convenient to conceal this elementary and obvious truth for the simple reason that it helps people to forget that human nature, like external nature, can be studied scientifically. Until recently biology and psychology, the two younger sciences which have been exceedingly irreverent to traditional beliefs, have not used mathematics. They are only now reaching the stage of understanding what sorts of measurements are most useful to make, and calling in the services of the mathematician to help. If we go back far enough in history we find that primitive man probably devoted at least twenty thousand years to the task of recognizing the different sorts of stars in the heavens before it was possible to make measurements of their position and to express the times of their appearance with numbers. After the emergence of the first calendar-civilizations more than three thousand years passed before mathematical methods such as those which we shall now describe in the next chapter were introduced into the study of astronomy. Science has its firm foundation in the recognition of what the world is like. Nothing but confusion has resulted, and can result, when mathematics is used before we are quite clear about the sort of things with which we are dealing and what sort of measurements it is useful to make. Only then can we decide what sort of mathematics is a useful instrument for increasing knowledge. The immense success which has resulted from applying mathematics to the study of the world when some of its features have been clearly delineated by careful observation has fostered a blind reverence which is precipitating a real crisis in our own culture, especially in the field of psychology where the amount of arithmetic devoted to intelligence-testing is out of all proportion to its substantial basis of enduring fact. We have not fully replaced the sacramental by the instrumental attitude to the use of number.

EXERCISES ON CHAPTER 5

1. Given that

$$\sqrt{2} = 1\cdot4142$$
$$\sqrt{3} = 1\cdot7321$$
$$\sqrt{5} = 2\cdot2361$$

find correct to three places of decimals $\sqrt{27}$, $\sqrt{18}$, $\sqrt{12}$, $\sqrt{24}$, $\sqrt{10}$, and $\sqrt{30}$.

2. If the hypotenuse of a right-angled triangle is 1 unit of length, find the third side when the second side is $\frac{3}{4}$, $\frac{2}{3}$, and $\frac{4}{5}$ of the hypotenuse.

3. Make up any arithmetical series of five terms. Call the sum S. Write the series backwards underneath so that the last term comes under the first term, etc. Add the two together, thus getting 2S. Verify arithmetically that the sum of an arithmetical progression (A.P.) of n terms when the first term is f and the last term is l is $\frac{n}{2}(f + l)$.

4. Repeat this with another arithmetical series.

5. Write down the abstract number series f, $f + d$, $f + 2d$, etc. If there are n terms, express l in terms of f, n, and d. Express f in terms of n, l and d. Express the last term but two in terms of (a) n, f, and d, and (b) n, l, and d. In this way build up the general rule without using proper numbers.

6. Find the fifth term, the tenth term, and the sum of ten terms in the following arithmetical progressions. First apply the formulae you

have found, then check your results by writing out the first ten terms and adding them up.

1	3	5 . . .		-6	-2	$+2$ . . .	
1	4	7 . . .		a	$+0$	$-a$	$-2a$ . . .
5	10	15 . . .		3	$+\frac{4}{3}$	$-\frac{1}{3}$ . . .	
$\frac{1}{2}$	1	$1\frac{1}{2}$ . . .					

7. Find the *n*th term and the sum of *n* terms in the foregoing arithmetical progressions. Find the first term and the differences between two successive terms in the A.P. in which the sixth term is 13 and the twelfth term is 25.

8. Find the sum of the first *n* natural numbers (1, 2, 3, . . .).

9. Find four numbers between 6 and 15 such that together with 6 and 15 they form six terms of an A.P.

10. Find three terms between 1 and 3, which together with 1 and 3 form five terms of an A.P.

11. Show how to insert *n* numbers between *f* and *l* so that together they form an A.P. of $n + 2$ terms, with first term *f* and last term *l*.

This is sometimes called inserting *n* arithmetic means between *f* and *l*. It is rather a stupid name, but it is a useful thing to know. It enables you, for instance, to find a given number of points at equal distances apart on a straight line.

12. Build up the formula for the sum of a geometrical series of *n* terms, *f* being the first term, *fr* the second term, fr^2 the third term, and so on.

Show that it is $\dfrac{f(r^n - 1)}{r - 1}$.

13. Find the fifth term and the sum of five terms in the following geometrical series:

1, 2, 4, . . .
$0 \cdot 9, 0 \cdot 81, 0 \cdot 729, \ldots$
$\frac{3}{4}, \frac{3}{8}, \frac{3}{16}, \ldots$
$x^5, a.x^4, a^2x^3, \ldots$
$1, 3, 3^2, \ldots$

Check your results arithmetically.

14. Find the nth term and the sum of n terms in the foregoing geometrical series.

15. Insert two numbers between 5 and 625 so that the four terms form a geometrical progression. This is sometimes called inserting two geometric means between 5 and 625.

16. Insert three geometric means between $\frac{1}{3}$ and $\frac{16}{243}$.

17. Find the formula for inserting n geometric means between two numbers of which the first is f and the second is l.

18. Make up a geometrical series in which the first term is f and r (of the formula in example 12) is a fraction less than 1. Write out ten terms of the series. What would you expect the last term to be if you went on for ever?

19. Remembering that if you can make a quantity as small as you like you can ignore it compared with quantities which have a definite value, see whether you can show, by examining the formula in example 12, that the sum of a diminishing geometrical series which goes on for ever (first term a, common ration r) cannot be larger than $\frac{a}{1-r}$.

20. You can write any recurring decimal in the following way:

$$0{\cdot}666\ldots = 0{\cdot}6 + 0{\cdot}06 + 0{\cdot}006\ldots$$

Use the result of the last example to express the following recurring decimals as proper fractions:

$$0{\cdot}\dot{6}$$
$$0{\cdot}252525\ldots$$
$$0{\cdot}791791791791\ldots$$

21. The expression $\frac{a}{1-r}$ is called the sum to infinity of the diminishing series $a, ar, ar^2, \ldots$ because if we go on adding terms we get nearer and nearer to a total of $\frac{a}{1-r}$, but cannot get beyond it.

Find the sum to infinity of the following geometrical series:

$$1 + \tfrac{1}{2} + \tfrac{1}{4}\ldots$$
$$1 + \tfrac{2}{10} + \tfrac{4}{100} + \tfrac{8}{1000}\ldots$$

22. Find the nth term

(*a*) in the series of hexagonal numbers, shown in Fig. 77 and the alternative hexagonals 1, 6, 15, 28, 45, etc.
(*b*) in the series of stellate numbers. (Fig. 77)

Check your formula by drawing figures of the third and fifth numbers.

23. Find by experiment (diagram) and formula how many different arrangements there are of the four aces in a pack of cards, the four aces and four kings, all three kinds of picture cards, all cards lower than 6 (excluding aces).

24. Using a diagram to check the formula, find how many different sets, irrespective of order (i.e. combinations of cards), can be obtained by taking three cards, any one of which may be either a king or a queen, from a full pack, or four cards, any one of which may be a king, queen, or jack, or five cards, any one of which may be a king, queen, jack, or ace.

25. How many different peals can be rung with six bells, all different, using all the bells?

26. How many different scores can be obtained from (*a*) three, (*b*) five tosses of a die?

27. A committee consists of chairman, secretary, treasurer, and four ordinary members. In how many different ways can they sit at a straight table on the platform behind the speaker if (*a*) no places are reserved, (*b*) the middle seat is reserved for the chairman, (*c*) the secretary and the treasurer must sit on either side of the chairman, who is occupying the middle seat, and (*d*) the secretary sits on the right and the treasurer on the left of the chairman occupying the middle seat.

28. A bag contains six coloured balls (all different). How many different pairs of two colours can be drawn from it if (*a*) each pair is replaced, and if (*b*) each pair is left out, when withdrawn?

THINGS TO MEMORIZE

1. In an arithmetical series in which the first term is f and the last term is l, the sum to n terms is $\frac{n}{2}(f + l)$, or if f is the first term and

d is the difference between each two successive terms, the sum to n terms is

$$\frac{n}{2}\left\{2f + (n-1)d\right\}$$

2. In a geometric series in which the first term is a and the common ratio is r, the sum to n terms is

$$\frac{a(r^n - 1)}{r - 1}$$

If r is a positive fraction less than unity, the sum to infinity of a geometric series is

$$\frac{a}{1 - r}$$

3. The number of combinations of n things taken r at a time is

$$\frac{n(n-1)(n-2)\ldots(n-r+1)}{r!} \text{ or } \frac{n!}{r!\,(n-r)!}$$

4. The number of permutations of n things taken r at a time is

$$\frac{n!}{(n-r)!}$$

* Footnote (see p. 215).

The series $1 + \frac{1}{2} + \frac{1}{3} + \frac{1}{4} + \ldots$

This series never chokes off, because, however far we have gone, we can always add an extra batch of terms with sum more than $\frac{1}{2}$.

Suppose we have added n terms. Take the next n terms

$$\frac{1}{n+1} + \frac{1}{n+2} + \ldots + \frac{1}{2n}$$

for the next batch. The smallest is $\frac{1}{2n}$, so the sum of the terms in the batch is more than $n \times \frac{1}{2n} = \frac{1}{2}$.

We can keep on doing this for ever, so our series has a sum bigger than

$$\tfrac{1}{2} + \tfrac{1}{2} + \tfrac{1}{2} + \ldots \text{ for ever;}$$

that is, it never chokes off.

If a series does choke off, you will find that however many terms you take in a new batch, the sums of successive batches will grow smaller and smaller—though perhaps not regularly—until they get too small to matter.

CHAPTER VI

The Size of the World

OR

WHAT WE CAN DO WITH TRIGONOMETRY

In 332 B.C. Egypt surrendered to Alexander the Great. To celebrate the conqueror a city was founded where the sacred river discharges into the Mediterranean. A mixed population made up of drafts of Egyptians, Greeks, and Jews was settled in it. Alexandria drew into itself all the learning of the ancient world, the arts of medicine, dyeing, machinery, and navigation. Alexander died in 323 B.C. Egypt then became an independent state under the Alexandrian general Ptolemy. The Ptolemaic dynasty lasted till Egypt fell to the Roman armies. Ptolemy himself celebrated his rise to power by founding the first organized centre of essentially secular learning—museum, library, and university—in the history of mankind. The three hundred years which intervened before the advent of Caesar's armies led to the burning of the first library of Alexandria saw perhaps the most astonishing efflorescence of intellectual adventure in the history of mankind. The only parallel to it is the four hundred years which elapsed between the simultaneous publication of the *De Revolutionibus* of Copernicus and the *De Fabrica Humani Corporis* of Vesalius in 1543 and the burning of the Reichstag in 1933. Under Roman rule Alexandria retained its position as the intellectual centre of the civilized world, as it likewise remained the great centre of the handicrafts and an important port of Mediterranean trade. A second library was set up. A second brief spell of activity in mathematics and medicine supervened in the second and third centuries A.D. before Christianity became the imperial religion. When the monks of St. Cyril destroyed the schools of pagan science, the second library was rifled of its useful contents and packed with superstitious rubbish long before it was destroyed by Moslem conquerors in the sixth century. During its successive stages Alexandrian science was a culture distinct from that of either Greece or Rome. It was pre-eminently cosmopolitan. It drew its personnel from men of widely different national and racial origins.

The burning of the first library of Alexandria was an unmixed calamity. The collapse of the second phase in the Alexandrian culture need not be regarded in the same light. It had reached the limits of further development within the framework of its social equipment. Further advance was conditional upon a new synthesis, of which the Moslem eruption proved to be the necessary instrument. Arab culture brought together two streams of human achievement, a new number language from the East and the classical mathematics of the West. The first phase in the Alexandrian contribution is signalized by the invention of trigonometry. It gave back number and measurement to geometry. The second stage was a natural corollary of the first. Men were using numbers on the grand scale. Beside the new measurements of the heavens, the marches of Alexander and the miraculous sum of three hundred talents which he expended on the tomb of Hephaestion had become trivial quantities. A new arithmetic was indispensable. When the curtain falls on the last stage of Alexandrian culture, mathematics is occupied with the problem of calculation, groping for new methods, but still shackled with an antiquated script which barred the path to real progress.

The key to both developments is the fact that mathematics was once again in lively contact with the world's work. Two names which are prominently associated with the beginnings of the university of Alexandria are Aristarchus of Samos (310–250 B.C.) and Archimedes of Syracuse (287–212 B.C.). Aristarchus made the first estimate of the relative distances of the moon and the sun from the earth. Archimedes, who first showed how we can calculate π as accurately as we need to, was especially concerned with mechanics. Among other important contributions which he made we remember more particularly his principle of the lever and of floating bodies. In demonstrating the ratio of the weight and the distance from the fulcrum, Archimedes was not merely indulging Platonic aspirations to spiritual perfection and intellectual refinement. He used his knowledge to design catapults which were used against—and by—the Roman armies. He applied his knowledge of the density ratio to measure the purity of precious metals. The measurement of π went hand in hand with the introduction of machinery based on the use of the wheel. Archimedes helped the launching of a ship by suggesting the use of cogs. He invented for irrigation a pump which depends on the rotation of a screw. Very few of us realize the high level of mechanical arts in the Alexandrian world. About 100 B.C. Hero of Alexandria composed a book in which he described the principles of about a hundred mechanical appliances, which included a cyclometer, a theodolite, a double forcing pump, and the first model steam-engine. The social culture of the time was using science. The intellectual worker was not

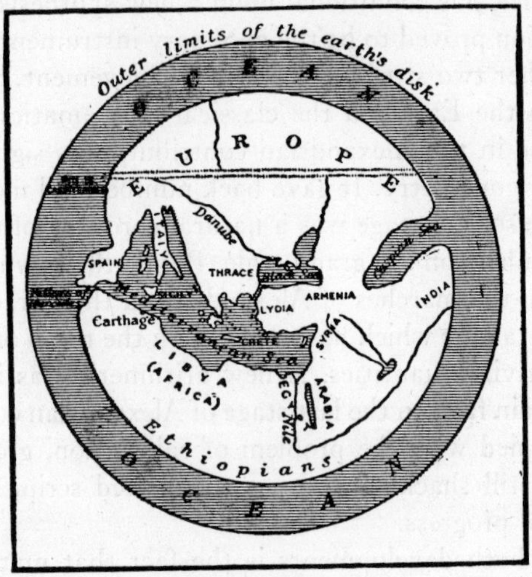

MAP OF THE WORLD BY HECATAEUS, 517 B.C.
Showing the primitive ideas held at the time of Pythagoras. From Breasted's *Ancient Times*

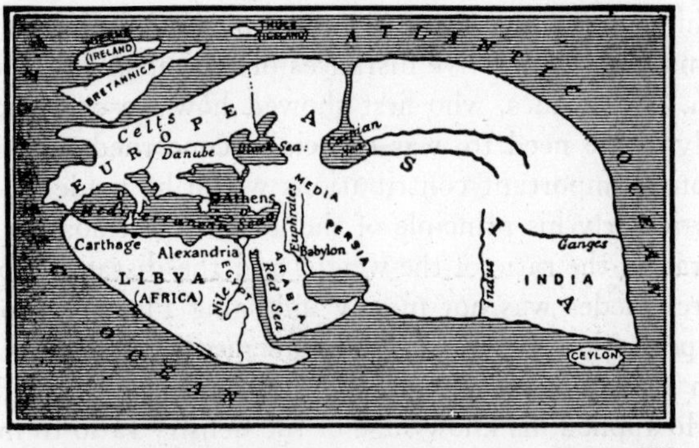

MAP OF THE WORLD ACCORDING TO ERATOSTHENES, ABOUT 250 B.C.

FIG. 81.—BEGINNINGS OF THE SCIENCE OF MAPS

hampered by the machine-wrecking ideology which is now eclipsing the culture of Western Europe. Inventions were welcome.

The substantial link which connected Alexandrian mathematics with the real world is illustrated by the fact that Hipparchus compiled a list of 1,080 fixed stars. Archimedes himself made the first known model in which the rotation of the celestial sphere and the changing positions of the stars were represented by the motion of a wheel. It is probable that he first used tables of angles like the one given on p. 160 in Chapter 4. Hipparchus, the Alexandrian astronomer, who lived about a hundred years later (*c.* 150 B.C.), made a table of sines, and used it to find the distance of the moon from the earth. By the time when Alexandria became a part of the Roman Empire the distances of the sun and the moon from the earth, as also the radius and the circumference of the earth, moon, and sun, had been determined. The circumference of the earth as determined by

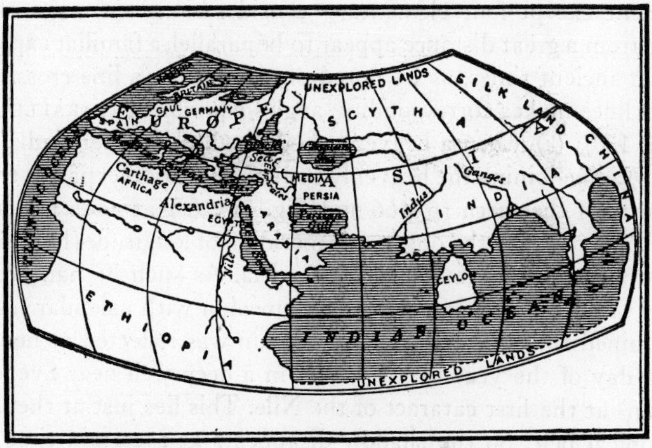

PTOLEMY'S MAP OF THE WORLD, ABOUT 200 A.D.

FIG. 81A.—BEGINNINGS OF THE SCIENCE OF MAPS

Eratosthenes (275–194 B.C.) and Poseidonius (*c.* 100 B.C.) was only about fifty miles out. Hipparchus (see Chapter 8) made star maps in latitude and longitude. Marinus of Tyre (*c.* A.D. 150) began the construction of maps in which lines of terrestrial longitude and latitude are laid down. You can get a very vivid picture of the close connexion between the rapid development of astronomy and the practical achievements of navigation and land-surveying during this period by comparing three world-pictures in Figs. 81–81A. The first is the world as the Greeks knew it. The second is as it was known at the time (*c.* 200 B.C.) when Eratosthenes measured the circumference of the earth. The third is that of Ptolemy (*c.* A.D.150), who lived in the second phase of the Alexandrian culture. The work of Ptolemy (not the general, of course) is mainly a compilation based on that of Hipparchus and his contemporaries.

If you go back to Fig. 53 and recall how we can measure the height of a cliff when trespassers near the base are prosecuted, you will see at once that measurement of the distances of heavenly bodies is possible if we can measure two angles with an astrolabe and the distance between the places where the angles are measured. As a matter of fact it is not even necessary to measure the last if we know the radius and circumference of the earth and the latitudes and longitudes of the two places. The earth measurement of Eratosthenes links up the rules of geometry with geography and astronomy. The extraordinary thing about this achievement is its simplicity. It requires no mathematical equipment except four elementary considerations: (*a*) rays of light coming from a great distance appear to be parallel, a familiar experience of life in ancient times, as we noted on p. 144; (*b*) a line crossing two parallel lines makes corresponding angles equivalent (PARALLEL RULE ONE, p. 130); (*c*) when a heavenly body is directly overhead ("at its zenith") a line joining the heavenly body to the observer passes through the centre of the earth (p. 166 and Fig. 58); (*d*) at noon the sun lies above some point on the observer's meridian of longitude (Figs. 62–63). Eratosthenes was librarian of Alexandria. As such he had access to records of events of importance in connexion with calendar festivals. He obtained the information that the sun was reflected at noon on a certain day of the year by the water in a deep well near Syene (now Assouan) at the first cataract of the Nile. This lies just at the limit of the tropical belt. So the shadow disappears at a certain time of the year, when the sun is at its zenith at noon. The reflection in the well records when the sun is directly overhead, i.e. vertical to the horizon. On the same day at Alexandria, five hundred miles due north of Syene, the shadow of a pillar at noon showed the sun $7\frac{1}{2}°$ south from the vertical. If sunbeams are parallel (Figs. 82 and 107), this means that the radii connecting the ends (Alexandria and Syene) of an arc 500 miles long with the centre of the earth make an angle of $7\frac{1}{2}°$. Now $7\frac{1}{2}°$ goes into the 360° of the entire circle approximately fifty times. So the entire circumference of the earth is fifty times 500 miles, i.e. 25,000 miles. The radius of the earth may be obtained by using the value of π given as a first approximation by Archimedes. On p. 181 we saw that the circumference of any circle is π times the diameter. In other words, the radius (r) can be got by dividing the circumference by 2π. If $\pi = 3\frac{1}{7}$ and the circumference (c) is 25,000:

$$25{,}000 = 2 \times 3\tfrac{1}{7} \times r$$

$$\text{i.e. } r = \frac{7 \times 25{,}000}{22 \times 2} = \frac{175{,}000}{44}$$

This is approximately 4,000 miles.

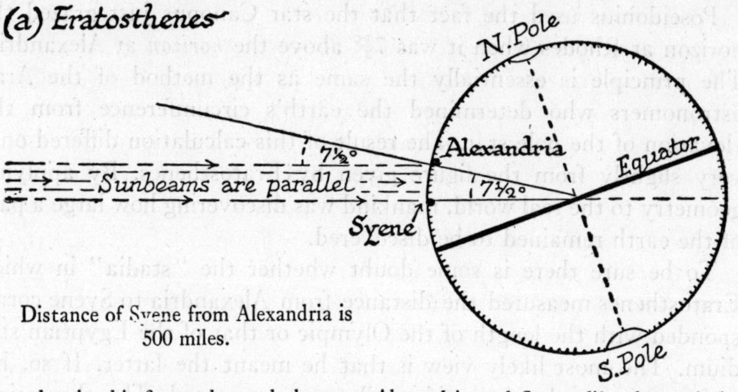

Distance of Syene from Alexandria is 500 miles.

Note that in this figure the angle between Alexandria and Syene, like the angle between Alexandria and Rhodes in the one below, is exaggerated for the sake of clarity.

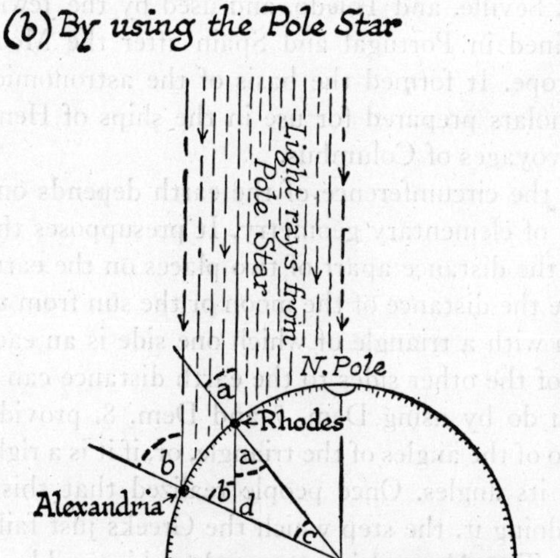

$a + d + c = 180°$ (Dem. 5)

$a + c = 180° - d = b$

$\therefore$

$a + c = b$ or $c = b - a$

Hence the angle at the earth's centre made by the arc with its ends at Rhodes and Alexandria (or any two other places, one so many miles due north of the other) is the difference between the zenith distances of the pole star at the two places. If D is the distance due north, the circumference of the earth is:

$$\frac{D \times 360}{c}$$

FIG. 82.—THE MEASUREMENT OF THE EARTH
(Refer also to Fig. 107)

Poseidonius used the fact that the star Canopus just grazed the horizon at Rhodes when it was $7\frac{1}{2}°$ above the *horizon* at Alexandria. The principle is essentially the same as the method of the Arab astronomers who determined the earth's circumference from the elevation of the pole star. The result of this calculation differed only very slightly from the figure given by Eratosthenes. By applying geometry to the real world, mankind was discovering how large a part of the earth remained to be discovered.

To be sure there is some doubt whether the "stadia" in which Eratosthenes measured the distance from Alexandria to Syene corresponded with the length of the Olympic or that of the Egyptian stadium. The most likely view is that he meant the latter. If so, his estimate was only about fifty miles out, as stated. The theoretical interest of the return to the doctrine of Aristarchus, and indeed to that of Pythagoras, when Copernicus and Kepler made new discoveries about planetary motion, has somewhat eclipsed the very great practical value of the Ptolemaic astronomy which was taught in the Moorish universities of Cordova, Seville, and Toledo, and used by the Jewish astronomers who remained in Portugal and Spain after the Moors were driven out of Europe. It formed the basis of the astronomical tables which Jewish scholars prepared for use in the ships of Henry the Navigator and the voyages of Columbus.

The measurement of the circumference of the earth depends on a very simple application of elementary geometry. It presupposes that we are able to measure the distance apart of two places on the earth. When we try to measure the distance of the moon or the sun from the earth, we have to begin with a triangle of which one side is an earth distance, and the ratio of the other sides to the earth distance can be calculated. This we can do by using Dem. 7 and Dem. 8, provided that we can measure two of the angles of the triangle, or, if it is a right-angled triangle, one of its angles. Once people realized that this is possible and set about doing it, the step which the Greeks just failed to take was inevitable. The Alexandrians started making tables of ratios of the sides of a right-angled triangle. They socialized the achievements of Greek geometry in the new size language of trigonometry. We shall leave the discussion of how to measure heavenly distances until we have explained how the first trigonometrical dictionaries, the tables of sines, etc., were compiled.

HOW THE FIRST TABLE OF SINES WAS MADE.—There are two trains which we might have added to our railway time-table on p. 160

without recourse to any additional information. We shall add them now. First refer to Figs. 42 and 50 to recall that

$$\sin A = \cos (90° - A)$$
$$\cos A = \sin (90° - A)$$

The ratios of angles which are very near to 0° and to 90° are obtainable without any difficulty from these rules. In Fig. 83 a right-angled

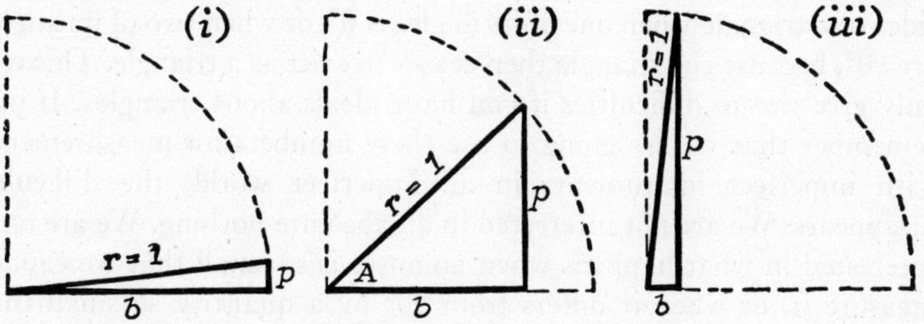

FIG. 83.—RATIOS OF SMALL ANGLES, ETC.

The circle is drawn with radius 1 unit long. The hypotenuse (r) is in each case 1 unit ($r = 1$).

$$\sin A = \frac{p}{r} = p, \text{ and } \cos A = \frac{b}{r} = b$$

triangle is drawn with the angle A at the centre of a quarter-circle the radius of which is the hypotenuse of the triangle and is of unit length. So

$$\sin A = p$$
$$\cos A = b$$

If we make the angle smaller and smaller till it is practically 0°, as in Fig. 83 (i), b approaches nearer and nearer to r. So when $A = 0$, $b = 1$. Hence

$$\cos 0° = 1$$

At the same time p vanishes, so that

$$\sin 0° = 0$$

If we make the angle larger and larger, as in Fig. 83 (iii), till it is practically 90°, p approaches nearer and nearer to r, and when A = 90°, p = 1. Hence

$$\sin 90° = 1$$

Meanwhile b is getting smaller and smaller, and vanishes when A = 90°. So that

$$\cos 90° = 0$$

It may strike you as somewhat queer to talk about the ratio of the sides of a triangle when one of its angles is 0°, or when two of its angles are 90°, because the triangle then ceases to exist as a triangle. This will only give rise to difficulties if you have ideals about triangles. If you remember that we are going to use these numbers for measurements with imperfect instruments in an imperfect world, the difficulty disappears. We are not interested in an absolute nothing. We are only interested in what happens when an angle is so small that we cannot measure it, or when it differs from 90° by a quantity so small that we cannot measure it. To assure yourself that the result does not make nonsense, you need only take the fact that cos A is very near to 1, when A is very small. Since sin (90° – A) = cos A, sin (90° – A) must be very near to 1 when 90° – A is very nearly a right angle, i.e. when A is very small. Conversely, if sin A is very near to 1 when A is very near to 90°, cos A must be very near to 1 when A is very small, because cos A = sin (90° – A). The tangent of the angle A is $\frac{p}{b}$. Since p becomes smaller and smaller when A is approaching 0°,

$$\tan 0° = 0$$

As A approaches 90°, p becomes larger while b becomes smaller. That is to say, the ratio $\frac{p}{b}$ grows beyond all bounds. The sign used to indicate that a quantity is getting too large to measure is ∞, i.e.

$$\tan 90° = \infty$$

This again is consistent with what we know already. We have seen (p. 157) that

$$\tan A = \frac{\sin A}{\cos A}$$

So when A = 0, tan A is 0 divided by 1, which is 0. When A is 90°, tan A is 1 divided by 0, i.e. 1 divided by a quantity so small that we cannot measure it. Such a quantity could only be made up to 1 by multiplying it by something too big to measure. We may thus extend our table on p. 160 by inserting the new items:

Angle (A°)	sin A	cos A	tan A
90	1	0	∞
60	$\frac{\sqrt{3}}{2}$	$\frac{1}{2}$	$\sqrt{3}$
45	$\frac{1}{\sqrt{2}}$	$\frac{1}{\sqrt{2}}$	1
30	$\frac{1}{2}$	$\frac{\sqrt{3}}{2}$	$\frac{1}{\sqrt{3}}$
0	0	1	0

It is more satisfactory to put down the numbers in the form in which we shall use them. If you look up the table of square roots you will find that $\sqrt{2} = 1{\cdot}414$ correct to three places, i.e. for use with instruments which yield consistent results up to but not beyond the one-in-a-thousand level. For the same purpose $\sqrt{3}$ is $1{\cdot}732$. So the table may be rewritten in the more convenient form:

Angle (A°)	sin A	cos A	tan A
90	1·000	0·000	∞
60	0·866	0·500	1·732
45	0·707	0·707	1·000
30	0·500	0·866	0·577
0	0·000	1·000	0·000

To fill up this table with other items, the practical method would be to make very large-scale diagrams such as the one which we used to calibrate the shadow pole (Fig. 66). This was based on Dem. 11. In Fig. 84

$$\sin 30° = \frac{AB}{AC} \text{ and } \sin 15° = \frac{AB}{AD}$$

$$\frac{\sin 15°}{\sin 30°} = \frac{AC}{AD}$$

Since $\sin 30° = \frac{1}{2}$

$$\sin 15° = \frac{\frac{1}{2}AC}{AD}$$

In the original drawing of Fig. 84, which was made sitting up in bed, so that no great effort to attain accuracy was attempted, AC was $6 \cdot 3$ centimetres and AD was $12 \cdot 2$ centimetres, which makes $\sin 15° = 0 \cdot 258$. Similarly

$$\sin 7\tfrac{1}{2}° = \frac{0 \cdot 258 \cdot ED}{EF}$$

The measurements in the original figure were $EF = 12 \cdot 4$ centimetres, $ED = 6 \cdot 3$ centimetres. This makes $\sin 7\tfrac{1}{2}° = 0 \cdot 131$.

There is no better way of getting used to sines, cosines, and tangents

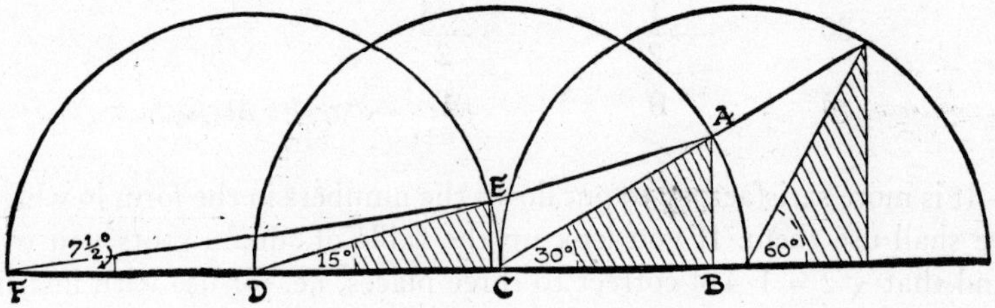

FIG. 84.—METHOD FOR MAKING TABLE OF SINES BY SCALE DIAGRAM

than to make a table for yourself of all the angles indicated in Figs. 65 and 66 in Chapter 4. When you have done so, you will be more ready to appreciate the next step, *which saves us the trouble of doing so.* Closer study of the same figure leads to a demonstration which allows us to calculate sines, etc., without making a scale diagram, so long as we have a few angles to take as a basis. These we have already included in the last table. The demonstration which follows is essentially the one used by Hipparchus to construct the first trigonometrical table.

The demonstration represented in Fig. 85 shows us how to find the sine or the cosine of half an angle if we know the sine or cosine of the angle itself. It is based on Dem. 11. The only additional dissection is that the triangle POQ is cut up into two right-angled triangles by OS at right angles to PQ. The two right-angled triangles are equivalent by TRIANGLE RULE TWO because

$$SO = SO$$

The enclosed $\angle SOP = 90° - \tfrac{1}{2}A = \angle SOQ$

$$OP = 1 = OQ$$

So if PS is y units long, PS = $\frac{1}{2}$PQ and PQ = $2y$. Since the radius of the circle is 1 unit long, OQ = OP = 1. The figure shows

$$\cos A = \frac{x}{OQ} = x \quad . \; . \; . \; . \; . \; . \; . \qquad \text{(i)}$$

$$\cos \tfrac{1}{2}A = \frac{PR}{PQ} = \frac{1+x}{2y} \quad . \; . \; . \; . \qquad \text{(ii)}$$

Also from the triangle POS

$$\cos \tfrac{1}{2}A = \frac{y}{PO} = y \quad . \; . \; . \; . \; . \; . \; . \qquad \text{(iii)}$$

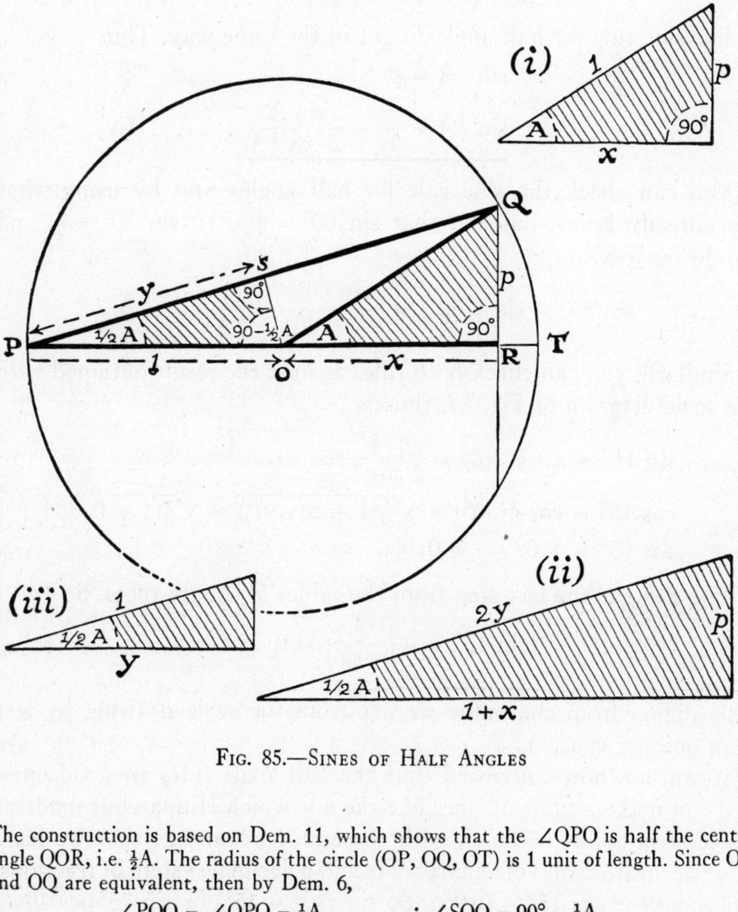

FIG. 85.—SINES OF HALF ANGLES

The construction is based on Dem. 11, which shows that the ∠QPO is half the centre angle QOR, i.e. $\frac{1}{2}$A. The radius of the circle (OP, OQ, OT) is 1 unit of length. Since OP and OQ are equivalent, then by Dem. 6,

∠PQO = ∠QPO = $\frac{1}{2}$A $\qquad$ ∴ ∠SOQ = 90° − $\frac{1}{2}$A.

Combining (i), (ii), and (iii), we have

$$\cos \tfrac{1}{2}A = \frac{1 + \cos A}{2 \cos \tfrac{1}{2}A}$$

$$2(\cos \tfrac{1}{2}A)^2 = 1 + \cos A$$

$$(\cos \tfrac{1}{2}A)^2 = \tfrac{1}{2}(1 + \cos A)$$

$$\cos \tfrac{1}{2}A = \sqrt{\tfrac{1}{2}(1 + \cos A)} \quad . \ . \ . \ . \quad (a)$$

Before going further, test this. You already know that $\cos 60° = 0{\cdot}5$ and $\cos 30° = \frac{1}{2}(\sqrt{3})$. From the new rule

$$\cos 30° = \cos \tfrac{1}{2}(60°) = \sqrt{\tfrac{1}{2}(1 + \cos 60°)} = \sqrt{\tfrac{1}{2}(1{\cdot}5)} = \sqrt{\tfrac{3}{4}}$$

$$\text{i.e.} \qquad \cos 30° = \tfrac{1}{2}(\sqrt{3})$$

The sine rule for half angles is got in the same way. Thus

$$\sin A = p$$

$$\sin \tfrac{1}{2}A = \frac{p}{2y} = \frac{\sin A}{2 \cos \tfrac{1}{2}A} \quad . \ . \ . \ . \quad (iv)$$

You can check the sine rule for half angles first by using what you already know, namely, that $\sin 60° = \frac{1}{2}(\sqrt{3})$, $\sin 30° = \frac{1}{2}$, and $\cos 30° = \frac{1}{2}(\sqrt{3})$:

$$\sin 30° = \sin \tfrac{1}{2}(60°) = \frac{\sin 60°}{2 \cos 30°} = \frac{(\tfrac{1}{2}\sqrt{3})}{2(\tfrac{1}{2}\sqrt{3})} = \tfrac{1}{2}$$

Similarly you can check both rules against the result obtained with the scale diagram of Fig. 84, thus:

$$\sin 15° = \sin \tfrac{1}{2}(30°) = \frac{\tfrac{1}{2}}{2 \cos 15°}$$

$$\cos 15° = \cos \tfrac{1}{2}(30°) = \sqrt{\tfrac{1}{2}(1 + \cos 30°)} = \sqrt{\tfrac{1}{2}(1 + 0{\cdot}866)}$$

$$\text{i.e.} \qquad \cos 15° = \sqrt{0{\cdot}933} = 0{\cdot}966$$

You can get the last step from the tables of square roots. So

$$\sin 15° = \frac{0{\cdot}5}{2(0{\cdot}966)} = 0{\cdot}259$$

This differs from the value we got from the scale drawing by less than one per cent.

If you are now convinced that the half-angle rules are good ones, you can make a table of sines like the one which Hipparchus made at Alexandria about 150 B.C., with the added advantage that we have more accurate tables of square roots and a decimal system of fractions. We have got $\cos 15° = 0{\cdot}966$. So $\sin (90° - 15°)$ or $\sin 75° = 0{\cdot}966$.

We have also got sin 15° = 0·259. So cos (90° – 15°) or cos 75° = 0·259. We next get cos $7\frac{1}{2}$°, using tables of square roots as before:

$$\cos 7\tfrac{1}{2}^\circ = \cos \tfrac{1}{2}(15^\circ) = \sqrt{\tfrac{1}{2}(1\cdot966)} = \sqrt{0\cdot983} = 0\cdot991$$

$$\sin 7\tfrac{1}{2}^\circ = \frac{\sin 15^\circ}{2 \cos 7\frac{1}{2}^\circ} = \frac{0\cdot259}{2(0\cdot991)} = 0\cdot131$$

This gives us

$$\cos 7\tfrac{1}{2}^\circ = 0\cdot991 = \sin 82\tfrac{1}{2}^\circ$$
$$\sin 7\tfrac{1}{2}^\circ = 0\cdot131 = \cos 82\tfrac{1}{2}^\circ$$

From cos 75° = 0·259 and sin 75° = 0·966:

$$\cos 37\tfrac{1}{2}^\circ = \cos \tfrac{1}{2}(75)^\circ = \sqrt{\tfrac{1}{2}(1\cdot259)} = \sqrt{0\cdot629} = 0\cdot793$$

$$\sin 37\tfrac{1}{2}^\circ = \sin \tfrac{1}{2}(75)^\circ = \frac{0\cdot966}{2(0\cdot793)} = 0\cdot609$$

This gives us

$$\cos 37\tfrac{1}{2}^\circ = 0\cdot793 = \sin 52\tfrac{1}{2}^\circ$$
$$\sin 37\tfrac{1}{2}^\circ = 0\cdot609 = \cos 52\tfrac{1}{2}^\circ$$

From cos 45° = 0·707 = sin 45°:

$$\cos 22\tfrac{1}{2}^\circ = \cos \tfrac{1}{2}(45)^\circ = \sqrt{\tfrac{1}{2}(1\cdot707)} = \sqrt{0\cdot853} = 0\cdot924$$

$$\sin 22\tfrac{1}{2}^\circ = \frac{0\cdot707}{2(0\cdot924)} = 0\cdot383$$

This gives us:

$$\cos 22\tfrac{1}{2}^\circ = 0\cdot924 = \sin 67\tfrac{1}{2}^\circ$$
$$\sin 22\tfrac{1}{2}^\circ = 0\cdot383 = \cos 67\tfrac{1}{2}^\circ$$

We can now tabulate all our results, calculating the fourth column in the following table from $\tan A = \dfrac{\sin A}{\cos A}$:

TABLE OF TRIGONOMETRICAL RATIOS IN INTERVALS OF $7\frac{1}{2}$°

Angle (A°)	sin A	cos A	tan A
90	1·000	0·000	∞
$82\frac{1}{2}$	0·991	0·131	7·56
75	0·966	0·259	3·73
$67\frac{1}{2}$	0·924	0·383	2·41
60	0·866	0·500	1·73
$52\frac{1}{2}$	0·793	0·609	1·30
45	0·707	0·707	1·00
$37\frac{1}{2}$	0·609	0·793	0·77
30	0·500	0·866	0·58
$22\frac{1}{2}$	0·383	0·924	0·41
15	0·259	0·966	0·27
$7\frac{1}{2}$	0·131	0·991	0·13
0	0·000	1·000	0·00

Of course if you like you can go on making the interval smaller: $\frac{1}{2}(7\frac{1}{2}) = 3\frac{3}{4}$; $\frac{1}{2}(3\frac{3}{4}) = 1\frac{7}{8}$; $\frac{1}{2}(1\frac{7}{8}) = \frac{15}{16}$, etc. Hipparchus, who published, as far as we know, the first table of sines, did not go further than we have gone. If you have actually checked all the arithmetic so far, you will have grasped how a table of sines, etc., can be built up, and you will not be likely to forget it quickly.

Let us now stop to ask what advantage we have gained. To begin with, we have made scientific map-making and surveying on a scale adequate for long-range geographical work possible. The method used for the cliff illustrated in Fig. 53 presupposes, first, that you can

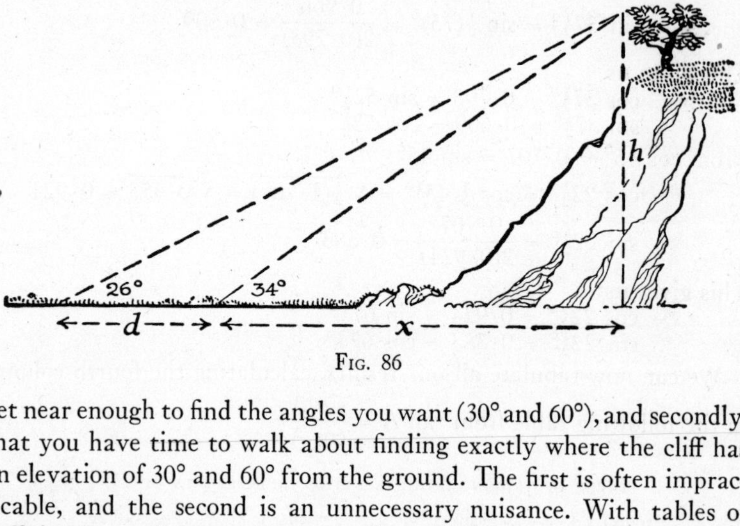

FIG. 86

get near enough to find the angles you want (30° and 60°), and secondly, that you have time to walk about finding exactly where the cliff has an elevation of 30° and 60° from the ground. The first is often impracticable, and the second is an unnecessary nuisance. With tables of sufficiently small intervals, all you have to do is to sight the angle of a distant object, then walk *any* measured distance away from it in a direct line, and measure a second angle. In Fig. 86 the measured distance is *d*, and the angles are 34° and 26°. To make a map we can get all we want, namely, the height of the hill and the horizontal distance to the spot vertically below it. Calling the height *h* and the horizontal distance from the nearest place of observation *x*, we look up the tables and find

$$\tan 34° = 0{\cdot}674 \qquad \tan 26° = 0{\cdot}488$$

We will suppose that the measured distance *d* is 64 yards. You will see at once that

$$\frac{h}{x} = \tan 34° \text{ or } x = \frac{h}{0{\cdot}674} \quad . \quad . \quad . \qquad \text{(i)}$$

Also $$\frac{h}{x+64} = \tan 26° \text{ or } h = 0{\cdot}488(x+64) \quad . \qquad \text{(ii)}$$

Combining (i) and (ii), we get

$$h = 0{\cdot}488\left(\frac{h}{0{\cdot}674} + 64\right) = \frac{0{\cdot}488}{0{\cdot}674}h + 64(0{\cdot}488)$$

So that $$h - \frac{0{\cdot}488}{0{\cdot}674}h = 64(0{\cdot}488) \text{ or } h\left(1 - \frac{0{\cdot}488}{0{\cdot}674}\right) = 31{\cdot}232$$

Hence $$0{\cdot}276h = 31{\cdot}232$$

$$h = \frac{31{\cdot}232}{0{\cdot}276} = \underline{113{\cdot}16 \text{ yards or } 339\tfrac{1}{2} \text{ feet.}}$$

Once we have h, we can also get x at once from (i), i.e.

$$x = \frac{113{\cdot}16}{0{\cdot}674} = 167{\cdot}9 \text{ yards.}$$

Try again with four-decimal values of tan 34° and tan 26°. You will get the better values $h = 112{\cdot}76$ yards, $x = 167.2$ yards. This tells you how far your previous results can be trusted.

SOLUTION OF TRIANGLES

The last example shows us indirectly how to calculate one side of a triangle if another side and two angles are known. We can also derive

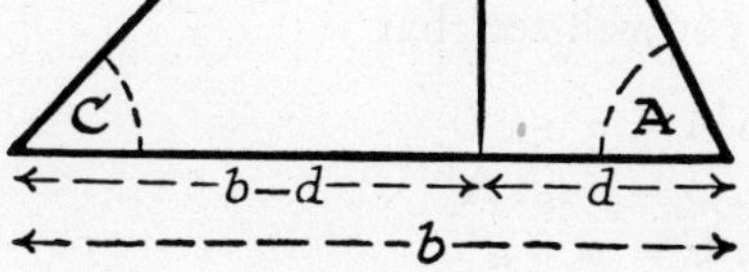

$$\sin A = \frac{p}{c} \quad \therefore p = c \sin A$$

$$\sin C = \frac{p}{a} \quad \therefore p = a \sin C$$

$$\cos A = \frac{d}{c} \quad \therefore d = c \cos A$$

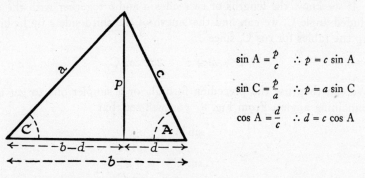

Fig. 87

simple formulae by which we can calculate without making a scale diagram any of the two angles or sides of a triangle, if we know enough about it in order to draw it. That is to say, if we know (*a*) the lengths of its three sides, or (*b*) the length of two sides and the included angle, or (*c*) the length of one side and two of its angles. The dissections are shown in Fig. 87.

If we know *three sides a, b, c* in the figure (Fig. 87) we see (Dem. 8) that

$$\begin{aligned} p^2 &= c^2 - d^2 \\ &= a^2 - (b-d)^2 \\ \therefore\quad c^2 - d^2 &= a^2 - b^2 + 2bd - d^2 \\ \therefore\quad c^2 &= a^2 - b^2 + 2bd \end{aligned}$$

Since $\cos A = d \div c$, i.e. $d = c \cos A$

$$\begin{aligned} \therefore\quad c^2 &= a^2 - b^2 + 2bc \cos A \\ \text{or}\quad a^2 &= b^2 + c^2 - 2bc \cos A \\ \therefore\quad \cos A &= \frac{c^2 + b^2 - a^2}{2bc} \end{aligned}$$

In the same way we can show that

$$\cos B = \frac{a^2 + c^2 - b^2}{2ac}$$

$$\cos C = \frac{a^2 + b^2 - c^2}{2ab}$$

So if we know *a, b, c* we can get cos A, cos B, or cos C, and the tables of cosines give us what A, B, and C are.

If we know the lengths of two sides *a* and *b* together with the included angle C, we can find the length of the third side *c* by looking up the tables for cos C, since

$$c^2 = a^2 + b^2 - 2ab \cos C$$

We can then use the preceding formula or a simpler one to get the remaining angles. From Fig. 87 you will see that

$$\begin{aligned} \sin A &= p \div c \\ \therefore\quad p &= c \sin A \\ \sin C &= p \div a \\ \therefore\quad p &= a \sin C \\ \therefore\quad c \sin A &= a \sin C \\ \therefore\quad \frac{\sin A}{a} &= \frac{\sin C}{c} \\ \therefore\quad \sin A &= \frac{a \sin C}{c} \end{aligned}$$

Thus we can find the angle A and hence B, since B = 180° − (A + C).

Similarly, if we know two angles (A, C) and a side (a), we can get the side c, since

$$c = \frac{a \sin C}{\sin A}$$

Since $B = 180° - (A + C)$, we can now get b, since

$$b^2 = a^2 + c^2 - 2ac \cos B$$

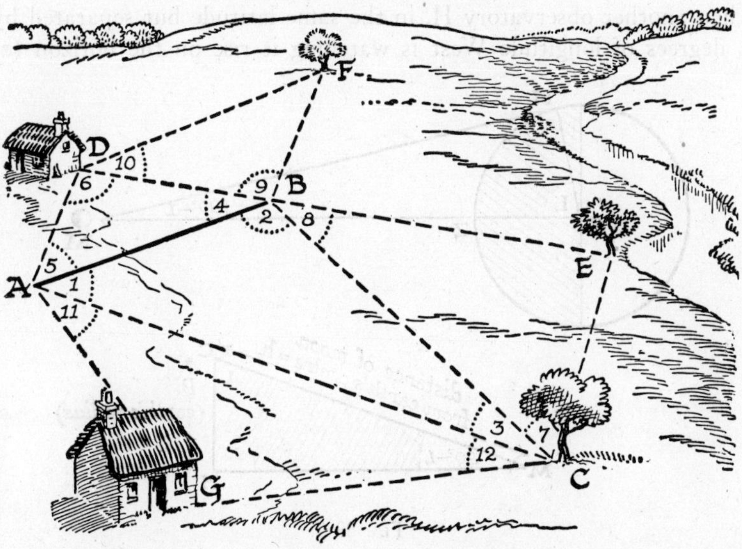

FIG. 87A.—TRIANGULATION IN DISTRICT MAP-MAKING

In surveying a district the surveyor first measures accurately a fixed distance AB with his chain or steel tape. This is the only necessary measurement of length. From the end A of the tape line AB he sights with his theodolite the angle (1) between B and C, a conspicuous object such as a tree. Then walking to the other end of it he sights the angle (2) between A and C. One side (AB) and two angles of the triangle ABC are now known. So he can calculate the lengths of BC and AC by the use of the sine formula and tables of sines. These can be used in turn to get the sides of the triangles BEC and AGC. To do this he first sights the tree E making the angle (8) between E and C, then the angle (7) between B and E. He then knows two angles of the triangle BEC and the calculated length of BC. Similarly he sights G from A and C. Proceeding in this way he sights in other directions the farm D and the tree F from AB, thus mapping all the landmarks.

THE DISTANCE OF THE MOON

Hipparchus calculated the moon's distance as approximately a quarter of a million miles. His estimate was not more than 5 per cent out. The method is essentially similar to finding the height of a cliff by measuring its altitude simultaneously at two stations a known distance apart. In practice this is a little complicated, and involves the last two formulae, which are given in case you wish to refer to books on astronomy for details. You will be able to grasp the underlying principle by imagining how it could be done with all the resources of modern radio equipment. We will suppose that one observatory Z sees the moon exactly at its zenith, i.e. vertically overhead, at exactly the same moment when another observatory H, in the same latitude but separated by L degrees of longitude West is watching it rise on the horizon (or

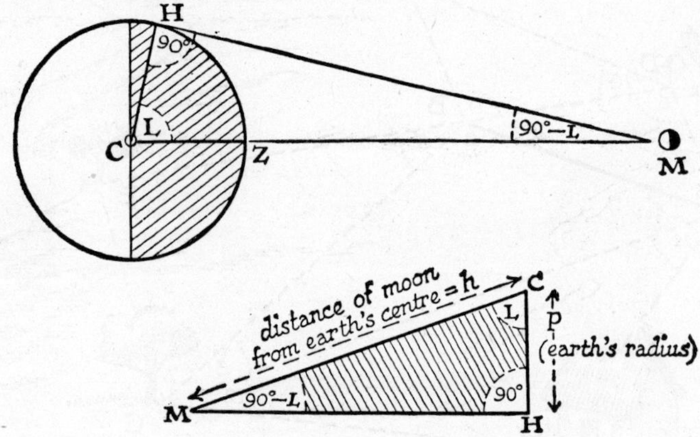

FIG. 88

H might be L degrees East watching it set at the same time). From Fig. 88 you will see that we now have a right-angled triangle, such that

$$\sin(90° - L) = \frac{\text{earth's radius}}{\text{moon's distance}}$$

$$\cos L = \frac{\text{earth's radius}}{\text{moon's distance}}$$

Suppose we find that L is actually $89\frac{1}{16}°$. On looking up the tables in intervals of $\frac{15}{16}$ we find that $\cos 89\frac{1}{16}° = 0{\cdot}0163$. So we may put

$$0{\cdot}0163 = \frac{4000}{\text{moon's distance}} \text{ in miles}$$

$$\text{Moon's distance} = \frac{4000}{0{\cdot}0163} = \underline{245{,}000 \text{ miles (approx.)}}$$

Once we have the moon's distance, it is easy to get the radius and circumference of the moon. The method is shown in Fig. 89. All you have to do is to measure the angle between opposite spots on the boundary of the full moon. If we call this angle A and neglect the earth's radius as small, compared with the moon's distance:

$$\sin \tfrac{1}{2}A = \frac{\text{moon's radius}}{\text{moon's distance}}$$

If A is found to be half a degree, i.e. $\frac{1}{2}A = \frac{1}{4}°$, we find from tables that $\sin \frac{1}{4}° = 0\cdot0044$, i.e.

$$0\cdot0044 = \frac{\text{moon's radius}}{245000}$$

This gives 0·0044 (245,000) miles, or approximately 1,100 miles for

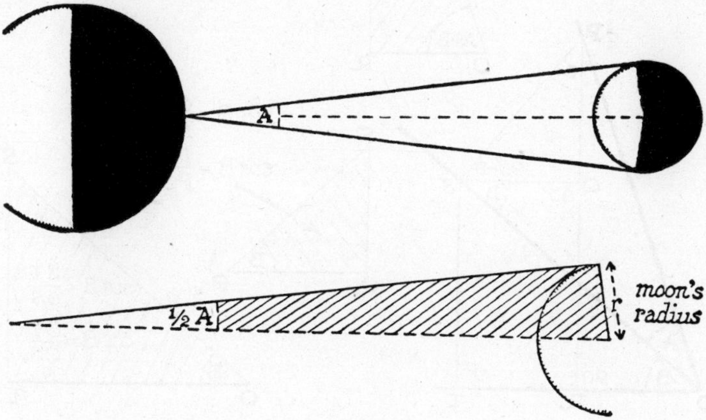

FIG. 89

the moon's radius. The best measurements yield 1,081 miles. We can now fulfil a former promise, and find π in the sky. The circumference of the moon will be 2π times this quantity, i.e.

$$2 \times 3\tfrac{1}{7} \times 1{,}081 = 6{,}800 \text{ miles approximately}$$

Thus the circumference of the moon is only about four and a half times the distance between London and Moscow.

Later on we shall have more to say about the kind of measurements which the Alexandrians made with cruder instruments than ours, and less facilities for making observations at different places widely separated by distances which have been accurately measured. At this point in the narrative you will have realized that for astronomical purposes tables of angles with very small intervals are needed for making good measurements. Various formulae have been devised for doing this. The half-angle formulae which we have used are particular

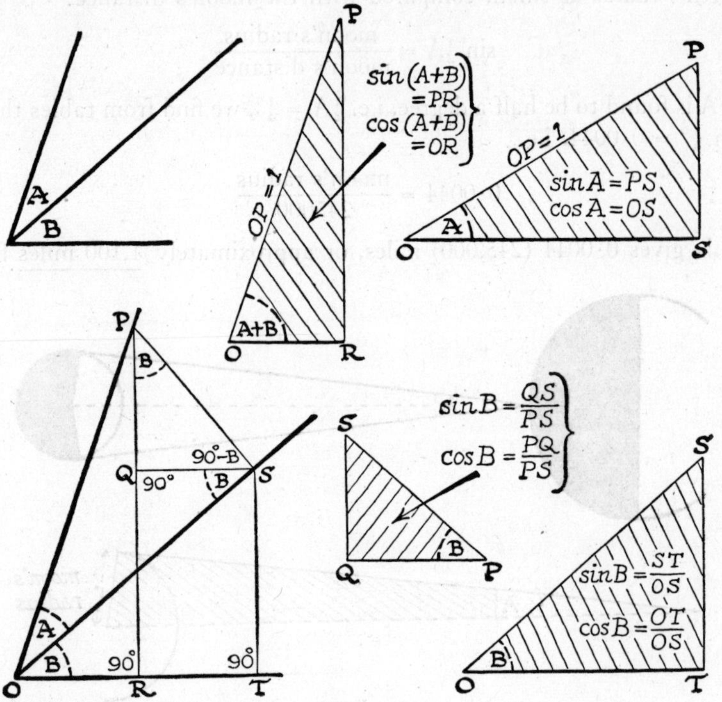

FIG. 90

The angle POT between the lines PO and OT is the sum of A and B.
The dissection is as follows:

(*a*) From P drop a perpendicular (PS) on the middle line OS.
(*b*) From P drop a perpendicular (PR) on OT.
(*c*) From S drop a perpendicular (SQ) on PR.
(*d*) From S drop a perpendicular (ST) on OT.

cases of two more general rules. The demonstration of these rules is given in Fig. 90. The rules are:

$$\sin (A + B) = \sin A \cos B + \cos A \sin B$$
$$\cos (A + B) = \cos A \cos B - \sin A \sin B$$

These particular formulae are important to remember because they are used later when we come to see how the Reformation geometry discovered a new use for the angle ratios. The demonstration, though difficult to remember because it does not recall any previous figure, is not difficult to follow. To simplify matters, we have made one length (OP) 1 unit long. Looking at the figure, you see

$$\sin(A+B) = PR = PQ + QR = PQ + ST = (PS)\cos B + (OS)\sin B$$
$$= \sin A \cos B + \cos A \sin B$$
$$\cos(A+B) = OR = OT - RT = OT - QS = (OS)\cos B - (PS)\sin B$$
$$= \cos A \cos B - \sin A \sin B$$

Check these rules for yourself, like this:

$$\sin 75° = \sin(45° + 30°) = \sin 45° \cos 30° + \cos 45° \sin 30°$$
$$0{\cdot}707\,(0{\cdot}866 + 0{\cdot}500) = 0{\cdot}966^{*}$$

FINDING A VALUE FOR π.—We have taken the value of π as $3\frac{1}{7}$ in getting the radius of the moon and earth. Actually the only estimate which we have so far shown how to get was in the neighbourhood of $3\frac{1}{4}$. In the Old Testament (2 Chron. iv. 2) we read: "Also he made a molten sea of ten cubits from brim to brim, round in compass, and five cubits the height thereof, and a line of thirty cubits did compass it about." The circumference was thus six times the radius, or three times the diameter. That is to say, the ancient Hebrews, like the Babylonians, were content with taking π as 3. About the time when the celebrated evolutionary trial was taking place in Tennessee a Bill was introduced into the legislature of one of the backward agricultural states of America with the object of restoring to π its Biblical value. No doubt this figure is good enough for making an ox-wagon wheel to lumber along a Biblical road. If the Bill had passed, the only logical

* A second connexion between the ratios of angles is sometimes useful, and will be used in Chapter 9. It gives us a direct way of finding the cosine of an angle if we know the sine or *vice versa*. In the right-angled triangle on the right $h = 1$, so $\sin A = p$ and $\cos A = b$.

From Dem. 8 we have

$$1^2 = p^2 + b^2$$
i.e. $$1 = (\sin A)^2 + (\cos A)^2$$

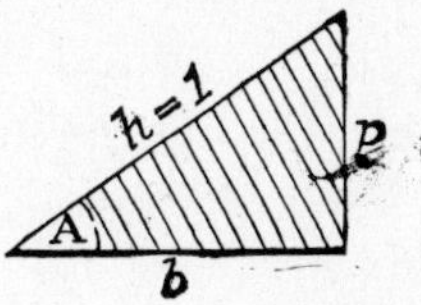

It is usual in textbooks to write for the squares of sin A and cos A:

$$(\sin A)^2 = \sin^2 A \quad \text{and} \quad (\cos A)^2 = \cos^2 A$$

Testing this by using the fact that $\sin 30° = \frac{1}{2}$, we get

$$1 = (\tfrac{1}{2})^2 + \cos^2 A$$

So $\cos^2 A = \frac{3}{4}$, or $\cos A = \frac{\sqrt{3}}{2}$.

course would have been to give up steam tractors and Ford cars. When the Alexandrians, like Archimedes and Hero, began to design machines with wheels they needed something better.

Once we have tables of sines and tangents it is easy to get a value for π as accurately as we need to have it. The method which Archimedes used makes it fairly clear that he had some such tables before those of Hipparchus. The history of science never confirms the popular belief that discoveries are made singly by the isolated genius. They are invariably made about the same time by a number of different people. This is a commonplace of scientific history, though historians of science rarely disclose the simple explanation. Discoveries repeat themselves because intellectual work proceeds along the lines laid down by the social culture which the individual discoverer inherits.

From Dem. 12 we learned that the ratio of the boundary to the diameter of a circle is the same for all circles, and the length of the boundary of a circle lies between (*a*) the boundary of a polygon of n equivalent sides drawn (circumscribed) around and just touching the circle with its sides, and (*b*) the boundary of a polygon of n equivalent sides drawn (inscribed) within the circle and just touching it at the angles. If c is the boundary of the circle and d the diameter,

$$c = \pi d$$

So if the diameter is 1 unit (i.e. r, the radius, is $\frac{1}{2}$), $c = \pi$. Having refreshed your memory by going back to the figures illustrating Dem. 12 in Chapter 4, you will find no difficulty with Fig. 91. On the left is partly drawn a polygon of n equivalent sides circumscribed about a circle of diameter 1 unit ($r = \frac{1}{2}$). The polygon is made up of $2n$ right-angled triangles, of which the perpendicular (p) of the centre angle $A\left(\frac{360°}{2n}\right)$ forms part of the boundary. So the boundary of the circumscribed polygon (P_c) is $2n$ times p. From the figure you see that

$$p = \tfrac{1}{2} \tan \frac{360°}{2n}$$

$$\therefore \quad P_c = n . \tan \frac{360°}{2n}$$

For instance, if the figure is a hexagon (six sides)

$$P_c = 6 \tan \left(\frac{360°}{12}\right) = 6 . \tan 30° = 6(0 \cdot 58) = 3 \cdot 48$$

FIG. 91.—HOW ARCHIMEDES FOUND A VALUE FOR π

$$\text{The angle } A = \frac{360°}{2n}$$

when the polygon has n equivalent sides

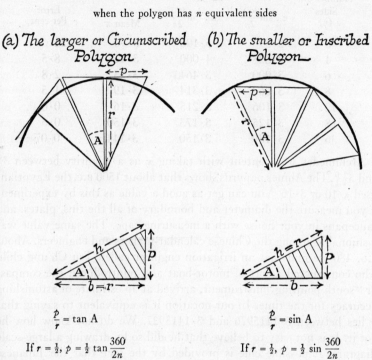

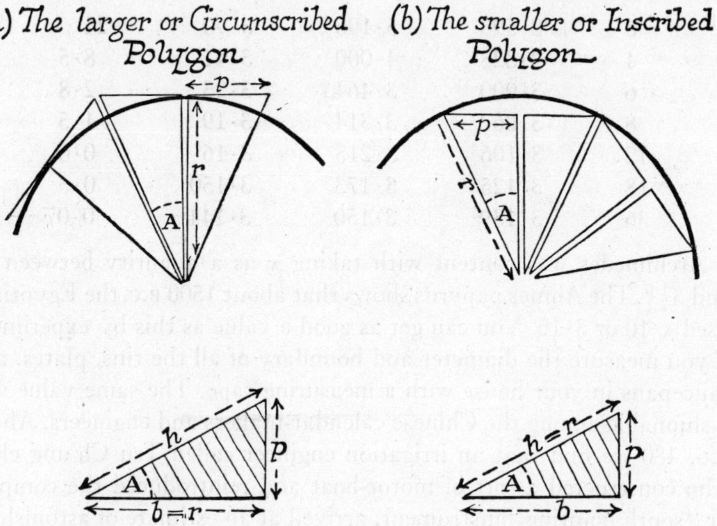

$\frac{p}{r} = \tan A$ $\qquad$ $\frac{p}{r} = \sin A$

If $r = \frac{1}{2}$, $p = \frac{1}{2} \tan \frac{360}{2n}$ $\qquad$ If $r = \frac{1}{2}$, $p = \frac{1}{2} \sin \frac{360}{2n}$

Similarly you will see from the figure that the boundary (P_i) of the inscribed polygon of n equivalent sides can be found from the corresponding equation:

$$P_i = n \,.\, \sin\left(\frac{360°}{2n}\right)$$

For instance, if the figure is a hexagon,

$$P_i = 6 \,.\, \sin \frac{360°}{12} = 6 \,.\, \sin 30° = 6(0{\cdot}50) = 3{\cdot}00$$

So the value of π lies between $3{\cdot}48$ and $3{\cdot}00$. If we take the common average, we can write this as $3{\cdot}24 \pm 0{\cdot}24$.

We have learned from Dem. 12 that we can make the plus and minus margin as small as we like, if we make the number of sides n of the polygon sufficiently large. With a table of sines and tangents this is quickly done. You can work out the following for practice*:

Number of Sides (n)	P_i $n \cdot \sin\frac{360°}{2n}$	P_c $n \cdot \tan\frac{360°}{2n}$	Mean π	Error Per cent
3	2·598	5·196	3·90	24
4	2·828	4·000	3·41	8·5
6	3·000	3·464	3·23	2·8
8	3·062	3·314	3·19	1·5
12	3·106	3·215	3·16	0·6
18	3·125	3·173	3·150	0·3
36	3·139	3·150	3·144	0·07

Archimedes was content with taking π as a quantity between $3\frac{1}{7}$ and $3\frac{10}{71}$. The Ahmes papyrus shows that about 1500 B.C. the Egyptians used $\sqrt{10}$ or 3·16. You can get as good a value as this by experiment if you measure the diameter and boundary of all the tins, plates, and saucepans in your house with a measuring tape. The same value was fashionable among the Chinese calendar-makers and engineers. About A.D. 480 we find that an irrigation engineer called Tsu Ch'ung chih, who constructed a sort of motor-boat and reintroduced the compass or "south pointing" instrument, arrived at an estimate of astonishing accuracy for the time. In our notation it is equivalent to saying that π lies between 3·1415926 and 3·1415927. We do not know how he got it. It is not easy to believe that he did so by drawing a large-scale diagram. A possible clue is provided by the fact that the Japanese were using a method similar to that which was just being applied in Europe about A.D. 1700. It depends on the Chinese (so-called Pythagoras) theorem about right angles. So it may have been derived from a procedure which was already known to the Chinese at a date little later than the time of Archimedes. It has a special interest, which will emerge later. The Japanese way depends on splitting the circle into tiny rectangles. It is based on the fact that the area of a circle is πr^2 (p. 182), where r is the radius, so that if the radius is 1 unit of length, the area of the circle is π units of area.

It is even tempting to wonder whether the Japanese method was not suggested, like the figure which was reproduced from a very ancient Chinese work in Chapter 2, by drawings made on tiles. If you trace a circle on graph paper, you will see that the area of the circle lies between that of two sets of superimposed oblong strips, white and

* See Note on p. 286.

shaded in Fig. 92 at the bottom. In each half of the circle there will be one more of the outer or longer strips than the inner or shorter, drawn as in the two quarter-circles at the top of Fig. 92. The quarter-circle of Fig. 93 is enclosed by five rectangular strips of the same width,

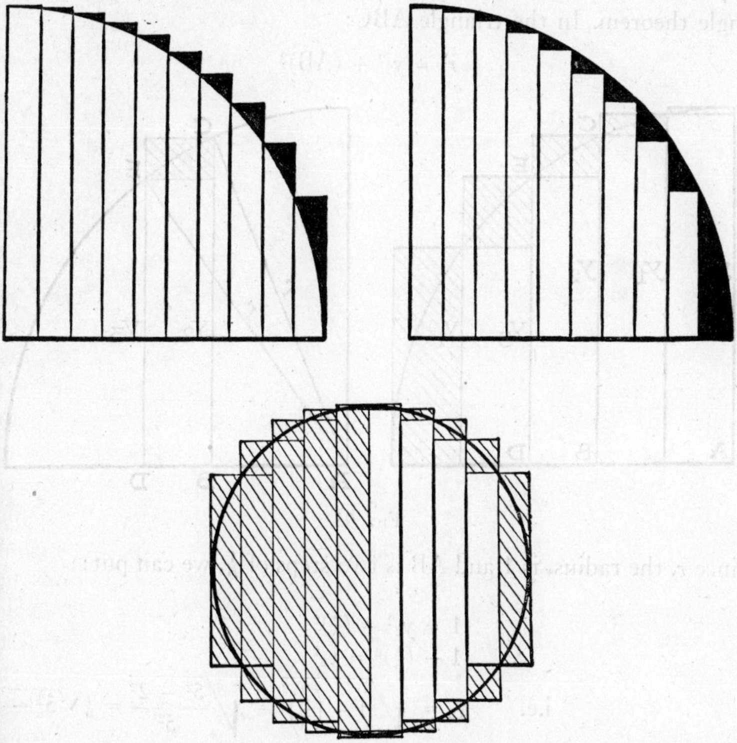

FIG. 92.—THE JAPANESE METHOD FOR GETTING π

and itself encloses four superimposed rectangular strips of the same width. From the way the rectangles are drawn you will see why the fifth inner rectangle vanishes. If the radius of the circle is 1 unit of length, the width of each strip is $\frac{1}{5}$. The area of all the rectangles of the outer series is

$$\frac{1}{5}y_0 + \frac{1}{5}y_1 + \frac{1}{5}y_2 + \frac{1}{5}y_3 + \frac{1}{5}y_4$$
$$= \frac{1}{5}(y_0 + y_1 + y_2 + y_3 + y_4)$$

In a complete circle the corresponding rectangular strips would amount to four times this, i.e.

$$A_c = \frac{4}{5}(y_0 + y_1 + y_2 + y_3 + y_4)$$

Similarly for the area of all the inner strips in the full circle we may write:

$$A_i = \tfrac{4}{5}(y_1 + y_2 + y_3 + y_4)$$

The values of y_1, y_2, etc., depend on using Dem. 8, the Chinese right-angle theorem. In the triangle ABC:

$$r^2 = y_2^2 + (AB)^2$$

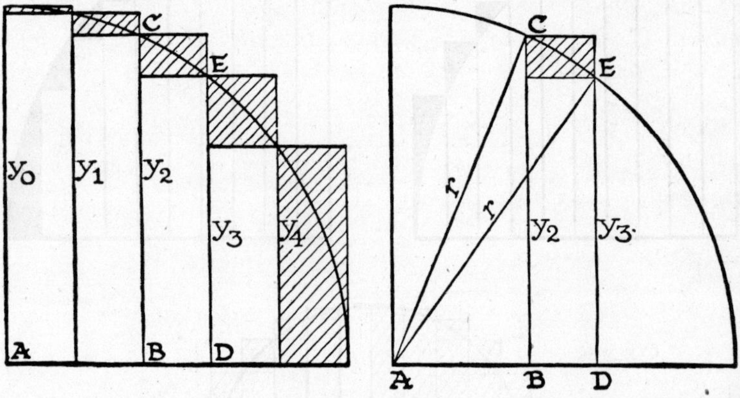

FIG. 93

Since r, the radius, is 1 and AB is two steps of $\tfrac{1}{5}$, we can put:

$$1 = y_2^2 + (\tfrac{2}{5})^2$$

$$\therefore \quad 1 - (\tfrac{2}{5})^2 = y_2^2$$

i.e. $$y_2 = \sqrt{1 - \left(\frac{2}{5}\right)^2} = \sqrt{\frac{5^2 - 2^2}{5^2}} = \tfrac{1}{5}\sqrt{5^2 - 2^2}$$

Similarly in the triangle AED

$$1^2 = y_3^2 + (\tfrac{3}{5})^2$$

$$\therefore \quad y_3 = \tfrac{1}{5}\sqrt{5^2 - 3^2}$$

In the same way $$y_1 = \tfrac{1}{5}\sqrt{5^2 - 1^2}$$

$$y_4 = \tfrac{1}{5}\sqrt{5^2 - 4^2}$$

And $y_0 = 1 = \tfrac{5}{5}$.

So we may now write

$$A_c = \tfrac{4}{5}[\tfrac{5}{5} + \tfrac{1}{5}\sqrt{5^2 - 1^2} + \tfrac{1}{5}\sqrt{5^2 - 2^2} + \tfrac{1}{5}\sqrt{5^2 - 3^2} + \tfrac{1}{5}\sqrt{5^2 - 4^2}]$$

$$\therefore A_c = \frac{4}{5^2}[5 + \sqrt{5^2 - 1^2} + \sqrt{5^2 - 2^2} + \sqrt{5^2 - 3^2} + \sqrt{5^2 - 4^2}] \quad (i$$

Likewise

$$A_i = \frac{4}{5^2}[\sqrt{5^2 - 1^2} + \sqrt{5^2 - 2^2} + \sqrt{5^2 - 3^2} + \sqrt{5^2 - 4^2}] \quad . \qquad \text{(ii)}$$

This gives us

$$A_c = \tfrac{4}{25}(5 + \sqrt{24} + \sqrt{21} + 4 + 3) = 3\cdot 44$$

and

$$A_i = \tfrac{4}{25}(\sqrt{24} + \sqrt{21} + 4 + 3) \qquad = 2\cdot 64$$

Since the area of the circle, the radius of which is of unit length, lies between A_c and A_i, and π is the area of a circle of which the radius is 1 unit long, π lies between 3·44 and 2·64. As a first approximation $\pi = 3\cdot 04 \pm 0\cdot 40$.

With a similar figure in which the radius is divided into ten equal parts, so that there are ten outer and nine inner rectangles, you should now be able to get for yourself

$$\begin{aligned} A_c = \frac{4}{10^2}(10 &+ \sqrt{10^2 - 1^2} + \sqrt{10^2 - 2^2} + \sqrt{10^2 - 3^2} \\ &+ \sqrt{10^2 - 4^2} + \sqrt{10^2 - 5^2} + \sqrt{10^2 - 6^2} \\ &+ \sqrt{10^2 - 7^2} + \sqrt{10^2 - 8^2} + \sqrt{10^2 - 9^2}) \end{aligned}$$

$$\begin{aligned} A_i = \frac{4}{10^2}(&\sqrt{10^2 - 1^2} + \sqrt{10^2 - 2^2} + \sqrt{10^2 - 3^2} \\ &+ \sqrt{10^2 - 4^2} + \sqrt{10^2 - 5^2} + \sqrt{10^2 - 6^2} \\ &+ \sqrt{10^2 - 7^2} + \sqrt{10^2 - 8^2} + \sqrt{10^2 - 9^2}) \end{aligned}$$

In this way, with the aid of a table of square roots, and calling π_n the value of π we get when the radius is divided into n equivalent strips, we can build up a table like this:

$$\begin{aligned} \pi_5 &= 3\cdot 04 \pm 0\cdot 40 \\ \pi_{10} &= 3\cdot 10 \pm 0\cdot 20 \\ \pi_{15} &= 3\cdot 12 \pm 0\cdot 14 \\ \pi_{20} &= 3\cdot 13 \pm 0\cdot 10 \end{aligned}$$

If you work these out, you will have discovered for yourself that there is no need to make a new figure each time. The rule for getting π can be expressed as a pair of series, the sum of the outer rectangles being:

$$\frac{4}{n^2}(n + \sqrt{n^2 - 1^2} + \sqrt{n^2 - 2^2} + \sqrt{n^2 - 3^2} + \sqrt{n^2 - 4^2} \;.\;.\;.)$$

The sum of the inner rectangles will be the same with the first term within the brackets left out. If you recall what was said in Chapter 3,

p. 92, about verbs like "put up" and "visit," which include the meaning of other verbs, you may be interested to meet an example of the higher abstractions mentioned in that context. The last rule can be written for the outer rectangle strips:

$$\frac{4}{n^2}\sum_{r=0}^{r=n}\sqrt{n^2 - r^2}$$

The verb (or "operator") Σ with its two adverbs $r = n$ above and $r = 0$ below means, "Add up all quantities like . . . formed by giving r the values of every whole number from 0 to n." Of course when $r = 0$, $\sqrt{n^2 - r^2} = n$, and when $r = n$, $\sqrt{n^2 - r^2} = 0$. The corresponding rule for the inner rectangle strips would be:

$$\frac{4}{n^2}\sum_{r=1}^{r=n}\sqrt{n^2 - r^2}$$

If you recall earlier discussion on the use of series (Chapter 5), you will ask whether it is possible to get this series into a form so that, when n is very big, you can make it choke off at any convenient point, as you can neglect the later terms in the series representing a recurring decimal fraction. The Japanese actually succeeded in doing this, quite independently of Western influence, at the end of the seventeenth century. Matsunaga gave an estimate of π which in our notation is a decimal fraction correct to fifty figures. We shall leave the solution of the problem till we can approach it in its proper historical setting, when we return to the discussion of series in a later chapter. What we have done already is enough to suggest the possibility of finding a series for π which can be stretched out to any order of precision which measurement demands.

A third way in which we can reach an estimate of π introduces us to a literal revolution in the measurement of the angle. We have called the degree the unit of the priestly calendar-makers, and the right angle the unit of the builders of the city-state. Another way of measuring the angle might be called the wheelwright's way, which we may call the unit of the machine age. The machine unit, which is called a RADIAN, is the angle joining to the centre the ends of an arc equivalent in length, when straightened out, to the radius of the circle to which it belongs (Fig. 94). If we straightened out a semicircle it would be π times the radius, since the whole boundary is $2\pi r$. So two right angles are equivalent to π radians, or one right angle = $\frac{1}{2}\pi$ radians, and one degree in the Babylonian measure is $\frac{\pi}{180}$ radians. Conversely, one radian is $\frac{180}{\pi}$, about $57\frac{1}{2}$ Babylonian degrees. It is well to memorize these identities using r and $^{\circ}$ as adjectives:

$$180^{\circ} = \pi^{r} \text{ (i.e. } \pi \textit{ radians)}$$
$$90^{\circ} = \tfrac{1}{2}(\pi)^{r}$$
$$1^{\circ} = \left(\frac{\pi}{180}\right)^{r}$$
$$1^{r} = \left(\frac{180}{\pi}\right)^{\circ}$$

This way of measuring the angle makes the unit depend on the

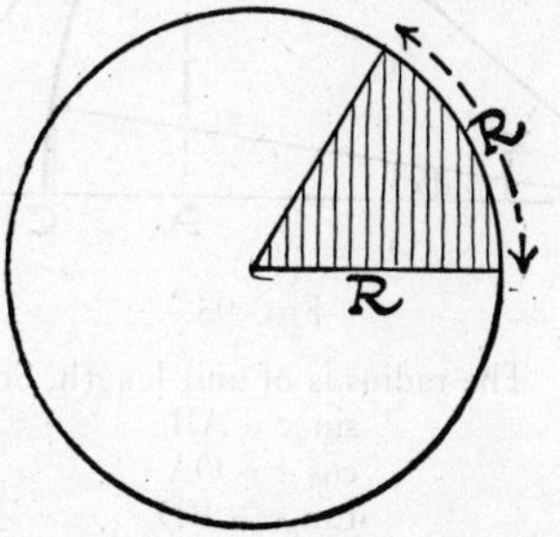

FIG. 94.—THE MACHINE UNIT OF ANGULAR MEASURE

The RADIAN is the angle unit which represents the amount which a wheel has revolved when the rim has covered a distance equivalent to the spoke. Hence 2π radians are equivalent to 360 Babylonian degrees.

revolution of a wheel when the rim has covered a distance equivalent to the spoke. If the spoke (radius) is of unit length, 1 unit of length corresponds with 1 unit of angular revolution. So the length of an arc (in the same units) is the same number as the number of radians in the angle formed by joining its ends to the axle (or centre). So in Fig. 95 the angle x = BC if $r = 1$.

If you compare Fig. 95 with Fig. 57, you will see that, since the radius of the circle is of unit length, the tangent of the angle x is the number of units of length of the tangent BD to the circle at B, and since OB = r = 1, $\sin x$ = AB (the perpendicular), and $\cos x$ = OA (the base). But since

$$\tan x = \frac{\sin x}{\cos x}$$
$$\cos x = \frac{\sin x}{\tan x} = \frac{AB}{BD}$$

As already explained, if $r = 1$, it is also true, in radian measure, that $x = BC$. BC is greater than AB. If you divide a quantity by a larger quantity, the result is less than unity. So $\frac{AB}{BC}$ is less than 1, i.e. $\frac{\sin x}{x} < 1$. Also BD is greater than BC. If you divide one quantity

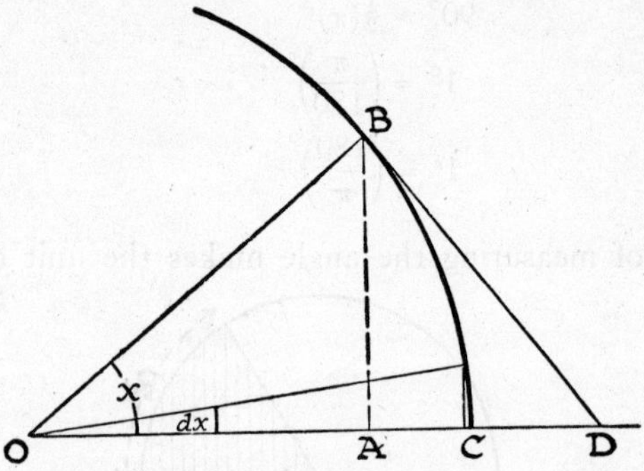

FIG. 95

The radius is of unit length. So
$\sin x = AB$
$\cos x = OA$
$\tan x = BD$

by a second, the result is larger than you get by dividing the same quantity by one still larger than the second. Hence:

$$\frac{AB}{BC} \text{ is greater than } \frac{AB}{BD}$$

$$\frac{\sin x}{x} > \cos x$$

So when x is measured in radians, $\frac{\sin x}{x}$ lies between $\cos x$ and 1. If x becomes very small (dx in Fig. 95), $\cos x$ becomes practically 1. You can also see that the perpendicular and the arc become practically indistinguishable, i.e. $\frac{\sin x}{x}$ becomes practically 1. So the upper limit of $\frac{\sin x}{x}$ is 1, and the lower limit is $\cos x$. From this we can get the limits between which π lies.

In other words $\sin x$ lies between x and x times $\cos x$,when x is measured in radians. So $\sin 5°$ or $\sin \left(\frac{5\pi}{180}\right)^r$ lies between $\frac{5\pi}{180}$ and

$\frac{5\pi}{180}$ times cos $\left(\frac{5\pi}{180}\right)^r$ or $\frac{5\pi}{180}$ times cos 5°. From the tables, sin 5° = 0·0872 and cos 5° = 0·9962. If

$$\sin x = x . \cos x$$

we get $$0{\cdot}0872 = 0{\cdot}9962 \times \frac{5\pi}{180}$$

$$\pi = 3{\cdot}15$$

Likewise, if $$\sin x = x$$

we get $$0{\cdot}0872 = \frac{5\pi}{180}$$

$$\pi = 3{\cdot}14$$

The mean is $\pi = 3{\cdot}145 \pm 0{\cdot}005$.

The above value is based on four-figure tables. These are not adequate for angles less than about 5° because the number of significant figures in the sine of the angle is not enough to give more than three significant figures in the result. We have now found by three methods that π lies very near to $3\frac{1}{7}$ or 3·143. To five decimals, if we take the trouble to persevere, the value is 3·14159. . . . By using this to get the radian or circular measure of an angle, you get good values for the sine of small ones, if you take $\sin x = x$. An historical table of the values assigned to π may interest you because it shows you how π stretches out as we approach the machine age.

TABLE OF VALUES OF π

Babylonians and Hebrews and earliest Chinese	3·0
Egyptians (*c.* 1500 B.C.)	3·16
Archimedes (240 B.C.) (interested in wheels)	between 3·140 and 3·142
Chinese calendar-makers and engineers:	
Liu Hsing (*c.* A.D.25)	3·16
Wang Fun (*c.* A.D. 250)	3·15
Tsu Ch'ung chih (*c.* A.D. 480) (interested in machinery)	between 3·1415926 and 3·1415927
Hindus and Arabs:	
Aryabhata (*c.* A.D. 450)	3·1416
Al Kashi (*c.* A.D. 1430)	3·1415926535897932

TABLE OF VALUES OF π—*continued.*

European:	
Vieta (*c.* A.D. 1593)	between 3·1415926537 and 3·1415926535
Ceulen (*c.* A.D. 1610)	correct to thirty-five decimal places
Wallis (*c.* A.D. 1650) and Gregory (*c.* A.D. 1668)	unlimited series
Japanese:	
Takebe (*c.* A.D. 1690)	unlimited series
Matsunaga (*c.* A.D. 1720)	correct to fifty decimal places in our notation

At the present time π is known to seven hundred correct decimal places. Vieta obtained his value by working out the limits from a polygon of 393,216 sides. The later values are based on series. As a matter of fact ten decimal places are enough to give the circumference of the earth within a fraction of an inch, and thirty decimals would give the boundary of the entire visible universe within a fraction too small to be measured by the most powerful modern microscope. So you have no need to be disappointed with the result we have obtained for most practical purposes. For designing the best aeroplane engines, it is only necessary to know four decimal places (3·1416).

ALEXANDRIAN ASTRONOMY.—Some account has already been given of the amazing achievements in earth measurements during the first phase of the Alexandrian culture. The measurement of celestial distances is greatly simplified today by the fact that we possess reliable wheel-driven clocks. The Alexandrian artificers improved on the timekeeping methods of their predecessors by devising clocks which depended on a continuous flow of water through a vessel which siphoned off like the arrangement in Fig. 2. Although these devices were highly ingenious, they did not meet the requirements of navigation. They were not portable. So for measurement of longitude they had to resort to more complicated astronomical observations than the simple method which we can use today. Hipparchus, as mentioned earlier, made a tolerably accurate estimate of the distance of the moon from the earth. The ingenuity of the methods used by these astronomers is well illustrated by the pioneer work of Aristarchus.

Aristarchus attempted to make an estimate of the relative distances of the sun and moon from the earth and their relative sizes by observing the angle (α) in Fig. 96 between the moon as seen in the early hours of morning, the sun, and the earth when exactly half the surface of

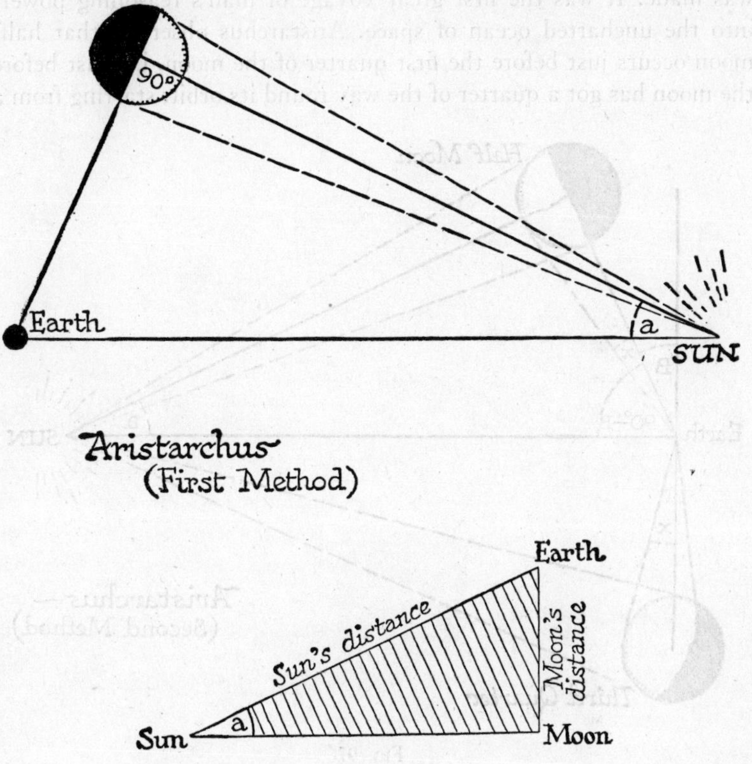

FIG. 96

the moon is visible, i.e. at half-moon. In the new dictionary language which we have now learned, the figure shows that

$$\sin \alpha = \frac{\text{moon's distance from the earth}}{\text{sun's distance from the earth}}$$

With the crude instruments at his disposal he concluded that the angle was 3°. He had no tables of angle ratios, so using a highly ingenious, though to us long-winded, application of Euclidean geometry, he showed that the sun's distance is between eighteen and twenty times the moon's distance from the earth. Not content with this method, he used a second one to check his result. The principle of this is not difficult to follow. What is fascinating about it is the daring resourcefulness of the performance, when one considers the time at which it was made. It was the first great voyage of man's reasoning powers into the uncharted ocean of space. Aristarchus observed that half-moon occurs just before the first quarter of the moon, i.e. just before the moon has got a quarter of the way round its orbit, starting from a

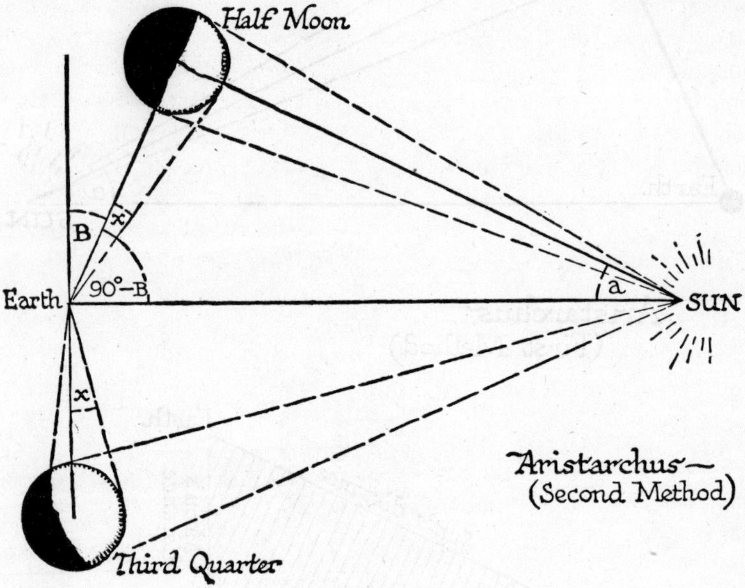

Fig. 97

position between sun and earth. At the quarter a little more than half the face of the moon is seen, as you will recognize in Fig. 97, where the half-moon of the first quarter and the moon when exactly at the third quarter, i.e. exactly three-quarters of the way round its orbit from new moon, are drawn together. If the angle of the full moon in Fig. 89 is called $2x$, the angle of the half-moon is x. When the moon is exactly at its first or (as in Fig. 97) its third quarter, the angle between the two furthest points across the moon's disc is just over x. If we call B the angle through which the moon revolves between half-moon and first quarter, the angle between the moon, the earth, and the sun is $90° - \text{B}$. But this angle is also $90° - \alpha$. So $\alpha = \text{B}$. Aristarchus made the delay between half-moon and first quarter six hours or a quarter of a day, i.e., if we take the lunar month as 28 days, $\frac{1}{4 \times 28}$ of a complete cycle during which the moon revolves through 360°. So B is $(\frac{360}{112})°$, or roughly 3°; and since $\alpha = B$, this confirms the previous estimate. Taking the moon's distance as 240,000 miles, we see that Aristarchus made the distance of the sun equivalent to $4\frac{1}{2}$ million miles. Actually it is about 93 million miles, a value within 10 per cent of which was given by Eratosthenes. His instruments were not suitable for measuring the very small angle between half-illumination and first or third quarter, or between moon, sun, and earth, which comes to the same thing. What is more important is the fact that before there were telescopes to map out the mountains of the moon it was quite impossible to get a very accurate estimate of the boundary of the half-moon. The two estimates of Aristarchus involved the same instrumental error. A high level of accuracy in astronomical measurements presupposes a high level of technical development in machinery.

We cannot go into further details of these first earth and sky surveys. The following passages from Carl Snyder's *World Machine* will give you a vivid picture of the achievements of Alexandrian astronomy:

"Ptolemy, in his treatise, describes another simple method, and there were doubtless others still. They did not agree very closely; the distance is, in reality, a troublesome quantity to compute, because it varies. . . . And with the circumference of the earth fixed, they knew that the moon was somewhere around 240,000 miles from the earth. They could likewise note that its apparent or visual diameter is half a degree, and, the distance known, could compute that this mild-mannered orb was in reality a colossal thing—a body some 2,000 miles through, that is, a quarter of the diameter of our massy earth. . . . Living in that same wonderful day was another giant, Apollonius of Perga, styled 'the great geometer.' His was the glory 'twas said, to have applied geometry to the problem of the heavens. Evidently by this was meant the higher geometry, for, as we have seen, Bion and Aristarchus and Eratosthenes and many another had already given good account of themselves in the use of geometrical methods. Apollonius developed the theory of conic sections, and introduced the idea of epicycles as an explanation of the motions of the planets. This latter idea was borrowed by Hipparchus, 'greatest observing astronomer of antiquity,' and it was doubtless the example of Apollonius which led him to the discovery of the idea of parallax usually attributed to him. . . . Be this as it may, the problem of the shadow cone, as is clear from the pages of Ptolemy, had been worked out by Hipparchus, apparently with great precision, but with the strange result of confirming the calculations of Aristarchus. He, too, found the distance of the sun about twenty times that of the moon, or from 1379 to 1472 half diameters of our globe. Ptolemy, a couple of centuries later, tries his hand at the matter, but with no better success; indeed, he reduces the distance to 1210 such half diameters. . . . The theorem of Hipparchus gave not merely the relative but also the absolute measures of the solar and lunar distances, hence a direct measure of their size. Cleomedes tells us that Hipparchus computed the sun's bulk at 150 times that of the earth; Ptolemy made it 170 times. But Aristarchus, by what method he does not state, figured the diameter of the sun at between six and seven times that of the earth, hence about three hundred times its bulk. He sets the moon's diameter at one-third that of the earth—an error of but one twelfth; admirable, if yet imperfect approximations. The march of the mind had begun! . . . There is, in an oddly-jumbled work, *Opinions of Philosophers*, attributed, with slight probability, to familiar old Plutarch, a paragraph which says that Eratosthenes had engaged the same problem. True to his love of concrete measures, he gives the distance of the moon at 780,000 stadia, of the sun at 804,000,000 stadia. Marvellous prevision of the truth! For though he makes the distance of the moon only about twenty earth radii—too small by two-thirds of the reality—his figure makes the sun distant 20,000 radii, which, as nearly as we may estimate the stadium, was practically the distance that, after three centuries of patient investigation with micrometers and heliometers, is set down as the reality. . . . It is with a deepening interest, bordering even upon amazement, that we find yet another great investigator of antiquity announcing similar but quite distinct estimates. This was Poseidonius, the teacher of Cicero and of Pompey. . . . We have already noted that his measures of the earth, adopted by Ptolemy, was the sustenance of Columbus. He had closely studied the refraction of light, and gives us a really wonderful calculation as to the height of the earth's atmosphere. In the pages of Cleomedes we learn that he equally attempted to establish the distance of the stars. He puts the moon at two million stadia away, the sun at five hundred million! This, on his earlier estimate of the earth's diameter, would place the moon at fifty-two radii of the earth, which would be nearer than the computations of Hipparchus. It would make the sun's distance 13,000 radii. If we take his later figure (180,000 stadia), the distance would become 17,400 radii, an estimate which, considering the necessarily wide limits of error, does not differ greatly from that of Eratosthenes, and equally little from the truth. Compare it with the thirteen *hundred* radii of his forerunners! Compare it with the notions of Epicurus, almost his contemporary, a very wise and large-minded man in his way, who yet believed that the sun might be a body two feet across!"

What Aristarchus succeeded in showing is that the sun is *at least* 4½ million miles away, an epochal advance in man's knowledge of the universe he inhabits. The failure of Aristarchus to get a better result exposes the error in Plato's separation of brainwork and technology. The success of Eratosthenes and Apollonius, who gave excellent estimates which disclosed a realm of vast intellectual adventure for all who came after, exposes the poverty of Platonic idealism as a means of enriching man's intellectual life. In putting back measurement into geometry, and so bringing geometry back to earth, Alexandrian materialism attained a new vision of the grandeur of the heavens. The vastness of the prospect engulfed the "heavenly race of the gods" from whom Plato derived the ancestry of philosophers. The calendar reformed by the orders of Caesar, on the advice of Sosigenes, an Alexandrian astronomer, who introduced the leap year to compensate for the fact that the earth takes about six hours more than 365 days to go round the sun, ushers in a new social era. The ancient star religions were losing their social function as timekeepers. Astrology had made way for the secular science of astronomy in the great centre of Mediterranean shipping, where the most prominent landmark surviving to our own time is the "Sailor's Pillar." The intellectual fruits of these discoveries were set forth in a systematic form in the *Almagest* of Ptolemy, about A.D. 150, a book which played an important part in the astronomy of the Arabs, who translated it and transmitted it to Europe. From its pages the pioneers of the Great Navigations learned the art of map-making and of finding the position of a ship at sea. They also learned how much of the world remained to be explored.

ALEXANDRIAN ARITHMETIC.—You will possibly have noticed, perhaps with some regret, that astronomy which is of any use to the mariner for finding the position of a ship at sea, and a value of π which is good enough for machinery, both involve a good deal of arithmetic. The sort of arithmetic which was encouraged by Greek idealists, as we have described it in the last chapter, does not help us to make laborious calculations. Logistic, as they called aids to rapid calculations with the counting frame, was despised by the Athenians. The more practical Alexandrians necessarily adopted a different point of view. At the outset, we find Archimedes grappling with the task of making numbers suitable to the work which numbers are called on to perform. He seems to have realized the advantage of expressing π as a series, and he was the first mathematician to make the discovery that a series of diminishing fractions can choke off. He gave the sum of unlimited geometric series like the following:

$$\frac{1}{2} \quad \frac{1}{4} \quad \frac{1}{8} \quad \frac{1}{16} \quad \frac{1}{32} \quad \frac{1}{64} \quad \frac{1}{128} \cdots$$

The method he used is the same as the one which we use to show that the unlimited recurring decimal $0\cdot\dot{1} = \frac{1}{9}$. Each term in the series is half its predecessor; so we subtract half the series from the series itself, thus:

$$S = \tfrac{1}{2} + \tfrac{1}{4} + \tfrac{1}{8} + \tfrac{1}{16} + \tfrac{1}{32} + \tfrac{1}{64} \ldots$$
$$\tfrac{1}{2}S = \ldots \tfrac{1}{4} + \tfrac{1}{8} + \tfrac{1}{16} + \tfrac{1}{32} + \tfrac{1}{64} \ldots$$

Whence $S - \frac{1}{2}S = \frac{1}{2}$ or $\frac{1}{2}S = \frac{1}{2}$, i.e. $S = 1$. However long we go on, the sum of the series chokes off at 1. The advantage of series like this for representing measurements to any required order of precision can be seen by comparing the sum of the first five and the first ten terms:

0·5	0·5
0·25	0·25
0·125	0·125
0·0625	0·0625
0·03125	0·03125
0·96875	0·015625
	0·0078125
	0·00390625
	0·001953125
	0·0009765625
	0·9990234375

By taking the first five terms we get 0·97 correct to two decimals. This is roughly 3 per cent less than 1. By taking ten terms we get 0·9990, which is only one in a thousand out. You will shortly see that the rapidity with which the series chokes off was much more difficult for the Alexandrians to recognize with the numbers which they actually used than it is for ourselves using decimal fractions. The Attic Greek numeral system used the first nine letters of the Greek alphabet for 1 to 9, the next nine letters for 10 to 90, the next nine for 100 to 900. To do this they added three archaic letters (digamma, san, koppa) to the ordinary alphabet to make the letters up to 27. Using our own familiar alphabet, this is the same as putting:

a	b	c	d	e	f	g	h	i
1	2	3	4	5	6	7	8	9
j	k	l	m	n	o	p	q	r
10	20	30	40	50	60	70	80	90
s	t	u	v	etc.				
100	200	300	400	etc.				

In this notation the number 17 would be represented by *jg*, the number 68 would be *oh*, and 259 *tni*. You may now find it easier to see how the Platonists mixed up their notions about God and the number 3. To get beyond 999 they had to start all over again, using the same letters with ticks to signify higher decimal orders. Archimedes wrote a tract in which he made an estimate of the number of grains of sand in the world. This was by no means a useless performance in an age when people's ideas of how big things could be were confined by the number of letters which they had at their disposal. In the *Sand Reckoner* Archimedes hit on two of the most powerful peculiarities which reside in the modern number script. He proposed that all high numbers should be represented by multiples of simple powers of ten. He also hit upon the law which underlies the modern calculating device called *logarithms*. The rule can be seen by putting side by side any simple geometric series and its parent series, e.g.

1	2	3	4	5	6	7	8	9	10
2	4	8	16	32	64	128	256	512	1,024

If you want to multiply any two numbers in the bottom series, all you have to do is to look up the corresponding numbers in the parent series, add them, and the result is got by taking the number in the bottom series corresponding with the number represented by their sum in the parent series. Thus to multiply 16 by 32, add the corresponding parent numbers (logarithms, as we call them today), $4 + 5 = 9$. The number (antilogarithm, as we call it today) in the bottom series corresponding with 9 in the top series is 512, which is the answer required. Test this rule by building up other series, e.g. 3, 9, 27, 81, 243, 729, etc. In the shorthand of modern algebra, the rule can be written in the mathematical sentence:

$$a^m \times a^n = a^{m+n}$$

Archimedes did not succeed in reforming the number script of his contemporaries, nor in making tables of logarithms by which any multiplication can be carried through rapidly. Such a change would have meant uprooting the social culture of his time. People were still using the old notation for *low* numbers. His brilliant failure shows that we cannot afford to let the mass of mankind be uneducated, however much entertainment the eugenist may get from reflecting upon his superiority to the rest of his fellows. An advance like that proposed by Archimedes must arise from a sense of common need. It is not enough that a few isolated men of genius should recognize what is wanted. The mathematician needs the co-operation of the plain man, just as much as the plain man needs the mathematician if he is to enjoy a punctual system of wheel-driven transport.

This Attic alphabet was a millstone about the necks of the Alexandrians. The first stage of the Alexandrian culture was signalized by tremendous achievements in the art of measurement as applied to astronomy and mechanics. It introduced calculations of appalling magnitude to people who used a number script which introduces an entirely new set of symbols at each decimal order. The second stage of the Alexandrian culture is characterized by a serious attempt to tackle the problem of devising simple and rapid means of calculation. This brought back number into geometry in another way. Geometrical figures such as those of Dem. 2 and Dem. 4 were used to suggest calculating devices. We have already referred to the arithmetic of Nichomachus of Alexandria to illustrate the practical importance of these demonstrations. Two names of far greater importance are those of Diophantus (*c.* A.D. 250) and Theon (*c.* A.D. 350).

Diophantus anticipated the greater part of the algebra of the Hindus and the Arabs. As Hindu mathematics begins about a hundred and fifty years after his death there is reason to suspect that his work became known in the East *via* Persia. We shall refer to his contributions in a later context. For the present it will suffice to notice that Diophantus was the first person to *use* a mathematical gerund, the part of speech which includes the characteristics both of a noun and of a verb (see Chapter 3). Before Diophantus multiplication was confined to numbers treated like nouns. It was not clearly recognized that a new grammatical convention had been introduced by such equations (Dem. 2) as

$$a(b + c) = ab + ac$$
$$a(b - c) = ab - ac$$
$$(a + b)(c + d) = ac + ad + bc + bd$$
$$(a + b)(c - d) = ac - ad + bc - bd$$

These equations raise a problem of which the solution is contained in the *Law of Signs* which Diophantus first used for calculation. By a geometrical figure we can make a model of the quantity $(a + b)$ by joining a line a units long to a line b units long. We can also represent $(a - b)$ as the number of units of lengths by which a line a units long exceeds a shorter line b units long. We have shown in Dem. 2 that we can represent products like $a(b + c)$ or $a(b - c)$ by rectangular figures. We have shown in Dem. 4 that we can represent products like $(a + b)$ $(a + b)$ and $(a + b)$ $(a - b)$, or, what comes to the same thing, $(a + b)$ $(c + d)$ and $(a + b)$ $(c - d)$. What would be the result of multiplying expressions like $(a - b)$ $(a - b)$ or $(a - b)$ $(c - d)$? The geometrical representation of this problem is seen in Fig. 98. The shaded rectangle of area $(a - b)$ $(c - d)$, together with the three

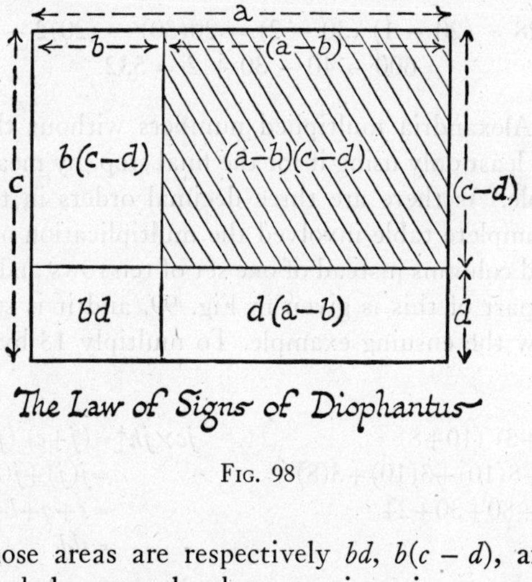

The Law of Signs of Diophantus

FIG. 98

rectangles whose areas are respectively bd, $b(c - d)$, and $d(a - b)$, makes up the whole rectangle whose area is ac, i.e.

$$(a - b)(c - d) + bd + b(c - d) + d(a - b) = ac$$
$$\therefore \quad (a - b)(c - d) + bd + bc - bd + ad - bd = ac$$
$$\therefore \quad (a - b)(c - d) + bc + ad - bd = ac$$

Take away bc and ad from each side and add bd to each, then

$$(a - b)(c - d) = ac - ad - bc + bd$$

Now compare this expression with these:

$$(a + b)(c + d) = ac + ad + bc + bd$$
$$(a + b)(c - d) = ac - ad + bc - bd$$

You will see that in each case the numbers in the result are got by multiplying in turn each of the numbers of one multiplier by each of the numbers in the other. The signs which precede the numbers follow the rules*:

$$
\begin{array}{ccccc}
+ & \times & + & = & + \\
+ & \times & - & = & - \\
- & \times & - & = & +
\end{array}
\qquad - \times + \text{ or } + \times -
$$

This adds a new rule for simplifying work on the abacus. If we want to multiply 19 by 28, we have

$$19 \times 28 = (20 - 1)\ (30 - 2) = 20(30) - (20)2 - 30 + 2$$
$$600 - 40 - 30 + 2 = 532$$

Theon of Alexandria multiplied numbers without the use of the abacus, or at least only using it for the final step, by means of a multiplication table. As there are three decimal orders in the alphabetic script, the complete table involved the multiplication of three sets of nine rows and columns instead of one set of ten rows and columns, like our own. A part of this is given in Fig. 99, and it is sufficient to be able to follow the ensuing example. To multiply 13 by 18, the steps would be:

$$
\begin{aligned}
13\times18 &= (10+3)\ (10+8) & jc\times jh\dagger &= (j+c)\ (j+h)\\
&= 10^2+8(10)+3(10)+3(8) & &= j(j)+j(h)+c(j)+c(h)\\
&= 100+80+30+24 & &= s+q+l+kd\\
&= 234 & &= tld
\end{aligned}
$$

Alternatively,

$$
\begin{aligned}
13\times18 &= (10+3)\ (20-2) & jc\times jh &= (j+c)\ (k-b)\\
&= 10(20)-2(10)+3(20)-3(2) & &= j(k)-j(b)+c(k)-c(b)\\
&= 200-20+60-6 & &= t-k+o-f\\
&= 234 & &= tld
\end{aligned}
$$

You can develop a sympathetic attitude towards the Alexandrians by making up sums like these and working them out by a multiplication

* In using the sign rule remember that $-(a+b-c)$ means the same as $-1(a+b-c)$ $= (-a-b+c)$, e.g.

$$y^2 + x^2 = 2cx + (y^2 + x^2 - 2cx) = 2y^2 + 2x^2$$
$$y^2 + x^2 + 2cx - (y^2 + x^2 - 2cx) = 4cx$$

† We have put *jc* because the Alexandrian numbers represented addition by juxtaposition. To distinguish this from multiplication, which is represented by juxtaposition in modern algebra, we have inserted brackets where multiplication is indicated.

PART OF THE ALEXANDRIAN MULTIPLICATION TABLE

(Roman alphabet substituted for Greek letters)

	1 a	2 b	3 c	4 d	5 e	6 f	7 g	8 h	9 i	10 j	20 k	30 l	40 m	50 n	60 o	70 p	80 q	90 r
2 = b	b	d	f	h	j	jb	jd	jf	jh	k	m	o	q	s	sk	sm	so	sq
3 = c	c	f	i	jb	je	jh	ka	kd	kg	l	o	r	sk	sn	sq	tj	tm	tp
4 = d	d	h	jb	jf	k	kd	kh	lb	lf	m	q	sk	so	t	tm	tq	uk	uo
5 = e	e	j	je	k	ke	l	le	m	me	n	s	sn	t	tn	u	un	v	vn
6 = f	f	jb	jh	kd	l	lf	mb	mh	nd	o	sk	sq	tm	u	uo	vk	vq	wm
7 = g	g	jd	ka	kh	le	mb	mi	nf	oc	p	sm	tj	tq	un	vk	vr	wo	xl
8 = h	h	jf	kd	lb	m	mh	nf	od	pb	q	so	tm	uk	v	vq	wo	xm	yk
9 = i	i	jh	kg	lf	me	nd	oc	pb	qa	r	sq	tp	uo	vn	wm	xl	yk	zj
10 = j	j	k	l	m	n	o	p	q	r	s	t	u	v	w	x	y	z	—

FIG. 99

table like that in Fig. 99. Of course, if you want to multiply fairly large numbers you will have to increase the size of your table.

Theon also dealt with a practical problem which has arisen in our attempt to make a table of angle ratios. We had to use a table of square roots. The method of getting a square root of numbers like $\sqrt{3}$ and $\sqrt{2}$ given on p. 174 is extremely laborious. This is the method which

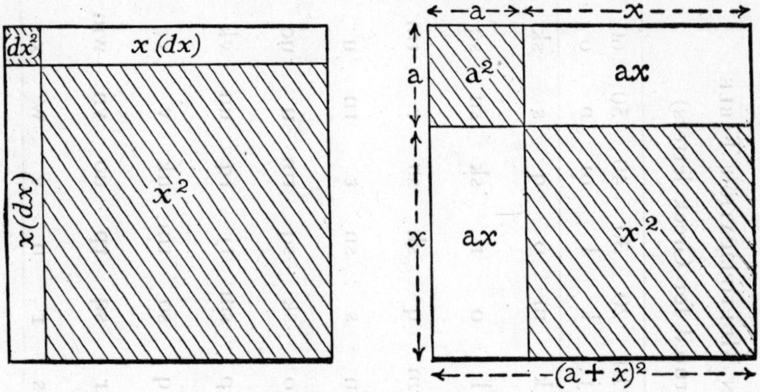

Theon's Differential Method to get a Square Root

FIG. 100

Theon used. It is shown in Fig. 100. On the right is the same figure as was given for Dem. 4 representing

$$(x + a)^2 = x^2 + 2ax + a^2$$

The figure on the left is essentially the same, but instead of a we have written dx, which does not mean d multiplied by x, but a quantity very small compared with x (dwarf x). As before

$$(x + dx)^2 = x^2 + 2x(dx) + (dx)^2$$

or $$(x + dx)^2 - x^2 = 2x(dx) + (dx)^2$$

The figures show you that $(dx)^2$ is very small compared with the two rectangles $x(dx)$, so we should not be much out if we put

$$(x + dx)^2 - x^2 = 2x(dx)$$

or $$dx = \frac{(x + dx)^2 - x^2}{2x}$$

You can see that this is very little out by the following arithmetical example. The quantity 1·01 may be written (1 + 0·01), in which 0·01 may stand for dx and 1 for x, since 0·01 is very small compared with 1. We then get approximately

$$dx = \frac{(1\cdot 01)^2 - 1^2}{2} = \frac{1\cdot 0201 - 1}{2} = 0\cdot 01005$$

The value obtained (0·01005) differs from the original one ($dx = 0\cdot 01$) by only 0·00005.

To get a square root by using this formula we first make a guess. For instance, we know that $\sqrt{2}$ is between 1 and 2, since $1^2(= 1)$ is less than 2 and $2^2(= 4)$ is greater than 2. Since $14^2 = 196$, a good guess is 1·4. This is a little too small, so we may put $\sqrt{2} = 1\cdot 4 + dx$.

$$(1\cdot 4 + dx)^2 = 2$$

Then from the formula,

$$\begin{aligned} dx &= \frac{(1\cdot 4 + dx)^2 - (1\cdot 4)^2}{2(1\cdot 4)} \\ &= \frac{2 - (1\cdot 4)^2}{2(1\cdot 4)} = \frac{2 - 1\cdot 96}{2\cdot 8} \\ &= 0\cdot 014 \quad \text{(approx.)} \end{aligned}$$

So we have approximately

$$(1\cdot 4 + 0\cdot 014)^2 = 2$$

$$\text{or} \quad 1\cdot 414 = \sqrt{2}$$

This, of course, will be a little out. So we take it as a second approximation, and proceed to a third, putting d^2x for the new dwarf x, i.e.* $(1\cdot 414 + d^2x)^2 = 2$.

$$\therefore \quad d^2x = \frac{2 - (1\cdot 414)^2}{2(1\cdot 414)}$$

This gives $d^2x = 0\cdot 0002$. So as a third approximation we can give $\sqrt{2} = 1\cdot 4142$. Comparing these successive approximations, we find:

$$(1\cdot 4)^2 = 1\cdot 96 \qquad \text{error 2 per cent}$$

$$(1\cdot 414)^2 = 1\cdot 999396 \qquad \text{,,} \quad 0\cdot 03 \text{ per cent}$$

$$(1\cdot 4142)^2 = 1\cdot 99996164 \qquad \text{,,} \quad 0\cdot 002 \text{ per cent}$$

We can continue like this as long as we need to do so.

* Note carefully d^2x does *not* mean d squared multiplied by x. It is shorthand for second dwarf x. The ^{2} is an adjective, not a verb.

Theon was the last of the Alexandrian mathematicians of importance. His daughter, Hypatia, edited the works of Diophantus and taught mathematics in Alexandria. She was murdered by the monks

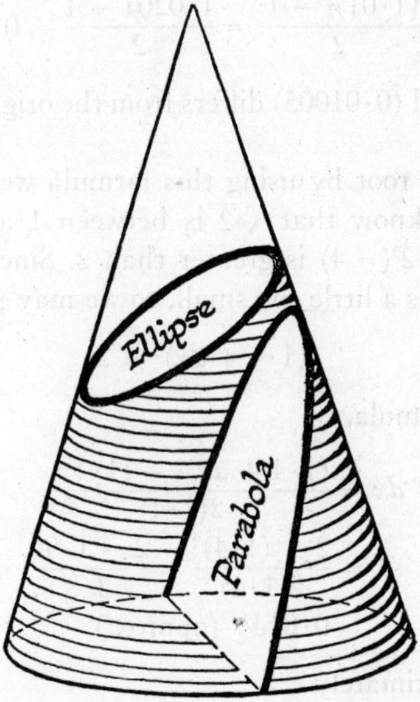

FIG. 101.—CONIC SECTIONS

Apollonius, who lived about 230 B.C., broke away from Plato's rule and studied curves which cannot be drawn with a compass and rule. In particular he studied three curves which correspond with the boundary of a slice of a cone. Two are shown here. The ellipse is the figure which represents the orbits of the planets. The parabola represents the path of a cannon ball. A third conic section will be used, when we describe (Chapter 11) the expansion of the gas in an internal-combustion engine. Using Euclid's geometry of solid figures, Apollonius anticipated some of the leading principles of the Reformation geometry. When men began to bother about the orbits of the planets with new observations supplied by the invention of the telescope, and when artillery and wheel-driven mechanisms came into general use, they were using projection maps for navigation. These projection maps, based on the principle of latitude and longitude, were the death-blow to Plato's geometry and the embryo of the Reformation geometry which will be studied in Chapter 9.

of St. Cyril, who attached more importance to philosophy than to mere chastity. Gibbon describes how they scraped her naked body with oyster shells. "Je me contente de remarquer," observes Voltaire, "que St. Cyrille était homme et homme de parti, qu'il a pu se laisser trop comporter à son zèle; que, quand on met des belles dames toutes nues, ce n'est pas pour les massacrer; que St. Cyrille a sans doute demandé pardon à Dieu de cette action abominable, et que je prie le père des miséricordes d'avoir pitié de son âme."

Theon's method of arriving at a square root introduces us to a conception which plays a very important part in the modern branch of mathematics called the *differential calculus*. The method used by Archimedes for getting the value of π illustrates the principle which lies at the root of the *integral calculus*. The invention of latitude and longitude by Hipparchus and the curves of Apollonius (Fig. 101), another brilliant Alexandrian, embody the basic conception of the *Reformation geometry*. Diophantus laid the foundations of *algebra*. The germs of almost every important advance of the sixteenth and seventeenth centuries of our own era can be found in the achievements of the Alexandrians. That they progressed so far and yet failed to advance further is not explained sufficiently by saying that Alexandrian civilization participated in the downfall of the Roman Empire. It had reached the limits of further growth within the social culture which it had inherited. The next great advance came because a less sophisticated people were equipped with a number script which could meet the requirements of Alexandrian mathematics. The essentially novel feature of the Hindu culture was that men who were not advanced mathematicians had invented what the most brilliant mathematicians of Alexandria had failed to invent, a symbol (0) for *nothing*. There is no more fitting epitaph for the decay of Alexandrian science and mathematics than two lines from the poem of Omar Khayyám, himself foremost among the Arab mathematicians who brought together the fruits of the Hindu and Alexandrian contributions to human knowledge:

> . . . the stars are setting, and the caravan
> Starts for the DAWN OF NOTHING, oh make haste . . .

CHAPTER 6

DISCOVERIES AND TESTS

1. Use the formula $\cos^2 A + \sin^2 A = 1$ to find:

(*a*) cos 40° and sin 50°, given that sin 40° = 0·6428.

(*b*) cos 75° and sin 15°, given that cos 15° = 0·9659.

2. Using the half-angle formula,

If $\sin 20^\circ = 0{\cdot}3420$, $\cos 20^\circ = 0{\cdot}9397$, find $\sin 10^\circ$, $\cos 10^\circ$, $\tan 20^\circ$, and $\tan 10^\circ$.

3. If $\sin 40^\circ = 0{\cdot}6428$, and $\cos 40^\circ = 0{\cdot}7660$, find $\sin 50^\circ$, $\cos 50^\circ$, $\tan 50^\circ$, $\sin 20^\circ$, $\cos 20^\circ$, $\tan 20^\circ$.

4. If $\sin 50^\circ = 0{\cdot}7660$, $\sin 43^\circ = 0{\cdot}6820$, $\sin 23\tfrac{1}{2}^\circ = 0{\cdot}3987$, find the following:

$\cos 50^\circ$	$\tan 50^\circ$	$\cos 21\tfrac{1}{2}^\circ$	$\tan 21\tfrac{1}{2}^\circ$
$\cos 25^\circ$	$\tan 25^\circ$	$\cos 43^\circ$	$\tan 43^\circ$
$\cos 47^\circ$	$\tan 47^\circ$	$\cos 40^\circ$	$\tan 40^\circ$
$\cos 23\tfrac{1}{2}^\circ$	$\tan 23\tfrac{1}{2}^\circ$	$\cos 66\tfrac{1}{2}^\circ$	$\tan 66\tfrac{1}{2}^\circ$

5. If $\cos 40^\circ = 0{\cdot}7660$, $\sin 40^\circ = 0{\cdot}6428$, $\cos 15^\circ = 0{\cdot}9659$, $\sin 15^\circ = 0{\cdot}2588$, $\cos 26\tfrac{1}{2}^\circ = 0{\cdot}8949$, and $\sin 26\tfrac{1}{2}^\circ = 0{\cdot}4462$, use the formulae for $\sin (A + B)$ and $\cos (A + B)$ to find:

$\cos 55^\circ$	$\sin 55^\circ$	$\cos 66\tfrac{1}{2}^\circ$	$\sin 66\tfrac{1}{2}^\circ$
$\cos 41\tfrac{1}{2}^\circ$	$\sin 41\tfrac{1}{2}^\circ$	$\cos 56\tfrac{1}{2}^\circ$	$\sin 56\tfrac{1}{2}^\circ$

6. Using the values in the previous examples, see whether you can find what the correct formula is for $\sin (A - B)$ and $\cos (A - B)$. Verify your result by reference to the figure in Chapter 9, p. 465.

7. In books on trigonometry $\dfrac{1}{\sin A}$ is called cosec A, $\dfrac{1}{\cos A}$ is called sec A, and $\dfrac{1}{\tan A}$ is called cot A. These are abbreviations for secant, cosecant, and cotangent. Use the method for demonstrating that $\cos^2 A + \sin^2 A = 1$ to build up the following formulae which are sometimes used in higher mathematics:

$$1 + \cot^2 A = \operatorname{cosec}^2 A$$
$$1 + \tan^2 A = \sec^2 A$$

8. Solve the cliff problem in Fig. 53 by using the sine formula for the solution of triangles, first to get the distance from the nearest point of observation to the top of the cliff, and then the height.

9. If in Fig. 87 you make A greater than 90° and drop the perpen-

dicular p on to the side b extended beyond the corner A, show that the cosine formula becomes

$$a^2 = b^2 + c^2 + 2bc \cos (180° - A)$$

and the sine formula becomes

$$\frac{\sin (180° - A)}{a} = \frac{\sin B}{b} = \frac{\sin C}{c}$$

10. If the formulae for the solution of triangles when A is less than 90° are

$$a^2 = b^2 + c^2 - 2bc \cos A$$

$$\text{and } \sin A = \frac{a \sin B}{b} = \frac{a \sin C}{c}$$

and when A is greater than 90° are

$$a^2 = b^2 + c^2 + 2bc \cos (180° - A)$$

$$\text{and } \quad \sin(180° - A) = \frac{a \sin B}{b} \text{ etc.}$$

what is the connexion between:

(*a*) cos A and cos (180° − A)

and (*b*) sin A and sin (180° − A)

If you could find a geometrical meaning for the sines and cosines of angles greater than 90°, what would you conclude to be the numerical values of the sine, cosine, and tangent of 150°, 135°, 120°? Verify your result, using the sign rule of Diophantus and the formula $\cos^2 A + \sin^2 A = 1$.

11. Two men start walking at the same time from a crossroads, both walking at 3 miles per hour. Their roads diverge at an angle of 15°. How far apart will they be at the end of two hours?

12. From a base line AB, 500 yards long, the bearings of a flagstaff from A and B are 112° and 63° respectively. Find the distance of the flagstaff from A.

13. From a boat out at sea the elevation of the top of a cliff is found to be 24°. The boatman rows 80 feet straight towards the cliff, and the elevation of the top of the cliff is now 47°. What is the height of the cliff?

14. Three villages A, B, and C are connected by straight, level roads. AB = 6 miles, BC = 9 miles, and the angle between AB and BC is 130°. What is the distance between A and C?

15. A boat sails 8 miles due south. It then changes its direction and sails for 11 miles in a line bearing 54° east of north. How far will it then be from its starting-point?

16. From the formulae for sin (A + B) and cos (A + B) find the formula for sin 2A, sin 3A, cos 2A, and cos 3A.

17. From the formulae for sin (A + B) and sin (A – B), cos (A + B) and cos (A – B), show that

$$\sin C + \sin D = 2 \sin \frac{C+D}{2} \cos \frac{C-D}{2}$$

$$\cos C + \cos D = 2 \cos \frac{C+D}{2} \cos \frac{C-D}{2}$$

$$\sin C - \sin D = 2 \cos \frac{C+D}{2} \cdot \sin \frac{C-D}{2}$$

$$\cos C - \cos D = -2 \sin \frac{C+D}{2} \cdot \sin \frac{C-D}{2}$$

Hence show how the half-angle formulae can be built up from the formulae for the addition of angles. Hint: C + D = 2A, C – D = 2B.

18. Using trigonometrical tables, find the limits between which π lies by considering the boundaries and areas of the inscribed and circumscribed figures with seventy-two sides.

19. Use the fact that sin x is very nearly equal to x, when x is a very small angle measured in radians, to obtain values for sin $\frac{1}{2}$°, sin 1°, and sin $1\frac{1}{2}$°, taking π as 3·1416.

20. Since the moon's rim almost exactly coincides with that of the sun in a total eclipse, the angular diameter of the sun (cf. Fig. 89) may be taken as roughly half a degree. Taking the sun's distance as 93 million miles, find the diameter of the sun, using the fact that for small angles measured in radians sin x = x and cos x = 1.

21. Tabulate in steps of one degree, the angles 1° to 10° in radians, and tabulate in degrees taking steps of quarter-radians the angles from 0 to 2 radians.

22. In the next few examples take the earth's radius as 3,960 miles.

The ancient Inca capital Quito, Kisumu on Lake Victoria in Kenya, and Pontianak in Borneo are all within half a degree from the equator. The longitude of Quito is 78° W. of Greenwich, Kisumu 35° E., and Pontianak 109° E. Find the shortest distance between each two of these places, using the value $3\frac{1}{7}$ for π.

23. Archangel, Zanzibar, and Mecca are all within about a degree of longitude 40° E. The latitude of Archangel is $64\frac{2}{3}$° N. The latitude of Mecca is $21\frac{1}{3}$° N., and of Zanzibar 6° S. What are the distances between them?

24. With the aid of a figure show that the length of a degree measured along latitude x is $x \cos L$, if x is the length of a degree at the equator.

25. If Winnipeg and Plymouth are within a third of a degree of latitude 50° N., find the distance between them if Plymouth is 4° W. of Greenwich and Winnipeg is 97° W.

26. Reading and Greenwich have the same latitude, 51° 28′ N., and the longitude of Reading is 59′ W. How far is Reading from Greenwich?

27. Two places are on the same meridian of longitude. The latitude of A is 31° N. B is 200 miles from A. What is the latitude of B?

28. Using the method given on p. 276 for multiplying 19 by 28, illustrate the law of signs by multiplying:

(*a*) 13 by 27 (*c*) 15 by 39
(*b*) 17 by 42 (*d*) 21 by 48
(*e*) 28 by 53

29. Do the multiplications given in Example 28 with the aid of the Alexandrian multiplication table.

30. Sum the following geometrical progressions to n terms:

(*a*) $3 - 9 + 27 \ . \ . \ .$ (*c*) $2\frac{1}{4} - 1\frac{1}{2} + 1 \ . \ . \ .$
(*b*) $\frac{1}{4} - \frac{1}{8} + \frac{1}{16} \ . \ . \ .$ (*d*) $1 - \frac{2}{3} + \frac{4}{9} \ . \ . \ .$

Check your results arithmetically by finding the sum to five terms.

31. Find (*a*) the $2n$th term and (*b*) the $(2n + 1)$th term of the series $a, - ar, ar^2, - ar^3$, etc.

THINGS TO MEMORIZE

1. $\cos \frac{1}{2}A = \sqrt{\frac{1}{2}(1 + \cos A)}$.

$\sin \frac{1}{2}A = \dfrac{\sin A}{2 \cos \frac{1}{2}A} = \sqrt{\frac{1}{2}(1 - \cos A)}$.

2. $\cos^2 A + \sin^2 A = 1$; $\sin A = \sqrt{1 - \cos^2 A}$; $\cos A = \sqrt{1 - \sin^2 A}$.

3. $\sin (A \pm B) = \sin A \cos B \pm \cos A \sin B$.

$\cos (A \pm B) = \cos A \cos B \mp \sin A \sin B$.

4. $a^2 = b^2 + c^2 - 2bc \cos A = b^2 + c^2 + 2bc \cos (180° - A)$.

5. $\dfrac{\sin A}{a} = \dfrac{\sin B}{b} = \dfrac{\sin C}{c} = \dfrac{\sin (180° - A)}{a}$.

6. When x is measured in radians, if x is very small,

$$\sin x = x = \tan x$$
$$\cos x = 1$$

7. $- \times - = +$ $\qquad - \div - = +$

$- \times + = -$ $\qquad - \div + = -$

$+ \times + = +$ $\qquad + \div - = -$

8. $\sin 0° = 0 = \tan 0°$ $\qquad \sin 60° = \dfrac{\sqrt{3}}{2} = \cos 30°$

$\cos 0° = 1 = \tan 45°$

$\sin 30° = \frac{1}{2} = \cos 60°$ $\qquad \sin 45° = \dfrac{1}{\sqrt{2}} = \cos 45°$

Footnote to p. 258: *Values of* π

We have found values for π by using the two approximate equations $\pi = n \sin \pi/n$ and $\pi = n \tan \pi/n$ with various values of n, and in the fourth column of the table we give the mean of the two values of π derived from these equations, so that this column contains $\frac{1}{2}n(\sin \pi/n + \tan \pi/n)$. With the help of formulae to be demonstrated later, we can work out expressions for the errors of these approximations to π, when n is large, but you may have difficulty in following the rest of this footnote until you have read a few more pages ahead.

One of the formulae, given on p. 502, is

$$\sin a = a - \frac{a^3}{3!} + \frac{a^5}{5!} - \frac{a^7}{7!} + \dots$$

where a is an angle given in radian measure. If we put $a = \pi/n$, we find

$$n \sin \frac{\pi}{n} = \pi - \frac{\pi^3}{6n^2} + \frac{\pi^5}{120n^4} - \dots$$

and, *if n is large*, the last term given on the right and all others after it are negligible, so that, approximately,

$$n \sin \frac{\pi}{n} = \pi - \frac{\pi^3}{6n^2}$$

In a similar manner we find, again approximately, that

$$n \tan \frac{\pi}{n} = \pi + \frac{\pi^3}{3n^2}$$

and $$\tfrac{1}{2}n\left(\sin \frac{\pi}{n} + \tan \frac{\pi}{n}\right) = \pi + \frac{\pi^3}{12n^2}$$

CHAPTER VII

The Dawn of Nothing

OR

HOW ALGEBRA BEGAN

To introduce the next stage in the narrative we cannot do better than quote Dantzig's admirable book *Number: The Language of Science.** "This long period of nearly five thousand years saw the rise and fall of many a civilization, each leaving behind it a heritage of literature, art, philosophy, and religion. But what was the net achievement in the field of reckoning, the earliest art practised by man? An inflexible numeration so crude as to make progress wellnigh impossible, and a calculating device so limited in scope that even elementary calculations called for the services of an expert. . . . Man used these devices for thousands of years without making a single worth-while improvement in the instrument, without contributing a single important idea to the system. . . . Even when compared with the slow growth of ideas during the dark ages, the history of reckoning presents a peculiar picture of desolate stagnation. When viewed in this light, the achievement of the unknown Hindu, who some time in the first centuries of our era discovered the principle of position, assumes the proportion of a world event."

During the first centuries B.C. and A.D. a "matchstick" number script was being used in China. This was essentially hieroglyphic, a representation of computation carried out with bits of stick. The use of symbols like $\equiv$ $\doteq$ for 3 and 2 is nearer to the hard reality of the counting board than the more sophisticated literal numeration of the Hebrews, Romans, and Greeks, whose practice was to introduce new symbols for each column in the counting frame (Fig. 6). Thus in Roman script the signs I, X, C, M stand for the columns of units tens, hundreds, and thousands. Repetition of X three times (XXX) meant three beads on the ten column, and repetition of I twice meant two beads on the unit column. If the Romans had written 32 as (III) (II) there would have been nothing to distinguish it from 320, 302, 3,200, 3,002, etc. The same applies to the matchstick notation. If we write 32 as $\equiv$ $=$, what is to distinguish it from any of the other numbers mentioned? There is one simple way of getting over this, namely,

* New York: The Macmillan Company.

to use some sign, at first a dot, then a circle (0), to stand for the *empty* column of the abacus. Thus 320 would be ≡ =. and 302 would be ≡.= Before the introduction of the . or 0, ≡ had become Ƶ, and = had become Z, the original form of our 3 and 2. This practice began in India at some time between 100 B.C. and A.D. 150. It was not primarily a mathematical discovery in the academic sense. It was a practical one. The Hindu word for (0) is *sunya*, which means *empty*. The identification of 0 with "nothing" or zero was an afterthought. The same discovery was made independently by the Maya calendar-civilization which flourished about A.D. 500. The Mayas adopted a vertical arrangement of number symbols of the matchstick type in their stone monuments.

The epochal character of this step has been universally recognized. Laplace, the brilliant mathematical astronomer who told Napoleon that God is not a necessary hypothesis in natural science, refers to it in a significant passage:

"It is India that gave us the ingenious method of expressing all numbers by means of ten symbols, each symbol receiving a value of position, as well as an absolute value; a profound and important idea which appears so simple to us now that we ignore its true merit, but its very simplicity, the great ease which it has lent to all computations, puts our arithmetic in the first rank of useful inventions; and we shall appreciate the grandeur of this achievement when we remember that it escaped the genius of Archimedes and Apollonius, two of the greatest men produced by antiquity."

The same surprise is expressed by Dantzig:

"Particularly puzzling to us is the fact that the great mathematicians of Greece did not stumble on it. Is it that the Greeks had such a marked contempt for applied science, leaving even the instruction of their children to the slaves? But if so, how is it that the nation that gave us geometry, and carried this science so far, did not create even a rudimentary algebra? Is it not equally strange that algebra, that cornerstone of modern mathematics, also originated in India, and at about the same time that positional numeration did?"

No doubt it is impossible to give a complete answer to such questions. Still it is not so difficult to see some light on them. One reason why the mathematicians of antiquity were unable to accomplish this feat is that they inherited a social culture which forced them to use a number script evolved before the need for elaborate calculations with large numbers was keenly felt. In such a situation advance could only come from a less sophisticated people, who did not begin to write numbers until large numbers were being used freely. The volume of world trade expanded considerably during the time of the Roman Empire. A problem which occurs in the *Lilavati*, and is quoted below, illustrates how the first Hindu arithmeticians were preoccupied with problems of taxation, debt, and interest. The difficulty of understanding why it should have been the Hindus who took this step, why it was not taken by the great mathematicians of antiquity, why it should have first been taken by the practical man, is only insuperable if we seek for the explanation of intellectual progress in the genius of a few gifted individuals, instead of in the whole social framework of custom thought which circumscribes the greatest individual genius. What happened in India about A.D. 100 had happened before. Maybe it is happening now in Soviet Russia. At a certain stage in the history of culture the eruption of a less sophisticated community proves to be a turning-point. History chooses the foolish things of this world to confound the wise, and the weak things to bring to naught the mighty. To the mathematician this essential social truth is not flattering. It is foolishness. To the eugenist it is a stumbling-block. To accept it is to recognize that every culture contains within itself its own doom, unless it pays as much attention to the education of the mass of mankind as to the education of the exceptionally gifted people.

An answer to the other question, why the Greeks failed to develop algebra, and why the Hindus and Arabs succeeded where they had failed, will emerge in the course of this chapter. The invention of *sunya* or "0" liberated the human intellect from the prison bars of the counting-frame. Once there was a sign for the empty column, "carrying over" on slate, paper, or other material for writing was just as easy as carrying over on the abacus. The new script was a perfect model of the mechanical action, and it had an advantage that the mechanical model lacked. It could stretch as far as necessary in either direction. If you have an abacus with, say, four columns (e.g. M, C, X, I), you get into difficulties when you start calculating with numbers larger than 9,999. On paper it is just as easy to handle mechanically sums like

9,999,999,999,999,999

as to handle quantities like 9,999. Then again, many simple characteristics of series of numbers, as we have illustrated by means of the Zeno paradox in the first chapter, are recognized at once. Their meaning does not lie buried in the obscurity of a literal notation. As a matter of fact, isolated men of genius in Alexandria, like Diophantus and Theon, did tackle the same kind of problems as the Hindus and Arabs, who succeeded them. Their algebra was hopelessly complicated by the fact that they used the same symbols for words and proper numbers. So they could not confine the use of letter to abstract numbers. A fruitful interest in the rules which apply to the use of numbers began precisely when a new social culture, springing from the working life of a community with no fetters of agelong custom, provided the apparatus for handling numbers with ease, and suggested practical problems for numerical solution. The Greeks lacked the social impulse to develop an algebra. The Alexandrians felt the need and lacked the social equipment. The Hindus had the social equipment, when the need arose. We shall discuss separately in this chapter three currents which contributed to the algebra of the Hindus and the Arabs: first, the need for simple rules of calculation, or *algorithm*, as arithmetic was called in the thirteenth century, after the Arab algebraist, Al Khwarismi; secondly, the solution of practical problems involving numbers, i.e. the "solution of *equations*"; and finally, the renewed study of *series*.

Our knowledge of Hindu mathematics begins with the *Lilavati* of Aryabhata about A.D. 470. This author discusses the rules of arithmetic, uses the law of signs of Diophantus, gives a table of sines in intervals of $3\frac{3}{4}°$, and evaluates π as $3 \cdot 1416$. In short, Hindu mathematics starts where Alexandrian mathematics left off. Just a little later, in the sixth century, comes Brahmagupta, who follows the same themes as Aryabhata: calculation, series, equations. These early Hindu mathematicians had already stated the laws of "ciphers" or *sunya* on which all our arithmetic depends, namely

$$a \times 0 = 0$$
$$a + 0 = a$$
$$a - 0 = a$$

They used fractions freely without the aid of metaphorical units like minutes and seconds, writing them as we do, except that they did not use a bar. Thus seven-eights was written $\begin{smallmatrix}7\\8\end{smallmatrix}$. About A.D. 800 Baghdad became a centre of learning under a Moslem Caliphate. Exiles from the Alexandrian schools which had been closed after the rise of Christianity had brought pagan science into Persia at an earlier date. Greek philosophical works had also been brought thither by banished Nestorian heretics. Jewish scholars were set by the Caliph to translate Syriac and Greek texts into Arabic. The works of Ptolemy, Euclid, Aristotle, and a host of other authors of classical scientific treatises were circulated from Baghdad to the Moorish universities which were set up in various countries, notably Spain, during the ninth and tenth centuries.

The Arab nomads who conquered and overran the ruins of the Roman Empire had no priesthood. Within the world of Islam timekeeping broke asunder from any association with a pre-existing priestly caste. Jewish and Arabic scholars were set to the task of making calendars. They improved on the astronomical tables of the Alexandrians and Hindus, and they brought to their task the advantage of the simple number script which the Hindus had invented. Among the famous mathematicians first and foremost comes Alkarismi (Al Khwarismi), who lived in the ninth century A.D. Another great mathematician, Omar Khayyám, lived in the twelfth century A.D. You will recall the close connexion between this new awakening of interest in mathematics and the secular task of keeping time, in the words of the *Rubaiyat:*

"Ah but my computations, people say,
Have squared the Year to human compass, eh?
If so, by striking from the Calendar
Unborn to-morrow and dead yesterday. . . ."

This quotation reminds us that the intellectual and even the literary awakening of Europe in the fourteenth and fifteenth centuries had very little to do with the Byzantine cult of decorative art. The metre of Fitzgerald's translation is based on the original. The poetry of modern Europe in both rhyme and metre is, like our chemistry and our algebra, the debt of our social heritage to the Moorish occupation of Spain and South France. Provençal ballad poetry was modelled on the songs sung by the Troubadours, when the works of Arab mathematicians were being translated into European languages. Of later Arab writers, Al Karki and Al Kayami of the eleventh century are especially important. A later Hindu arithmetician Bhaskara in the twelfth century is also noteworthy. The translations of these works were the foundations of European mathematics.

The two chief foci for the introduction of Arabic and Hindu

mathematics to the backward Nordic peoples of Europe were the Moorish universities of Spain and Sicilian trade in the Mediterranean. A Sicilian coin with the date 1134 Anno Domini is the first extant example in Christendom of the official use of the so-called Gobar numerals, the Hindu numbers as modified by the western Arabs. In Britain the earliest case is said to be the rent roll of the St. Andrew's chapter in 1490. Italian merchants were using them for their obvious advantages in commercial calculations in the thirteenth century. The change did not come about without obstruction from the representatives of custom thought. An edict of A.D. 1259 forbade the bankers of Florence to use the infidel symbols, and the ecclesiastical authorities of the University of Padua in A.D. 1348 ordered that the price list of books should be prepared not in "ciphers," but in "plain" letters. Three social elements contributed to the diffusion of the Moorish culture. The first is that the Christian religion, in replacing the Roman Pantheon, had taken over the social function of the priests as calendar-makers, as we shall see more clearly in the next chapter. As the custodians of the calendar, the monks were interested in mathematics. Thus Adelard of Bath disguised himself as a Moslem (about A.D. 1120), studied at Cordova, and translated the works of Euclid and Alkarismi, together with the Arabic astronomical tables. Gerard of Cremona about the same time studied at Toledo. He translated about ninety Arabic texts, including the Arabic edition of Ptolemy's *Almagest*. The heretical ecclesiastic Paciulo, who had the good fortune not to be found out, translated the arithmetic of Bhaskara, and introduced Theon's method of getting square roots. Of equal importance is the independent culture of the rising merchant-class. A foremost figure among the mercantile mathematicians is Leonardo Fibonacci, whose *Liber Abaci* (A.D. 1228) was the first mercantile arithmetic. His name is remembered for a quaint series of numbers, entitled the Fibonacci series. It is:

$$0 \quad 1 \quad \frac{1}{2} \quad \frac{2}{4} \quad \frac{3}{8} \quad \frac{5}{16} \quad \frac{8}{32} \quad \frac{13}{64} \quad \frac{21}{128} \quad \text{etc.*}$$

As far as its author was concerned, this seems to have been a *jeu d'esprit*. Oddly enough a use has been found for it quite recently in applying Mendel's laws of heredity to the effects of brother-sister incest.

*If the nth term is $\frac{u_n}{v_n}$, its connexion with its predecessors is

$$\frac{u_n}{v_n} = \frac{u_{n-1} + u_{n-2}}{2v_{n-1}}$$

Fibonacci, who was the despair of his teachers as a boy, found mathematics interesting by applying it to the social needs of his class. He came to make up series for fun, when he had learned to use equations to solve practical problems in interest and debt. Leonardo was patronized by the atheistical Frederick II under whose encouragement the University of Salerno became a centre from which Jewish physicians carried the Moorish learning into the ecclesiastical centres of learning in Northern Europe. The third stream of diffusion is represented by these Jewish physicians. "Physician and algebraist" was a term still used in Spain until quite recently, just as surgeon and barber went together in the Middle Ages. Maybe the intellectual accomplishments of barbers were underrated.

Before proceeding to an account of the new arithmetic or Algorithm, it will help us at a later stage if we pause to recognize what latent possibilities of the new numerals immediately impressed themselves on the imagination of the unsophisticated pupils of the Moorish culture. Stifel, whom we have already met as a commentator of the Apocalyptic "mysterium," was not referring to the number 666 when he wrote, "I might write a whole book concerning the marvellous things relating to numbers." He was referring to new connexions which suggested themselves when mankind acquired a script which could reproduce the mechanical work of the counting-frame without any need for the device itself. Consider the number MMCCCXXXII (2,332) in our notation. The Roman figures are a label for two beads on the first (units) column, three beads on the second, three on the third, and two on the fourth (thousands) column. The essence of the old systems was that each symbol (M, C, etc.) stood for a particular column, or in the case of Hebrew and Attic Greek a particular bead in a particular column. Written in Gobar numerals, reading from left to right, 2,332 give us the number of beads in the successive columns without recourse to any new symbols. For practical purposes the symbols stand for the beads only. The columns themselves are distinguished by the position of the numbers, an empty column being represented by "0." However, position itself can be described by the use of numbers, as you will see by considering the meaning of the number 6,666,666. This means that if we had an abacus going up to millions, i.e. with seven columns, there would be six beads in the seventh (millions), six in the sixth (hundred thousands), six in the fifth (ten thousands), six in the fourth (thousands), and so on. Now a million is $(10\times10\times10\times10\times10\times10)$ i.e. six tens multiplied together, or 10^6. Similarly a hundred thousand is 10^5. In other words, each bead in the seventh column stands for 10^6. Each bead in the sixth column stands for 10^5, each bead in the fifth column stands for 10^4, each bead in the fourth column for 10^3, and each bead in the third column for 10^2. Putting this in a simple rule, we may say that 10^n is the value of each bead in the $(n + 1)$th column. The consequences of this rule, found out by Stifel, apparently excited him almost as much as the number 666, which led to his conversion to the Reformed doctrine.

Consider what it meant. First, we have found a *physical* model for 10^n which takes us far beyond the confines of Greek geometry. Greek geometry could give us a model for 10^1, i.e. a line 10 units long, a model for 10^2, i.e. a square of side 10 units long, a model for 10^3, i.e. a cube of side 10 units long. Beyond that point (see p. 90) the number n, put where we put it in the top right-hand corner, to mean the operation of multiplying n tens together, had no physical equivalent in the real world. With the new number script 10^{12} (a billion) meant the value which would be given to each bead in the thirteenth column of a counting-frame with thirteen or more columns, if such were made. So the horizon of large numbers widened out immeasurably. What of smaller numbers? We have said nothing of the first column. To see the implications of the new way of translating 10^n we have to arrange the geometric series in the descending order in which the *index* numbers (n) occur in the number script, thus:

7th column	*6th column*	*5th column*	*4th column*	*3rd column*	*2nd column*
1,000,000	100,000	10,000	1,000	100	10
10^6	10^5	10^4	10^3	10^2	10^1

You now see that n goes down one step when the value of the bead is reduced through dividing by ten. So the index number n of the first column should be one less than 1, i.e. 0. Indeed we may go further. One less than 0 is -1, so 1 divided by 10 is 10^{-1}. Thus we can stretch the horizon of the index numbers backwards to any degree of smallness thus:

. .	10,000	1,000	100	10	1	$\frac{1}{10}$	$\frac{1}{100}$	$\frac{1}{1000}$	. . .
	10^4	10^3	10^2	10^1	10^0	10^{-1}	10^{-2}	10^{-3}	

A second marvellous thing relating to these numbers is that they can equally well give us the meaning of a^n when a is any number besides 10. This is another way of saying that the advantages of the Hindu numerals have nothing to do with the mysterious properties of 10. On the contrary the mysterious properties of 10 are merely due to the fact that Hindu numerals were introduced to fit a counting-frame on which the index numbers went up one when the value of the beads went up ten. Ten itself was chosen in the first place simply because man used his ten fingers to count. Suppose we were all one-armed, as our militarists would like us to be. We should then count in fives as the military Romans did to some extent by using the intervals V, L, D, for 5, 50, and 500. The first column of the counting-frame would have five beads, each worth one, the second column five beads each worth five, the third column five beads each worth five times five, the fourth five beads each worth five times five times five. When we had counted all the beads on the first column we should switch them back and put one bead in the second column, leaving the first empty. When we had counted five in the second we should switch back all of them and put one out in the third. So if we used 0 for the empty column we should write 1, 2, 3, 4; as we do in the decimal system, but five would be 10, and twenty-five would be 100. Using the words themselves for our own notation, we should have the symbols:

One to five	1	2	3	4	10
Six to ten	11	12	13	14	20
Eleven to fifteen	21	22	23	24	30
. . . . . .					
Twenty-one to twenty-five	41	42	43	44	100
One hundred and twenty-one to one hundred and twenty-five	441	442	443	444	1,000

The multiplication table for this system is given in Fig. 102 with a table for addition. Having worried it out for yourself, you may then multiply the number corresponding with 29 ("104") in our notation by 31 (i.e. "111"), using exactly the same method as the one we use ourselves, except that the tables of multiplication and addition will have to be those in Fig. 102. Thus

104		104
111	or if you are more used	111
104	to the other way	104
104		104
104		104
12,044		12,044

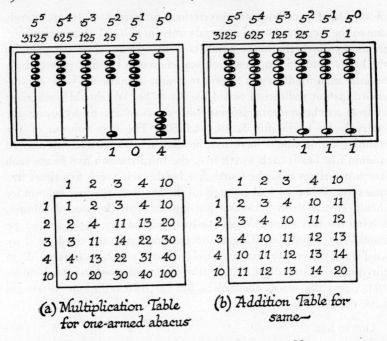

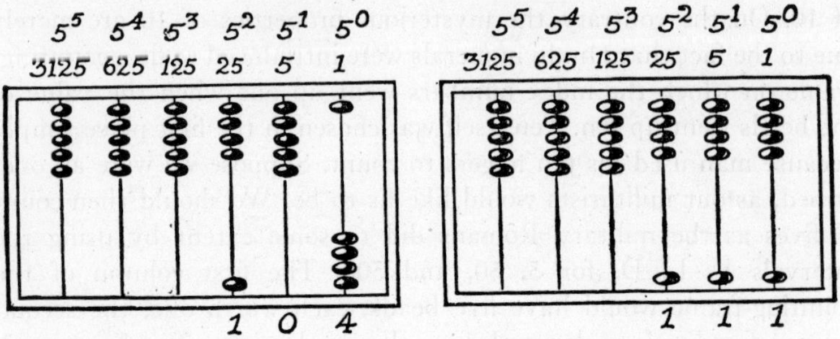

	1	2	3	4	10
1	1	2	3	4	10
2	2	4	11	13	20
3	3	11	14	22	30
4	4	13	22	31	40
10	10	20	30	40	100

(a) Multiplication Table for one-armed abacus

	1	2	3	4	10
1	2	3	4	10	11
2	3	4	10	11	12
3	4	10	11	12	13
4	10	11	12	13	14
10	11	12	13	14	20

(b) Addition Table for same—

FIG. 102.—THE ABACUS OF THE ONE-ARMED MAN

The principle of the abacus is that the value of a bead in successive columns from left to right is given by:

$$\ldots x^5 \quad x^4 \quad x^3 \quad x^2 \quad x^1 \quad x^0$$

In our notation $x = 10$. For the abacus drawn here $x = 5$.

104 in the notation of the one-armed abacus would be 1(25) + 0(5) + 4(1), i.e. 29 in the notation of the ten-finger abacus which we use.

111 in the notation of the one-armed abacus would be 1(25) + 1(5) + 1(1), i.e. 31 in the notation of the ten-finger abacus which we use.

The number "12,044" means 1(625) 2(125), 0(25), 4(5), 4(1), i.e. 899, which is what you get by putting

$$\begin{array}{r} 29 \\ 31 \\ \hline 87 \\ 29 \\ \hline 899 \end{array} \quad \text{or} \quad \begin{array}{r} 29 \\ 31 \\ \hline 29 \\ 87 \\ \hline 899 \end{array}$$

If human communities were bred like stock, they could select for the disease known as *lobster claw*. The moral qualities which most eugenists would wish to perpetuate are not much less repulsive. A community with this deformity might use a two-finger abacus. One would be 1, 2 would be 10, 3 would be 11, 4 would be 100, 5 would be 101, 6 would be 110, 7 would be 111, and 8 would be 1,000. There would be no multiplication table to learn except $1 \times 1 = 1$, and the only addition would be $1 + 1 = 10$. Square roots would be easy, and the only disadvantage would be the large amount of paper which would be used. You can make up sums in the dual notation, which greatly intrigued Laplace, if you want further proof that the interesting properties of 10 are due to the nature of the Hindu arithmetic rather than the converse, as most of us grow up to believe.

ALGORITHMS.—The scope of the new arithmetic is set forth in the introduction to one of the earliest books on the new *Craft of Nombrynge* (A.D. 1300) to be written in the English language. "Here tells that ther ben 7 spices or partes of the craft. The first is called addicion, the secunde is called subtraccion. The thyrd is called duplacion. The 4 is called dimydicion. The 5 is called multiplicacion. The 6 is called diuision. The 7 is called extraccion of the Rote."

You will already have grasped the fact that the number symbols of the Hindus were different from all other number symbols which preceded them. Those of their predecessors had been labels with which you recorded a calculation you were going to carry out, or had already performed, on the counting-frame. The Hindu numerals swept away the necessity for this clumsy instrument. Addition and subtraction could be done as easily "in one's head" as on the abacus itself. Carrying over "in one's head" in the language of modern physiology means that the brain receives from small changes of tone in the muscles of the eye-socket and fingers with which we count precisely the same sequence of nerve messages as those which accompany carrying over on the counting-frame. Carrying over two means that we have started all over again twice with the beads of one column and have to put two beads in the next column on the left to register the fact. The reason why this is possible is that the use of 0 or *sunya* for the empty column makes the number of figures precisely equivalent to the number of columns on the counting-frame.

The algorithm of multiplication which we use is based on the same principle as Egyptian duplation. This, as our quotation shows,

completed side by side with it for some time. In Dem. 2 we learned that

$$a(b + c + d) = ab + ac + ad$$

So multiplying 532 by 7, i.e. 7 times (500 + 30 + 2), is the same thing as

$$7(500) + 7(30) + 7(2)$$

To begin with, this would be written:

$$\begin{array}{r} 532 \\ 7 \\ \hline 14 \\ 210 \\ 3{,}500 \\ \hline 3{,}724 \end{array} \qquad \text{or} \qquad \begin{array}{r} 532 \\ 7 \\ \hline 3{,}500 \\ 210 \\ 14 \\ \hline 3{,}724 \end{array}$$

This was soon shortened to:

$$\begin{array}{r} 532 \\ 7 \\ \hline 3{,}724 \end{array} \qquad \text{or} \qquad \begin{array}{r} 532 \\ 7 \\ \hline 3{,}724 \end{array}$$

Once this step was made by applying the rule of "carrying over," a simple method for multiplying numbers of any size followed naturally. Thus

$$532\ (732) = (532)\ 700 + (532)\ 30 + (532)\ 2$$

This can be written in the form suitable for addition in either of two ways, the one on the right being better because it is suitable for approximation, especially when decimal fractions are used:

$$\begin{array}{rl} 532 & \\ 732 & \\ \hline 1{,}064 & 2(532) \\ 15{,}960 & 30(532) \\ 372{,}400 & 700(532) \\ \hline 389{,}424 & \end{array} \qquad \begin{array}{rl} 532 & \\ 732 & \\ \hline 372{,}400 & 700(532) \\ 15{,}960 & 30(532) \\ 1{,}064 & 2(532) \\ \hline 389{,}424 & \end{array}$$

The earliest commercial arithmetics which used the Arabic Hindu algorithms put down the numbers which are carried over, thus:

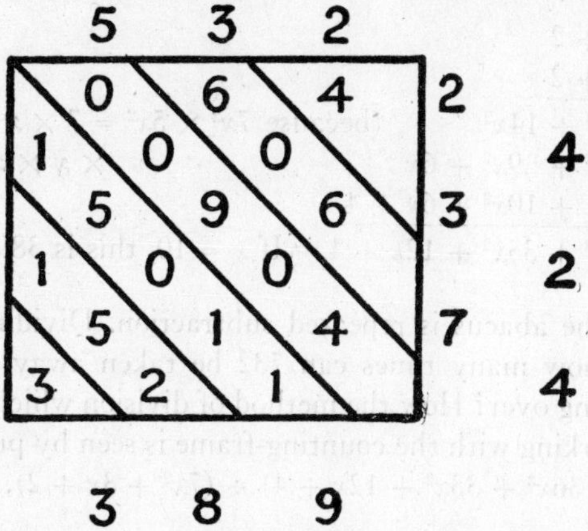

The answer was read off by adding the columns diagonally. Multiplication, as we carry it out, presupposes that we have access to a table for multiplication. The identification of number symbols with the beads instead of with the columns reduces the size of the table necessary. We only need to be able to multiply up to ten times ten, and this is an undertaking vastly less formidable to the human memory than learning the Alexandrian multiplication tables used by Theon. Duplation lingered on side by side with our own method of multiplying because the full advantage of the latter is only reaped when the table has been committed to memory, so that continual reference can be dispensed with. This could not happen till there were new schools to meet the requirements of the mercantile class. Germany took the lead in this development. The craft of nombrynge was so important in Germany during the fourteenth century that it could boast a guild of *Rechenmeister*. You must not imagine that there is even at the present time any absolute uniformity in the various algorithms in use. In Europe the two alternative ways of carrying out multiplication (left-right and right-left) are both practised today very much as they were used by the Arabs. There is less uniformity in the methods of division, and the one taught in English schools is not exactly like any of the Arabic ones. It is a comparatively late device first used, as far as we know, by Calandri in 1491. If you do not know why we divide in the way we do, the best way to understand it is to use abstract numbers for the value of each bead on the counting-frame, giving the value

1 for the first column, x for the second, x^2 for the third, and x^3 for the fourth, etc. We can rewrite the previous multiplication:

$$\begin{array}{r} 5x^2 + 3x + 2 \\ 7x^2 + 3x + 2 \\ \hline 35x^4 + 21x^3 + 14x^2 \qquad\qquad \\ 15x^3 + 9x^2 + 6x \qquad \\ + 10x^2 + 6x + 4 \\ \hline 35x^4 + 36x^3 + 33x^2 + 12x + 4 \end{array}$$

(because $7x^2 \times 5x^2 = 7 \times x \times x \times 5 \times x \times x = 35x^4$, etc.)

(If $x = 10$, this is 389,424)

division on the abacus is repeated subtraction. Dividing 389,424 by 732 means, how many times can 732 be taken away from 389,424, leaving nothing over? How the method of division which we use corresponds to working with the counting-frame is seen by putting it in the form $(35x^4 + 36x^3 + 33x^2 + 12x + 4) \div (7x^2 + 3x + 2)$, thus:

$$7x^2 + 3x + 2)\ 35x^4 + 36x^3 + 33x^2 + 12x + 4\ (5x^2 + 3x + 2$$

$$\begin{array}{r} 35x^4 + 15x^3 + 10x^2 \qquad\qquad\quad \\ \hline 21x^3 + 23x^2 + 12x + 4 \\ 21x^3 + 9x^2 + 6x \qquad \\ \hline 14x^2 + 6x + 4 \\ 14x^2 + 6x + 4 \\ \hline 0 \quad\ 0 \quad\ 0 \end{array}$$

Taking away $5x^2$ times $7x^2 + 3x + 2$ empties the fifth column of the frame.

Taking away $3x$ times $7x^2 + 3x + 2$ empties the fourth column.

Taking away 2 times $7x^2 + 3x + 2$ empties the remaining columns.

The fact that we still use the commercial idiom "borrow one" in subtraction and division reminds us that the laws of calculation were developed in response to the cultural needs of the mercantile class. The use of abstract numbers for the value of the beads shows you why the laws of arithmetic are just the same for the one-armed abacus as for the ten-finger abacus. The use of number symbols which could represent a counting-frame with as many columns as we need is a parable of the growing volume of trade which necessitated operations with large numbers. The popularity of the new methods grew, as Europe absorbed from the East the social invention which made it convenient to dispense with the counting-frame altogether. Paper and printing, like *sunya*, came from the East. The "dawn of nothing" was also the dawn of cheap material for writing.

We have anticipated later discoveries than those of the Arabs by pointing to some of what Stifel called the marvellous things relating to the Hindu numbers to suggest a simple answer to the question Dantzig asks in the passage quoted at the beginning of this chapter. How the search for general rules about the behaviour of numbers was prompted by the flood of light which the new symbols shed is well illustrated by the fact that all the algorithms for fractions now used were invented by the Hindus. The Greek treatment of fractions never advanced beyond the level of the Egyptian Rhind papyrus. Fractions were dealt with metaphorically by imagining smaller units, just as we divide tons into hundredweights, and these into pounds, and pounds into ounces. This inability to treat a fraction as a number on its own merits is the explanation of a practice which continued for several millennia. The mathematicians of antiquity went to extraordinary pains to split up fractions like $\frac{2}{43}$ into a sum of unit fractions, e.g. $\frac{2}{43} = \frac{1}{30} + \frac{1}{86} + \frac{1}{645}$ or $\frac{1}{43} + \frac{1}{86} + \frac{1}{129} + \frac{1}{258}$. As this example shows, the procedure was as useless as it was ambiguous. A simple explanation of such apparent perversity is that the first calculators were trying to put side by side two fractions and see whether one was larger than the other in the same way as we might compare two weights like 1 stone 1 pound 1 ounce with 1 hundredweight, 1 stone and 1 pound. When we remember that the Greeks and Alexandrians continued this extraordinary performance, there is nothing remarkable about the small progress which they achieved in their arithmetic. What is remarkable is that a few of them like Archimedes should have discovered anything at all about series of numbers involving fractional quantities.

Equipped with their simple and eloquent number symbols, the Hindus broke away completely from this metaphorical way of dealing with fractions. They wrote fractions as we write them, and as they had an arithmetic which lent itself to rapid calculation without mechanical aids, they experimented with them as with whole numbers. Thus Mahavira (A.D. 850) gave our rule for dividing one fraction by another in the same words which a school teacher might use today: "Make the denominator the numerator and then multiply." The three fundamental rules are recognized by the use of geometrical figures such as the one given in Chapter 3 (cf. Fig. 103) as soon as we have a sensible way of writing down fractions. We have illustrated the rule for multiplication, namely:

$$\frac{a}{b} \times \frac{c}{d} = \frac{ac}{bd} \quad \text{e.g.} \quad \frac{3}{5} \times \frac{4}{7} = \frac{12}{35}$$

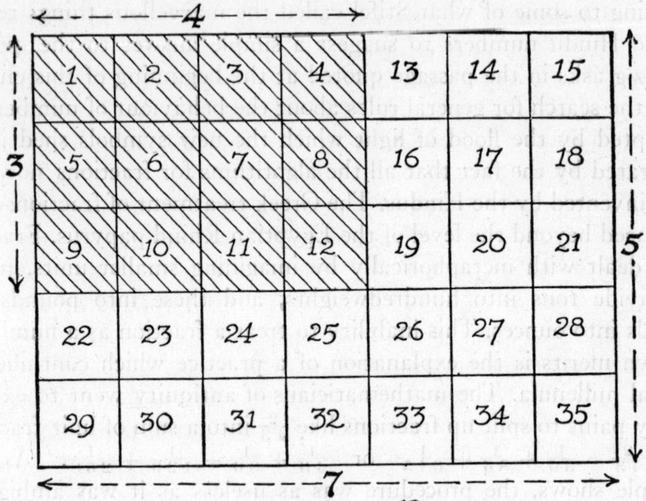

$$\frac{3}{5} \times \frac{4}{7} = \frac{12}{35}$$

FIG. 103.—MULTIPLICATION OF FRACTIONS

The rule for division simply depends on remembering that division is the "inverse" operation, i.e. $\frac{a}{b} \div \frac{c}{d}$ means "Find the number which when multiplied by $\frac{c}{d}$ gives $\frac{a}{b}$." This can be put in abstract numbers:

$$x \times \frac{c}{d} = \frac{a}{b}.$$

$$\therefore \quad \frac{cx}{d} = \frac{a}{b}$$

Applying the diagonal rule, we get

$$x = \frac{ad}{bc} \quad \text{e.g.} \quad \frac{3}{5} \div \frac{4}{7} = \frac{7 \times 3}{4 \times 5} = \frac{21}{20}$$

Similarly the rule for addition and subtraction follows from the rule for multiplication thus:

$$\frac{a}{b} \pm \frac{c}{d} = \frac{1}{b}\left(a \pm \frac{bc}{d}\right) = \frac{1}{bd}(ad \pm bc)$$

$$= \frac{ad \pm bc}{bd} \quad \text{e.g.} \quad \frac{3}{5} \pm \frac{4}{7} = \frac{21 \pm 20}{35}$$

The answer to Dantzig's question supplied by this line of development does not seem very obscure. In so far as algebra was developed in connexion with the practical need for rules to make calculations quickly and easily, it progressed rapidly as soon as people began to use and write numbers in such a way that the rules were easy to recognize, and, if recognized, were easy to apply. The cogency of this consideration in contradistinction to the fashion of saving further work by invoking a peculiar racial aptitude for arithmetic is even better illustrated by the last "spices" of the craft of "nombrynge," the "extraccion of the Rote," or, as we now say, the extraction of square roots. This was the parent of one of the marvellous things relating to numbers discovered by Stifel and his contemporaries. We saw how Stifel stretched the paper counting-frame of the Hindu numbers backwards to represent tenths, hundredths, thousandths, etc., by imaginary columns with index numbers -1, -2, -3, etc., to the right of the units column. If we make a gap or put a dot at the right of it to show which is the units column, the numbers 125 in 1·125 mean 1 tenth, 2 hundredths, 5 thousandths, just as the same numbers read to the left of the dot in 5210·1 mean 5 thousands, 2 hundreds, and 1 ten. The way this practice grew up was directly associated with the rule for using prime numbers to simplify extraction of square roots. The Hindus and Arabs greatly improved on the simple trigonometrical tables of the Alexandrians in connexion with their own studies in astronomy. This, as we have seen, requires tables of square roots. The advantage of stretching the counting-frame to the right of the units column to represent fractions in descending order diminishing by one-tenth at each step, was grasped in principle by the Arabian mathematicians. If they wanted $\sqrt{2}$ they would put it in the form

$\sqrt{\frac{200}{100}} = \frac{1}{10}\sqrt{200}$ for a first approximation, $\sqrt{\frac{20000}{10000}}$ or $\frac{1}{100}\sqrt{20000}$ for a second approximation, $\sqrt{\frac{2000000}{1000000}}$ or $\frac{1}{1000}\sqrt{2000000}$ for a third approximation, and so on. Trial at once shows that $\sqrt{200}$ is roughly 14, which, divided by 10 came to be written 1 4. Similarly the nearest whole number for $\sqrt{2000000}$ is 1,414 and this, divided by 1,000, was written with a gap 1 414 to indicate that the 414 is what we call the decimal fraction part of the square root. Tables of square roots printed in this form are given by the *Rechenmeister* Adam Riese in 1522. Independently as a natural offspring of the same process Al kashi of Samarkand gives his value for π as 3 14159 . . .

correct to nine decimals about A.D. 1400. The decimal point to mark the gap was introduced by Pelazzi of Nice about 1492. In England it is written above the line, in America on the line. On the Continent a comma on the line marks the gap. The introduction of the typewriter makes it fairly certain that the English custom will be superseded by the American or Continental one. By the time of Adam Riese people had grasped the essential truth that the rules which govern the arithmetic of a numeral system based on the principle of position are exactly the same, whatever value *x* we give to the beads of a particular column. In other words, addition, multiplication, division, subtraction, etc., are exactly the same for decimal fractions as for whole numbers, the only precaution necessary being to arrange the numbers suitably to show where the point should come (e.g. the left-right method of multiplication), or to put in the decimal point at the right place by common sense.

Stevinus, who was a warehouse clerk, put in charge of the provisioning of his army by William of Orange, advocated the legal adoption of a decimal system as early as 1585. The idea was revived by Benjamin Franklin and others at the time of the American Revolution, and thoroughly carried out in the end by the initiative of the National Assembly of France. England still clings to an antiquated jumble of weights and measures, and has not yet completely succeeded in introducing the Gobar numerals into the House of Commons. The scientific ignorance of English politicians is much the same as it was in the days when Government offices had not yet exchanged the tally-sticks of our Palaeolithic for the counting-frames of our Neolithic forbears. Charles Dickens refers to this belated reform in an entertaining passage:

"Ages ago a savage mode of keeping accounts on notched sticks was introduced into the Court of Exchequer, and the accounts were kept much as Robinson Crusoe kept his calendar on the desert island. A multitude of accountants, bookkeepers, and actuaries were born and died. . . . Still official routine inclined to those notched sticks as if they were pillars of the constitution, and still the Exchequer accounts continued to be kept on certain splints of elm wood called *tallies*. In the reign of George III an inquiry was made by some revolutionary spirit whether, pens, ink and paper, slates and pencils being in existence, this obstinate adherence to an obsolete custom ought to be continued, and whether a change ought not to be effected. All the red tape in the country grew redder at the bare mention of this bold and original conception, and it took until 1826 to get these sticks abolished. In 1834 it was found that there was a considerable accumulation of them; and the question then arose, what was to be done with such worn-out, worm-eaten, rotten old bits of wood? The sticks were housed in Westminster, and it would naturally occur to any intelligent person that nothing could be easier than to allow them to be carried away for firewood by the miserable people that lived in that neighbourhood. However, they never had been useful, and official routine required that they should never be, and so the order went out that they should be confidentially burned. It came to pass that they were burned in a stove in the House of Lords. The stove, overgorged with these preposterous bits of wood, set fire to the panelling: the panelling set fire to the House of Commons; the two Houses were reduced to ashes; architects were called in to build others; and we are now in the second million of the cost thereof."

The failure of Stevinus to persuade the Dutch Republic to adopt the decimal system of fractions is an historical portent with a lesson for our own time. The Dutch merchants were too much occupied with theology to pay attention to a pressing practical reform which had sprung from their own cultural needs. The world had to wait till the middle classes had outgrown the doctrinal disputation of the Protestant Reformers. Today we can see just as clearly the need for educational reforms which spring from the working life of another social group which is in process of becoming a governing class. Fascist Europe, like Spain in the time of the Dutch war of independence, has chosen the path of reaction and cultural decadence with an outburst of brutality hardly less savage than the accomplishments of the Inquisition. Will Soviet Russia be too much concerned about the squabbles of its Hegelian calvinists and its holistic Arminians to tackle such serious issues as a rationally planned language for mankind? Perhaps we must leave the issue to a happier period, when the movement towards a rationally planned use of the instruments of human welfare in a different social context breaks down the Bastille of custom thought. Meanwhile the duty of reasonable men and women is clear. We must remember that when the middle classes had climbed to the apex of their prosperity, Erasmus, Servetus, and Stevinus seemed closer to the brain and heart of European culture than were Luther, Knox, and Calvin by whose orders Servetus was committed to the flames. In the long run the builders of the City of God are not necessarily its most respected citizens. Calvin hoped to build the

City of God in Geneva. A monument to Servetus, who discovered the circulation of the blood before Harvey, is the judgment of history on the dialectic of Calvin.

EQUATIONS.—Alexandrian mathematicians had been forced to pay attention to the art of calculation by the problems they encountered in astronomy and mechanics. The early Hindu mathematicians devoted a great deal of attention to problems involving numbers such as arise in trade. When we speak of this early Hindu work as *algebra*, we must remember that the words algebra and arithmetic are used in schoolbooks in a somewhat different sense from that in which they are used in histories of mathematics. What is called arithmetic nowadays does not correspond with the *arithmetika* of the Greeks, dealt with in Chapter 5. The arithmetic of our schools is made up partly of rules for calculation based on the Hindu and Arab algorithms and partly of the solution of numerical problems without using the abstract number symbols of what is ordinarily called algebra. The simple and consistent rules for using abstract numbers and the shorthand symbols for mathematical verbs and operators have been evolved very slowly. Diophantus was the first person to attempt anything of the kind, and for many centuries mathematicians dealt with problems involving numbers on entirely individualistic lines. Each writer would use a shorthand which he understood himself without attempting to introduce a universal convention. So he was forced to fall back on the language of everyday life when he attempted to explain his methods to other people. Mathematicians use the term "algebra" to mean rules for solving problems about numbers of one kind or another, whether the rules are written out in full (*rhetorical* algebra), or more or less simplified by abbreviations (*syncopated* algebra), or expressed with the aid of letters and operative signs exclusively (*symbolic* algebra). The problems in commercial arithmetic which we learn to solve at school correspond with what the mathematician calls rhetorical algebra. There was no continuous line of evolution in the use of a shorthand symbolism. Individual authors used abbreviations of one kind or another, sometimes substituting letters for numbers. The Arabs used syncopated expressions corresponding with what we would call equations. Individual authors among the first converts to the Moorish learning, like the Dominican friar Jordanus (about A.D.1220), replaced words altogether by symbols. His contemporary, Leonardo of Pisa (Fibonacci) did the same. The following examples, which show the transition from pure rhetorical algebra to modern algebraic shorthand, are not given to exhibit a continuous historical sequence so much as to bring into clear historical perspective the fact that size language grew by imperceptible stages out of the language of everyday life.

Regiomontanus, A.D. 1464:
3 Census et 6 demptis 5 rebus aequatur zero.

Pacioli, A.D. 1494:
3 Census p 6 de 5 rebus ae 0.

Vieta, A.D. 1591:
3 in A quad − 5 in A plano + 6 aequatur 0

Stevinus, A.D. 1585:
3 ② − 5 ① + 6 ⊙ = 0.

Descartes, A.D. 1637:
$3x^2 - 5x + 6 = 0.$

The advance from "rhetorical" discussion of rules for solving problems to symbolism of the modern sort was wellnigh impossible for the Greeks, who had already exhausted the letters of the alphabet for proper numbers. Although the Hindu numerals removed this obstacle to progress, there was at first no social machinery to impose the universal use of devices for representing operators. The only operative symbol which was transmitted to us by the Arabs from Hindu sources is the square-root sign ($\surd$). In medieval Europe the social machinery which paved the way for this tremendous economy in the language of size emerged in a somewhat surprising way. Our word "plus" is short for "surplus." In the medieval warehouses the marks "+" and "−" were chalked on sacks, crates, or barrels to signify whether they exceeded or fell short of the weight assigned. These signs were introduced into general use by one of the first products of the printing press —Widman's *Commercial Arithmetic*, published in 1489 at Leipzig— and one of the first to use them for solving equations was Stevinus who, as already mentioned, was a merchant's clerk. An English commercial arithmetic by Record, published a century later, introduced "×" and "=". From this point onwards the shorthand first used by Descartes was generally adopted, and mathematics was liberated from the clumsy limitations of everyday speech. Again you will notice how a turning-point in the history of mathematics arose from the common social heritage rather than through an invention of isolated genius.

The transition from rhetorical to symbolical algebra is one of the most important things to understand in mathematics. What is called solving an equation is putting it in a form in which its meaning is obvious. The rules of algebra tell us how to do this. The really difficult step consists in translating our problem from the language of everyday life into the language of algebra. At this point the mathematician himself may go astray, because the mathematician may have less opportunity for understanding the problem as stated in the language of everyday life than the plain man who is not a mathematician. Once a problem has been translated into a mathematical sentence (or equation), we can safely trust the mathematician to do the rest. What remains is a problem in the peculiar grammar of mathematics. The danger lies in trusting the mathematician to do the translation.

To understand the art of translating from the language of everyday life to the language of size we have to face a very common difficulty in learning any foreign language. We cannot easily make sense of a sentence in a foreign language merely by looking up the words in the dictionary. Every language has its own particular idiosyncrasies of word order or idiom. If we do not understand something about the idiom of a language we may go badly astray, like the French Huguenot pastor who preached a sermon for the benefit of English tourists. He took for his text: "The devil goeth about as a roaring lion, seeking whom he may devour." The discourse was divided into three headings: first, "who the devil he is," second, "what the devil he is doing," third, "where the devil he is going." So we shall supplement what we have said about the grammar of language in an earlier chapter by the following three rules and two cautions.

Rules.—(i) Translate separately each separate item of information (stated or implied) into the form "By or with something do something to get something."

(ii) Combine the statements so as to get rid of any quantities which you do not want to know about. To do this you may have to add to statements explicitly made others which are only implied.

(iii) Get the final statement in the form "The number I want to know (x) can be got ($=$) by putting down an ordinary number."

Cautions.—(iv) See that all numbers representing the same kind of quantities are expressed in the same units, e.g. if money all pounds or all shillings, etc., if distance all yards or all miles, etc., if time all seconds or all hours, etc.

(v) Check the result.

To illustrate translation of verbal statements about numbers into the idiom of algebraical symbolism we shall now give six problems which can be put in the form of the simplest sort of equations which the Hindu mathematicians gave rhetorical rules for solving. Before doing so a further word of explanation may not be amiss. When you are fluent in the use of a foreign language, you translate into the correct idiom, one way or the other, straight away. When you are beginning, you have to go step by step. To show you that *solving problems is not a special gift but merely the art of applying fixed rules of grammar*, we shall go step by step with the problems which follow. Of course, you will not need to construe sentence by sentence when you have got used to the trick of translation. You will then put down the equation which represents the verbal statement in one or two steps.

Example I.—The current account of a local trade-union committee is four times the deposit account, the total of the two being £35. How much is there in each account?

First statement: The current account is four times the deposit account, i.e. "By 4 multiply the number of pounds in the deposit account to get the number of pounds in the current account."

$$4d = c \quad . \quad . \quad . \quad . \quad . \quad . \quad \text{(i)}$$

Second statement: The two together make £35, i.e. "The number of pounds in the current account must be added to the number of pounds in the deposit account to get £35."

$$c + d = 35 \quad . \quad . \quad . \quad . \quad . \quad . \quad \text{(ii)}$$

Combining both statements, we get

$$\begin{aligned} 4d + d &= 35 \\ \therefore \quad 5d &= 35 \\ \therefore \quad d &= \tfrac{35}{5} \\ \therefore \quad &= 7 \end{aligned}$$

The deposit account is £7, and the current account is £(35 – 7) = £28. Check: 4 × £7 = £28.

Example II.—A train leaves London for Edinburgh at 1 o'clock, going at 50 miles per hour. Another train leaves Edinburgh for London at 4 o'clock, going at 25 miles per hour. If Edinburgh is 400 miles from London, when do they meet?

What we are told allows us to get how far the trains have got in any time. What we want to get is the time which elapses before they are both the same distance from Edinburgh, or the same distance from London. As this time is assumed to be after the second train has started we will reckon it from 4 o'clock, i.e. the time (t) required is so many hours after 4 o'clock.

First statement: Train A leaves London at 1 o'clock, i.e. "Add 3 (time between 1 o'clock to 4 o'clock) to the number of hours after 4 o'clock when the trains meet to get the number of hours (T) train A has been travelling."

$$3 + t = \mathrm{T} \quad . \quad . \quad . \quad . \quad . \quad . \quad . \quad \text{(i)}$$

Second statement: Train A travels at 50 miles per hour away from London, i.e. "By 50 multiply the time (T) the train has been running when they meet to get the distance (D) from London when they meet."

$$50\mathrm{T} = \mathrm{D} \quad . \quad . \quad . \quad . \quad . \quad \text{(ii)}$$

Third statement: The second train leaves Edinburgh at 4 o'clock, travelling at 25 miles per hour, i.e. "By 25 multiply the time (t) after 4 o'clock when the trains meet to get the distance from Edinburgh where they meet."

$$25t = d \quad . \quad . \quad . \quad . \quad . \quad . \quad . \quad \text{(iii)}$$

Fourth statement: The distance from London to Edinburgh is 400 miles, i.e. "From 400 subtract the distance (d) from Edinburgh where they meet to get the distance (D) from London where they meet."

$$400 - d = \mathrm{D} \quad . \quad . \quad . \quad . \quad . \quad . \quad . \quad \text{(iv)}$$

Combine (i) and (ii) $\quad 50(3 + t) = \mathrm{D} \quad . \quad . \quad . \quad . \quad . \quad . \quad . \quad$ (v)

Combine (iv) and (iii) $\quad 400 - 25t = \mathrm{D} \quad . \quad . \quad . \quad . \quad . \quad . \quad$ (vi)

Combine (v) and (vi)

$$50(3 + t) = 400 - 25t$$

Divide both sides by 25 to reduce arithmetic.

$$2(3 + t) = 16 - t$$
$$\text{or} \quad 6 + 2t = 16 - t$$
$$2t + t = 16 - 6$$
$$3t = 10$$
$$t = \frac{10}{3}$$
$$= 3\tfrac{1}{3} \text{ (hours after 4 o'clock)}$$
$$= 3 \text{ hours 20 minutes after 4 o'clock}$$
$$= 7.20 \text{ p.m.}$$

Check: $50(3 + 3\frac{1}{3}) + 25 \times 3\frac{1}{3} = 400$

Example III.—How much tea at 2s. 3d. (27d.) per lb. must be added to 50 lb. of tea at 3s. (36d.) to get a mixture worth 2s. 6d. (30d.)?

First statement: Some tea (x) is to be added to 50 lb. we have already got, i.e. "x lb. must be added to 50 lb. to get the number of lb. (N) in the mixture."

$$50 + x = \text{N} \quad . \quad . \quad . \quad . \quad . \quad . \quad . \quad . \quad \text{(i)}$$

Second statement: This tea is to be sold at 30d. a lb., i.e. "By 30 multiply the amount (in lb.) of the mixture to get the total value (T)."

$$30\text{N} = \text{T} \quad . \quad . \quad . \quad . \quad . \quad . \quad . \quad . \quad \text{(ii)}$$

Third statement: The price of the x lb. added is 27d. per lb., i.e. "By 27 multiply the number of lb. added to get the value (v) in pence of the added quantity."

$$27x = v \quad . \quad . \quad . \quad . \quad . \quad . \quad . \quad . \quad \text{(iii)}$$

Fourth statement: The original 50 lb. of tea was worth 3s. (36d.) per lb., i.e. "By 36 multiply 50 to get the value (V) in pence of the original 50 lb."

$$36 \times 50 = \text{V} \quad . \quad . \quad . \quad . \quad . \quad . \quad . \quad \text{(iv)}$$

Common sense adds the fifth statement which is implied but not stated: Add the value of the tea added to the value of the original 50 lb. to get the total value, i.e.

$$v + \text{V} = \text{T} \quad . \quad . \quad . \quad . \quad . \quad . \quad . \quad \text{(v)}$$

Combine (i) and (ii) $\quad 30(50 + x) = \text{T} \quad . \quad . \quad . \quad . \quad . \quad . \quad . \quad \text{(vi)}$

Combine (iii), (iv), (v) $\quad 27x + 36(50) = \text{T} \quad . \quad . \quad . \quad . \quad . \quad \text{(vii)}$

Combine (vi) and (vii)

$$\begin{aligned} 30(50 + x) &= 27x + 36(50) \\ 1{,}500 + 30x &= 27x + 1{,}800 \\ 30x - 27x &= 1{,}800 - 1{,}500 \\ 3x &= 300 \\ x &= 100 \text{ (lb.)} \end{aligned}$$

Check: $$\frac{27 \times 100 + 50 \times 36}{150} = 30$$

Example IV.—The race of Achilles on p. 20.

First statement: The speed of the hero is ten times the speed of the tortoise, i.e. "By 10 multiply the speed (s) of the tortoise to get the speed (S) of Achilles."

$$10s = S \quad . \; . \; . \; . \; . \; . \; . \; . \; . \; . \quad \text{(i)}$$

Second statement: Achilles starts 100 yards behind the tortoise, i.e. "To 100 add the distance (d) which the tortoise has gone when he is overtaken to get the distance (D) Achilles has run (in yards) when he catches up."

$$100 + d = D \quad . \; . \; . \; . \; . \; . \; . \; . \; . \; . \quad \text{(ii)}$$

To connect these statements we have to remember that the speed is the distance divided by the time (t), which is obviously the same in both cases (i.e. the time when the tortoise is overtaken is the time when Achilles catches him up). So we may add two more implied statements.

Third statement: The distance which the tortoise goes till he is overtaken must be divided by the time he runs to get his speed.

$$\frac{d}{t} = s \quad . \; . \; . \; . \; . \; . \; . \; . \; . \; . \; . \quad \text{(iii)}$$

Fourth statement: The distance that Achilles goes before he catches up must be divided by the time he runs to get the speed of Achilles.

$$\frac{D}{t} = S \quad . \; . \; . \; . \; . \; . \; . \; . \; . \; . \; . \quad \text{(iv)}$$

Combine (i) and (iii) $$\frac{10d}{t} = S \quad . \; . \; . \; . \; . \; . \; . \; . \; . \; . \; . \quad \text{(v)}$$

Combine (ii) and (iv) $$\frac{100 + d}{t} = S \quad . \; . \; . \; . \; . \; . \; . \; . \; . \; . \quad \text{(vi)}$$

Combine (v) and (vi) $\frac{10d}{t} = \frac{100 + d}{t}$

Multiply both sides by *t*

$$10d = 100 + d$$
$$10d - d = 100$$
$$9d = 100$$
$$d = \frac{100}{9}$$
$$= 11\tfrac{1}{9} \text{ (yards)}$$

Example V.—When I am as old as my father is now, I shall be five times as old as my son is now. By then my son will be eight years older than I am now. The combined ages of my father and myself are 100 years. How old is my son? (*Week-End Book.*)

First statement: When I am as old as my father I shall be five times as old as my son is now, i.e. my father is now five times as old as my son is now. This means, "By 5 multiply my son's age (*s*) to get my father's age (*f*)."

$$5s = f \quad . \; . \; . \; . \; . \; . \; . \; . \; . \; . \; . \quad \text{(i)}$$

Second statement: When I am as old as my father my son will be eight years older than I am now. Split this up thus: (A) From my father's age (*f*) take mine (*m*) to get how long it will be (*l*) before I am as old as he is.

$$f - m = l \quad . \; . \; . \; . \; . \; . \; . \; . \; . \; . \quad \text{(A)}$$

(B) These *l* years must be added to my son's age (*s*) to get how old he will be (S years) when I am as old as my father is now.

$$l + s = S \quad . \; . \; . \; . \; . \; . \; . \; . \; . \; . \quad \text{(B)}$$

(C) Eight must be added to my present age to get my son's age years hence.

$$m + 8 = S \quad . \; . \; . \; . \; . \; . \; . \; . \; . \; . \quad \text{(C)}$$

Combine (B) and (C) $m + 8 = l + s$ . . . . (D)

Combine (A) and (D) $m + 8 = f - m + s$

or $2m + 8 = f + s$ . . . . (ii)

Third statement: The combined ages of my father and myself are

100 years, i.e. "My father's age must be added to mine to get 100 (years)."

$$m + f = 100$$
$$\text{or} \quad m = 100 - f \quad \ldots\ldots \quad \text{(iii)}$$

Combine (i) and (ii) $\quad 5s + s = 2m + 8$

$$6s = 2m + 8 \quad \ldots\ldots \quad \text{(iv)}$$

Combine (i) and (iii) $\quad 100 - 5s = m \quad \ldots\ldots \quad$ (v)

Combine (iv) and (v) $\quad 6s = 2(100 - 5s) + 8$

$$6s = 200 - 10s + 8$$
$$6s + 10s = 200 + 8$$
$$16s = 208$$
$$s = \frac{208}{16}$$
$$= 13 \text{ (years)}$$

i.e. My son is 13 years old now.

Example VI.—(An early Hindu problem from the *Lilavati* of Aryabhata, *c.* A.D. 450.) "A merchant pays duty on certain goods at three different places. At the first he gives $\frac{1}{3}$ of his goods, at the second $\frac{1}{4}$ of what he has left, and $\frac{1}{5}$ of the remainder at the third. The total duty is twenty-four coins. What had he at first?"

First statement: At the first place he gives a third of his goods away, i.e. "From what he had (x) take $\frac{1}{3}$ of its worth to get what he had left (y) when he got to the second place."

$$x - \tfrac{1}{3}x = y$$
$$\text{or} \quad \tfrac{2}{3}x = y \quad \ldots\ldots \quad \text{(i)}$$

Second statement: At the second place he pays a quarter of its worth, i.e. "From what he had when he arrived take $\frac{1}{4}$ of its worth to get what he had (z) when he went on."

$$y - \tfrac{1}{4}y = z$$
$$\text{or} \quad \tfrac{3}{4}y = z \quad \ldots\ldots \quad \text{(ii)}$$

Third statement: He paid one-fifth of the residue at the third place and this made the total duties up to twenty-four coins, i.e. "To $\frac{1}{5}$ of what he had when he got there add the duty he paid at the second ($\frac{1}{4}y$) and the duty he paid at the first ($\frac{1}{3}x$) to get 24."

$$\tfrac{1}{5}z + \tfrac{1}{4}y + \tfrac{1}{3}x = 24 \quad \ldots\ldots \quad \text{(iii)}$$

Combine (ii) and (iii)

$$(\tfrac{3}{4} \times \tfrac{1}{5})y + \tfrac{1}{4}y + \tfrac{1}{3}x = 24$$
$$\text{or} \quad \tfrac{2}{5}y + \tfrac{1}{3}x = 24 \quad \ldots\ldots \quad \text{(iv)}$$

Combine (i) and (iv)

$$(\tfrac{2}{5} \times \tfrac{2}{3})x + \tfrac{1}{3}x = 24$$
$$\text{or} \quad \tfrac{3}{5}x = 24$$
$$x = \frac{5 \times 24}{3}$$
$$= 40$$

.e. he had forty coins' worth.

These examples have been worked out step by step with great letail to show you that solving problems by algebra is simply translation according to fixed grammatical rules. As stated, you need not go hrough all these steps when you have become fluent in the use of number language. Once you are at home in it, you will find it much nore quick to put down first of all an abstract number for the one vhich you want to find and then write down everything you are told about it, till you have a sentence which stands by itself. For instance, Example V may be worked out more snappily like this:

Let son's age be x years:

Then father's age is $5x$ years:

My age is $(100 - 5x)$ years; and

$$5x - (100 - 5x) + x = 100 - 5x + 8$$
$$\therefore \quad 16x = 208$$
$$\therefore \quad x = 13$$

All the problems which we have translated so far can finally be boiled down to a mathematical sentence which only contains one abstract number standing for the unknown quantity which we are looking for. This can often be done even when the problem is about two unknown quantities, provided the connexion between them is simple and obvious. For instance, here is a problem about three unknown quantities which presents no difficulties.

Example VII.—In a tool-box there are three times as many tacks s nails, and three times as many nails as screws. The total number f tacks, nails, and screws in the box is 1,872. How many of each are here? You can translate this thus. The number of nails is one-third he number of tacks ($n = \frac{1}{3}t$). The number of screws is one-third the number of nails ($s = \frac{1}{3}n$). The number of all three ($t + n + s$) is 1,872, i.e.

$$t + \tfrac{1}{3}t + \tfrac{1}{3}(\tfrac{1}{3}t) = 1{,}872$$
$$t(1 + \tfrac{1}{3} + \tfrac{1}{9}) = 1{,}872$$
$$\tfrac{13}{9}t = 1{,}872$$
$$t = \frac{9 \times 1{,}872}{13} = 1{,}296$$

Thus the number of tacks is 1,296, the number of nails one-third of this number, i.e. 432, and the number of screws one-third of 432, i.e. 144. (Check: 1,296 + 432 + 144 = 1,872.)

When more than one unknown quantity occurs in a problem we can only boil down the verbal statement to a mathematical sentence containing a single abstract number, provided that one of the unknown quantities is so many times another, or differs from the other by a known amount. When we cannot do this we can still solve the problem, provided we can make as many distinct equations as there are unknown quantities. For instance, here is a simple problem of this sort.

Example VIII.—Two pounds of butter and three pounds of sugar cost two shillings and sevenpence. Three pounds of butter and two pounds of sugar cost three shillings and threepence. What is the price of each? This problem means: (i) That twice the cost of a pound (b) of butter (in pence) added to three times the cost of a pound (s) of sugar (in pence) amounts to 31 pence, i.e.

$$2b + 3s = 31$$

(ii) That three times the cost of a pound of butter added to twice the cost of a pound of sugar amounts to 39 pence, i.e.

$$3b + 2s = 39$$

We have now two equations and two abstract numbers, and can get rid of either of them by a simple trick which is called solving "simultaneous equations." We can do anything we like to one side of an equation so long as we do exactly the same to the other side, and if we multiply both sides of the first equation by three and both sides of the second by two we now have two equations in which one term containing an abstract number is identical, viz.

$$6b + 9s = 93$$
$$6b + 4s = 78$$

ubtracting $6b + 4s$ from $6b + 9s$ is the same thing as subtracting 8 from 93, and the results of the two subtractions are therefore the ame, i.e. $5s = 15$. Hence $s = 3$ (pence). We can get b by putting the alue of s into either of the original equations; thus $2b + 9 = 31$, .e. $2b = 22$ and $b = 11$ (pence). The price of sugar is therefore three-ence, and of butter elevenpence a pound.

The general rule for solving two simultaneous equations where , b, c, d, e, f stand for known numbers and x and y for unknown umbers in the final statement of the problem may be put in this vay. If

$$ax + by = c$$
$$dx + ey = f$$

Then to get rid of x multiply the first by d and the second by a,

$$dax + dby = dc$$
$$dax + eay = fa$$

ubtract the second from the first:

$$(db - ea)y = dc - fa$$

We have now a simple equation with only one abstract number y, he others being stated in the problem itself. Alternatively, of course, ve might, if it involved multiplying by smaller numbers, prefer to nultiply the first equation by e and the second by b, getting rid of and leaving x

$$(ea - db)x = ce - bf$$

Although the Hindus and Arabs made little use of operative symbols vhich stand in modern algebra for mathematical verbs when we ranslate a problem from everyday speech into the language of size nd order, as we have done in the foregoing examples, they gave rammatical rules which are substantially those which have been iven in Chapter 3. Alkarismi distinguished between two general rules. The first he called *al-muqabalah*, or, as our textbooks say, collecting ike terms. In modern shorthand this is the rule for avoiding redun-dancy, illustrated by:

$$q + 2q = x + 6x - 3x$$
$$\therefore \quad 3q = 4x$$

The other rule, the name for which has been assimilated into our own language, was *al-gebra*, i.e. transferring quantities from one side o an equation to another, e.g. in our shorthand:

$$bx + q = p$$
$$bx = p - q$$

Alkarismi gives the rule which we now use for solving equation containing the square of an unknown number which we are trying tc

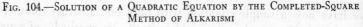

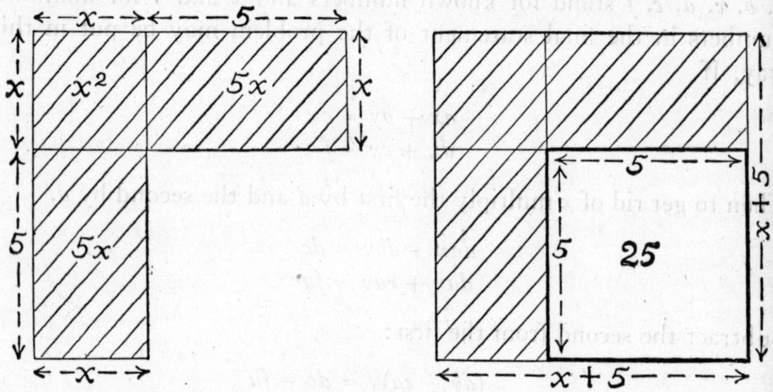

FIG. 104.—SOLUTION OF A QUADRATIC EQUATION BY THE COMPLETED-SQUARE METHOD OF ALKARISMI

(i) $x^2 + 10x = 39$ (ii) $x^2 + 10x + 25 = 25 + 39$
$(x + 5)^2 = 64 = 8^2$
$x + 5 = 8$

find. The method he gives is essentially the same as one first used b Diophantus. An actual example which is given by Alkarismi is:

$$x^2 + 10x = 39$$

The rule which Alkarismi gives is based upon a simple application c Dem. 4 in Chapter 4, and the figure is given in Fig. 104. Suppose yo draw a square on a line x units long and continue two adjoining sid of the square 5 units further, completing the two rectangles wit adjacent sides 5 and x units. You now have an L-shaped figure, th area of which is

$$x^2 + 5x + 5x = x^2 + 10x$$

If we complete the square with sides 5 units in the figure on the le of Fig. 104, as has been done on the right, the area is now

$$x^2 + 10x + 25$$
$$= (x + 5)^2$$

s we know from Dem. 4. The equation tells us that

$$\begin{aligned} x^2 + 10x &= 39 \\ x^2 + 10x + 25 &= 39 + 25 \\ &= 64 \\ \therefore \quad (x+5)^2 &= 8^2 \\ \therefore \quad x + 5 &= 8 \\ \therefore \quad x &= 8 - 5 \\ \therefore \quad x &= 3 \end{aligned}$$

lkarismi thus gives the rule for solving such equations. Calling the umber by which x is multiplied (10 in this illustration) the "roots," You halve the number of the 'roots' which in the present instance ves 5. This you multiply by itself. The product is 25. Add this to). The sum is 64. Now take the square root of this, which is 8, and ibtract from it half the number of 'roots,' which is 5. This is the oot of the square you sought for."

Nowadays we call the number corresponding with 10 in this equaon the *coefficient* of x. Replacing it by an abstract number at the benning of the alphabet to signify that it is a number we already know, hile replacing 39 in the same way, we say that, if:

$$x^2 + bx = c$$

$$x = \sqrt{\frac{b^2}{4} + c} - \frac{b}{2}$$

'ou will recognize $\frac{b^2}{4}$ as the square of half the coefficient of x, or, as lkarismi would say, the result of multiplying half the number of the roots" by itself.

We still call this rule for finding the value of x in an equation conining x^2 "completing the square" to remind us of the fact that the gebra of equations developed from the hieroglyphic way of solving problem by scale diagrams like those of Dem. 4. We still call equaons like the one which we have just solved "*quadratic equations*," om the Latin word *quadratum*, for a four-sided figure, though modern ooks on elementary algebra no longer use the figure to suggest the ıle. Here is a problem which you can solve by the rule we have just ven. There are easier ones given at the end of the chapter for practice.

Example IX.—Two hikers go out for the day, one walking a quarter f a mile an hour faster than the other. The faster one reaches the end of his journey half an hour earlier than the slower of the two Both walk 34 miles. At what rate does each walk?

First statement: The one who gets there first walks a quarter o a mile per hour faster, i.e. "To the speed of the slower (m miles pe hour) add $\frac{1}{4}$ mile per hour to get the speed of the faster (n miles pe hour)," or

$$\tfrac{1}{4} + m = n$$

$$\therefore \quad n = \frac{4m+1}{4} \quad \ldots\ldots\ldots \text{(i)}$$

Second statement: The faster walker took half an hour less, i.e "From the time (h hours) taken by the slower walker take $\frac{1}{2}$ to ge the time (H hours) taken by the faster one," or

$$h - \tfrac{1}{2} = \text{H} \quad \ldots\ldots\ldots \text{(ii)}$$

Third statement: The faster one walking H hours at n miles pe hour covers 34 miles, and the slower one walking h hours at m mile per hour covers 34 miles. This means "Divide 34 miles by the tim taken by each hiker to get the speed at which he travels," i.e.

$$n = 34 \div \text{H}$$

$$\therefore \quad \text{H} = \frac{34}{n} \quad \ldots\ldots\ldots \text{(iii}a\text{)}$$

$$m = 34 \div h$$

$$\therefore \quad h = \frac{34}{m} \quad \ldots\ldots\ldots \text{(iii}b\text{)}$$

Combine (iii) with (ii)

$$\frac{34}{m} - \frac{1}{2} = \frac{34}{n} \quad \ldots\ldots\ldots \text{(iv)}$$

Combine (iv) with (i)

$$\frac{34}{m} - \frac{1}{2} = \frac{34 \times 4}{4m+1}$$

Apply the diagonal rule

$$68 + 271m - 4m^2 = 272m$$

$$\therefore \quad -m - 4m^2 = -68$$

$$\therefore \quad m^2 + \tfrac{1}{4}m = 17$$

Apply Alkarismi's rule

$$m = \sqrt{\tfrac{1}{4}(\tfrac{1}{4})^2 + 17} - \tfrac{1}{2}(\tfrac{1}{4})$$

$$= \sqrt{\frac{1{,}089}{64}} - \frac{1}{8}$$

$$= \tfrac{33}{8} - \tfrac{1}{8}$$

$$= 4$$

Hence the speed (m) of the slower of the two is 4 miles per hour, and that of the faster is $4\frac{1}{2}$ miles per hour. (Check: The faster goes at $4\frac{1}{4} = \frac{17}{4}$ or $\frac{34}{8}$ miles per hour, i.e. takes 8 hours. The slower takes $8\frac{1}{2}$ hours, in which time he does $8\frac{1}{2} \times 4 = 34$ miles.)

The solution of equations by this rule brought the Arabs face to face with a limitation which we have already recognized in Greek geometry. In solving the two equations which we have used to illustrate the rule we have given only one answer. Now an equation need not have a single answer. Many questions in real life like "Have you stopped beating your wife?" do not yield to the legal preference for a simple answer "Yes" or "No." To a quadratic equation there are two answers, the answer we are looking for and its shadow answer. The Arab mathematicians who were accustomed to use the law of signs were very puzzled by this fact. According to the law of signs,

$$-a \times -a = a^2$$

$$\text{also} \quad +a \times +a = a^2$$

$$\therefore \quad \sqrt{a^2} = +a \text{ or } -a$$

or, as it is frequently written, $\pm a$. So every square-root sign represents an operation which gives two results, e.g.

$$100 = (\pm 10)^2$$

$$49 = (\pm 7)^2$$

If you go back to the equation which Alkarismi used to illustrate the rule, you will see that

$$x = 8 - 5$$

$$\text{or} \quad x = -8 - 5$$

$$\text{i.e.} \quad x = 3$$

$$\text{or} \quad x = -13$$

The Arabs recognized that both these answers check up as follows:

$$3^2 + 10(3) = 9 + 30 = 39$$

$$(-13)^2 + 10(-13) = 169 - 130 = 39$$

We have simply neglected the second answer because we have not yet found a physical meaning for mathematical gerunds like -3 or -13, which is the alternative answer to the equation illustrated in Fig. 105. We shall see later that the use of these parts of mathematical speech became clear when the Reformation geometry found a place for the position of a figure. The reason why Euclid's geometry only suggests one answer is because figures in Euclid's geometry are regarded as equal in all respects in spite of the fact that they happen

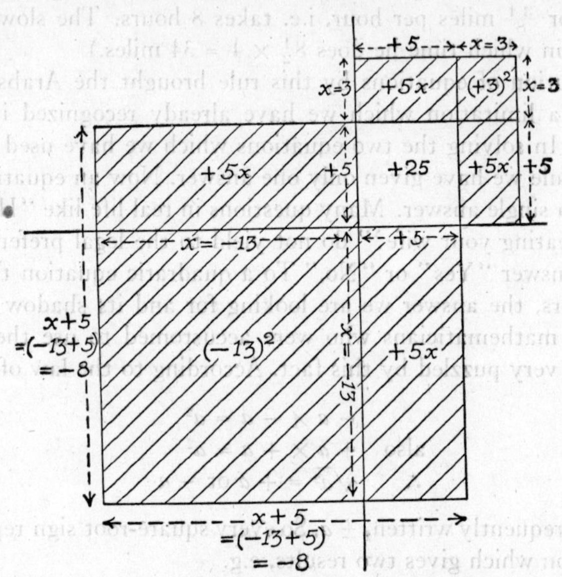

FIG. 105.—ALKARISMI'S PROBLEM IN REFORMATION GEOMETRY

In the previous figure we do not know what x is. The figure is merely used to suggest the numerical procedure. In the Reformation Geometry of the next chapter you will see that if we call quantities drawn upwards or rightwards plus units, we must call quantities measured downwards or leftwards minus units. The equation tells us that:

$$x + 5 = 8 \text{ or } -8$$

This means that the area of the whole square whose side is $x + 5$ is 64 square units. The lower large square is made up of two rectangles whose area is together:

$$2(5)\ (-13) = -130 \text{ square units,}$$

and two squares whose area together is:

$$(-13)\ (-13) + (+5)\ (+5)$$

or + 194 square units. The total area is:

$$194 - 130 = 64.$$

to be in totally different places. Here we must be content to notice that the two answers of a quadratic equation can both be ordinary quantities, i.e. positive numbers to which Alkarismi's rule applies. For instance, you may have heard some such riddle as this: "A number is multiplied by itself. The result is added to 6. On taking away 5 times the number, nothing is left. What was the number?" In algebraic shorthand the riddle can be translated.

$$x^2 - 5x + 6 = 0$$

We may write this

$$x^2 - 5x = -6$$

By applying Alkarismi's rule and the law of signs, the solution is

$$x = \sqrt{-6 + (-\tfrac{5}{2})^2} - (-\tfrac{5}{2})$$
$$x = \sqrt{-6 + \tfrac{25}{4}} + \tfrac{5}{2}$$
$$x = \pm \tfrac{1}{2} + \tfrac{5}{2}$$
$$= +2 \text{ or } +3$$

You will see that both these answers are consistent with the riddle proposed:

$$2^2 - 5(2) + 6 = 4 - 10 + 6 = 0$$
$$3^2 - 5(3) + 6 = 9 - 15 + 6 = 0$$

In the hands of the Hindus, the Arabs, and their immediate successors, algebra had grown out of its Euclidean clothes. It was beginning to feel the cold. There was worse to come. Some equations admit of no answer which is a positive number, and others do not admit of an answer which is either a positive or a negative number. This complication worried the Italian Cardan towards the end of the period of transition which intervened between the Alexandrian era and the invention of Reformation geometry. Playing with riddles like the one we have just set, Cardan stumbled upon a new sort of answer, such as we get when we change the numbers in the last riddle thus: "A number is multiplied by itself. The result is added to 5. On taking away twice the number, nothing is left. What was the number?" The translation in this case is

$$x^2 - 2x + 5 = 0$$
$$x^2 - 2x = -5$$
$$x = \sqrt{-5 + 1} + 1$$
$$= 1 \pm \sqrt{-4}$$
$$x = 1 \pm 2\sqrt{-1}$$

This raises the question: What on earth is the square root of -1? As a purely grammatical convention it is clearly the number which when multiplied by itself gives -1. A number which did this would give the correct answer as you can see by the two following checks, one where ± means + throughout, and the other in which it means −,

$$
\begin{array}{r}
\therefore \quad 1 \pm 2\sqrt{-1} \\
1 \pm 2\sqrt{-1} \\
\hline
1 \pm 2\sqrt{-1} \\
\pm 2\sqrt{-1} + 4(-1) \\
\hline
x^2 = 1 \pm 4\sqrt{-1} - 4
\end{array}
$$

$$\therefore x^2 - 2x + 5 = 1 \pm 4\sqrt{-1} - 4 - 2(1 \pm 2\sqrt{-1}) + 5 = 0$$

Although this shows us that our answer was perfectly grammatical, it does not get us any nearer to saying what the square root of − 1 is. By the law of signs + a multiplied by itself is + a^2, and − a multiplied by itself is also + a^2, so a number which when multiplied by itself would give a minus quantity is neither an ordinary number nor a gerund like − 2, which is a "back number" in the Reformation geometry. All we can say about it at present is that it is a part of speech which can be used grammatically in the kind of sentences which we call quadratic equations. The first mathematicians who encountered these quantities called them imaginary numbers, which left them in the clouds. As a matter of fact you will locate them literally in the clouds when we turn to the Reformation geometry. Like − 1, $\sqrt{-1}$ is a mathematical gerund. In Reformation geometry in Chapter 9 we shall see that − 5 is a direction and a number (Fig. 105). It means making a measurement 5 units backwards, and $\sqrt{-5}$ means $\sqrt{5}$ units measured straight up in the air. Both these examples of the mathematical gerund can now be used to describe movements which occur in the real world, because the Great Navigations gave us a geometry in which things could move about and have a definite position like a ship at sea. Today, multiplying by $\sqrt{-100}$ is no more difficult than saying what happens when a ship is blown up into the air 10 feet or sunk 10 fathoms deep by the explosion of a mine.

Alkarismi's rule for the solution of a quadratic equation is sometimes given in a more general form for the solution of equations in which the coefficient of x^2 is not *one*, as in the examples given. The equation

$$ax^2 + bx + c = 0$$

can be written

$$x^2 + \frac{bx}{a} = -\frac{c}{a}$$

Applying Alkarismi's rule

$$x = \sqrt{-\frac{c}{a} + \left(\frac{b}{2a}\right)^2} - \frac{b}{2a}$$

$$\therefore \quad x = \frac{-b \pm \sqrt{b^2 - 4ac}}{2a}$$

As a numerical example which you can check, the solution of

$$3x^2 - 7x = 6$$

is

$$x = \frac{7 \pm \sqrt{49 + 72}}{6}$$

$$= \frac{7 \pm 11}{6}$$

$$x = 3 \quad \text{or} \quad -\tfrac{2}{3}$$

SERIES.—The new number language brought to light new things about the Natural History of the natural numbers. It is not at all surprising that the Hindus and Arabs revived interest in the ancient Chinese number lore, and made some interesting discoveries of their own. Thus Aryabhata gives the rules for finding the sums of various series of numbers such as

$$\begin{array}{llll} 1 & 2 & 3 & 4 \ldots \\ 1^2 & 2^2 & 3^2 & 4^2 \ldots \\ 1^3 & 2^3 & 3^3 & 4^3 \ldots \end{array}$$

We have already seen that (Chapter 5) the sum of n terms of the series of n natural numbers is the nth triangular number. This suggests an explanation of the facility with which the Hindu mathematicians discovered expressions for the sum of series. For the natural numbers we have:

Sum of first n terms:

$$\begin{array}{lll} n & = & \\ 1 & 1 & = 1 \quad T_1 \\ 2 & 1 + 2 & = 3 \quad T_2 \\ 3 & 1 + 2 + 3 & = 6 \quad T_3 \\ 4 & 1 + 2 + 3 + 4 & = 10 \quad T_4 \\ 5 & 1 + 2 + 3 + 4 + 5 & = 15 \quad T_5 \text{ etc.} \end{array}$$

This table can be summarized by using the operator and adverbs of p. 262, thus:

$$\sum_{1}^{n}(1 + 2 + 3 \ . \ . \ . + n) = T_n = \frac{n(n+1)}{2}$$

To find the sum of the squares of the natural numbers we may first tabulate our results thus:

n	$\sum_{1}^{n}$	
1	1	= 1
2	1 + 4	= 5
3	1 + 4 + 9	= 14
4	1 + 4 + 9 + 16	= 30
5	1 + 4 + 9 + 16 + 25	= 55
6	1 + 4 + 9 + 16 + 25 + 36	= 91

Now we can split these sums into triangular numbers, as the following table shows:

n	Σ		
1	1 =	1 + 0 =	1 + 0
2	5 =	3 + 2 =	3 + 2(1)
3	14 =	6 + 8 =	6 + 2(4)
4	30 =	10 + 20 =	10 + 2(10)
5	55 =	15 + 40 =	15 + 2(20)
6	91 =	21 + 70 =	21 + 2(35)

We have now got the two triangular number series:

1 3 6 10 15 21 . . .

1 4 10 20 35 . .

Each term in the series formed by the sum of the squares of the first n natural numbers can be formed by adding the nth simple triangular number to twice the one before the nth or (n – 1th) triangular number of the second order, i.e.

$$T_n + 2 \times {}^2T_{n-1}$$

$$= \frac{n(n+1)}{2} + \frac{2(n-1)(n)(n+1)}{3.2}$$

$$= \tfrac{1}{2}n(n+1)\left[1 + \frac{2n-2}{3}\right]$$

$$= \frac{n(n+1)(2n+1)}{6}$$

Thus the sum of the first 7 terms in the series of squares of the natural numbers is:

$$\frac{7.8.15}{6} = 140$$

This you will see is correct by adding $49 = (7^2)$ to $91 = (\sum_1^6 n^2)$. You can proceed to get the sum of n terms in the series of cubes of the natural numbers in the same way. The series for which we want to get the rule is:

$$\begin{matrix} 1^3, & (1^3+2^3), & (1^3+2^3+3^3), & (1^3+2^3+3^3+4^3), & (1^3+2^3+3^3+4^3+5^3) \\ 1, & 9, & 36, & 100, & 225, \end{matrix}$$

You will probably see at once that this series is:

$$1^2, \quad 3^2, \quad 6^2, \quad 10^2, \quad 15^2,$$

So we may put

$$\sum_1^n n^3 = (T_n)^2 = \left[\frac{n(n+1)}{2}\right]^2 = \frac{n^2(n+1)^2}{4}$$

The next term of the series 1, 9, 36, 100, 225, i.e. the sum of the first 6 cube numbers would therefore be

$$\frac{36 \times 49}{4} = 441$$

This is correct, as you may see by adding $6^3 = 216$ to 225.

The fascination of these triangular numbers probably suggested what is called Pascal's Triangle, after the first French mathematician who paid attention to the subject of mathematical probability, the foundation of modern statistical theory. In reality the series of Pascal's triangle was given by Omar Khayyám. It is figured in the Precious Mirror of the Four Elements, written about A.D. 1300 by the Chinese mathematician Chu Shi Kei, who lived at the time when the Mogul Empire was sprawling into Eastern Europe. The fact bears testimony to the interest of triangular numbers in Eastern countries. This explains how easily the Hindu mathematicians dealt with series which present considerable scope for ingenuity, when we have to use the formal methods of algebra textbooks. Here is the so-called Pascal Triangle, which, like the so-called Theorem of Pythagoras, is really a product of a much earlier Eastern culture.

$$\begin{array}{ccccccccccccccc}
 & & & & & & & 1 & & & & & & & \\
 & & & & & & 1 & & 1 & & & & & & \\
 & & & & & 1 & & 2 & & 1 & & & & & \\
 & & & & 1 & & 3 & & 3 & & 1 & & & & \\
 & & & 1 & & 4 & & 6 & & 4 & & 1 & & & \\
 & & 1 & & 5 & & 10 & & 10 & & 5 & & 1 & & \\
 & 1 & & 6 & & 15 & & 20 & & 15 & & 6 & & 1 & \\
1 & & 7 & & 21 & & 35 & & 35 & & 21 & & 7 & & 1
\end{array}$$

Reading diagonally downwards from right to left we have the series of "unity, the source of all," the natural numbers, the simple triangular numbers, and successive higher orders of triangular numbers, as you will see by referring back to p. 220, Chapter 5. Reading horizontally we have

$$\begin{array}{llllllll}
1 & & & & & & & \\
1 & 1 & & & & & & \\
1 & 2 & 1 & & & & & \\
1 & 3 & 3 & 1 & & & & \\
1 & 4 & 6 & 4 & 1 & & & \\
1 & 5 & 10 & 10 & 5 & 1 & & \\
1 & 6 & 15 & 20 & 15 & 6 & 1 & \text{etc.}
\end{array}$$

There are, as Michael Stifel might have said, many marvellous things relating to these numbers. The first is that they show us how to write out fully the expression $(x + a)^n$ without multiplying out. You will see that successive multiplication of $(x + a)$ leads to a simple rule by looking at the following:

$$\begin{array}{lr}
x + a & = (x + a)^1 \\
\underline{x + a} & \\
x^2 + ax & \\
\underline{\quad ax + a^2} & \\
x^2 + 2ax + a^2 & = (x + a)^2 \\
\underline{\qquad x + a} & \\
x^3 + 2ax^2 + a^2x & \\
\underline{\qquad ax^2 + 2a^2x + a^3} & \\
x^3 + 3ax^2 + 3a^2x + a^3 & = (x + a)^3 \\
\underline{\qquad\qquad\qquad x + a} &
\end{array}$$

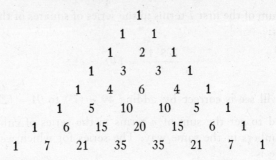

$$\begin{array}{l} x^4 + 3ax^3 + 3a^2x^2 + a^3x \\ \quad\quad ax^3 + 3a^2x^2 + 3a^3x + a^4 \\ \hline x^4 + 4ax^3 + 6a^2x^2 + 4a^3x + a^4 \quad\quad = (x+a)^4 \\ \quad\quad\quad\quad\quad\quad\quad\quad x + a \\ \hline x^5 + 4ax^4 + 6a^2x^3 + 4a^3x^2 + a^4x \\ \quad\quad ax^4 + 4a^2x^3 + 6a^3x^2 + 4a^4x + a^5 \\ \hline x^5 + 5ax^4 + 10a^2x^3 + 10a^3x^2 + 5a^4x + a^5 \quad\quad = (x+a)^5 \end{array}$$

Tabulating these results, we get:

$$\begin{aligned} (x+a)^1 &= x + a \\ (x+a)^2 &= x^2 + 2ax + a^2 \\ (x+a)^3 &= x^3 + 3ax^2 + 3a^2x + a^3 \\ (x+a)^4 &= x^4 + 4ax^3 + 6a^2x^2 + 4a^3x + a^4 \\ (x+a)^5 &= x^5 + 5ax^4 + 10a^2x^3 + 10a^3x^2 + 5a^4x + a^5 \end{aligned}$$

The numbers in front of each term, or "coefficients," in these expressions are series in Omar Khayyám's triangle. Thus we should expect $(x + a)^6$ to be

$$x^6 + 6ax^5 + 15a^2x^4 + 20a^3x^3 + 15a^4x^2 + 6a^5x + a^6$$

You will find that it is so. There is thus a simple rule for writing down $(x + a)^n$. It is called the Binomial Theorem. If you go back to Chapter 5, p. 220, you will recall that the series

$$1,\ 4,\ 6,\ 4,\ 1$$

is the same as

$${}^4C_0\quad {}^4C_1\quad {}^4C_2\quad {}^4C_3\quad {}^4C_4$$

i.e. $1,\ \frac{4}{1},\ \frac{4.3}{2.1},\ \frac{4.3.2}{3.2.1},\ 1.$

Similarly, the coefficients of $(x + a)^6$ may be written

$$1,\ 6,\ 15,\ 20,\ 15,\ 6,\ 1$$

$${}^6C_0\quad {}^6C_1\quad {}^6C_2\quad {}^6C_3\quad {}^6C_4\quad {}^6C_5\quad {}^6C_6$$

$$1,\ \frac{6}{1},\ \frac{6.5}{2.1},\ \frac{6.5.4}{3.2.1},\ \frac{6.5.4.3}{4.3.2.1},\ \frac{6.5.4.3.2}{5.4.3.2.1},\ 1$$

So we can write down the result of multiplying out $(x + a)^n$ as

$$x^n + n.ax^{n-1} + \frac{n(n-1)}{2.1}a^2x^{n-2} + \frac{n(n-1)(n-2)}{3.2.1}a^3x^{n-3}$$
$$+ \frac{n(n-1)(n-2)(n-3)}{1.2.3.4}a^4x^{n-4} \ldots + a^n$$

Omar Khayyâm, who discovered the Binomial Theorem, was a sturdy materialist who believed in applying reason to the real world, and replanning it "nearer to the heart's desire." We do not know whether he used it to help him in the computations which struck dead yesterdays from the calendar. Perhaps he just played with it for fun, as Leonardo of Pisa played with the Fibonacci series. In the new mathematics which followed on the trail of the Reformation geometry, it turned out to be an exceedingly valuable instrument for a great variety of uses. One use which you can test out for yourself is an arithmetical device. To find $(4\cdot84)^8$ it is not necessary to go through a long series of multiplication sums. We can put

$$\begin{aligned}(4\cdot84)^8 &= (4\times1\cdot21)^8\\ &\quad 4^8\times(1\cdot21)^8\\ &\quad 4^8\times(1+\tfrac{21}{100})^8\end{aligned}$$

Applying the binomial theorem, we get

$$\left(1+\frac{21}{100}\right)^8 = 1 + 8\left(\frac{21}{100}\right) + \frac{8.7}{2.1}\left(\frac{21}{100}\right)^2 + \frac{8.7.6}{3.2.1}\left(\frac{21}{100}\right)^3 + \frac{8.7.6.5}{4.3.2.1}\left(\frac{21}{100}\right)^4 \text{ and so on}$$

$$= 1 + 8(0\cdot21) + 28(0\cdot0441) + 56(0\cdot009261) \text{ and so on}$$

The advantage of this is that we have a series of numbers getting smaller and smaller, and we can stop adding more terms at any convenient place. For instance:

$$(1\cdot01)^{10} = 1 + 10(0\cdot01) + \frac{10.9}{2.1}(0\cdot0001) + \frac{10.9.8}{3.2.1}(0.000001) \text{ and so on}$$

$$= 1 + 0\cdot1 + 0\cdot0045 + 0\cdot000120 + 0\cdot0000021 \text{ and so on}$$

The answer correct to 7 places is:

1.1046221

The use of triangular numbers as a way of discovering how series are built up led Newton and his followers to a trick which is used in physical sciences to suggest laws which describe quantitative changes in the real world. This trick depends on the use of vanishing triangles, to which we have already referred in an earlier chapter on ancient number lore. You will recall how the vanishing triangle of the series of the triangular numbers of the second order exposes their pedigree, thus:

$$\begin{array}{ccccccccc} & & & & 0 & & & & \\ & & & 1 & & 1 & & & \\ & & 3 & & 4 & & 5 & & \\ & 3 & & 6 & & 10 & & 15 & \\ 1 & & 4 & & 10 & & 20 & & 35 \end{array}$$

If we make a vanishing triangle for any series which vanishes at the same point, we may represent it by using abstract numbers in this way:

$$\begin{array}{ccccccccc} & & & & 0 & & & & \\ & & & D_1^3 & & D_2^3 & & & \\ & & D_1^2 & & D_2^2 & & D_3^2 & & \\ & D_1^1 & & D_2^1 & & D_3^1 & & D_4^1 & \\ x_1 & & x_2 & & x_3 & & x_4 & & x_5 \end{array}$$

Each D term in the triangle is the difference between the two terms on either side of it in the row below. The adverbs n and m in D_m^n refer to the diagonal order of the rows and the horizontal order within the rows; thus D_3^2 means a term in the second row of *differences* occupying the third place from the left in the row.

A vanishing triangle has peculiarities of its own apart from the particular set of numbers which make it up. To see what they are, first look at the vanishing triangle of 3 rows below:

$$\begin{array}{ccccc} & & 0 & & \\ & D_1^1 & & D_2^1 & \\ x_1 & & x_2 & & x_3 \end{array}$$

We can write down the last term from the first, thus:

$$x_2 - x_1 = D_1^1$$
$$x_3 - x_2 = D_2^1$$
$$\text{but} \quad D_2^1 - D_1^1 = 0$$
$$\text{so} \quad D_2^1 = D_1^1$$
$$x_3 = x_1 + 2D_1^1$$

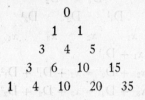

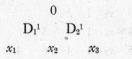

Now find the last term in the x row from the first diagonal column for the vanishing triangle of 4 rows:

$$
\begin{array}{ccccccc}
 & & & 0 & & & \\
 & & D_1^2 & & D_2^2 & & \\
 & D_1^1 & & D_2^1 & & D_3^1 & \\
x_1 & & x_2 & & x_3 & & x_4
\end{array}
$$

Now

$$
\begin{aligned}
x_2 &= x_1 + D_1^1 \\
x_3 &= x_2 + D_2^1 = x_2 + D_1^1 + D_1^2 \\
x_4 &= x_3 + D_3^1 = x_3 + D_2^1 + D_2^2 \\
&= x_3 + D_1^1 + D_1^2 + D_1^2 \\
\therefore \quad x_4 &= x_1 + 3D_1^1 + 3D_1^2
\end{aligned}
$$

If you form a vanishing triangle of 5 rows in the same way, you will find that

$$x_5 = x_1 + 4D_1^1 + 6D_1^2 + 4D_1^3$$

Similarly for vanishing triangles of 6 or 7 rows:

$$
\begin{aligned}
x_6 &= x_1 + 5D_1^1 + 10D_1^2 + 10D_1^3 + 5D_1^4 \\
x_7 &= x_1 + 6D_1^1 + 15D_1^2 + 20D_1^3 + 15D_1^4 + 6D_1^5
\end{aligned}
$$

You can easily test the last two expressions by using them to get the 6th and 7th terms of the series given at the top of p. 331. Thus $x_7 = 1 + 6(3) + 15(3) + 20(1) + 15(0) = 6(0) = 84$. The coefficients of the diagonal terms may now be tabulated thus:

n	x_n	Coefficient					
2	x_2	1					
3	x_3	1	2				
4	x_4	1	3	3			
5	x_5	1	4	6	4		
6	x_6	1	5	10	10	5	
7	x_7	1	6	15	20	15	6

You will recognize that these coefficients are none other than the numbers of Omar Khayyám's triangle and the Mirror of the Precious Elements, the only point to confuse you being that the coefficients of the series for the nth term, e.g. the 7th, are the coefficients of the binomial expression $(x + a)^{n-1}$, e.g. $(x + a)^6$. So we can write for any series which gives a vanishing triangle of n rows

$$x_n = ax_1 + bD_1^1 + cD_1^2 + dD_1^3 + eD_1^4 + fD_1^5 \ldots$$

The series continues till the differences vanish, and the coefficients a, b, c, etc., are the coefficients of

$$(x + a)^{n-1}$$

If
$$(x + a)^{n-1} = (x + a)^m$$

the coefficients are

$$1, \frac{m}{1}, \frac{m(m-1)}{2.1}, \frac{m(m-1)(m-2)}{3.2.1}, \frac{m(m-1)(m-2)(m-3)}{4.3.2.1} \ldots$$

and we can rewrite these, putting $(n - 1)$ for m:

$$1, \frac{(n-1)}{1}, \frac{(n-1)(n-2)}{2.1}, \frac{(n-1)(n-2)(n-3)}{3.2.1} \ldots$$

So the law of the vanishing triangle of n rows is

$$x_n = x_1 + (n-1)D_1^1 + \frac{(n-1)(n-2)}{2.1}D_1^2 + \frac{(n-1)(n-2)(n-3)}{3.2.1}D_1^3 \ldots$$

The $(n - 1)$th difference vanishes. So the series has $(n - 1)$ terms ending in the $(n - 2)$th difference (D_1^{n-2}). We can find how any set of numbers which can make a vanishing triangle is built up by using this rule. Take, for instance, the following series:

1 5 12 22 35 51 . . .

We only need the first four terms to form a vanishing triangle,

0
3 3
4 7 10
1 5 12 22

The law of this triangle is obtained by putting the correct values of x_1, D_1^1, D_1^2, D_1^3 in:

$$x_n = x_1 + (n-1)D_1^1 + \frac{(n-1)(n-2)}{2.1}D_1^2 + \frac{(n-1)(n-2)(n-3)}{3.2.1}D_1^3 \ldots \text{ and so on.}$$

Since $D_1^3 = 0$ the last term vanishes, and all subsequent ones do, so

$$x_n = 1 + (n-1)(4) + \frac{(n-1)(n-2)}{2.1}(3)$$

$$= 1 + 4n - 4 + \frac{3n^2 - 9n + 6}{2}$$

$$= \tfrac{1}{2}(3n^2 - n)$$

or $\quad \tfrac{1}{2}n(3n-1)$

This is the rule for building up the pentagonal numbers obtained in Chapter 5 by the hieroglyphic or figurate method. You can practise for yourself the use of this trick by finding how the following sets of numbers are built up and checking the result:

1	7	19	37	61 . . .
1	8	21	40	65 . . .
0	3	8	15	24 . . .
0	2	6	12	20 . . .
4	7	12	19	28 . . .
2	5	15	33	60 . . .

To commit the binomial theorem to memory you can find the values of $(1{\cdot}02)^7$, $(1{\cdot}03)^4$, $(2{\cdot}006)^6$ correct to 5 decimal places without multiplication, and make up a table of squares between 1·000 and 2·000 in intervals of 0·001 correct to 3 decimals. When you have finished it you will have seen the Dawn of Nothing with—

> "The beauty and bright faith of those
> Who made the Golden Journey to Samarkand."

FUTURE OF NUMBER SYMBOLS.—We have traced what progress immediately resulted when the human race was equipped with a more eloquent number system than the obscure letter symbols of the Greeks and Semites or the clumsy figures of the Sumerians and Egyptians. A vast waste of time in education could be eliminated at once if countries like Britain, which still cling to antiquated weights and measures, adopted a uniform system in which all units increased in multiples of the base of the numeral system. Countries which have the decimal system of weights and measures have done this. However, the base of the decimal system is not necessarily the best *base* to choose. We have seen that there is nothing sacred, no holy *tetraktys*, as the Pythagoreans sang, about the number 10. The arithmetic of a *positional* number script based on 5 (Fig. 102) would be just as easy. The five times row in the multiplication table would be the easiest to remember, instead of the ten times row.

In planning a rational future for human communication, we must always ask whether there is not a grain of truth in the conservatism which has obstructed progress. The fact is that some quite reasonable, though insufficient, arguments have been used to oppose the decimal system of measures by mathematicians who for long clung to the old sexagesimal fractions of degrees, minutes, and seconds, and by practical men who were accustomed to measures and weights (like the English monetary system) which go up in multiples of 12. For the purpose of calculation 10 is a bad number, however holy its devotional associations and however venerable its biological antecedents. It has only three exact divisors: 1, 2, 5. The number 12 has 1, 2, 3, 4, 6 as its divisors, and the number 60 has 1, 2, 3, 4, 5, 6, 10, 12, 15, 20, 30. A large number of factors is a great advantage in rapid calculation. So it would be an improvement on our present standards to make a Hegelian compromise of the English and French systems by adding two numbers to the Hindu number script, and making a positional notation based on the twelve-fingered abacus with weights and measures adjusted accordingly. You can make up sums and tables for yourself in the number script with base 12.

1	2	3	4	5	6	7	8	9	♀	♂	10
(1	2	3	4	5	6	7	8	9	10	11	12)

As explained on p. 69 the Sumerian priesthoods very nearly succeeded in devising a 60-base system with the chief merits of the Hindu numerals. The calendar makers of the extinct civilizations of Central America went further. They used the principle of vertical position and a zero. The base 20 was sometimes used consistently. Successive orders were then 1, 20, 400 and 8,000. The glyphs for 400, 8,000 and 7,613 then corresponded with those for 360, 7,200 and 6,853 in Fig. 106. The inconsistency in the third position betrays the social origin of numeral scripts. The Mayan calendar had 20-day as well as 30-day months and a primitive 360 as well as a 365-day year. The most usual value of the successive orders seems to have been 1, 20, 360, 7,200 in accordance with their primitive social function rather than the more sophisticated advantages of rapid calculation.

We have seen how the grammar of number was perfected to meet new social needs, when the Moslem world extended its boundaries from India to Spain. We have seen what our barbarian ancestors owed to these poets and mathematicians with a darker skin than ours. As we now turn to the contributions which Northern Europe has made to the grammar of size, we may recall our debt to an older

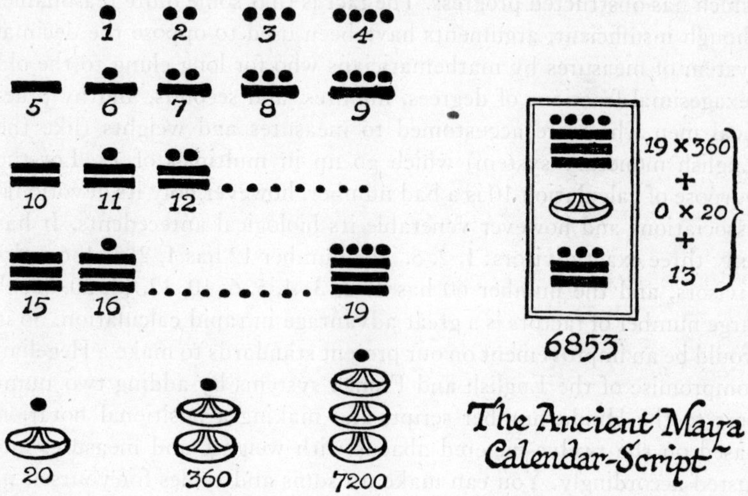

FIG. 106

The principle of position employed in the Mayan script of which the base was twenty is as follows. The lowest group of symbols represents the units column of the abacus, that above 20's, that above 360, that above 7,200.

civilization in the lines of the song which was sung at the Gate of the Sun in Flecker's poem:

> "Away, for we are ready to a man
> Our camels sniff the evening and are glad,
> Lead on, O Master of the Caravan,
> Lead on, the MERCHANT PRINCES of Baghdad. . . ."

CHAPTER 7

DISCOVERIES AND TESTS

1. In Mr. Wells's story, the two-toed sloth was the dominant species of Rampole Island. Suppose the two-toed sloth had evolved a brain as good as Mr. Blettsworthy's, it would have a number system

with a base 2, 4, or 8. Make multiplication tables for the systems of numeration it might use. Multiply 24 by 48 in all three systems, and check your results. You will find it easier if you assume that it first learnt to calculate with a counting-frame and make diagrams of the three different kinds of counting-frames.

2. You already know and can check by multiplication that

$$(x + a)(x + b) = x^2 + (a + b)x + ab.$$

The expression $x^2 + 5x - 6$ is built up in the same way, a being -1 and b being 6. So it is the product of the two factors $(x - 1)(x + 6)$. You can check this by dividing $x^2 + 5x - 6$ by $(x - 1)$ or by $(x + 6)$, and by multiplying $(x - 1)$ and $(x + 6)$ together. In the same way, write down the factors of the following by noticing how they are built up, checking each answer first by division and then by multiplication.

(*a*) $a^2 + 10a + 24$
(*b*) $p^2 + 5p + 6$
(*c*) $x^2 - 3x + 2$
(*d*) $m^2 + 4m + 3$
(*e*) $x^2 - 10x + 16$
(*f*) $f^2 + f - 20$
(*g*) $t^2 - 3t - 40$
(*h*) $q^2 - 10q + 21$
(*i*) $c^2 - 12c + 32$
(*j*) $n^2 + 8n - 20$
(*k*) $h^2 + 12h + 20$
(*l*) $z^2 + z - 42$
(*m*) $y^2 - y - 42$
(*n*) $b^2 - b - 20$

3. By direct multiplication you can show that

$$(ax + b)(ax - b) = a^2x^2 - b^2$$

an

$$(ax + by)(ax - by) = a^2x^2 - b^2y^2$$

Notice that the expression $4x^2 - 25$ is built up in this way from $(2x - 5)(2x + 5)$, etc., and write down the factors of:

(*a*) $x^2 - 36$
(*b*) $9x^2 - 25$
(*c*) $4x^2 - 100$
(*d*) $100y^2 - 25$
(*e*) $64x^2 - 49$
(*f*) $81x^2 - 64$
(*g*) $25x^2 - 16$
(*h*) $49p^2 - 169^2$
(*i*) $256t^2 - 169s^2$
(*j*) $4p^2 - 9q^2$
(*k*) $p^2 - 81q^2$
(*l*) $25n^2 - 9$
(*m*) $36t^2 - 16s^2$
(*n*) $9a^2 - 49b^2$

Using the "surd" sign ($\sqrt{\ }$), write down the factors of:

(o) $3 - x^2$ (r) $x^2 - 2$
(p) $2 - 3x^2$ (s) $2a^2 - 3$
(q) $5x^2 - 3$ (t) $7a^2 - 3b^2$

4. By direct multiplication show that

$$(ax + b)(cx + d) = acx^2 + (ad + bc)x + bd$$

Notice that the expression $6x^2 - 7x - 20$ is built up in the same way from the two factors $(3x + 4)(2x - 5)$, in which $a = 3$, $b = 4$, $c = 2$, and $d = -5$. In this way find the factors of the following and check by numerical substitution:

(a) $3x^2 + 10x + 3$ (h) $20x^4 + x^2 - 1$
(b) $6x^2 + 19x + 10$ (i) $15 + 4x - 4x^2$
(c) $6p^2 + 5p + 1$ (j) $6n^2 - n - 12$
(d) $3t^2 + 22t + 35$ (k) $15x^2 + 7x - 2$
(e) $6n^2 + 11n + 3$ (l) $7x - 6 - 2x^2$
(f) $6q^2 - 7q + 2$ (m) $15 - 4x - 4x^2$
(g) $11p^2 - 54p + 63$ (n) $7x - 6x^2 + 20$

5. By direct multiplication you can show that

$$(ax + by)(cx + dy) = acx^2 + (ad + bc)xy + bdy^2$$

The expression $6x^2 + 7xy - 20y^2$ is built up in the same way by multiplying the two factors $(3x - 4y)(2x + 5y)$, in which $a = 3$, $b = -4$, $c = 2$, and $d = 5$. In this way write down the factors of the following, and check your answers by division and multiplication:

(a) $6a^2 + 7ax - 3x^2$ (h) $36p^2 + 3pqr - 5q^2r^2$
(b) $15a^2 - 16abc - 15b^2c^2$ (i) $14d^2 + 11de - 15e^2$
(c) $6a^2 - 37ab - 35b^2$ (j) $3t^2 - 13ts - 16s^2$
(d) $2a^2 - 7ab - 9b^2$ (k) $9m^2 + 9mn - 4n^2$
(e) $6f^2 - 23fg - 18g^2$ (l) $6q^2 - pq - 12p^2$
(f) $21m^2 + 13ml - 20l^2$ (m) $4l^2 - 25lm + 25m^2$
(g) $12n^2 - 7mn - 12m^2$

6. In arithmetic you are used to reducing a fraction like $\frac{14}{21}$ to the simpler form $\frac{2}{3}$ by noticing that it is built up as $\frac{2 \times 7}{3 \times 7}$. In the same way

use your knowledge of how to find factors to simplify the following fractions, checking by numerical substitution:

(a) $\dfrac{x+y}{x^2+2xy+y^2}$

(b) $\dfrac{(x-y)}{x^2-y^2}$

(c) $\dfrac{(x+y)}{x^2-y^2}$

(d) $\dfrac{x-y}{x^2-2xy+y^2}$

(e) $\dfrac{ax+ay}{ax^2-ay^2}$

(f) $\dfrac{42x^2yz}{56xyz^2}$

(g) $\dfrac{x^2+3x+2}{x^2+5x+6}$

(h) $\dfrac{x^2+2x+1}{x^2+3x+2}$

(i) $\dfrac{x^2-1}{2x^2+3x-5}$

(j) $\dfrac{9x^2-49}{3x^2+14x-49}$

(k) $\dfrac{a^4b+ab^4}{a^4-a^3b+a^2b^2}$

(l) $\dfrac{8a^3-1}{4a^2+4a+1}$

(m) $\dfrac{2x^3-3x^2+4x-6}{x^3-2x^2+2x-4}$

7. Express the following in the simplest form:

(a) $\dfrac{a}{b}+\dfrac{a}{c}$

(b) $\dfrac{a^2b+ab^2}{a+b}$

(c) $x+y-\dfrac{9x^2-4y^2}{3x+2y}$

(d) $a+2b+\dfrac{4b^2}{a-2b}$

(e) $\dfrac{a}{x+1}+\dfrac{3a}{2x+2}-\dfrac{5a}{4x+4}$

(f) $\dfrac{a+2b}{3}-\dfrac{a-3b}{4}$

(g) $\dfrac{7a}{4x+8y}-\dfrac{3a}{2x+4y}$

(h) $x^2+2xy+y^2-\dfrac{x(x^2+3xy+4y^2)}{x+y}$

8. Express as a single fraction in its simplest form:

(a) $\dfrac{1}{x+1}+\dfrac{1}{x-1}$

(b) $\dfrac{1}{x+1}-\dfrac{1}{x-1}$

(c) $\dfrac{1}{a-b}-\dfrac{1}{a+b}$

(d) $\dfrac{a}{a-b}+\dfrac{b}{a+b}$

(e) $\dfrac{x}{x-y}-\dfrac{y}{x+y}$

(f) $\dfrac{x-y}{x+y}+\dfrac{xy}{x^2-y^2}$

(g) $\dfrac{x}{2y}-\dfrac{x-y}{2(x+y)}$

(h) $\dfrac{y-5}{y-6}-\dfrac{y-3}{y-4}$

(i) $\dfrac{x^2 + y^2}{x^2 \quad y^2} - \dfrac{y}{x - y} + \dfrac{x}{x + y}$

(j) $\dfrac{x + p}{x + q} + \dfrac{x + q}{x + p} - \dfrac{2(x - p)(x - q)}{(x + p)(x + q)}$

(k) $\dfrac{1}{t^2 - 6t + 5} - \dfrac{2}{t^2 + 2t - 3} + \dfrac{1}{t^2 - 2t - 15}$

(l) $\dfrac{1}{n} + \dfrac{1}{n - 1} - \dfrac{1}{n + 1} + \dfrac{2n}{n^2 - 1}$

(m) $\dfrac{t}{t^2 - 1} + \dfrac{1}{t - 1} - \dfrac{1}{t + 1}$

9. If, following the suggestion of Stevinus, we call $\frac{1}{100}$, 10^{-2}, illustrate by using concrete numbers for a and b the following rules:

$$10^a \times 10^b = 10^{a+b}$$
$$10^a \div 10^b = 10^{a-b} \text{ (} a \text{ greater than } b \text{ or less than } b\text{)}$$
$$(10^a)^b = 10^{ab} = (10^b)^a$$

Test the general rules

$$n^a \times n^b = n^{a+b} \text{ etc.}$$

using numbers other than 10.

10. Applying the diagonal rule of p. 101 and the methods of the preceding examples, solve the following equations:

(a) $\dfrac{x + 2}{3} - \dfrac{x + 1}{5} = \dfrac{x - 3}{4} - 1$

(b) $\dfrac{x + a}{a + b} + \dfrac{x - 3b}{a - b} = 3$

(c) $\dfrac{1}{2x - 3} + \dfrac{x}{3x - 2} = \dfrac{1}{3}$

(d) $\dfrac{3}{x - 1} - \dfrac{2}{x - 2} = \dfrac{1}{x - 3}$

(e) $\dfrac{2x - 1}{x - 2} - \dfrac{x + 2}{2x + 1} = \dfrac{3}{2}$

(f) $\dfrac{x}{x - 2} - \dfrac{x}{x + 2} = \dfrac{1}{x - 2} - \dfrac{4}{x + 2}$

11. (*a*) A man travelled 8 miles in $1\frac{3}{4}$ hours. If he rode part of the way at 12 miles per hour and walked the rest at 3 miles per hour, how

far did he have to walk? (*b*) A train usually travels at 40 miles an hour. On a journey of 80 miles a stoppage of 15 minutes takes place. By travelling the rest of the way at 50 miles an hour the train arrives on time. How far from the start did the stoppage take place?

(*c*) A manufacturer cuts the price of his goods by $2\frac{1}{2}$ per cent. By what percentage must the sales increase after the cut to produce an increase of 1 per cent in the gross receipts?

12. Solve the following equations:

(*a*) $x^2 + 11x - 210 = 0$

(*b*) $x^2 - 3x = 88$

(*c*) $12x^2 + x = 20$

(*d*) $(3x + 1)(8x - 5) = 1$

(*e*) $3x^2 - 7x - 136 = 0$

(*f*) $2(x - 1) = \dfrac{x - 1}{x + 1}$

(*g*) $x(x - b) = a(a - b)$

(*h*) $\dfrac{1}{x + 1} - \dfrac{1}{2 + x} = \dfrac{1}{x + 10}$

13. (*a*) Find three consecutive whole numbers the sum of whose squares is 110.

(*b*) A square lawn with one side lying due north and south has a border 6 feet wide taken off its south edge. It is then lengthened by adding a strip 3 feet wide on the west side. If the present area of the lawn is 500 square feet, what was the length of the side of the original lawn?

(*c*) The circumference of the hind wheel of a wagon is 1 foot more than the circumference of the front wheel. If the front wheel makes 22 more revolutions than the hind wheel in travelling a mile, find the radius of each wheel.

(*d*) In a right-angled triangle ABC the hypotenuse is 9 inches longer than one of the other sides AC. The remaining side is 2 inches less than half AC. Find the lengths of the sides.

14. The working of Example V on p. 313 can be done in another way. The three statements are:

(i) $5s = f$ (ii) $2m + 8 = f + s$ (iii) $m = 100 - f$

From (i) substitute 5*s* for *f* in (ii) and (iii). Then,

$$2m + 8 = 5s + s$$

and $$m = 100 - 5s$$

Rearranging, we get $$2m - 6s = -8 \quad \ldots\ldots\ldots \quad \text{(iv)}$$

$$m + 5s = 100. \quad \ldots\ldots\ldots \quad \text{(v)}$$

We have here two unknown quantities and two equations. We can get rid of one unknown by combining the two equations. We combine the equations by subtracting the left-hand and right-hand sides separately. Before we do this we must decide which unknown we will try to get rid of or eliminate. The easiest one to eliminate will be *m*. To get *m* to vanish when we add the left-hand sides we must multiply (v) by 2. We then obtain

$$2m - 6s = -8 \quad \ldots\ldots\ldots \quad \text{(vi)}$$

$$2m + 10s = 200 \quad \ldots\ldots\ldots \quad \text{(vii)}$$

Subtracting both sides, we get

$$-16s = -208$$

or $$16s = 208$$

$$s = 13$$

In the present instance this is all we need to know, but if we wanted to know *m*, we put $s = 13$ in either (iv) or (v), and we have then a simple equation which we can solve for *m*.

Usually it is necessary to multiply both equations by a different factor, as in the following example.

$$3x + 4y = 15. \quad \ldots\ldots\ldots \quad \text{(i)}$$

$$2x + 5y = 17. \quad \ldots\ldots\ldots \quad \text{(ii)}$$

To eliminate *x* multiply (i) by 2 and (ii) by 3.

$$6x + 8y = 30$$

$$6x + 15y = 51$$

Subtract both sides: $$-7y = -21$$

$$y = 3$$

Put the value obtained for *y* in (i):

$$3x + 12 = 15$$

$$3x = 3$$

$$x = 1$$

Check by putting the values obtained for x and y in (ii):

$$2 + 15 = 17$$

In order to find two unknown quantities we must have two equations which make two different statements about them.

The method for solving simultaneous equations can be summarized thus:

Step I.—Arrange your equations so that like terms (e.g. x's) come under one another.

Step II.—Decide which unknown to eliminate.

Step III.—Multiply each term of the first equation by the coefficient of the selected unknown in the second equation and *vice versa.*

Step IV.—Subtract the left-hand sides and the right-hand sides of your equations.

Step V.—Solve the resulting simple equation.

Step VI.—Substitute the value obtained in one of your original equations and thus find the second unknown.

Step VII.—Check by substituting for both unknowns in the other original equation.

Equations involving three unknowns can be solved in a similar manner. Three equations are required. By taking them in two pairs we can eliminate one unknown from each pair, and thus obtain two equations with two unknowns.

$$2x + 3y = 4z$$
$$3x + 4y = 5z + 4$$
$$5x - 3z = y - 2$$

Rearrange:

$$2x + 3y - 4z = 0 \quad \ldots\ldots\ldots \quad \text{(i)}$$
$$3x + 4y - 5z = 4 \quad \ldots\ldots\ldots \quad \text{(ii)}$$
$$5x - y - 3z = -2 \quad \ldots\ldots\ldots \quad \text{(iii)}$$

Eliminate y from (i) and (iii) by multiplying (iii) by -3:

$$2x + 3y - 4z = 0$$
$$-15x + 3y + 9z = 6$$
$$17x - 13z = -6 \quad \ldots\ldots\ldots \quad \text{(iv)}$$

Eliminate y from (ii) and (iii) by multiplying (iii) by -4.

$$3x + 4y - 5z = 4$$
$$-20x + 4y + 12z = 8$$
$$23x - 17z = -4 \quad \ldots\ldots \quad \text{(v)}$$

(iv) and (v) can now be solved for x and z as before. By substituting the values obtained in (i) y can be found and all three values checked from (ii) and (iii).

Solve the following equations:

(*a*) $x = 5y$
$x - y = 8$

(*b*) $3y = 4x$
$8x - 5y = 4$

(*c*) $x = 5y - 4$
$10y - 3x = 2$

(*d*) $60x - 17y = 285$
$75x - 19y = 390$

(*e*) $x + y = 23$
$y + z = 25$
$z + x = 24$

(*f*) $2x + 7y = 48$
$5y - 2x = 24$
$x + y + z = 10$

15. The following problems lead to simultaneous equations:

(*a*) The third term of an A.P. is 8, and the tenth term is 30. Find the seventh term.

(*b*) The fourth term of an A.P. is $-\frac{1}{8}$ and the seventh term is $\frac{1}{64}$. Find the first term.

(*c*) In a room, twice the length is equal to three times the breadth. If the room were 3 feet wider and 3 feet shorter it would be square. Find the measurements of the room.

(*d*) A hall seats 600 people, with chairs in rows across the hall. 5 chairs are taken out of each row to provide a passage down the middle. In order to seat the same number of people, 6 more rows have to be added. Find the original number of chairs in a row.

(*e*) Two towns P and Q are 100 miles apart on a railway line. There are two stations R and S between them. The distance between R and S is 10 miles more than the distance between P and R, and the distance between S and Q is 20 miles more than the distance between R and S. Find the distance between R and S in miles.

16. Give the nth term of the following series:

(*a*) by using triangular numbers,
(*b*) by using vanishing triangles:

(i) 1, 6, 15, 28, 45
(ii) 1, 6, 18, 40, 75
(iii) 1, 20, 75, 184, 365, 636
(iv) 1, 7, 19, 37, 61, 91
(v) 1, 4, 10, 19, 31, 46
(vi) 1, 5, 13, 25, 41, 61

17. Expand the following,
(*a*) by the binomial theorem,
(*b*) by direct multiplication:

(i)	$(x + 2)^5$	(iv)	$(2x + 1)^6$
(ii)	$(a + b)^3$	(v)	$(3a - 2b)^4$
(iii)	$(x + y)^4$	(vi)	$(x - 1)^7$

Check your results by repeated division.

18. Using the binomial theorem, calculate to four decimal places:

(i)	$(1{\cdot}04)^3$	(iii)	$(1{\cdot}12)^4$
(ii)	$(0{\cdot}98)^5$	(iv)	$(5{\cdot}05)^3$

19. Represent 272 and 8,573 in Maya calendar-script, and multiply 27 by 343 in the Maya calendar-notation as it would have been done if the Arabs had reached America before Columbus.

THINGS TO MEMORIZE

1. If $x^2 + ax + b = 0$

$$x = \frac{-a \pm \sqrt{a^2 - 4b}}{2}$$

2. $a^0 = 1$, whatever a is, apart from 0

$$a^{-n} = \frac{1}{a^n}$$

3. $$(a + b)^n = a^n + na^{n-1}b + \frac{n(n-1)}{1.2}a^{n-2}b^2 + \frac{n(n-1)(n-2)}{1.2.3}a^{n-3}b^3 \ldots + b^n$$

NUMBER GAMES TO ILLUSTRATE ALGEBRAIC SYMBOLISM

1. Think of a number. Multiply the number above it by the number below it. Add 1. Give me the answer. The number you thought of is (the square root of the answer).

The explanation of this puzzle is as follows. Let the number thought of be a. The number above is $a + 1$, the number below is $a - 1$, and $(a - 1)(a + 1) = a^2 - 1$. Add 1 and you get a^2. By taking the square root of the number given you get the number thought of.

This sort of game can go on indefinitely, and will provide good practice in the use of symbols and factorization. Here are some more.

2. Think of a number less than 10. Multiply it by 2. Add 3. Multiply the answer by 5. Add another number less than 10. Give the answer. To tell what the numbers thought of are, subtract 15 from the answer. Then the digit in the tens place is the first number thought of, and the digit in the units place is the second number thought of.

In algebraic language.

$$(2a + 3)5 + b = 10a + b + 15$$

3. Think of a number. Square it. Subtract 9. Divide the answer by the number which is 3 more than the number you first thought of. Give the answer. What is the number thought of? Explain this in algebraic language.

4. Think of a number. Add 2. Square the answer. Take away four times the first number. Give the answer. What is then umber thought of? Explain this, and make up some more for yourself.

5. Express in symbolic form the statement: if each of two different numbers is exactly divisible by a whole number x, their sum and their difference are each also divisible by x. Hence use the methods on pages 209 and 300 to explore the following rules for the decimal notation:

(*a*) A number is divisible by 5 if its last digit is 5 or 0.

(*b*) A number is exactly divisible by 3 if the sum of its digits is exactly divisible by 3, and by 9 if the sum of its digits is exactly divisible by 9.

(*c*) A number is divisible by 4, if the last two; by 8, if the last three; by 16 if the last four digits are divisible by the same number (i.e. 4, 8, 16 as the case may be). N.B.—Use (*b*) and (*c*) in the last example to find a rule for factors of 6 and 12.

(*d*) From the fact that 1001 is exactly divisible by 7, 11, and 13, justify the rule that a number of 6 digits is divisible by one of these numbers if the difference between the number represented by the first three and last three digits (in their appropriate order) is so divisible. Extend the rule to any numbers of more than 3 digits.

CHAPTER VIII

The World Encompassed

OR

SPHERICAL TRIANGLES

As early as the time when the Great Pyramids were built, and possibly at a far earlier date, the ancient priesthoods of Egypt and Sumeria were well acquainted with two facts about the stars. One is that the same interval of time always elapses between the moments when any two particular stars cross the meridian, i.e. reach their highest point in the heavens on the great imaginary circle which passes through the north point of the horizon, the pole star, the zenith,* and the south point. The other is that at any particular place the angle between a star and the horizon line (its altitude) or the zenith (its zenith distance) is always the same at the moment when it is making its meridian transit. The ancient calendar-priesthoods had to rely on hour-glasses, like the ones which used to be sold to time the boiling of an egg, for recording the times of transit, and as they did not travel much, they did not fully realize the importance of what they knew. When the priests had ceased to be practical men, and another class of practical men, the Phoenician mariners, were gathering new information about the heavens, a second step of great importance was made. The maritime Greeks already knew that the difference between the meridian zenith distance of any two stars measured at two different places is the same. Thus at Memphis (Lat. 30° N.) Sirius transits 46½° S., and Aldebaran roughly 14° S. At London (Lat. 51½° N.) Sirius transits 68° S., and Aldebaran roughly 35½° S. In each case the local difference is 32½°. The maritime peoples of the ancient world recognized that this was because the stars have a fixed relation to each other, and because the earth itself is round. One reason why they knew the world was round was because the circular shadow of the earth could be seen when it occupied a position in the heavens in line with the sun and moon during a lunar eclipse. They were also well acquainted with the daily experience of ships sinking on the horizon, and they had learned from travel that new constellations appeared or familiar ones sank

* Refer to Figs. 4, 8, and 13 in Chapter 2 to make sure you know the meaning of altitude, zenith distance, and azimuth before reading this chapter.

below the horizon, as they sailed further south or north. Till about 250 B.C. they had very little knowledge of distances. About that time

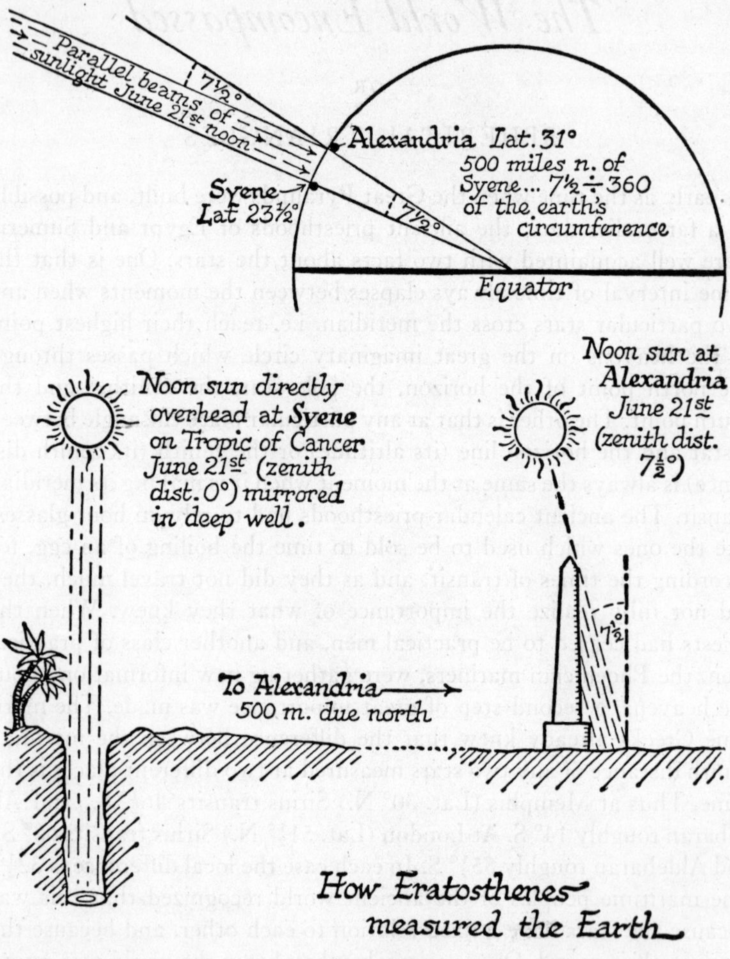

FIG. 107

Note that at noon the sun lies directly over the observer's meridian of longitude. Syene and Alexandria have nearly the same longitude. So the sun, the two places, and the earth's centre may be drawn on the same flat slab of space.

Eratosthenes made the first measurements of the size of the earth. This was followed by the invention of maps. The first maps were maps of the heavens. Earth maps depended on star maps, and grew by easy stages out of them. Hipparchus, whom we have mentioned in Chapter 6, mapped the position of a thousand and eighty fixed stars.

The construction of star maps provided the necessary technical foundation for the Great Navigations, and we shall see later that map-making played a great part in stimulating the discovery of new mathematical tools in the period which followed them. In A.D. 1420 Henry, then Crown Prince of Portugal, built an observatory on the headland of Sagres, one of the promontories which terminate at Cape St. Vincent, the extreme south-west point of Europe. There he set up a school of seamanship under one Master Jacome from Majorca, and for forty years devoted himself to cosmographical studies while equipping and organizing expeditions which won for him the title of Henry the Navigator. For the preparation of maps, nautical tables, and instruments he enlisted Arab cartographers and Jewish astronomers, employing them to instruct his captains and assist in piloting his vessels. Peter Nunes declares that the prince's master mariners were well equipped with instruments and those rules of astronomy and geometry "which all map-makers should know." The development of astronomy once more became part of the everyday life of mankind, and the new impetus it received from the growth of maritime commerce was reinforced by the introduction of the clock and the telescope, two new technical inventions which emerged from the world's everyday work in a different social context.

Between the fall of Alexandrian civilization and the rise of European navigation considerable progress in the mathematics of map-making, or, as it is sometimes called, *spherical trigonometry*, was made by the Arabs, though all the basic principles were laid down earlier. Some of this chapter is likely to prove difficult, unless you have done Exercise 10 on p. 283, and it may be well to skim pages 429–434 before reading it. Later chapters do not depend on it, and it is only put in because it helps you to understand how mathematics grew to meet the practical requirements of human life. If you have any turn for carpentering, it will also show you how you can apply mathematics to astronomical problems for which you can collect your own data with home-made instruments.

THE CONSTRUCTION OF A STAR MAP

On a country walk we recognize our whereabouts by familiar landmarks. The mariner's landmarks are the stars. If you were stranded on an uninhabited island after weeks of fever, you could tell whether you were south or north of the equator by the appearance of the heavens. North of it you would be able to see the pole star, and at some time of the year the Great Bear. South of it you would not see the pole star, you would see the Southern Cross and other constellations which are not seen in the latitude of London and New York. If you live south of the equator, you cannot find your latitude by taking the altitude of the pole star, as explained on p. 171 in Chapter 4, because there is no bright star which shines very nearly above the south pole. Star maps, which the Alexandrians were the first to construct, show you how to find your latitude in any part of the earth by the bearings of any star which is not obscured, as the pole star often is obscured, by clouds. With their aid and the accurate knowledge of Greenwich time, the mariner can also find his longitude at any hour of the night from the position of any star. So he does not have to wait for noon each day to find where his ship is located.

In an ordinary globe the position of a place is represented by where two sets of circles cross. One set of "great" circles, which all intersect at the poles, have the same radius as the globe itself. These are the meridians of longitude which are numbered according to the angles which they make with each other at the poles when the globe is viewed from above or below, and equally, of course, by the fraction of the circumference of the equator (or of any circle bounding a flat slab parallel to the slab bounded by the equator) cut off by them. Thus the angle between Long. 15° W. and 45° W. at the pole is also the angle formed by joining to its centre the ends of the arc which is $\frac{45° - 15°}{360°}$ or $\frac{1}{12}$ of the circumference of any circle parallel to the equator. The other set of circles are the small* circles of latitude. These are numbered by the angle between any point on the boundary, the earth's centre, and a point on the equator in the same meridian of longitude as the point of the boundary chosen. Thus the angle between Lat. 15° N. and Lat. 45° N. is the angle at the earth's centre made by an arc $\frac{1}{12}$ of the circumference of a circle of longitude (or of the equator itself). Circles of latitude form the boundaries of flat slabs ("planes") drawn at right angles to the polar axis round which the earth rotates, i.e. the axis round which the sun and stars appear to turn. Circles of longitude bound the rim of flat slabs ("planes") which intersect at the poles.

* One circle of latitude (0°, the equator) is a great circle, i.e. a circle with the same radius as the sphere on which it is traced.

This way of mapping out the world arose from the discovery that the fixed stars all appear to rotate at the same rate in circular arcs lying in parallel layers at *right angles* to the line which joins the eye to the pole in the heavens (i.e. approximately speaking, to the pole star in the northern hemisphere). The elevation of this line above the horizon (which, as we saw on p. 171, is the latitude of the observer) is different at different places. It becomes greater as we sail due north, i.e. towards the pole star, and less as we go due south, i.e. away from the pole star. At any particular place one and the same star always has the same elevation above the pole, and hence makes the same angle with the zenith as it crosses the meridian. The fact that the stars appear to rotate in circular arcs lying in parallel layers at right angles to the polar axis is shown by the fact that the difference between the meridian zenith distances of any star at two places is the same as the difference between the elevation of the pole as measured at the same two places, and it can be demonstrated directly by fixing a shaft pointing straight at the celestial pole and fixing a telescope (or a piece of steel tube) so that it can rotate at any required angle about the shaft itself as axis (Fig. 108). If the telescope is now clamped at such an angle as to point to a particular star, we can follow the course of the star throughout the night by simply rotating it on its free axis without lowering it or raising it. If it is set by very accurate modern clockwork so that it can turn through 360° in a sidereal day (i.e. the time between two meridian transits of any star whatever), it will always point to the same star. The fact that any particular star crosses the meridian exactly the same number of minutes after or before any other particular star suggested to the astronomers of antiquity that they were spaced out on great fixed circles all intersecting at the celestial poles.

Thus each star can be given a position in the great imaginary sphere of the heavens, fixed by the crossing of two circles (Fig. 109), a great circle of *Right Ascension* (comparable to our meridian of longitude) cutting all other similar circles at the celestial poles, and a small circle of *Declination* (comparable to our parallels of latitude), all lying on planes at right angles to the polar axis. A circle of declination is numbered in the same way as circles of latitude by the angle which the two points where it and the celestial equator are cut by the meridian make at the centre of the earth (Fig. 110). What we call the earth's polar axis is only the axis about which the stars appear to rotate, and what we call the plane of the earth's equator is therefore only the slab of the earth where it is cut by the plane of the heavenly equator. The line which joins an observer to the centre of the earth (see p. 166) goes

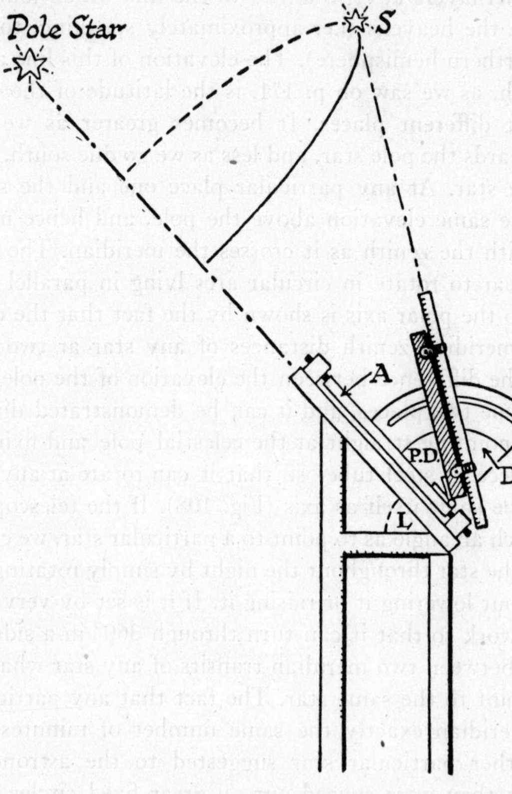

FIG. 108

A simple "equatorial" made with a piece of iron pipe and wood. The pipe which serves for telescope rotates around the axis A fixed at an angle L (latitude of the place) due north. When it is clamped at an angle PD (the "polar distance" of the star or 90° – Declin.) you can rotate it about A as the star (S) revolves, keeping S always in view.

through his zenith, cutting his parallel of latitude and a corresponding declination circle in the heavens. Any star on such a declination circle will pass directly above an observer anywhere on the corresponding circle of latitude once in twenty-four hours. So once the stars had been mapped out in this way to act as landmarks in navigation, it was an easy step to map out the globe in a similar way.

It is important to bear in mind that mapping stars in this way is merely a way of telling us in what direction we have to look or point a telescope in order to see them. The position of a star as shown on

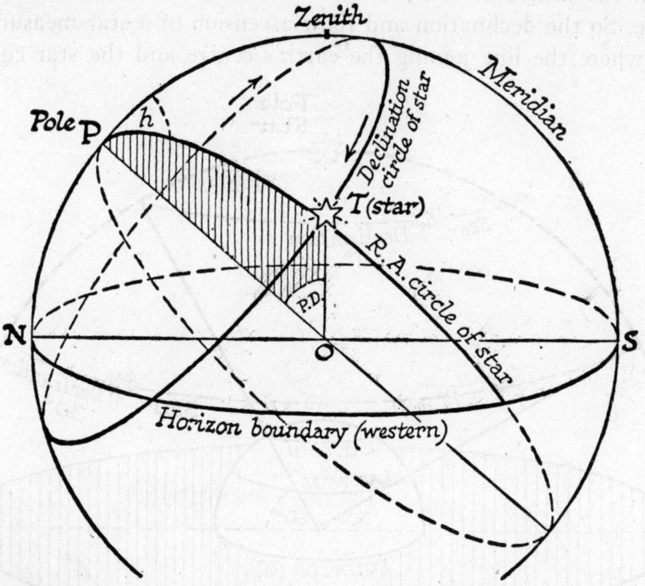

FIG. 109.—APPARENT ROTATION OF THE CELESTIAL SPHERE

The position of a star (T) in the celestial sphere may be represented by a point where a small circle of declination which measures its elevation above the celestial equator intersects a large circle of Right Ascension (R.A.). All stars on the same declination circle must cross the meridian at the same angular divergence from the zenith and are above the observer's horizon for the same length of time in each twenty-four hours. The arc PT or flat angle POT measures the angular divergence of the star from the pole (polar distance) and is hence 90° – Declin. All stars on the same great circle of R.A. cross the meridian at the same instant. The angle between two R.A. circles measures the difference between their times of transit. The angle *h* between the plane of the meridian and the R.A. circle of the star is the angle through which it has rotated since it crossed the meridian. If *h* is 15° it crossed the meridian one hour ago. So *h* is called the hour angle of the star. If the hour angle is *h* degrees, the star made its transit $h \div 15$ hours previously.

the star map has nothing to do with how far it is away from us. If you dug straight down following the plumb-line (see p. 166), you would eventually reach the centre of the earth; and the bottom of a straight well, as viewed from the centre of the earth, if that were possible, would therefore be exactly in line with the top. It has the same latitude and longitude as the latter, though it is not so far away from the earth's centre. The latitude or longitude of the bottom of a mine is the latitude and longitude of the spot where the line joining it with the centre of the earth continued upwards cuts the earth's surface. So the declination and right ascension of a star measure the place where the line joining the earth's centre and the star cuts an

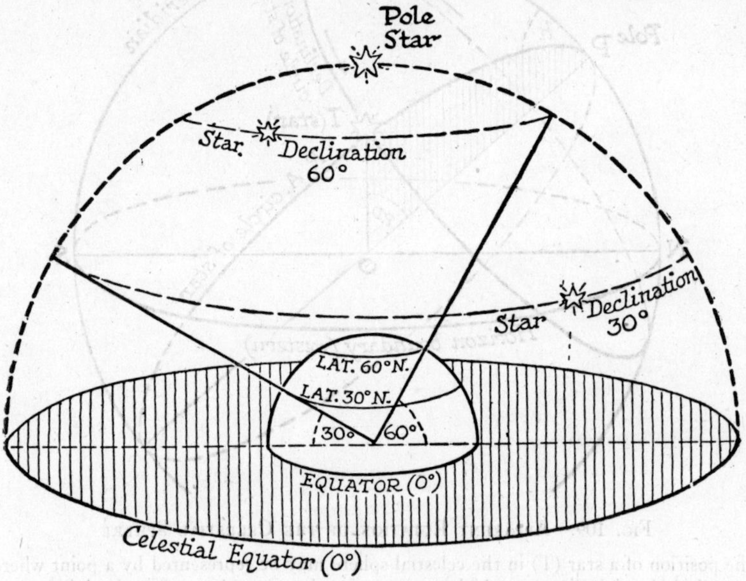

FIG. 110.—SMALL CIRCLES OF LATITUDE ON THE TERRESTRIAL AND OF DECLINATION ON THE CELESTIAL SPHERE

imaginary globe whose radius extends to the furthermost stars. In a total eclipse the sun and the moon have the same declination and R.A. just as the top and bottom of a mine have the same latitude and longitude. This means that the sun and moon are directly in line with the centre of the earth like the top and the bottom of a mine.

At noon the sun's shadow lies on the line joining the north and south points of the horizon. This is also the observer's meridian of longitude which joins the north and south poles. The sun itself lies at noon on the imaginary circular arc or celestial meridian which passes through the celestial pole and the zenith. The celestial pole is in line with the earth's pole and the earth's centre. The zenith (Chapter 4, p. 166) is in line with the observer and the earth's centre. So the celestial meridian, the earth's centre, and the observer's meridian of

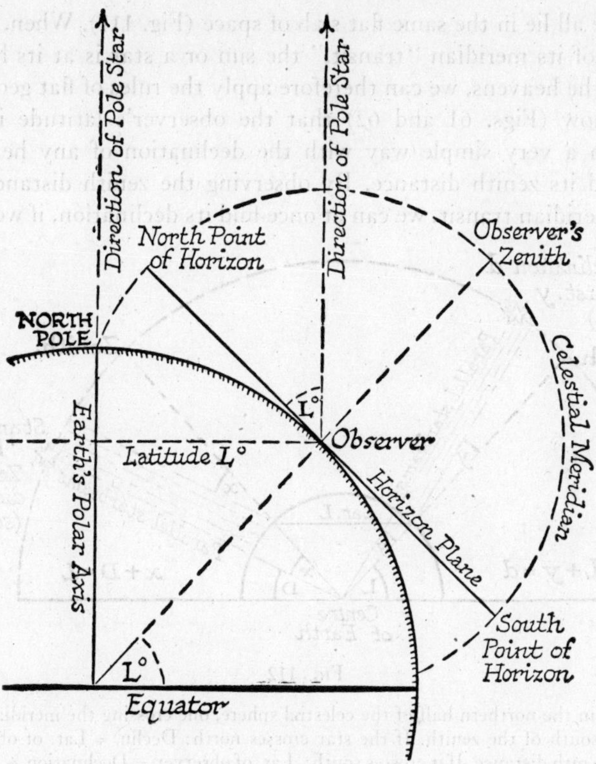

FIG. 111. — A STAR AT MERIDIAN TRANSIT LIES IN THE SAME PLANE AS THE OBSERVER, THE EARTH'S POLES, THE ZENITH, THE SOUTH AND NORTH POINTS OF THE HORIZON, AND THE EARTH'S CENTRE

A straight line which does not lie on some particular flat slab of space (or *plane*) can only cut it once. A straight line which passes through more than one point on a plane therefore lies on the same plane as the points through which it passes. The plane bounded by the observer's great circle of longitude and the earth's axis includes as points the earth centre, observer, and the earth's poles. The line joining zenith and observer passes also through the earth centre, i.e. through more than one point on this plane. Hence it lies wholly on the plane. The north and south points of the horizon are simply points where lines from the earth centre through the meridian of longitude pierce the horizon plane. They must also lie in the same plane as these lines. So south and north points, zenith and observer are all in the same plane with the earth centre and poles. A circle can only cut a plane in which it does not itself lie at two points. The circle drawn through the north and south points and the zenith passes through more than two points in the same plane, and therefore lies wholly on it. So any point on this imaginary circle (the celestial meridian) is also on it.

longitude all lie in the same flat slab of space (Fig. 111). When, at the moment of its meridian "transit," the sun or a star is at its highest point in the heavens, we can therefore apply the rules of flat geometry which show (Figs. 61 and 62) that the observer's latitude is connected in a very simple way with the declination of any heavenly body and its zenith distance. By observing the zenith distance of a star at meridian transit, we can at once find its declination, if we know

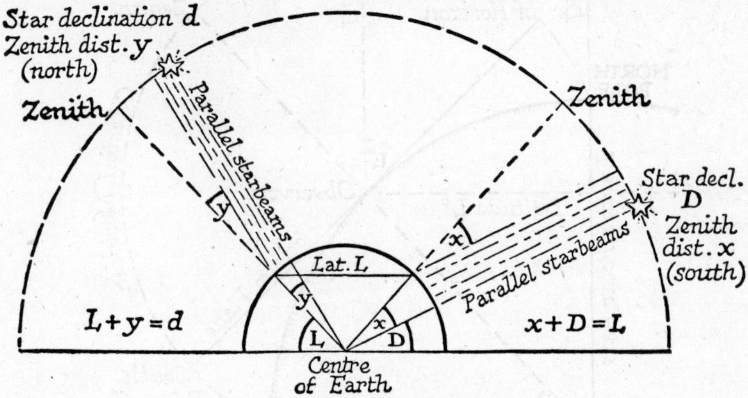

FIG. 112

Two stars in the northern half of the celestial sphere, one crossing the meridian north, the other south of the zenith. If the star crosses north: Declin. = Lat. of observer + meridian zenith distance. If it crosses south: Lat. of observer = Declination + meridian zenith distance, i.e. Declin. = Latitude of observer – meridian zenith distance.

our latitude, and conversely, if we have once determined its declination we can always determine our latitude. As there is always some star near the meridian this means that the mariner can determine his latitude at any time of the night with the aid of the star map or tables giving the declination of stars. For a star which transits north of the zenith (Figs. 112 and 113) in a northerly latitude the formula is simply

$$\text{Declination} = \text{Observer's latitude} + \text{meridian z.d.}$$

For a star which transits south of the zenith the formula is

$$\text{Declination} = \text{Observer's latitude} - \text{meridian z.d.}$$

The first formula holds for all situations if we reckon zenith distances

As explained in Chapter 4, p. 171, the observer's (O) latitude is the angle between the horizon and the celestial pole (P), i.e. ∠PON. Hence the angle ZOP is 90° – Lat. (L).

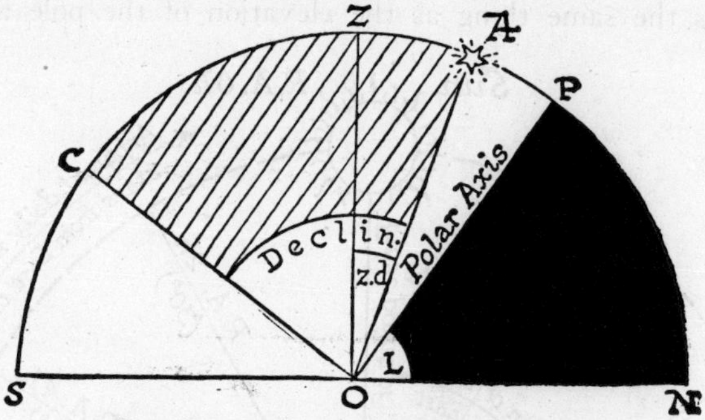

Star A transits north of the Zenith

For a star (A) which transits north of the zenith:

$$ZOP = AOP + \text{zenith distance (z.d.)}$$

Since the star's declination is the angle it makes with the celestial equator which is at right angles to the polar axis:

$$\begin{aligned} \text{Declin.} &= 90° - AOP \\ &= 90° - (ZOP - \text{z.d.}) \\ &= 90° - (90° - \text{lat.}) + \text{z.d.} \\ \therefore \quad \text{Declin.} &= \text{Lat.} + \text{z.d.} \end{aligned}$$

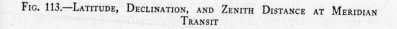

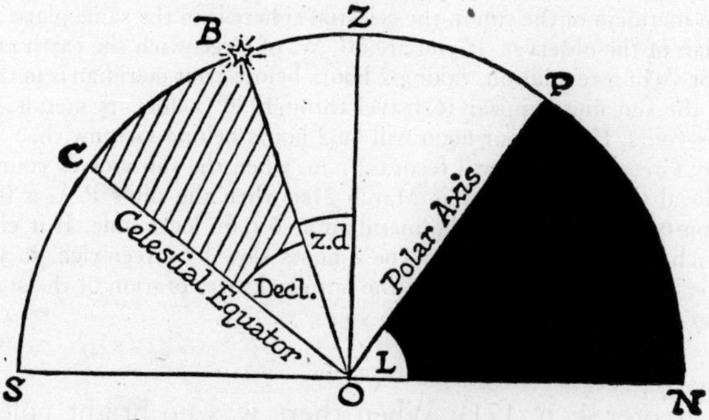

Star B transits south of the Zenith

For a star (B) which transits south of the zenith:

$$\text{Declin.} + \text{z.d.} = 90° - ZOP = 90° - (90° - \text{lat.})$$
$$\therefore \quad \text{Declin.} = \text{Lat.} - \text{z.d.}$$

FIG. 113.—LATITUDE, DECLINATION, AND ZENITH DISTANCE AT MERIDIAN TRANSIT

measured south of the zenith as negative and latitudes or declinations south of the terrestrial or celestial equators as negative. The observer's latitude is the same thing as the elevation of the pole above the

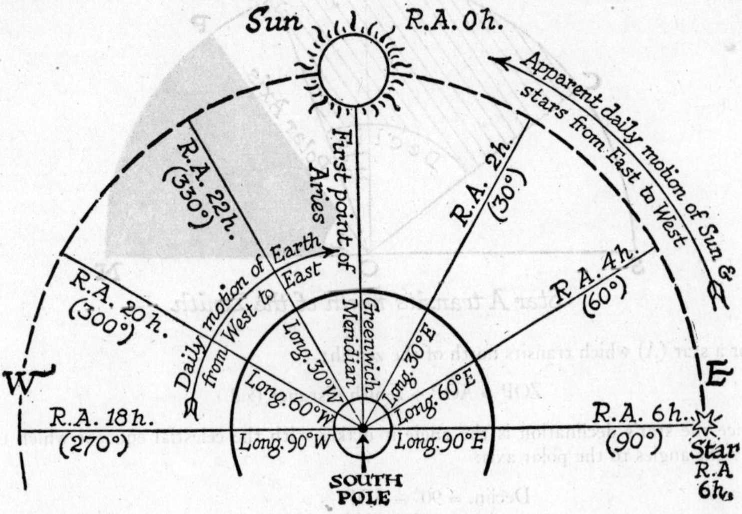

FIG. 114

Noon at Greenwich on March 21st. Showing relation of R.A. longitude and time. At noon the R.A. meridian of the sun in the celestial sphere is in the same plane as the longitude meridian of the observer. If you are 30° W. of Greenwich the earth must rotate through 30° or $\frac{1}{12}$ of a revolution, taking 2 hours before your meridian is in the plane of the sun's, or the sun must appear to travel through 30° before its meridian is in the same plane as yours. Hence your noon will be 2 hours behind Greenwich.
A clock set by Greenwich time will record 2 p.m. when the sun crosses your meridian, i.e. at noon local time. If the date is March 21st when the sun's R.A. is 0, a star of right ascension 6 hours will cross the meridian at 6 p.m. local time. If it crossed at 8 p.m. Greenwich time your clock would be 2 hours slow by Greenwich, so your longitude would be 30° W. The figure shows the anticlockwise rotation of the stars looking *northwards*, so the south pole is nearest to you.

horizon (Chapter 4, p. 171). When there was no bright pole star, as in Alexandrian times, this was done by taking the average altitude of any star near the pole when it was at its highest point above and its lowest point below the meridian. Of course this could be done at any particular place before people had begun to interpret it as we do.

Just as we can find the latitude of a place by observing the zenith distance of any star at meridian transit if we know its declination from the star map, we can also get our longitude by observing the times of meridian transit of any star, if we know its right ascension (Figs. 114, 115, and 116) on the star map and have a chronometer set by standard time. Circles of terrestrial longitude are nowadays numbered in degrees from 0° to 180° east and west of the Greenwich prime meridian (0°). Right ascension is always reckoned *east* of the

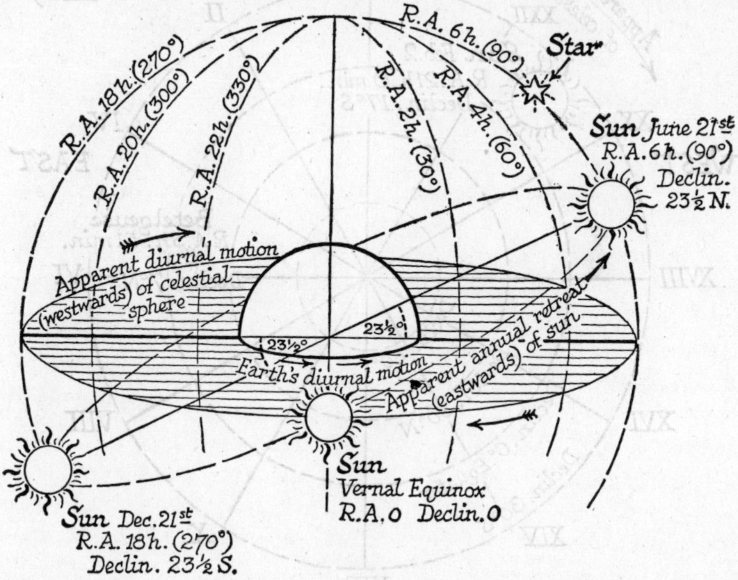

Fig. 115

The star shown (R.A. 6 hours) makes its transit above the meridian at noon on June 21st, and midnight on December 21st, i.e. it is a winter star like Betelgeuse.

celestial meridian on which the "First Point of Aries" lies. This is the Celestial Greenwich, and is denoted by the astrological symbol ♈. It is the position the sun occupies at the vernal equinox (March 21st). The celestial sphere appears to turn through 360° in 24 hours. So it is more convenient to number the circles of R.A. in hours and minutes, from 0 to 24 hours. Since it appears to rotate from east to west, a star which has the R.A. 13 hours 21 minutes (e.g. Spica in the constellation of Virgo) crosses the meridian 13 hours and 21 minutes after the sun crosses the meridian at the same place on the day of the vernal equinox. That is to say, it crosses the meridian at 1.21 a.m. local time. If at the moment of transit, the Radio announcer gave Greenwich time as 10.21 p.m., you would know (see footnote, p. 361) that you were 3 hours in advance of Greenwich time, and that when it was noon at Greenwich your local time was 3.0 p.m. So your longitude (see Fig. 63, p. 173) would be 3 × 15° = 45° *East* of Greenwich.

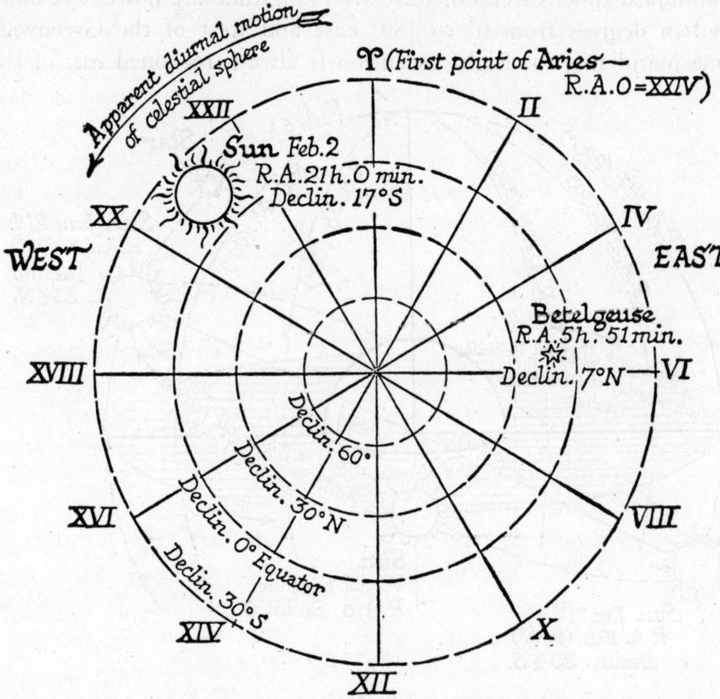

FIG. 116.—STAR MAP (OR PLANISPHERE) TO ILLUSTRATE RELATION OF RIGHT ASCENSION TO LOCAL TIME OF TRANSIT

If the sun's R.A. is x it transits x hours after the zero R.A. circle or First Point of Aries. If the star's R.A. is y, it transits y hours after ♈. The star therefore transits $y - x$ hours after the sun, i.e. its local time of transit is $(y - x)$. Hence

Star's R.A. − sun's R.A. = Local time of transit.

It may happen that the difference is negative, as in the example in the figure, the local time of transit being − 15.9, i.e. 15 hours 9 minutes *before* noon, which is the same as 8 hours 51 minutes after noon (8.51 p.m.). The figure shows that the sun transits 3 hours before ♈, and the star 5 hours 51 minutes after, making the time of transit as stated. The orientation is the same as in Fig. 114.

At other times of the year you would have to make allowance for the fact that the sun's position relative to the earth and fixed stars changes through 360° or 24 hours of R.A. in 365¼ days. The exact values of the sun's R.A. on each day of the year are given in the nautical almanacs, for the preparation of which modern Governments maintain their public observatories. Without tables you can calculate the time reckoned from local noon roughly as follows (Fig. 116). Since the stars reach the meridian a little earlier each night, the sun appears to retreat further east, and its R.A. increases approximately by $\frac{360}{365}$ or 1° or $\frac{1}{15}$ hour (4 minutes) in time units per day. Suppose, then, that Betelgeuse transits at a certain time on March 1st. The sun then has 20 days to retreat east before it reaches the First Point of Aries, i.e. it will cross the meridian 80 minutes (1 hour 20 minutes) before the First Point of Aries. If the R.A. of Betelgeuse is 5 hours 51 minutes, it crosses the meridian 5 hours and 51 minutes later than ♈, and hence 1 hour + 20 minutes + 5 hours 51 minutes = 7 hours 11 minutes after noon. So the local time is 7.11 p.m.* The sun's declination also changes from + 23½° on the summer solstice to – 23½° on the winter solstice. From the tables of its values in *Whitaker's* or the *Nautical Almanac* you can get your latitude from the sun's z.d. at noon on any day of the year, just as you could from the z.d. of a star at meridian transit.

When you look through the window of a moving train at a stationary one, you cannot be sure, as you pass it, whether you are, it is, or both you and it are moving relatively to the landscape. So there is nothing at first sight to tell us whether the celestial sphere revolves daily and the sun retreats annually around the earth, or whether the earth revolves on its own axis daily and moves annually in its orbit around the sun. Since the stars are immensely far away, all our calculations hold good either way, and the view which Hipparchus and the Arabs took is simpler for most practical purposes. But it is not simpler when we come to deal with another class of heavenly bodies. If any fixed star crosses the meridian so many hours and minutes after noon, it will do so again after the lapse of a year, when the sun has once more the same position relative to it and to the earth. This is not true of the planets which change their positions relative to the stars, so that the R.A. and declination of a planet are not fixed. The way in which the planets change their position attracted attention in very early times for several reasons. One is that several of them are exceedingly conspicuous — much brighter than the most brilliant stars. Another is

* For simplicity no reference is made to the correction called "*the equation of time*" explained in the Almanacs. Broadcast time is *Greenwich mean time*, plus one hour in "summer time," which differs from Greenwich local time by a few minutes varying in the course of the year. Mean time is used because the solar day (noon to noon) varies in length throughout the year, and a clock cannot be made to keep in step with it. So an average solar day is taken as the basis of time and the time of noon is shifted backwards and forwards by a certain number of minutes at different seasons. The difference is tabulated.

that they all move near the belt through which the sun and moon revolve. At certain times they may have the same R.A. as the moon, and if they also have the same declination within $\frac{1}{4}°$ they are eclipsed or "occulted" by it. Such events were watched for in ancient times. When there were no portable timepieces, the sky, with the moon or a planet as hour-hand, was the only clock available for identifying

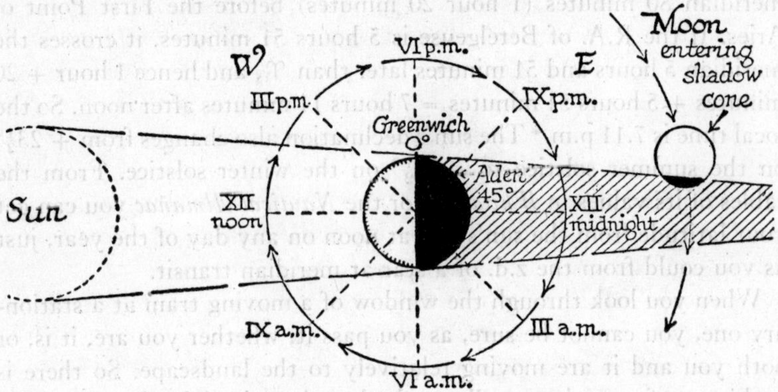

FIG. 116A.—FINDING LONGITUDE BY LUNAR ECLIPSE

Before the invention of the chronometer knowledge of local time and estimates of longitude depended upon observation of the interval between noon and some celestial signal such as an eclipse of the moon, or the occultation of a planet or star by the moon's disc. The interval was measured with hour glasses or crude clocks which would not keep time accurately over a long voyage. The principle of the method is shown in this figure, which is drawn like Fig. 114 with the South Pole nearest to the observer. You see the meridians on which Aden and Greenwich lie at the moment when a lunar eclipse is beginning. If your almanac tells you that it is calculated to begin at 6.0 p.m. by Greenwich time, and you observe it at nine hours after local noon at Aden (9.0 p.m. Aden time), you know that Aden time is three hours fast by Greenwich, and that Aden is therefore 45° East of the Greenwich meridian.

simultaneous moments at places far apart on the earth's surface. Eclipses and occultations were first used, originally those involving the moon. In this way it could be seen that noon was not simultaneous at all places. When tables of the moon's position had been worked out, the angular distance of the moon from any bright star could be used.

Before chronometers were invented there was no practicable way of finding longitude at sea except by using the moon's position. Most of the methods are complicated but the one based on an eclipse of the moon is readily explained. This was how the pilots of Columbus, Amerigo Vespucci, and Magellan, trained in Arab astrology, were able to define the position of America on the world map (see Fig. 116A). So knowing exactly where the planets are located was a matter of some practical importance in the period of the Great Navigations, when Copernicus and Kepler showed that their positions can be calculated more accurately and far more simply if we reject the common-sense view of the priestly astronomers.

To calculate the courses of the planets the flat geometry which we have learned so far is quite useless, for a simple reason which you will see easily enough if you consider the behaviour of the planet *Venus*. On one night of the year the difference between the R.A. of the sun and that of any particular fixed star will be 12 hours. So it will cross the meridian at midnight. On such occasions the earth and the celestial poles will lie in the same plane as the sun and the star. Venus never crosses the meridian after dark. It is always seen setting just after sunset, or rising just before sunrise (Fig. 117). According to the modern or Copernican view this is merely because it revolves *between* the sun and the earth. As the earth turns away from the sun it only becomes visible after our meridian has passed it by. As the earth turns towards the sun it ceases to be visible with the naked eye, because the sun rises, before our meridian reaches it. Thus we cannot find the R.A. or declination of Venus and trace the way it changes by finding its meridian zenith distance and time of transit. We can calculate them by finding its zenith distance when its position in the celestial sphere has apparently revolved through a measurable angle from the meridian if we use a different kind of geometry in making our calculations.

We have seen how to represent the position of a star in the heavenly sphere by small circles of declination parallel to the celestial equator and great circles of R.A. intersecting at the celestial poles. Such a map is true for all places, and is relevant to any time.* Similarly at any fixed moment at a particular place we can represent the position of a star by small circles of *altitude* parallel to the circular edge of the horizon and great circles of *azimuth* intersecting at the zenith (Fig. 118).

* The last statement is only approximately true, and requires several qualifications, the most important of which is the phenomenon of the "precession of the equinoxes" discovered by the Babylonian astronomers. The earth's axis of rotation changes its direction slowly in the course of centuries, so that what is now the pole star, i.e. the star almost directly over the north pole, is not the pole star of the time when the pyramids were built.

The altitude circles are numbered by their angular elevation above the horizon plane as declination or latitude circles are numbered by

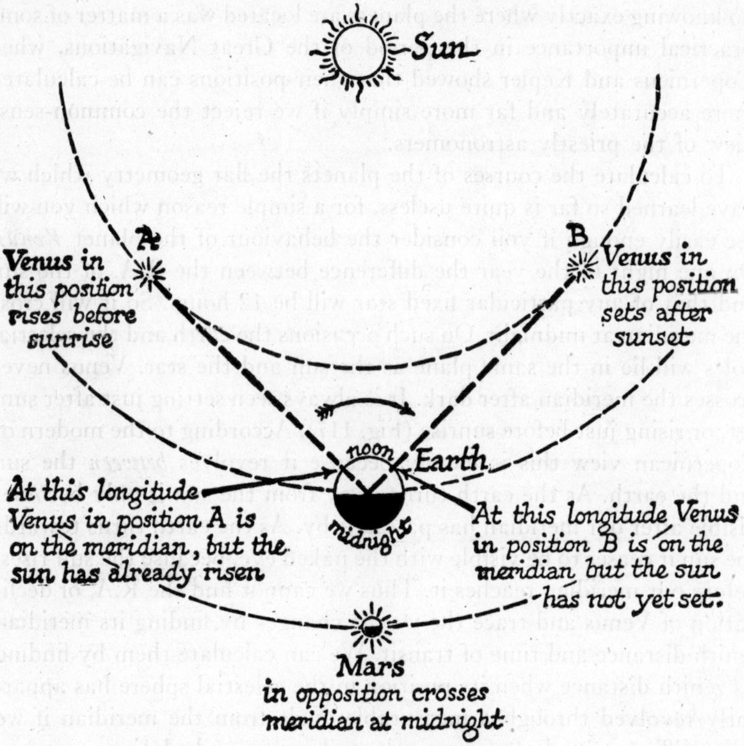
Sun
A
Venus in this position rises before sunrise
B
Venus in this position sets after sunset
noon
Earth
midnight
At this longitude Venus in position A is on the meridian, but the sun has already risen
At this longitude Venus in position B is on the meridian, but the sun has not yet set.
Mars in opposition crosses meridian at midnight.

FIG. 117

The inferior planets, Mercury and Venus, have always passed the meridian when they become visible or have not yet reached it when they cease to be visible. Earth seen with South Pole towards the reader.

their elevation above the equator plane. An azimuth circle is numbered in degrees off the meridian by joining to the observer the ends of an arc on the horizon plane intercepted by the meridian and the azimuth circle, in just the same way as a circle of longitude is numbered by the angle between the end of an arc of the equator intercepted by it, the centre of the earth, and the point where the equator is cut by the Greenwich meridian. The azimuth of a star is therefore its east/west bearing with reference to the meridian. If you have mounted your home-made astrolabe or theodolite of Fig. 119 to revolve vertically on a graduated base set so that 0° points due south or north, the azimuth of a star is the angle through which you have to turn the sighting tube (or telescope) on its base, and the altitude is obtained by subtracting from 90° the zenith distance. If the protractor is numbered

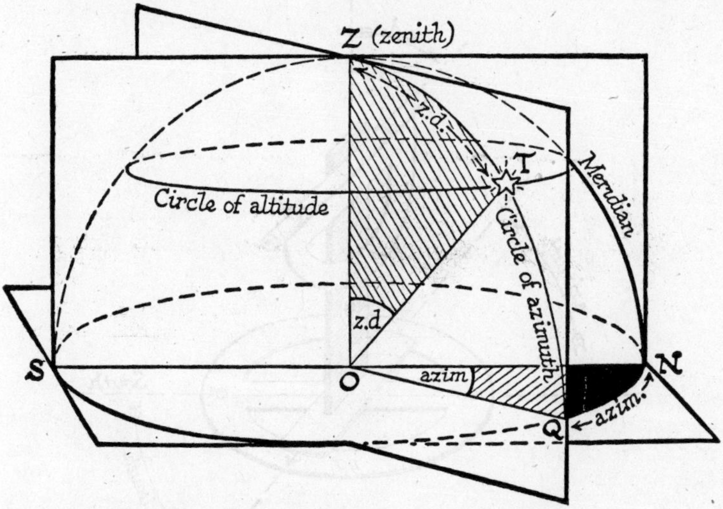

FIG. 118.—LOCAL CO-ORDINATES OF A STAR

The horizon bearing or altitude is 90° – z.d. The zenith distance z.d. is measured by the arc TZ or the flat angle ZOT in the azimuth plane. The meridian bearing or azimuth is the arc NQ which in degrees is the flat angle NOQ or the angle between the meridian plane NZS and the azimuth plane ZOQ.

reversibly from 0° to 90° and 90° to 0°, you can, of course, read off the altitude at once.

If you fix your telescope towards a star and turn it freely a little later to the place where the star is then seen, you sweep out an arc on the celestial sphere like the course of a ship on the high seas. If you think about the way in which ships actually sail, you will see that they never sail in the straight lines of Euclid's geometry. They have to sail in arcs of circles on the curved surface of the globe. The shortest arc between two points is the one which is least bent, hence the one with the greatest radius, which is the radius of the globe itself. So the shortest distance between two points for purposes of navigation is not the Euclidean straight line, but the "great" circle which passes through them. If two ships travel from A to B, one in the most direct course, the other without changing its latitude till it gets to the longitude meridian of B, and then along the latter until it reaches B, the two courses form a three-sided figure, of which the sides are circular arcs. Similarly, when a star appears to move along its declination

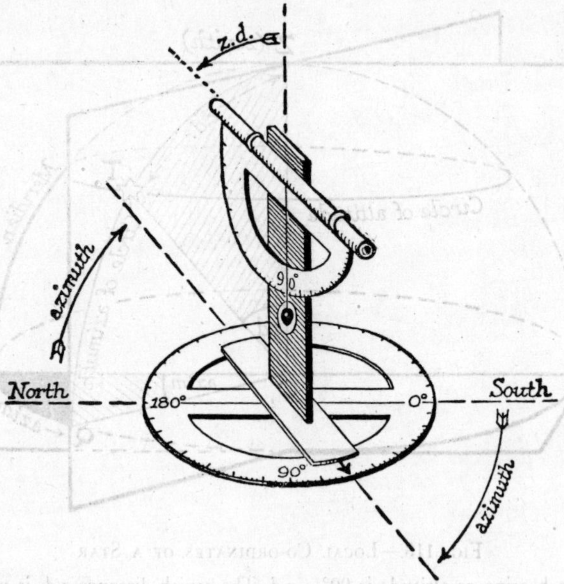

FIG. 119.—HOME-MADE APPARATUS FOR MEASURING AZIMUTH AS WELL AS Z.D., OR ALTITUDE OF A STAR

The materials are three blackboard protractors (you can make these with a fretwork set), a piece of iron tube (gas pipe), and a plumb-line.

circle in the heavens we have to rotate our eye horizontally along an arc of altitude and vertically along an arc of azimuth to follow its course. The apparent movement of the star and the movement of our eye or our telescope trace out a triangle with curved sides in the celestial dome. In reaching any point in the heavens a star has to rotate about the polar axis through a certain angle away from the meridian, while our telescope has turned through a definite angle about the zenith axis, and the star has turned through a certain angle along its declination circle, while our telescope has been tilted through a definite angle to the horizon plane. As the polar axis is fixed at a fixed angle to the horizon plane, we should expect that all these quantities are connected, just as a ship's shortest course is connected with the latitude and longitude of its port of departure and destination. For both problems we need to know what sort of connections to expect between the parts of figures which have curved sides.

SPHERICAL TRIANGLES

Fig. 120 shows a globe in which three flat planes have been sliced

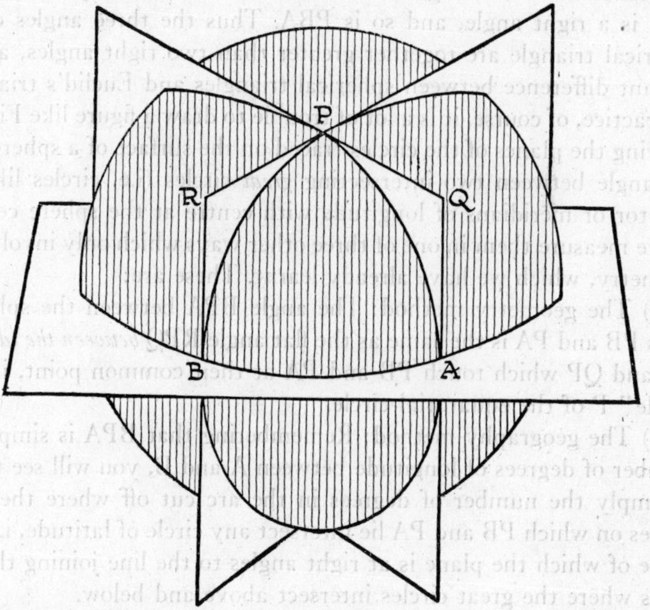

FIG. 120.—INTERSECTING FLAT PLANES ON WHICH THREE GREAT CIRCLES OF A SPHERE LIE

through two meridians of longitude (along PA and PB) and through the equator (AB). Each of these planes cuts the surface of the terrestrial sphere in a complete circle, the centre of which is the centre of the sphere. Where they intersect on the surface, they make the corners of a three-sided figure of which the sides are all arcs of *great circles*, i.e. circles with the same centre and the same radius as the sphere itself. Such a figure is called a spherical triangle. It has three sides, PA, PB, and AB, which we shall call b (opposite B), a (opposite A), and p. It has also three angles B, A, and P (PBA, PAB, and APB). What you already know about a map will tell you how these angles are measured.

The angle APB is simply the difference of longitude between the two points A and B marked on the equator, and it is measured by the inclination of the two planes which cut from pole to pole along the axis of the globe. You will notice therefore that, since the earth's axis is at right angles to the equator plane, the plane of AB is at right angles to the plane of PA and of PB; and since we measure angles where two great circles traced on a sphere cut one another by the angle between the planes on which the great circles themselves lie, the spherical angle PAB is a right angle, and so is PBA. Thus the three angles of the spherical triangle are together greater than two right angles, an important difference between spherical triangles and Euclid's triangles. In practice, of course, it is a lot of trouble to draw a figure like Fig. 120 showing the planes of the circles traced on the surface of a sphere, and the angle between two intersecting *great* circles (i.e. circles like the equator or meridians of longitude with centre at the sphere centre). So we measure them in one of three other ways which only involve flat geometry, which we have already learnt. These are:

(*a*) The geometry method: The angle BPA between the spherical sides PB and PA is the same as the flat angle RPQ *between the tangents* RP and QP which touch PB and PA at their common point, i.e. the "pole" P of the equatorial circle.

(*b*) The geography method: Remembering that BPA is simply the number of degrees of longitude between A and B, you will see that it is simply the number of degrees in the arc cut off where the great circles on which PB and PA lie intersect any circle of latitude, i.e. any circle of which the plane is at right angles to the line joining the two poles where the great circles intersect above and below.

(*c*) The astronomy method: This is illustrated in the next figure (Fig. 121), which shows the intersection of the plane of the celestial equator FEQO with the plane of the horizon NESO on the celestial sphere, the axis of which is cut by the pole of the celestial equator at P and the pole of the horizon circle, i.e. the zenith at Z. The angle QES between the arcs QE and SE is the angle QOS between their intersecting planes, and

$$\text{QOS} = 90^\circ - \text{QOZ}$$
$$\text{POZ} = 90^\circ - \text{QOZ}$$

So the angle between two spherical arcs is the angle between the poles of the great circles on which they lie.

The next thing to learn about spherical triangles is how to measure their sides. A spherical triangle is not primarily a figure which represents the distances between three objects at its corners so much as the difference in direction of three objects as seen from one centre. The side of a spherical triangle is the angle through which the eye or the telescope has to be turned to get directly from one corner to the other. The sides of spherical triangles, like their angles, are always

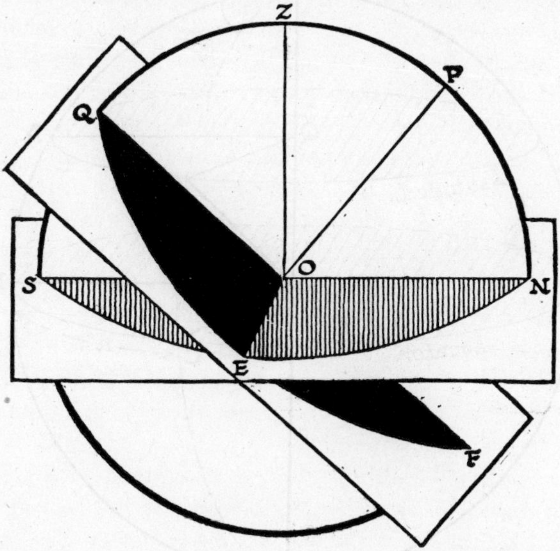

FIG. 121

The angles between two arcs (QE and SE) of great circles on a sphere is the angle (ZOP) between the poles of great circles Z and P.

measured in degrees or radians. Thus in Fig. 120 the side *a* (PB) and the side *b* (PA) are each equivalent to the latitude of the north pole $\left(90° \text{ or } \frac{\pi}{2} \text{ radians}\right)$, and the side *p* (AB) is the difference of longitude between A and B, and just happens in this special case to be the same as the angle P. In Fig. 121 the points Q, E, S form the apices of a spherical triangle on the celestial sphere. Two of the sides *s* (QE) and *q* (SE) are right angles. The third side *e* (SQ) is also equivalent to the angle E, which is equal to the flat angle POZ. The spherical angles Q and S are right angles, and you see again that the three angles of a spherical triangle make up more than two right angles.

A moment ago we saw that the latitude and longitude at the top and bottom of a mine are the same, because latitude and longitude measure the direction of an object as it would be seen from the centre of the earth, and, as seen from the centre of the earth, the top and bottom of the mine lie in exactly the same direction. Thus any three points in space can be represented by the corners of a spherical triangle traced

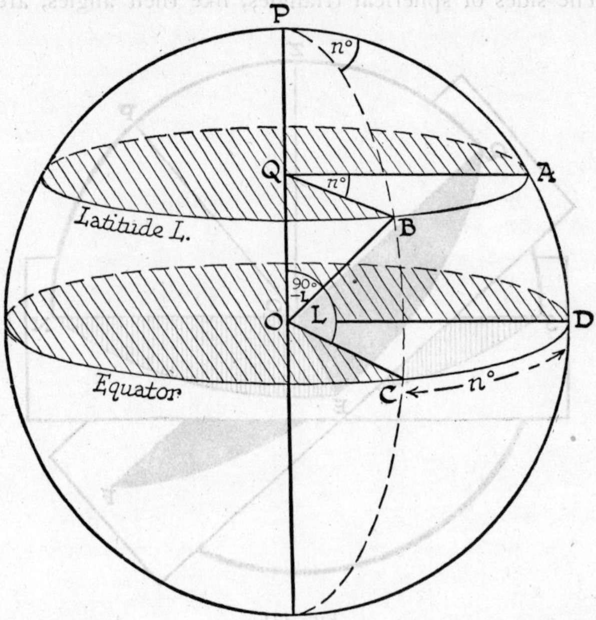

FIG. 122.—HOW TO CALCULATE THE LENGTH OF *n* DEGREES OF LONGITUDE MEASURED ALONG ANY PARALLEL OF LATITUDE.

CD are two points on the equator, AB two points on a parallel of latitude, PO is half the earth's axis, COD the plane of the equator, QAB the plane of the latitude of A and B, and OB is the earth's radius (R).

on the surface of a sphere which encloses all three. If all three points happen to be at the same distance from the centre of observation, we can express the sides of such a triangle in actual lengths instead of degrees or radians. The way in which this is done can be illustrated by a simple calculation which does not involve a spherical triangle, since parallels of latitude (other than the equator) are not great circles. If we know the number of degrees or radians in the angle joining the ends of an arc to the centre of the circle on which it lies, we also know its length. A difference of longitude of one degree anywhere along the equator is one three hundred and sixtieth of the earth's circumference, i.e. if the earth's radius (R) is taken as 3,960 miles, it is

$$2\pi \times 3{,}960 \div 360$$
$$= \tfrac{44}{7} \times 11 = 69 \text{ miles (approximately)}$$

Without any allowance for the slight flattening of the earth at the Poles, this is equivalent to a degree of latitude measured along a meridian of longitude or a degree measured along any great circle at the earth's surface.

A difference of longitude equivalent to one degree measured along any other parallel of latitude is easily determined as illustrated in Fig. 122, in which AB is n degrees of longitude measured along the latitude circle L and DC is n degrees along the equator. The circumference of the equatorial circle of which DC is an arc is $2\pi.\text{OC}$. One degree corresponds to $2\pi.\text{OC} \div 360$ and n degrees to $2\pi n.\text{OC} \div 360$. Hence

$$\text{DC} = 2\pi n.\text{OC} \div 360 \text{ and OC} = 360.\text{DC} \div 2\pi n$$

Likewise

$$\text{AB} = 2\pi n.\text{QB} \div 360 \text{ and QB} = 360.\text{AB} \div 2\pi n.$$

The angle QOB = 90° – L, and since the plane of QAB is at right angles to the polar axis, QOB is a right-angled triangle in which OB = R = OC and

$$\sin \text{QOB} = \text{QB} \div \text{OB}$$
$$\therefore \sin (90° - \text{L}) = \text{QB} \div \text{OC}$$
$$\therefore \cos \text{L} = \text{QB} \div \text{OC}$$
$$\therefore \text{QB} = \text{OC} \cos \text{L}$$
$$360.\text{AB} \div 2\pi n = 360\ \text{DC}.\cos \text{L} \div 2\pi n.$$
$$\therefore \text{arc AB} = \text{arc DC} \cos \text{L}$$
$$= n \times 69 \times \cos \text{L miles (approximately)}$$

SOLUTION OF SPHERICAL TRIANGLES

General expressions for "solution" of spherical triangles analogous to those given in Chapter 6, p. 286, can be found, and are used constantly in astronomy and mathematical geography for the reason already given. They depend on the corresponding formulae for flat triangles, and the only difficulty in understanding them is due to the fact that it is difficult to make clear diagrams of solid figures on a flat page. If we spent a fraction of what is now wasted in building battleships and aircraft carriers on equipping schools with cinematographs and making films of solid changing objects as they really are, all sorts of things which cannot now be grasped without a lot of effort and time by clever people could be quite easily understood by people like ourselves, who do not claim to be so clever. As it is, we shall have to use

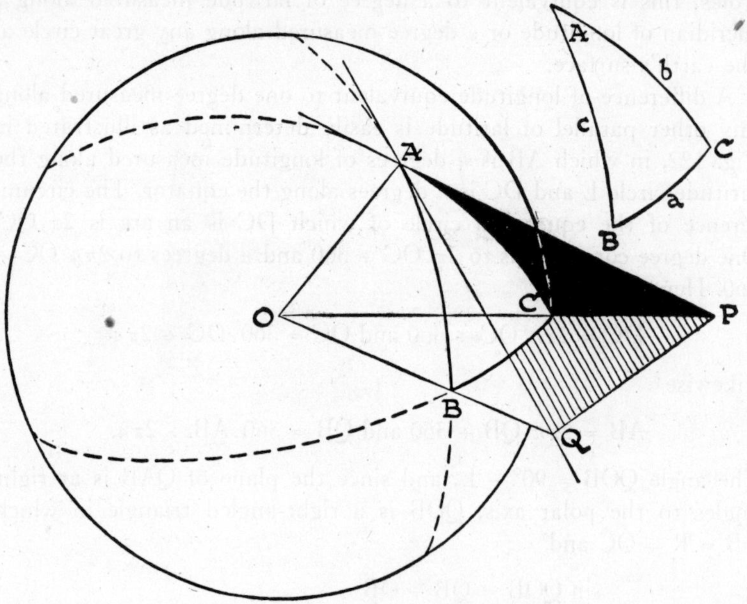

FIG. 123

a very simple model which you can make for yourself out of transparent paper in a couple of minutes.

The most important formula for solving spherical triangles tells us how to get the third side (*a*) when two sides (*b* and *c*) and the angle between them (A) are already known. The analogous formula for flat triangles is (p. 250):

$$a^2 = b^2 + c^2 - 2bc \cos A$$

Fig. 123 shows you a spherical triangle ABC formed by the intersection of three circles with their common centre O at the centre of the sphere. The edges of the flat planes in which the sides *a*, *b*, *c* lie meet along OA, OBQ, and OCP. The edges AQ and AP just graze the great circles of the arcs *c* and *b* at A, i.e. AQ is the tangent to *c* and AP to *b*. So OAQ and OAP are really right angles, though it is impossible to draw them as such in the flat. The edges of three planes in which the arcs *a*, *b*, *c* lie forms a flat triangle PAQ, of which the apical angle PAQ is equivalent to the angle A of the spherical triangle according to the definition of how we measure the angles of a spherical triangle.

To get a clear picture of the way in which the parts of the spherical

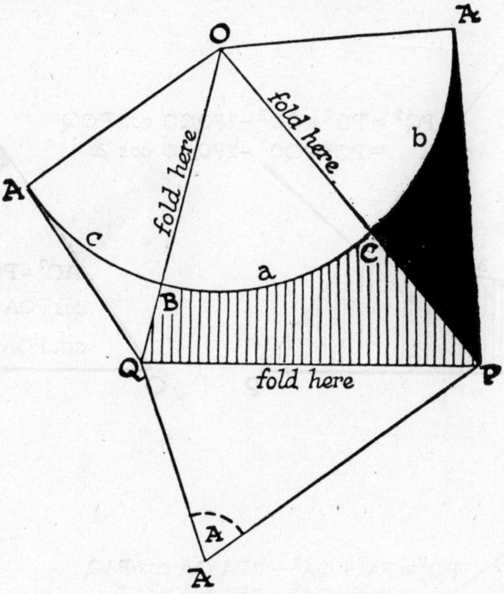

FIG. 124

triangle are related to the parts of the four flat triangles which form the sides of a little pyramid in which it lies, cut out a paper model drawn as in Fig. 124 and fold the parts together along the three edges where you are told to do so. All the facts required are indicated in the figures. When you have made the model, take it to pieces as in Fig. 124A so that you can see each triangle in the position which is most familiar. You then see, as indicated in Fig. 124A, by the rule for flat triangles:

$$PQ^2 = PO^2 + QO^2 - 2PO.QO \cos a$$
$$PQ^2 = PA^2 + QA^2 - 2PA.QA \cos A$$

$$\therefore \quad (PO^2 - PA^2) + (QO^2 - QA^2) - 2PO.QO \cos a + 2PA.QA \cos A = 0$$
$$\therefore \; 2PO.QO \cos a = 2AO^2 + 2PA.QA \cos A$$

Divide through by 2PO.QO, then

$$\cos a = \frac{AO}{PO}.\frac{AO}{QO} + \frac{PA}{PO}.\frac{QA}{QO}\cos A$$
$$= \cos POA \cos QOA + \sin POA \sin QOA \cos A$$
$$= \cos b \cos c + \sin b \sin c \cos A$$

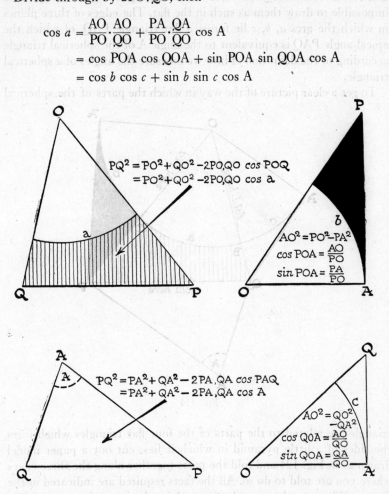

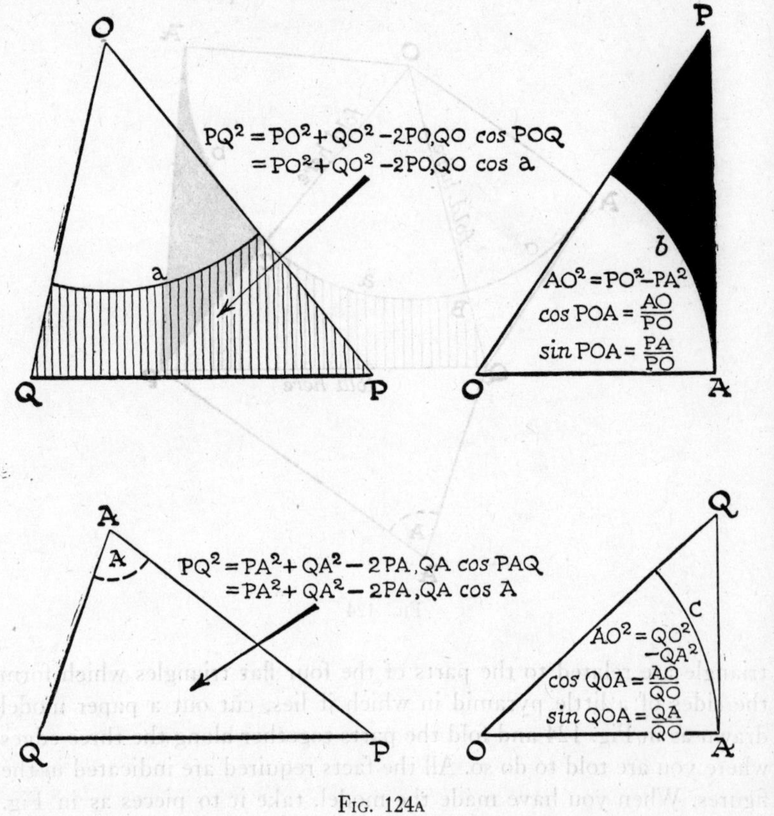

FIG. 124A

The formula for getting the third side (a), when you know the other two (b and c) and the included angle A, is, therefore:

$$\underline{\cos a = \cos b \cos c + \sin b \sin c \cos A}$$

Of course, once you know the way this is pieced together you just learn it by heart, or refer to a book when you want to use it.

CALCULATING A SHIP'S DIRECT COURSE

If you are a sensible person, you will not want to go through any more of this sort of thing until you have seen what earthly good comes out of it. The first example is of a kind which you can amuse yourself with for hours, if you have any map which gives the distances of sea

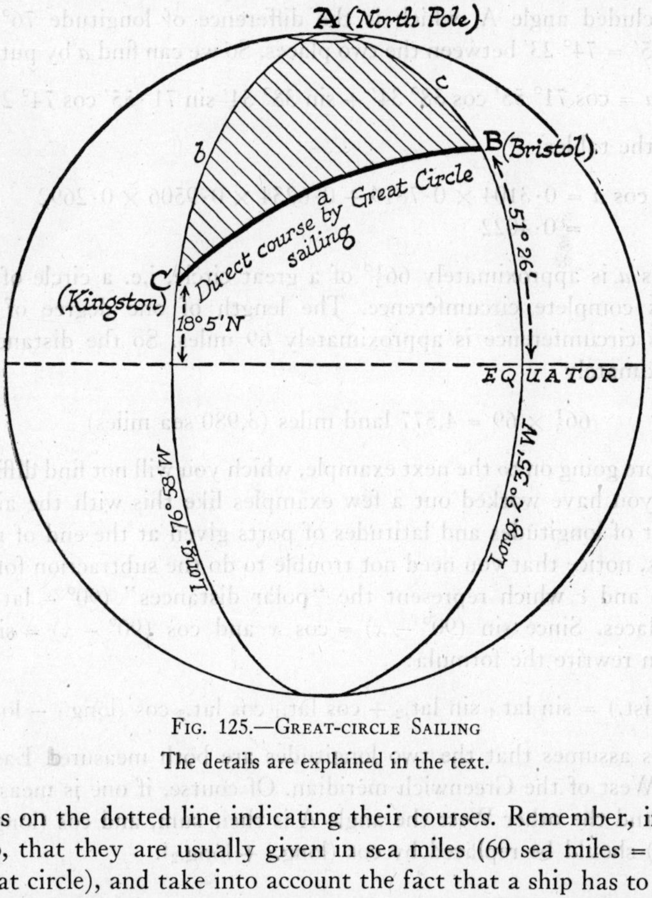

FIG. 125.—GREAT-CIRCLE SAILING

The details are explained in the text.

routes on the dotted line indicating their courses. Remember, if you do so, that they are usually given in sea miles (60 sea miles = 1° of a great circle), and take into account the fact that a ship has to steer round a few corners before it gets away from, or when it is approaching, land. Thus the map gives for the course from Bristol to Kingston in Jamaica 4,003 sea miles, about 25 miles in excess of the calculation which follows. This makes no allowance for getting out of the Bristol Channel and into port (see Fig. 125).

The latitude of Bristol is 51° 26′ N. of the equator, and therefore

38° 34′ from the pole, along the great circle of longitude 2° 35′ W. The latitude of Kingston is 18° 5′, i.e. it is 71° 55′ from the pole along the great circle of longitude 76° 58′ W. The arc joining the pole to Bristol (c), the arc joining the pole to Kingston (b), and the arc (a) of the great circle representing the course from Bristol to Kingston form a spherical triangle, of which we know two sides (b and c), and the included angle A, which is the difference of longitude 76° 58′ − 2° 35′ = 74° 23′ between the two places. So we can find a by putting

$$\cos a = \cos 71^\circ 55' \cos 38^\circ 34' + \sin 38^\circ 34' \sin 71^\circ 55' \cos 74^\circ 23'$$

From the tables:

$$\begin{aligned}\cos a &= 0{\cdot}3104 \times 0{\cdot}7819 + 0{\cdot}6234 \times 0{\cdot}9506 \times 0{\cdot}2692 \\ &= 0{\cdot}4022\end{aligned}$$

Thus a is approximately $66\frac{1}{3}°$ of a great circle, i.e. a circle of the earth's complete circumference. The length of one degree of the earth's circumference is approximately 69 miles. So the distance is approximately

$$66\tfrac{1}{3} \times 69 = 4{,}577 \text{ land miles } (3{,}980 \text{ sea miles})$$

Before going on to the next example, which you will not find difficult when you have worked out a few examples like this with the aid of the list of longitudes and latitudes of ports given at the end of most atlases, notice that you need not trouble to do the subtraction for the arcs b and c which represent the "polar distances" (90° − lat.) of the places. Since $\sin (90° - x) = \cos x$ and $\cos (90° - x) = \sin x$, we can rewrite the formula:

$$\cos (\text{dist.}) = \sin \text{lat.}_1 \sin \text{lat.}_2 + \cos \text{lat.}_1 \cos \text{lat.}_2 \cos (\text{long.}_1 - \text{long.}_2)$$

This assumes that the two longitudes are both measured East or both West of the Greenwich meridian. Of course, if one is measured East and the other West the angle A is their sum, and $\cos (\text{long.}_1 - \text{long.}_2)$ should be replaced by $\cos (\text{long.}_1 + \text{long.}_2)$.

DECLINATION OF A PLANET

As we have seen, the declination (or R.A.) of a planet like Venus or Mercury cannot be obtained by meridian observations, and the declination (or R.A.) of an outer planet like Mars or Jupiter can only be determined by meridian observations at periods when it transits during the hours of darkness. So it is impossible to trace the positions of any planet relative to the fixed stars in all parts of its course unless we can determine their declinations and right ascensions by some other method. It is easy to obtain the former in precisely the same way as we get a ship's course in great-circle sailing.

The local position of every star at any instant can be placed at the

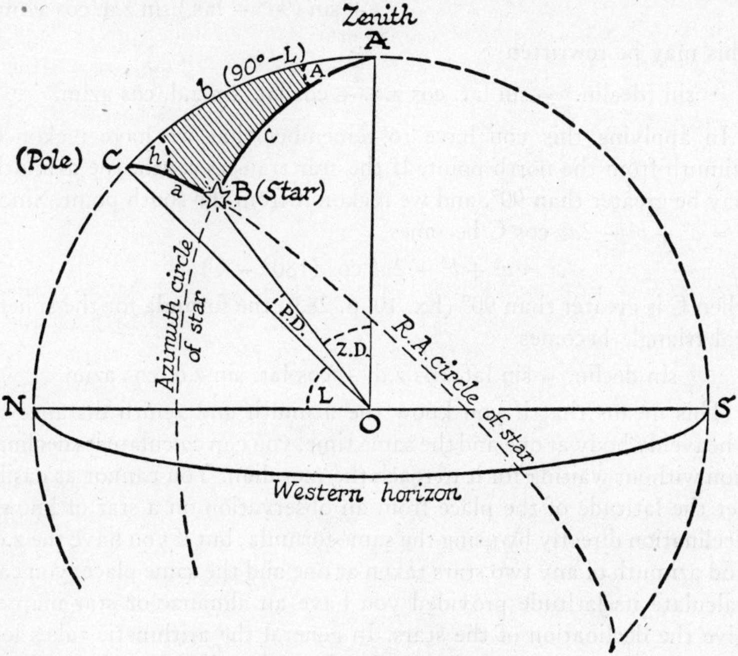

FIG. 126.—THE STAR TRIANGLE
Compare with Figs. 109 and 118.

corner of a spherical triangle (Fig. 126) like the Bristol-Kingston triangle of the last example. One side (*b*), like the polar distance of Kingston, is the arc between the celestial pole and the zenith along the prime meridian. The elevation of the pole is the latitude (L) of the observer. So $b = 90° - L$. One side (*c*) is the arc between the star and the zenith on its own great circle of azimuth. This arc is its zenith distance (c = z.d.). The angle A between its azimuth circle and the prime meridian which cuts it at the zenith is its azimuth (A = azim.). Between the ends of these two arcs passes the great circle of right ascension which joins the star to the celestial pole, and the length of the arc between the star and the pole on its R.A. circle is its polar distance. Since the celestial pole is 90° from the celestial equator, the star's polar distance, which is the third side of our spherical triangle, is the difference between one right angle and its declination ($a = 90° -$ declin.). Applying the formula we have

$$\cos(90° - \text{declin.}) = \cos(90° - \text{lat.}) \cos \text{z.d.} + \sin(90° - \text{lat.}) \sin \text{z.d.} \cos \text{azim.}$$

This may be rewritten

$$\sin(\text{declin.}) = \sin \text{lat.} \cos \text{z.d.} + \cos \text{lat.} \sin \text{z.d.} \cos \text{azim.}$$

In applying this you have to remember that we have reckoned azimuth from the north point. If the star transits south, the azimuth may be greater than 90°, and we reckon it from the south point. Since $c^2 = a^2 + b^2 - 2ab \cos C$ becomes

$$c^2 = a^2 + b^2 + 2ab \cos(180° - C)$$

when C is greater than 90° (Ex. 10, p. 283), the formula for the spherical triangle becomes

$$\sin \text{declin.} = \sin \text{lat.} \cos \text{z.d.} - \cos \text{lat.} \sin \text{z.d.} \cos \text{azim.}$$

This means that if you know the azimuth and zenith distance of a heavenly body at one and the same time, you can calculate its declination without waiting for it to reach the meridian. You cannot as easily get the latitude of the place from an observation on a star of known declination directly by using the same formula; but if you have the z.d. and azimuth of any two stars taken at one and the same place, you can calculate its latitude provided you have an almanac or star map to give the declination of the stars. In general the arithmetic takes less time than waiting about for one bright and easily recognized star to cross the meridian.

Another application of the formula just derived gives the direction of a heavenly body when rising or setting at a known latitude, or conversely the latitude from the rising or setting of a star. At the instant when a heavenly body is rising or setting its zenith distance is 90°. Since $\cos 90° = 0$ and $\sin 90° = 1$, the formula then becomes

$$\sin \text{declin.} = \cos \text{lat.} \cos \text{azim.}$$

On the equinoxes when the sun's declination is 0°,

$$\cos \text{lat.} \cos \text{azim.} = 0$$
$$\therefore \quad \cos \text{azim.} = 0$$
$$\therefore \quad \text{azim.} = 90°$$

That is to say, the sun rises due east and sets due west in all parts of the world that day. To find the direction of the rising or setting sun at latitude $51\frac{1}{2}°$ N. (London) on June 21st, when the sun's declination is $23\frac{1}{2}°$ N., we have only to put

$$\sin 23\tfrac{1}{2}° = \cos 51\tfrac{1}{2}° \cos \text{azim.}$$

From the tables, therefore:

$$0{\cdot}3987 = 0{\cdot}6225 \cos \text{azim.}$$
$$\therefore \quad \cos \text{azim.} = 0{\cdot}6405$$
$$\text{azim.} = 50\tfrac{1}{6}°$$

Thus the sun rises and sets $50\frac{1}{6}°$ from the meridian on the north side, or $90° - 50\frac{1}{6}° = 39\frac{5}{6}°$ north of the east or west point. Conversely, of course, you can use the observed direction of rising and setting to get your latitude.

ANOTHER THING ABOUT SPHERICAL TRIANGLES

How the declination of a planet changes is much less interesting than how its R.A. changes, because the way in which its R.A. changes is so much easier to explain if we assume that the earth and the planets revolve around the sun, as Aristarchus believed and Copernicus taught. This is not a book on astronomy, so we cannot spend any time on how Copernicus was led to this conclusion, but you should be able to worry it out from a book on astronomy if you understand clearly how the position of a planet is determined.

If you look at the star triangle shown in Fig. 126, you will see that the angle C between the arc which represents the star's polar distance and the arc *b*, which is the angle between the observer and the earth's pole (90° – lat.), is the angle through which the star has rotated since it was last on the meridian. Since the celestial sphere appears to rotate through 360° in 24 hours, i.e. 15° an hour, this angle C is sometimes called the hour angle of the star, because you can get the time (in hours) which has elapsed since the star made its transit by dividing the number of degrees by 15. If you know when the star crossed the meridian by local time, you also know how long has elapsed since the sun crossed the meridian because time is reckoned that way, and if you know the sun's R.A. on the same day, you know how long has elapsed since ♈ crossed the meridian. Thus all you have to do to get the star's R.A. is to add to its time of transit the sun's R.A.

So to get its R.A. from the star's altitude and azimuth at any observed time, we need to determine one of the other angles of a spherical triangle of which we already know two sides and the angle between them. For flat triangles the formula we should use (Chapter 6, p. 250) is

$$\sin C = c\frac{\sin A}{a}\left(\text{or } \sin C = c\frac{\sin B}{b}, \text{ if we knew B}\right)$$

For spherical triangles the corresponding sine formulae are

$$\sin C = \frac{\sin c \sin A}{\sin a}\left(\text{or } \sin C = \frac{\sin c \sin B}{\sin b}\right)$$

This can be worried out from the figure (see Appendix 1) or from the last formula by applying the rules of multiplication in algebra and remembering the rule (Chapter 6, p. 255) that if x is any angle:

$$\cos^2 x = 1 - \sin^2 x$$

First, however, you should notice that if we can get a when b, c, and A are known from

$$\cos a = \cos b \cos c + \sin b \sin c \cos A$$

we can also get c when a, b, and C are known from

$$\cos c = \cos a \cos b + \sin a \sin b \cos C$$

The demonstration of the sine formula is as follows. Rearrange the first of these, and then square both sides:

$$-\cos A \sin b \sin c = \cos b \cos c - \cos a$$
$$\cos^2 A \sin^2 b \sin^2 c = \cos^2 b \cos^2 c - 2\cos a \cos b \cos c + \cos^2 a$$

Now make the substitution

$$(1 - \sin^2 A)\sin^2 b \sin^2 c = (1 - \sin^2 b)(1 - \sin^2 c) - 2\cos a \cos b \cos c + (1 - \sin^2 a)$$

$$\therefore \sin^2 b \sin^2 c - \sin^2 A \sin^2 b \sin^2 c = 1 - \sin^2 b - \sin^2 c + \sin^2 b \sin^2 c - 2\cos a \cos b \cos c + 1 - \sin^2 a$$

After taking away $\sin^2 b \sin^2 c$ from both sides this becomes

$$-\sin^2 A \sin^2 b \sin^2 c = 2 - \sin^2 a - \sin^2 b - \sin^2 c - 2\cos a \cos b \cos c$$

Just by looking at this you can see that the right-hand side would be the same if we had started with

$$\cos c = \cos a \cos b + \sin a \sin b \sin C$$

in which case we should have found

$$-\sin^2 C \sin^2 a \sin^2 b = 2 - \sin^2 a - \sin^2 b - \sin^2 c - 2 \cos a \cos b \cos c$$

Hence we can put

$$-\sin^2 C \sin^2 a \sin^2 b = -\sin^2 A \sin^2 b \sin^2 c$$

Dividing by $-\sin^2 b$, we get

$$\sin^2 C \sin^2 a = \sin^2 A \sin^2 c$$

$$\therefore \quad \sin C \sin a = \pm \sin A \sin c$$

$$\text{or} \quad \sin C = \pm \frac{\sin A \sin c}{\sin a}$$

This is a little long-winded, but it is not difficult to apply, when you have regained your breath. In our original triangle of Fig. 126 A is the azimuth, c is the zenith distance, and a the polar distance (90° – declin.) of the star, i.e. $\sin a = \cos$ declin. Hence

$$\sin \text{hour angle} = \frac{\sin \text{azim.} \sin \text{z.d.}}{\cos \text{declin.}}$$

Suppose one of the stars in Orion is found to have the hour angle 10° when it is west of the meridian at 8.40 p.m. local time. It crossed the meridian $\frac{10}{15}$ hour = 40 minutes before, i.e. at exactly eight o'clock, and its R.A. is greater than that of the sun by 8 hours. If the sun's R.A. on that day were 21 hours 50 minutes, the sun would transit 2 hours 10 minutes before ♈, i.e. ♈ would transit at 2.10 p.m., and the star 8 hours 0 minutes – 2 hours 10 minutes = 5 hours 50 minutes after ♈. So its R.A. would be 5 hours 50 minutes.

The same formula also tells you how to calculate the times of rising and setting of stars in any particular latitude. At rising or setting the z.d. of a heavenly body is 90°, and sin 90° = 1. So the formula becomes

$$\sin \text{hour angle} = \frac{\sin \text{azim.}}{\cos \text{declin.}}$$

The azimuth of a rising or setting star can be found from the formula already given, i.e.

$$\cos \text{azim.} = \frac{\sin \text{declin.}}{\cos \text{lat.}}$$

As an example we may take the time of sunrise on the winter solstice in London (Lat. $51\frac{1}{2}$°). By the last formula the azimuth of the rising and setting sun is $50\frac{1}{6}°$ from the south point on the winter solstice. So at sunrise and sunset

$$\begin{aligned}\text{sin hour angle} &= \frac{\sin 50\frac{1}{6}°}{\cos(-23\frac{1}{2}°)}\\ &= \frac{0{\cdot}7679}{0{\cdot}9171}\\ &= 0{\cdot}8373\end{aligned}$$

Since 0·8373 is the sine of 56° 51′, the time which elapses between setting and rising and meridian transit (i.e. noon, since it is the sun with which we are dealing) is $56\frac{5}{6} \div 15$ hours, i.e. 3 hours 47 minutes. Thus sunrise would occur at 8.13 a.m., and sunset at 3.47 p.m. Daylight lasts roughly $7\frac{1}{2}$ hours. This calculation differs by about 6 minutes from the value given in Whitaker. This is partly due to approximations made in the arithmetic and partly due to other things about which you need not worry, because you will not find it difficult to put in the refinements when you understand the basic principles.

The same formula would apply to calculating the times of sunset or sunrise on June 21, when the lengths of day and night are reversed. As hinted in exercise 10 on page 283 and explained more fully at the end of this chapter on page 388,

$$\sin A = \sin(180° - A)$$

Since sin A = sin (180° – A), 0·8373 may be either sin 56° 51′ or sin (180° – 56° 51′), i.e. sin (123° 9′). A figure shows you at once which value to take. An equatorial star rising due east passes through 90° in reaching the meridian. A star south of the equator passes through a smaller and a star north of the equator through a larger arc. So if *the declination of a heavenly body is north* (*like the sun on June* 21), *we take the solution as sin* (180° – *A*), *and if south as sin A.* Thus the hour angle of sunrise and sunset on June 21 would be $(123\frac{1}{6} \div 15)$ hours = 8 h. 13 m., i.e. sunrise would be at 3.47 a.m. and sunset at 8.13 p.m.

THEORY OF THE SUN-DIAL

One last example of the use of spherical triangles is provided by what has now become a garden ornament. The sun-dial which you see in gardens or on the walls of old churches is an invention which is based on the same principles as great-circle sailing.

The sun-dial was invented by the Arabs, who made considerable progress in the study of spherical trigonometry, and it is quite different from the shadow clocks of antiquity. The ancient shadow clock or obelisk was a vertical pillar sometimes mounted on a circular stone base. The angle which the shadow of a vertical pole makes with the meridian is the sun's azimuth (Fig. 13), and the azimuth angle,

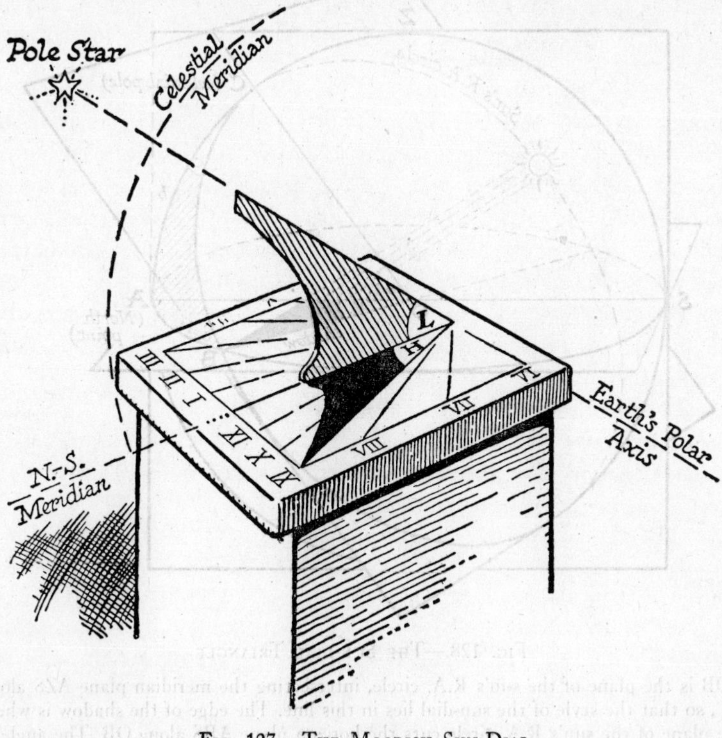

FIG. 127.—THE MOORISH SUN-DIAL

through which the shadow rotates when the sun has turned through a given angle, is not the same at all seasons. It depends on the sun's declination. So the length of a working hour as recorded by the shadow clock was not the same fraction of a day at different times of the year. Working time had no fixed relation to astronomer's time recorded by the hourglass or clepsydra (water clock).

The Moorish astronomers saw that this could be put right by setting the pole of the shadow clock along the earth's polar axis. When the style is set (Fig. 127) so that you would see the pole star if your eye followed the line along its upper edge, the scale can be graduated in divisions corresponding with equivalent intervals at all seasons of the year. That is to say, the "style" or pointer of the sun-dial is set along the meridian, and its edge is elevated at an angle equivalent to the latitude of the place for which it is made. So a sun-dial which keeps

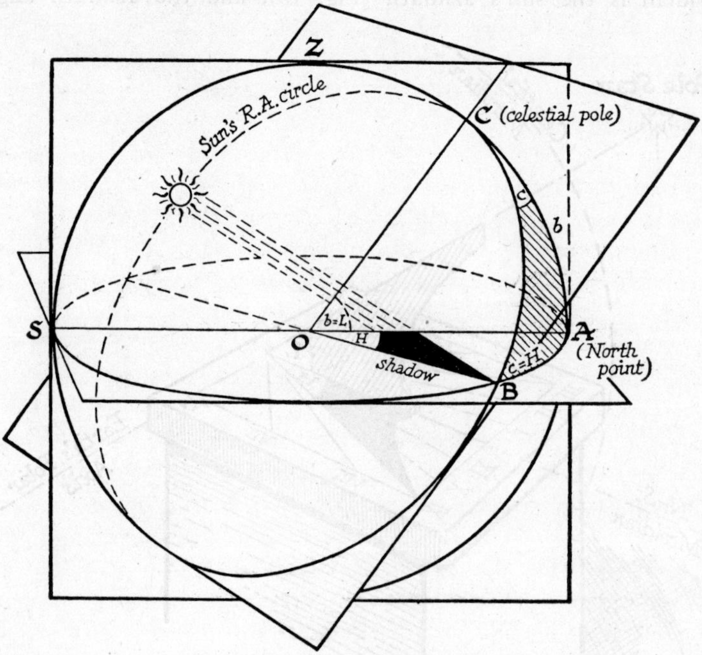

FIG. 128.—THE SUN-DIAL TRIANGLE

COB is the plane of the sun's R.A. circle, intersecting the meridian plane AZS along OC, so that the style of the sun-dial lies in this line. The edge of the shadow is where the plane of the sun's R.A. circle cuts the horizon plane ABS along OB. The angle C is the angle through which the sun has revolved around CO after crossing the meridian plane.

time in Seville, where a great Moorish university flourished in the tenth century of our era, will not keep time correctly in London.

The reason for this is explained by Fig. 128. Whatever the declination or R.A. of the sun happens to be on any day, it appears to revolve around the polar axis, where the planes of all the great circles of Right Ascension intersect. Suppose it has rotated through an hour angle C; any ray which strikes the edge of the style lies completely on the same plane as the great circle of R.A. on which the sun happens to lie.

This plane slices the horizon along the line which joins the observer O to the point where the sun's R.A. circle cuts the great circle which bounds the horizon. The arc (c) of the horizon circle between this point and the meridian is measured by the plane angle H through which the shadow turns while the sun revolves through an hour angle C. If C is the same, c = H is the same. In other words, when the sun has turned through an angle equivalent to x hours of solar time ($15x°$), the shadow has turned through an angle H, which is the same in summer or winter.

To make a sun-dial we have first to cut a style so that its upper edge is inclined to the base at an angle L = b, the latitude of the place where it will be used. Then the base must be put in line with the meridian, so that the upper edge points due north. All that remains is to graduate the scale in hours. On a summer holiday you can get some amusing practice in trigonometry by doing this. If at the same time you remember that the theory was worked out by the coloured conquerors of Spain when the people of Britain and Germany were barbarians, living in mud huts, ruled by ignorant priests and robber barons, it will also clear your mind of the sort of cant chanted by the white settlers of Kenya, General Hertzog, the apostles of selective immigration restrictions, and the pundits of German national socialism.

The theory of graduating the scale depends on a third formula for the solution of spherical triangles. In Fig. 128 you will see that the spherical triangle ABC is right-angled. Since the meridian plane is at right angles to the horizon plane, the angle A, which is the angle between these two planes, is 90°. In this triangle the parts which concern us are C, the hour angle of the sun, c = H, the angle of the shadow, and b = L, the latitude of the place. The last we know, and the first we can supply. The second is what we want to know to mark off the scale according to the values we give C, i.e. according to the time of the day.

If A = 90°, sin A = 1, so the second formula for right-angled spherical triangles becomes

$$\sin C = \frac{\sin c}{\sin a} \quad . \ . \ . \ . \ . \ . \ . \ . \ . \ . \ . \ . \ . \quad \text{(i)}$$

And since cos 90° = 0 the first formula becomes

$$\cos a = \cos b \cos c \quad . \ . \ . \ . \ . \ . \ . \ . \ . \ . \ . \quad \text{(ii)}$$

If we also apply the first formula to the two sides a, b and the included angle C

$$\cos c = \cos a \cos b + \sin a \sin b \cos C$$

$$\therefore \quad \cos C = \frac{\cos c - \cos a \cos b}{\sin a \sin b} \quad . \quad . \quad . \quad . \quad \text{(iii)}$$

Combining (i) and (iii) we get

$$\frac{\sin C}{\cos C} = \frac{\sin c}{\sin a} \times \frac{\sin a \sin b}{\cos c - \cos a \cos b}$$

$$\therefore \quad \tan C = \frac{\sin c \sin b}{\cos c - \cos a \cos b}$$

Multiply both sides by $\sin b$, then

$$\tan C \sin b = \frac{\sin c \sin^2 b}{\cos c - \cos a \cos b}$$

Substitute for $\cos a$ according to (ii)

$$\tan C \sin b = \frac{\sin c \sin^2 b}{\cos c - \cos c \cos^2 b}$$

$$= \frac{\sin c \sin^2 b}{\cos c(1 - \cos^2 b)}$$

$$= \frac{\sin c \sin^2 b}{\cos c \sin^2 b}$$

$$= \frac{\sin c}{\cos c}$$

$$= \tan c$$

Thus we have

$$\tan \text{(shadow angle)} = \sin \text{(latitude)} \times \tan \text{(hour angle)}$$

To get the angle we have to mark off for the edge of the shadow at 2.30 p.m. when the hour angle is $2\frac{1}{2}$ hours, or $2\frac{1}{2} \times 15° = 37\frac{1}{2}°$ for a sun-dial which will keep time in London, we put

$$\begin{aligned} \tan \text{shadow angle} &= \sin 51\tfrac{1}{2}° \times \tan 37\tfrac{1}{2}° \\ &= 0{\cdot}7826 \times 0{\cdot}7673 \\ &= 0{\cdot}6005 \end{aligned}$$

According to the tables of tangents $\tan 31° = 0{\cdot}6009$ and $\tan 30{\cdot}9° = 0{\cdot}5985$. So the required angle within a tenth of a degree is 31°.

You will now be able to work out the other graduation lines for the scale yourself according, of course, to the latitude of your home. If it happens to be New York, you must put sin 41° for sin lat.

TRIGONOMETRICAL RATIOS OF LARGE ANGLES

In using the formulae of this chapter correctly several points which have not been dealt with arise. One has been mentioned in connexion with the times of sunset and sunrise on the solstices (p. 382). The south point on the horizon is 180° from the north point. So if the azimuth of a star measured from the north point is A, it is (180° – A) measured from the south point. In the trigonometry of flat figures (p. 283) we saw that when an angle A of a triangle is less than 90°,

$$a^2 = b^2 + c^2 - 2bc \cos A \quad . \quad . \quad . \quad . \quad . \quad . \quad . \quad . \quad \text{(i)}$$

When A is more than 90°,

$$a^2 = b^2 + c^2 + 2bc \cos (180° - A) \quad . \quad . \quad . \quad . \quad \text{(ii)}$$

Similarly if two angles A and B are both less than 90°,

$$\frac{\sin A}{a} = \frac{\sin B}{b} \quad . \quad . \quad . \quad . \quad . \quad . \quad . \quad . \quad . \quad \text{(iii)}$$

If one of these angles of a flat triangle, e.g. A, is greater than 90°,

$$\frac{\sin (180° - A)}{a} = \frac{\sin B}{b} \quad . \quad . \quad . \quad . \quad . \quad . \quad . \quad \text{(iv)}$$

If we agree to say that cos (180° – A) means the same thing as – cos A, (or that – cos (180° – A) means the same thing as cos A), the single rule (i) includes (ii). Similarly, if we agree to say that sin (180° – A) means the same thing as sin A, the single rule (iii) includes (iv), whether a triangle has three angles none of which is greater than 90°, or one of which is greater than 90°. If we decide to do this we should say that cos 45° has the value + 0·7071 and cos 135° has the value – 0·7071. So if the answer to a problem is cos A = – 0·7071 and tables tell us that cos 45° = + 0·7071, we conclude that A is 180° – 45° = 135°. Similarly sin 30° has the same value as sin 150°, (+ 0·5); and the value 0·5 given in tables of angles from 0° to 90° as sin 30° should be read sin 30° or sin 150°. Thus we only need the one rule for the declination of a star, that when the azimuth angle is always reckoned from the south point (whether greater or less than 90°)

sin declin. = sin lat. cos z.d. – sin z.d. cos lat. cos azim.

At first sight this seems a paradox, because we have been used to thinking of sines, cosines, and tangents as ratios of side lengths in right-angled triangles of which no angle can be greater than 90°, and it therefore seems useless to talk of the sine or cosine of an angle of 150°. If we had started with figures drawn on a sphere, as all figures really are drawn on the earth's spherical surface, it would not necessarily seem so silly. The three angles of a spherical triangle make up more than two right angles, and one of the angles of a right-angled spherical triangle may be greater than 90°. Look at the matter in another way, as we did in Chapter 3, p. 91. It is easy to draw a geometrical diagram to show the meaning of a^n when $n = 1$ (a line), $n = 2$ (a flat square), $n = 3$ (a cube). We cannot make the same sort of figure to show the meaning of the operator 4 in the expression a^4. Yet we can do the same things with a^4 in arithmetic as we can do with a^1, a^2, a^3. So why should we say that sin 150° means nothing, merely because we cannot draw a flat right-angled triangle having one angle of 150°, or that cos 110° means nothing because we cannot draw a flat right-angled triangle with an angle of 110°?

After all, we can look on sine, cosine, and tangent as different ways of measuring an angle, and if so, it is not so odd that angles bigger than 90° should have sines, cosines, and tangents like angles less than 90°. Indeed, the measurement of an angle by its sine, cosine, or tangent does not necessarily imply drawing a triangle at all. An angle is ordinarily defined by the number of units of length in a circular arc of radius 1 unit. To say that the angle between two lines is one degree means that if we draw a circle of 1 inch radius around the point where they cross, the length of the small arc between the points where they cut the circle is $(2\pi \div 360)$ inches long. The sine of an angle may also be defined in units of length, as we have done in Chapter 6, p. 264. If PT is the chord joining the ends of the arc 2A, of a circle of unit radius, $\frac{1}{2}$PT, (PQ in Fig. 129), the half chord, is the sine of the half arc A. The line PT has just as much right to be called the chord of the large arc $360° - 2A$ as of the small arc 2A, and the arc $\frac{1}{2}(360° - 2A) = 180° - A$ has just as much right to be called the half angle whose sine is the half chord PQ as A itself. Accordingly, this way of measuring sines means that

$$\sin A = \sin (180° - A)$$

To make a figure representing the fact that $\cos (180° - A)$ behaves as if it were $-\cos A$ for purposes of calculation we have got to find a meaning for the operator " – ". We have already seen that Euclid's geometry does not help to illustrate calculations in which the – sign occurs. We shall now study a geometry that does.

Before you go on, there is one other thing worth thinking about. When you were drawing figures to illustrate the rules of Euclid's geometry, you were probably under the impression that Archimedes was tracing the flat figures of Euclid's geometry on the sand when

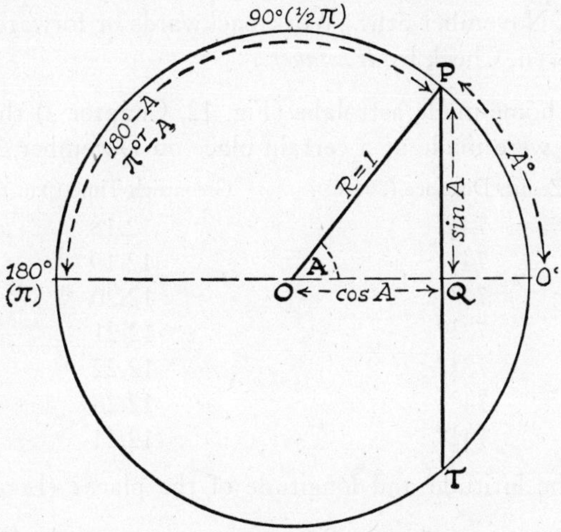

FIG. 129

he was murdered by Italian soldiers. You now know that he was really drawing spherical triangles on the curved surface of the earth. The only reason why Euclid's geometry meets the needs of draughtsmanship and architecture is that the dimensions of our drawings and buildings are very small compared with the earth's radius. If we go on tracing a straight line across the ocean long enough, we find that it is not a straight line in Euclid geometry. Inside the small slab of space which bounds our solar system the edge of a beam of light is for all practical purposes a straight line of Euclid, but when we say that light travels in straight lines to the furthest nebulae we do not necessarily mean that it travels in the straight lines of Euclid.

Chapter 8

TESTS

1. What is the sun's declination and right ascension on March 21st, June 21st, September 23rd, and December 21st?

2. What *approximately* is the sun's R.A. on July 4th, May 1st, January 1st, November 5th? (Work backwards or forwards from the four dates given. Check by *Whitaker*.)

3. With a home-made astrolabe (Fig. 12, Chapter 2) the following observations were made at a certain place on December 25th:

Sun's Zenith Distance (South)	Greenwich Time (p.m.)
$74\frac{1}{2}°$	12.18
74°	12.19
74°	12.20
$73\frac{1}{2}°$	12.21
$73\frac{1}{2}°$	12.22
74°	12.23
$74\frac{1}{2}°$	12.24

What was the latitude and longitude of the place? (Look it up on the map.)

4. Find the approximate R.A. of the sun on January 25th, and hence at what local time Aldebaran (R.A. 4 hours 32 minutes) will cross the meridian on that night. If the ship's chronometer then registers 11.15 p.m. at Greenwich, what is the longitude of the ship?

5. If the declination of Aldebaran is 16° N. (to the nearest degree) and its altitude at meridian transit is 60° from the southern horizon, what is the ship's latitude?

6. The R.A. of the star α in the Great Bear is nearly 11 hours. Its declination is 62° 5′ N. It crosses the meridian 4° 41′ north of the zenith on April 8th at 1.10 a.m. by the ship's chronometer. What is the position of the ship?

7. Suppose that you were deported to an island, but had with you a wrist watch and *Whitaker's Almanack*. Having set your watch at noon by observing the sun's shadow, you noticed that the star α in the Great Bear was at its lower culmination about 11 o'clock at night.

If you had lost count of the days, what would you conclude to be the approximate date?

8. On April 1st, 1895, the moon's R.A. was approximately 23 hours 48 minutes. Give roughly its appearance, time of rising, and transit on that date.

9. If the sun and the Great Bear were each visible throughout one whole 24 hours, and one only, in the year at a given locality on the Greenwich meridian, how could you determine the distance from London, if you also remembered that the earth's diameter is very nearly 8,000 miles, and the latitude of London is very nearly 51°?

10. If you observed that the sun's noon shadow vanished on one day of the year and pointed south on every other, how many miles would you be from the north pole?

11. On January 1st the sun reached its highest point in the heavens when the B.B.C. programme indicated 12.17 p.m. It was then 16° above the southern horizon. In what part of England did this happen?

12. The approximate R.A. and declination of Betelgeuse are respectively 5 hours 50 minutes and $7\frac{1}{2}$° N. If your bedroom faces east, and you retire regularly at 11.0 p.m., at what time of the year will you see Betelgeuse rising when you get into bed?

13. On April 13th, 1937, the shortest shadow of a pole was exactly equal to its height, and pointed north. This happened when the radio programme timed for 12.10 p.m. began. In what county were these observations made?

14. With a home-made astrolabe the following observations were made in Penzance (Lat. 50° N., Long. $5\frac{1}{2}$° W.) on February 8th:

	Least Zenith Distance	Greenwich Mean Time
Betelgeuse	$42\frac{1}{2}$° South	9.9 p.m.
Rigel	$58\frac{1}{2}$° ,,	8.24 ,,
Sirius	$67\frac{1}{2}$° ,,	10.0 ,,

Find the declination and R.A. of each star, and compare your results with the table in *Whitaker's Almanack* (p. 140). Note Greenwich "Mean" Time is not the true solar time reckoned from noon at Greenwich, but differs by a few minutes, the difference ("equation of time") being tabulated for each day of the year in *Whitaker* or the *Nautical Almanac*. On February 8th true noon at Greenwich occurred 14 minutes later than noon by Greenwich Mean Time.

15. By aid of a figure show that if the hour angle (h) of a star is the angle through which it has turned since it crossed the meridian (or if the sign is minus the angle through which it must turn to reach the meridian),

R.A. of star (in hours) = Sun's R.A. (in hours)

– (hour angle in degrees ÷ 15) + *local* time (in hours)

16. With the aid of a map on which ocean distances are given, work out the distances by great-circle sailing from ports connected by direct routes. What are the distances between London and New York, London and Moscow, London and Liverpool?

17. On April 26th, the sun's R.A. being 2 hours 13 minutes, the bearings of three stars were found to be as follows, by a home-made instrument:

	Azimuth	Zenith Distance	Local Time
Pollux	W. 80° from S.	45°	9.28 p.m.
Regulus	W. 28° " S.	41°	9.39 "
Arcturus	W. 7° " N.	31°	12.50 "

Find the declination and R.A. of each star and compare these rough estimates made at Lat. $50\frac{3}{4}$° N. with the accurate determinations given in *Whitaker's Almanack.*

18. To get the exact position of the meridian a line was drawn between two posts in line with the setting sun on July 4th at a place Lat. 43° N. At what angle to this line did the meridian lie? (Whitaker gives the sun's declination on July 4th as 23° N.) What was the approximate time of sunset?

19. If the R.A. of Sirius is 6 hours 42 minutes and its declination is $16\frac{3}{5}$° S. find its local times of rising and setting on January 1st at

Gizeh	Lat. 30° N.
New York	Lat. 41° N.
London	Lat. $51\frac{1}{2}$° N.

Check with planisphere.

THINGS TO MEMORIZE

1. If z.d. is measured north of the zenith the sign is +, if measured south of the zenith it is –. If latitude or declination is measured

north of the equator the sign is +, if south −. In all circumstances

Declination = Lat. of observer + *meridian* zenith distance

2. Star's R.A. = Time of transit + sun's R.A. on same day of year.

(Sun's R.A. 0. Declin. 0 March 21st
R.A. 12. Declin. 0 September 23rd
R.A. 6. Declin. + $23\frac{1}{2}°$ June 21st
R.A. 18. Declin. − $23\frac{1}{2}°$ December 21st)

3. In a spherical triangle

(*a*) $\cos a = \cos b \cos c + \sin b \sin c \cos \mathrm{A}$

(*b*) $\dfrac{\sin \mathrm{A}}{\sin a} = \dfrac{\sin \mathrm{B}}{\sin b} = \dfrac{\sin \mathrm{C}}{\sin c}$

4. For a heavenly body, azimuth being measured from the *south* point

(*a*) sin (declin.) = cos (z.d.) sin (lat.) − sin (z.d.) cos (lat.) cos (azim.)

(*b*) $\sin(\text{hour angle}) = \dfrac{\sin(\text{z.d.}) \sin(\text{azim.})}{\cos(\text{declin.})}$

(*c*) When setting and rising (z.d. = ± 90°)

$$\cos(\text{azim.}) = -\frac{\sin(\text{declin.})}{\cos(\text{lat.})},$$ (see p. 387).

$$\sin(\text{hour angle}) = \pm\frac{\sin(\text{azim.})}{\cos(\text{declin.})}$$

CHAPTER IX

The Reformation Geometry

OR

WHAT ARE GRAPHS?

THE mathematical syllabus of the University of Oxford in the fourteenth century took the student to the Bridge of Asses and left him there. It ended at the fifth proposition of the first of Euclid's twelve books. In the Moslem world a living body of secular learning had flourished side by side with the dead lexicography of the Koran, while, in Europe, book learning was mainly confined to a priesthood like the priesthood which guarded the calendar in the days of Nilotic civilization. For four centuries Europe absorbed and added little to what it had learned from its teachers. Meanwhile three technical developments conspired to set new problems for the mathematician. At the close of the fifteenth century a new era began. The manufacture of wheel-driven clocks, the introduction of artillery into warfare, the preparation of maps and astronomical tables for navigation forced mathematics to grapple with *time* in a new social context with a new technical equipment.

The Alexandrians and the Chinese had invented various devices which replaced the sun-dial, notably *clepsydras*, which were kept going by a flow of water. The principle involved was essentially the same as that represented in Fig. 2. Wheel-driven clocks were a later invention. The earliest we know was made in the latter end of the tenth century of our era. In the village communities of Northern Europe, as we are reminded by the derivation of our own word from the French *cloche* (a bell), the monks who rang the monastery bell were as essential to an orderly economic life based on the produce of the soil as the priesthood of the sacred Nile had been five thousand years before. In displacing its predecessors the Christian Church had taken over the archaic social function of the priesthood. The Pantheon was re-upholstered with saints whose martyrdoms, birthdays, or conversions marked the diurnal rhythms of the solar clock. Hour candles and clepsydras were kept at first. By the end of the tenth century clocks with wheels driven by a weight were to be found in the wealthier monasteries and churches. St. Paul's in London had a clock in A.D. 1286. Mechanical clocks were not sold for secular use till about the end of the fourteenth century. These early clocks were very crude instruments. The measurement of small intervals of time did not begin until Galileo demonstrated the principle of the pendulum. The application of this principle to the construction of pendulum clocks in the seventeenth century is one of the very few examples of a theoretical discovery which preceded its technical application before the era of electricity and dye chemistry. Chronometers for ships were not designed with sufficient accuracy for determining longitude until the compensated spring was invented a century later, although Gemma Regnier (Frisius), a Dutch mathematician, suggested in A.D. 1540 the method given in Chapter 4, p. 173.

The principle of the pendulum was the beginning of a new era in mechanics, the mechanics of movement as opposed to the Alexandrian mechanics of equilibrium. The first application of mechanical devices for offensive purposes seems to have been the use of a catapult contrivance in the campaigns of Alexander. The theoretical development of the mechanics of *poise* in the hands of Archimedes and his followers came immediately after. In 1241 the Mongol invaders of Hungary and Poland were using gunpowder. The introduction of artillery into European warfare in the fourteenth and fifteenth centuries created a new kind of mechanical problem—the calculation of the position of a swiftly moving body which could be propelled to great distances. The pendulum clock provided the instrument for measuring intervals of time small enough to record its progress. Within a century of the invention of paper, manuals of military science showing the use of trigonometry to calculate the distance of a target by sighting two angles as in Fig. 130 and 130A were circulated.

So the professional mathematician who was carried on board ships equipped with cannon in the great voyages of exploration during the sixteenth century was preoccupied with the problem of time and position in more ways than one. Three new social factors converged to bring the limitations of classical geometry to a focus in the social context where the solution was actually found. The astronomer who accompanied the ships of Henry the Navigator was trained in the Ptolemaic teaching which had survived the destruction of the Moorish learning. He used flat maps with parallels of latitude, and sometimes also with meridians of longitude. The Norwegians had long been acquainted with the "south pointing" instrument which the Chinese had used for a millennium or more, and perhaps made possible their long voyages across seas where stars are rarely visible. When

FIG. 130.—MATHEMATICS IN MILITARY AFFAIRS

In the upper figure the great medieval mathematician Tartaglia applies mathematics to artillery in a book published in 1546 at Venice. The lower one is the frontispiece of the *Arithmeticall Militare Treatise* of the brothers Digges, published in London in 1572.

gentlemen began to invest in merchant ventures the mariner's compass began to have a "cultural" as well as a practical interest. Compass-bearings and map-drawings together reproduce all the essential features of the new geometry which René Descartes first applied to the theoretical treatment of equations at the beginning of the seventeenth century. By then the study of curves had outgrown the use of rule and compass laid down by Plato. Copernicus, Tycho Brahe, Kepler, and Galileo, the last two equipped with the telescope, had made new and exact measurements of the orbits of the planets, tracing their positions in the form of a graph or map.

Contrary to Plato's teaching that the heavenly bodies move in circles because the circle is the most "perfect" figure, it was now found that the planets move in ellipses, a figure which Apollonius of Perga had studied by Euclidean constructions based on oblique sections of a cone. Omar Khayyám had actually solved cubic equations by using conic sections. Marinus of Tyre and his contemporary Ptolemy had made maps with parallels of latitude and longitude. Just as gunpowder was used for fireworks long before it transformed the tactics of warfare, every conception inherent in the Cartesian geometry had occurred to somebody centuries before it was made into an instrument which introduced a new epoch of mathematical invention.

Schoolboys heave a sigh of relief when they turn from the dullness of Euclid's demonstrations to the use of graphs, and many clever people have expressed surprise that a principle so simple should have waited so long for fulfilment. Surprise is perhaps more flattering to their vanity than to their social intelligence. The truth is that fruitful progress only occurs when a large number of people are thinking together about the same sort of thing. There would be less reason for surprise if we realized that clever people and people not so clever have a common need for each other, and that we cannot plan a future of higher intellectual progress for the human race if we place the needs of exceptionally gifted people in a false antithesis to the common needs of mankind. The more highly abstract mathematics becomes, the more clearly do we see the interconnection between the intellectual superstructure and the social foundations. The same social context produced a clock which dispensed with the need for the priestly innovations of catholicism, revolutionary wars in which success went to those who were in closest contact with mechanical amenities, exploration which enriched the merchant classes with the plunder of new territories, and a mathematical invention which could measure

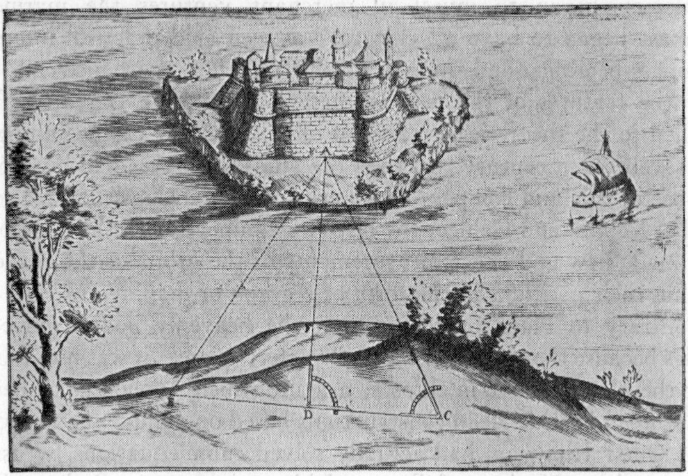

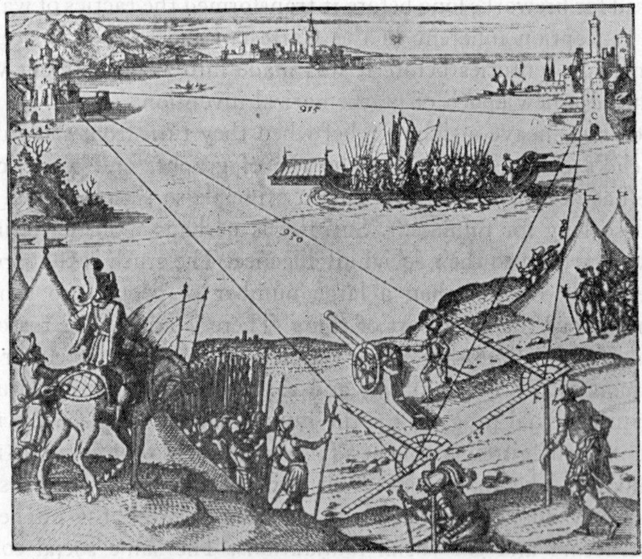

FIG. 130A.—MILITARY MATHEMATICS

These four prints taken from old books show one way in which solving the problem of motion had become a technical necessity in the period of Stevinus and Galileo. The upper one is from Bettino's *Apiaria* (Bologna 1645). The lower from Zubler's work on geometric instruments (1607).

the movement of the pendulum, the path of the cannon ball, the position of a ship at sea and the courses of the heavenly bodies.

POSITION AND MEASUREMENT.—The fundamental difference between the Cartesian geometry and the geometry of Euclid is that every quantity (or "magnitude") also has a direction or position attached to it. Thus a line is not just so many units of length. It is so many units of length drawn in a certain direction with reference to other lines. An area is not so many units of surface. It is the difference between so many units of surface in one situation and so many units of surface in another (Fig. 105). To say that a line is described by a direction as well as a quantity is literally true in the grammatical sense, because all the quantities of Cartesian geometry have an operative sign attached to them, "+" or "−", directing the way they are to be measured. The use of the signs in the sense of *direction* or *position* is a simple application of their more primitive use to mean adding or subtracting. It might have been made at any time in the three thousand years before Descartes if the development of mathematics were really independent of the common social heritage.

To illustrate how it naturally follows from addition and subtraction we will first confine ourselves to movement in a straight line. Fig. 131 shows a straight road running east and west from an old English village inn called "The Badger and Bagpipes." Four hundred yards along the road in an easterly direction is a village church. Four hundred yards from the inn to the west there is a second inn, "The Turtle and Toasting Fork." Suppose that a traveller, having refreshed himself at "The Badger and Bagpipes," sets out with the laudable intention of attending a week-night service at the church. Every step he goes *adds* a yard to his distance measured eastward from the inn, and by the time he reaches the church he has gone:

$$400 \text{ yards}$$

He is now thirsty and turns back for fluid relief. When he has gone another 300 yards back, i.e. in a westerly direction, where is he now? Holding to the traditional use of the signs, we say he is

$$400 - 300 = 100 \text{ yards}$$

from the place from which he started. He has taken away 300 yards from the easterly distance between his original position and the church.

If he walks another 100 yards he will have taken it all away. His distance from the inn will be

$$400 - 400 = 0 \text{ yards}$$

i.e. he will be back where he started. But by that time he may remember that there is better beer at "The Turtle and Toasting Fork." If he

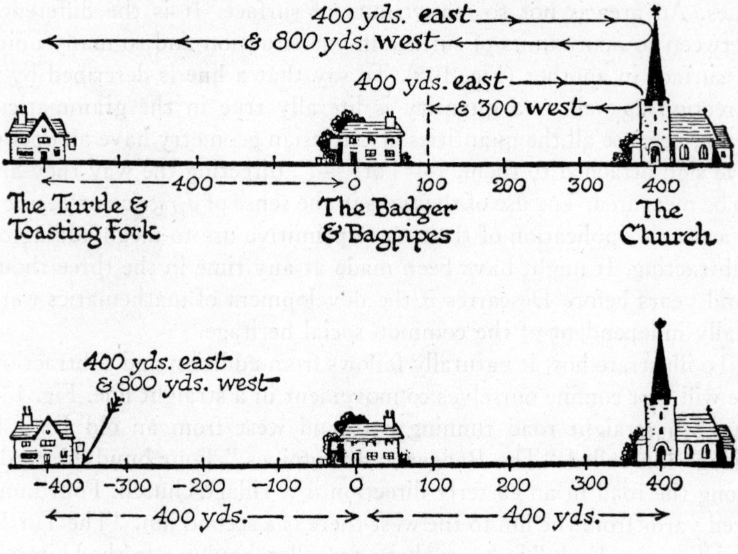

FIG. 131.—THE MEANING OF THE GERUND

keeps on walking another 400 yards west he comes to the second inn, having walked 800 yards from the church. To be consistent with what we have done before we should say that his distance from the place where he started is now:

$$400 - 800 = -400 \text{ yards}$$

To get his final position from what we know of his movements, we must represent 400 yards west of the place where he started as -400, if we call 400 yards east of the place where he started $+400$. So the meaning of "+" is its ordinary meaning, and the meaning of "−" is its ordinary meaning, if we make the gerund (verb and noun taken together) $+a$ mean a units of length east, or a units to the right, and the gerund $-a$ mean a units west or a units to the left.

At first you may not see any particular advantage in this addition to the rules of grammar. There would not be, if people spent all their time in churches or public-houses with only clepsydras to record the continuous flow of time. However, the social epoch into which we have now penetrated begins with the warning "Time, gentlemen, time!" It is the century of the pendulum clock. Fig. 132 shows a pendulum which ticks every two seconds. The displacements of the extremity, i.e. horizontal distance from its resting position when the clock stops, are represented as "+" and "−" quantities. The total swing is 12 centimetres, or ± 6 centimetres from the equilibrium position. Suppose we can record its position by successive snapshots using a camera provided with a very rapidly closing shutter. Starting from its extreme position, + 6 units to the right, we could draw up a table of our observations like this:

Time in secs.	Horizontal distance (cm.) traversed	Horizontal displacement (cm.)
0	0	+ 6
0·37	1	+ 5
0·51	2	+ 4
0·66	3	+ 3
0·80	4	+ 2
0·90	5	+ 1
1·00	6	0
1·10	7	− 1
1·22	8	− 2
1·33	9	− 3
1·44	10	− 4
1·62	11	− 5
2·00	12	− 6
2·36	13	− 5
2·52	14	− 4
2·64	15	− 3
2·80	16	− 2
2·90	17	− 1
3·00	18	0
3·10	19	+ 1

The second column might be called the classical method of recording where the pendulum is. The third is the Cartesian. Its advantage is that you see at once exactly *what kind of movement* the pendulum executes. It swings left and right symmetrically about the position it occupies, when the clock is stopped, returning to its original position like the solar clock which swings over the horizon.

Let us now return to the inn and observe the sequel of the visit. The traveller takes his departure at the inn door with renewed intentions for good, but without realizing that alcohol is apt to sidetrack the messages which our receptor organs telegraph to the brain. Owing

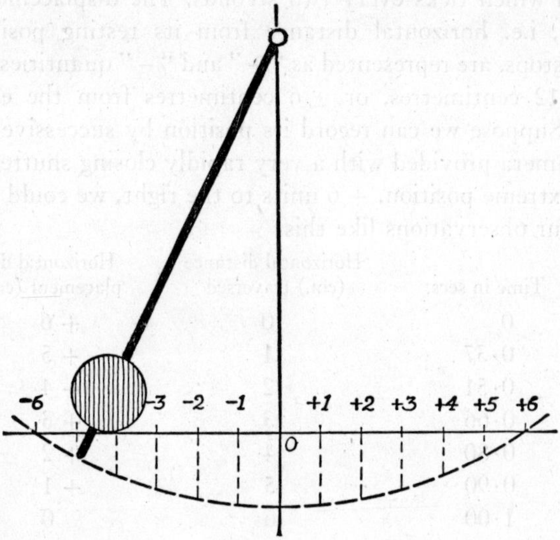

FIG. 132.—DISPLACEMENT OF THE PENDULUM OF THE CLOCK FROM POSITION AT REST

to the error of identifying the moon shining overhead with the church he tries to climb up the wall of the inn. In failing to satisfy his need for devotional exercise he has demonstrated the meaning of another gerund, $\sqrt{-1}$, or, as we more usually write it for short, "i." To see why ia (or $a\sqrt{-1}$) units means a units measured upwards into the heaven where his imagination has located the church militant, you have only to recall the Euclidean hieroglyph of the geometric mean (compare Fig. 133 with Fig. 64). From Dem. 8 in Chapter 4 we learned that the length of the perpendicular drawn from the right angle to the hypotenuse is the square root of the product of the two parts into which the length of the hypotenuse is divided, and Dem. 10 showed that a triangle of which one side is the diameter and the opposite angle touches the boundary of a semicircle is right-angled. If we draw a semicircle with its centre at the mid-point between the second inn and the church, we get a right-angled triangle by joining each to a point vertically above the centre. In Fig. 133 the unit of measurement is 100 yards. The church is + 4, and "The Turtle and

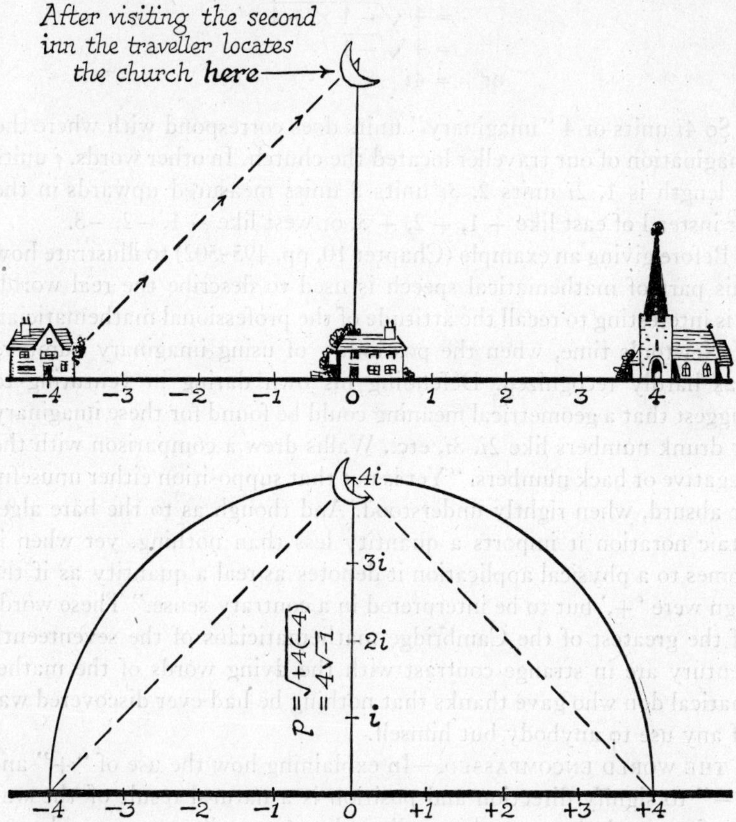

FIG. 133

Toasting Fork" inn is − 4 units from the centre. If we call the vertical height p, we know that if a is the first and b is the second distance,

$$p = \sqrt{ab}$$

In Euclidean geometry we should take no account of direction. This would be equivalent to saying

$$p = \sqrt{4 \times 4} = 4$$

To be consistent with what we have agreed to do in putting back

into geometry what Euclid left out, we are committed to a surprising result, i.e.

$$\begin{aligned} p &= \sqrt{-4 \times +4} \\ &= 4\sqrt{-1 \times +1} \\ &= 4\sqrt{-1} \\ \text{or} \quad &= 4i \end{aligned}$$

So $4i$ units or 4 "imaginary" units does correspond with where the imagination of our traveller located the church. In other words, i units of length is 1, $2i$ units 2, $3i$ units 3 units measured upwards in the air instead of east like + 1, + 2, + 3, or west like − 1, −2, −3.

Before giving an example (Chapter 10, pp. 495–502) to illustrate how this part of mathematical speech is used to describe the real world, it is interesting to recall the attitude of the professional mathematician of Newton's time, when the possibility of using imaginary numbers was hardly recognized. Defending his own daring in venturing to suggest that a geometrical meaning could be found for these imaginary or drunk numbers like $2i$, $3i$, etc., Wallis drew a comparison with the negative or back numbers. "Yet is not that supposition either unuseful or absurd, when rightly understood. And though as to the bare algebraic notation it imports a quantity less than nothing, yet when it comes to a physical application it denotes as real a quantity as if the sign were '+,' but to be interpreted in a contrary sense." These words of the greatest of the Cambridge mathematicians of the seventeenth century are in strange contrast with the dying words of the mathematical don who gave thanks that nothing he had ever discovered was of any use to anybody but himself.

THE WORLD ENCOMPASSED.—In explaining how the use of "+" and "−" to signify direction and position is a natural result of the way we first used them, we have allowed our traveller to roam along a straight road on his own legs and left him free to find heaven in his own imagination. Let us now see how they may be used to describe the movements of ships on sea roads which have no hedges, so that the mariner can steer his course as the crow flies. In Fig. 134 we have shown the world of the Great Navigations projected on parallels of latitude and meridians of longitude. The latter are not strictly parallel on the solid globe. They converge to the poles. At equal distances on the circumference of a circle round the world from north to south pole and back the surface of the world is divided by circles parallel to the equator, 90 of them north and 90 of them south so that in going from the north pole to the south and back we should have to cross 360 parallel lines of latitude, or, as we usually say, go through 360° of latitude. By lines joining the poles, reckoned from 0° to 180° east

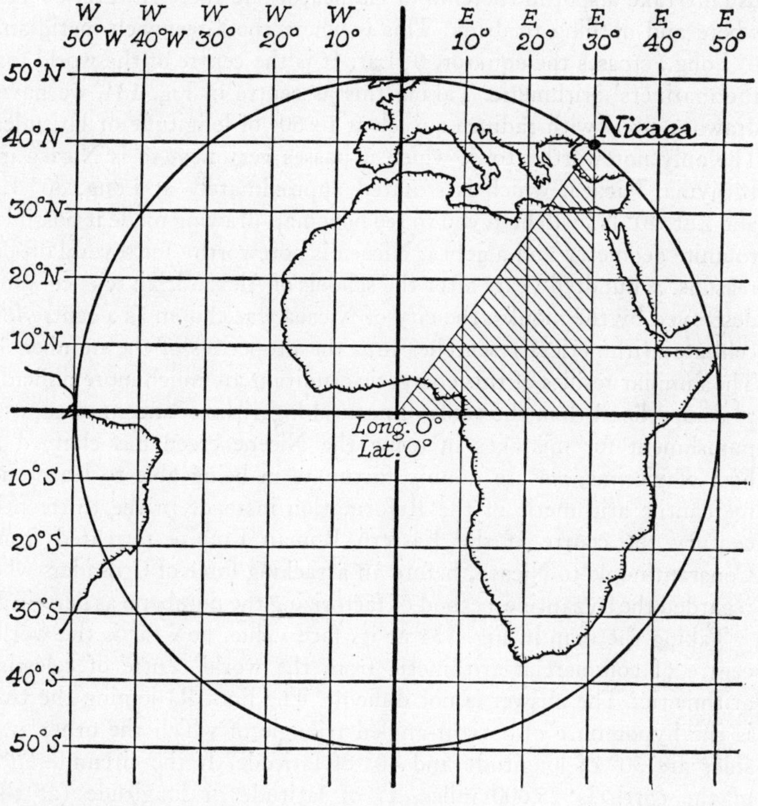

FIG. 134

and 0° to 180° west of the meridian which passes through Greenwich, any circle of latitude parallel to the equator is divided into 360 equal steps or degrees of *longitude*. In a projection map, the meridians are usually drawn parallel like the lines corresponding with the parallel circles of latitude, as if the world were flat. This introduces a big error in calculating long distances which can only be correctly calculated by the use of spherical triangles, as explained in Chapter 8, p. 376. For our present purpose we will neglect the correction and proceed as if the world were actually flat.

To indicate our position at sea or on the earth we only need to have some fixed spot to which we can refer our measurements, like the Badger and Bagpipes Inn of the last example. For navigation we usually take a spot in the Gulf of Guinea, where there is water everywhere and nothing to drink. This is where the Greenwich meridian, 0° Long., crosses the equator, 0° Lat. It is the centre of the world for the mariners' arithmetic. Taking this as centre in Fig. 134, we have drawn a circle with radius equivalent to 50° of longitude or latitude. The only noteworthy town which it passes very near to is Nicaea in Bithynia. Nicaea, which is situated approximately at Long. 30° E. and Lat. 40° N., will help you to see how map-drawing made it possible to unite geometry and algebra. Nicaea is noteworthy for several other reasons. A hundred years after the schools of Alexandrian science were destroyed by the monks, the city of Nicaea was chosen as a centre for celibate arithmetical researches into the properties of the number 3. The familiar results of this energetic erudition are much more difficult to comprehend than the table of natural logarithms, and since capital punishment for mistakes in using the Nicene creed has claimed a host of victims, we are doubly fortunate in being able to learn the mercantile arithmetic of the Reformation instead. In the thirteenth century the centre of the Eastern Roman Empire retreated from Constantinople to Nicaea, before an attacking force of Crusaders who regarded the Byzantine method of factorizing the number 3 as heretical.

Taking the map in Fig. 134 at its face value, how far is the world centre of commercial arithmetic from the world centre of celestial arithmetic? The answer is not difficult. The line (R) joining the two is the hypotenuse of a right-angled triangle of which the other two sides are 30° of longitude and 40° of latitude. If the circumference of the earth is 25,000 miles, 1° of latitude or longitude (at the equator) is $\frac{2500}{36}$, or $69\frac{1}{2}$ miles. So the other two sides of the triangle are $30 \times 69\frac{1}{2}$ and $40 \times 69\frac{1}{2}$ miles. By what we might now call the Chinese Compass Theorem, or Dem. 8,

$$
\begin{aligned}
R^2 &= (30 \times 69\tfrac{1}{2})^2 + (40 \times 69\tfrac{1}{2})^2 \\
&= (69\tfrac{1}{2})^2\,(30^2 + 40^2) \\
\therefore \quad R &= 69\tfrac{1}{2}\sqrt{900 + 1{,}600} \\
&= 69\tfrac{1}{2}\sqrt{2{,}500} \\
&= \pm\, 69\tfrac{1}{2}(50) \\
&= \pm\, 3{,}475 \text{ miles.*}
\end{aligned}
$$

* The error due to the earth's curvature is about 3 per cent, as you will see by using the formula on p. 376.

The two signs in this case remind us that R, the distance from the centre to the circumference, would be the same if measured in the opposite direction to some place on the boundary of the circle in

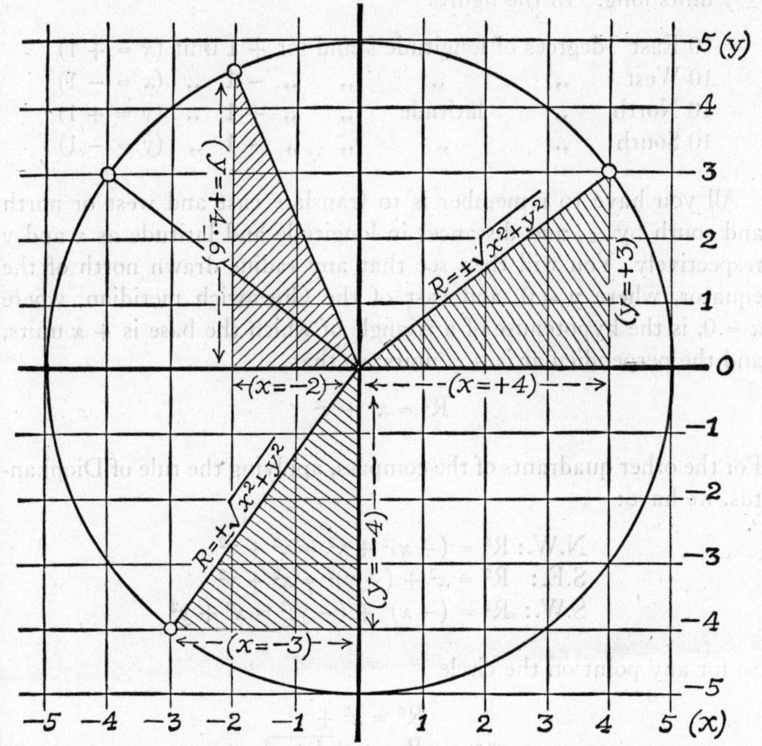

FIG. 135.—CARTESIAN EQUATION OF THE CIRCLE

At every point on the boundary of the circle of radius R, $R^2 = x^2 + y^2$; $x^2 = R^2 - y^2$; $y^2 = R^2 - x^2$, i.e.

$$R = \sqrt{x^2 + y^2};\ x = \sqrt{R^2 - y^2};\ y = \sqrt{R^2 - x^2}$$

Hence if $R = 5$ and $x = -2$,

$$y = \sqrt{5^2 - (-2)^2} = \sqrt{25 - 4} = \sqrt{21} = \pm\, 4{\cdot}6 \text{ (approx.)}$$

the South Atlantic. This simple calculation reveals how figures are described in Reformation geometry. The Cartesian line is not like the lines of Euclid, which can be equal in all respects in spite of the fact that they are obviously in different places. It is a particular line pointing in a particular direction, and starting from a particular place. In Fig. 135 we have redrawn the circle of Fig. 134 with four radii superimposed on the same framework. The only difference is one of vocabulary. We call a distance measured parallel to the equator $\pm x$ units, and any distance measured along a parallel of longitude $\pm y$ units long.* In the figure:

10 East	degrees of longitude	stand	for	+ 1	unit	($x = +1$)
10 West	,,	,,	,,	,,	− 1	,,	($x = -1$)
10 North	,,	latitude	,,	,,	+ 1	,,	($y = +1$)
10 South	,,	,,	,,	,,	− 1	,,	($y = -1$)

All you have to remember is to translate east and west or north and south by $\pm$, and distances in longitude and latitude as x and y respectively. You will then see that any radius drawn north of the equator, where $y = 0$, and east of the Greenwich meridian, where $x = 0$, is the hypotenuse of a triangle of which the base is $+ x$ units, and the perpendicular is $+ y$ units; so that

$$R^2 = x^2 + y^2$$

For the other quadrants of the compass, applying the rule of Diophantus, we have:

$$\text{N.W.: } R^2 = (-x)^2 + y^2 = x^2 + y^2$$
$$\text{S.E.: } R^2 = x^2 + (-y)^2 = x^2 + y^2$$
$$\text{S.W.: } R^2 = (-x)^2 + (-y)^2 = x^2 + y^2$$

So for any point on the circle

$$R^2 = x^2 + y^2$$
$$\text{or} \quad R = \sqrt{x^2 + y^2}$$

Be sure you know what this means by translating it back into the more familiar rhetorical algebra of the Hindus. It will then read: "In Cartesian geometry a circle is a figure of which the distance of the boundary from a fixed point called the centre can be got by taking the square root of the sum formed by adding together the squares of the horizontal and vertical distances from the centre to any spot on the boundary." So in the Reformation geometry the definition of a

* Do not confuse the y measurements of Fig. 135 with the ix measurements of Fig. 133. In Fig. 135 measurements represented by y correspond with distances along a road at right angles to the road which joins the two inns of Fig. 133 and not with distances upwards (ix) in a plane at right angles to the plane in which it lies. The distinction is merely a convention.

figure is an algebraic equation. We say that the circle is the figure of which the equation is

$$R = \sqrt{x^2 + y^2}$$

This is called the *Cartesian Equation of the Circle,* whose centre is at the point where $x = 0$ and $y = 0$.

A second familiar figure which will illustrate the difference between the Euclidean and the Cartesian standpoint is the right-angled triangle. Any line drawn across the Cartesian framework of longitude (x) and latitude (y) is the hypotenuse of a right-angled triangle of which the perpendicular is a meridian of longitude, and the base a parallel of latitude (Fig. 136). If the line passes through the world centre where the Greenwich meridian cuts the equator, or, as we shall now call it, the *origin* of reference, any right-angled triangle enclosed by a part of the line and a parallel of longitude or latitude is similar to any other right-angled triangle enclosed by any other part of the line and a parallel of longitude and latitude. This you will see without difficulty if you compare the two series of triangles at the right and left at the bottom of Fig. 136 with Fig. 43 to illustrate Dem. 5 in Chapter 4. If the line drawn across the framework passes through the origin like RS, the position and size of a right-angled triangle with its corner angle (A) at the origin, having for its base x, and for its perpendicular y, are fully described by the equation

$$\frac{y}{x} = \tan A$$

$$\text{or} \qquad y = (\tan A)x$$

In the diagram $x = 5$ and $y = 3$. So tan A, which is the *gradient* or slope (see Fig. 31) of RS, is $\frac{3}{5}$.

If a line PQ is drawn parallel to RS across the Cartesian frame cutting the Greenwich meridian ("y" axis) at $y = b$,

$$\tan A = \frac{y - b}{x}$$

$$\text{or} \qquad \underline{y = (\tan A)x + b}$$

We do not usually speak of this equation as the equation of the right-angled triangle. It is usually called the *Cartesian Equation of the Straight Line.* The reason is that describing a figure in Reformation geometry is really describing a line which bounds it, and the equation which describes a line — straight, or, like the boundary line of a circle, curved —, tells you how to find the latitude of any spot on the line if you know the longitude, or *vice versa.* The last equation

$$y = (\tan A)x + b$$

means that we can calculate the vertical height of any point on the

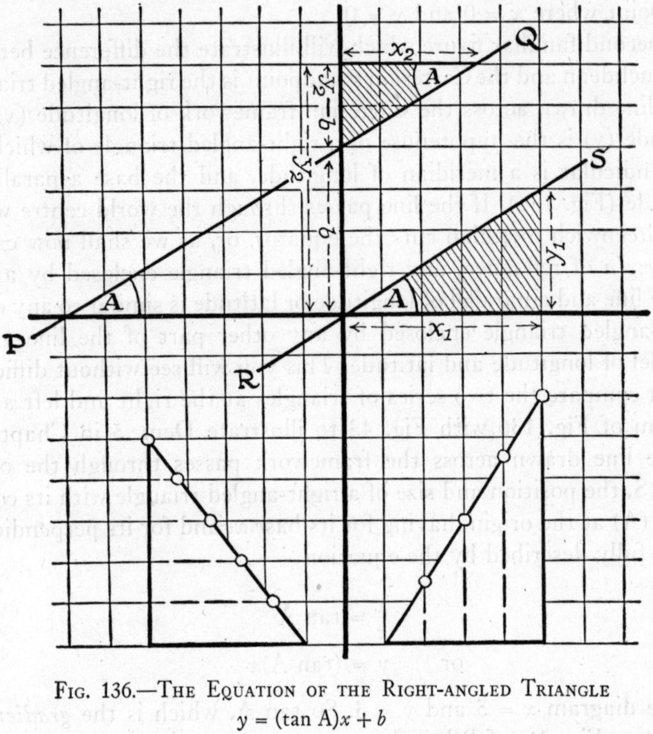

FIG. 136.—THE EQUATION OF THE RIGHT-ANGLED TRIANGLE
$y = (\tan A)x + b$

line if we know the horizontal distance of the point from the origin. For any particular line, we must know tan A and b. If the line goes through the origin, $b = 0$ and

$$y = (\tan A)\,x$$

If A is 0, $$y = b$$

This means that the line runs parallel to the equator ("x" axis) at the same vertical height b anywhere. If A is 45° or $\frac{1}{4}\pi$ radians, tan A = 1 (see p. 157), and

$$y = x + b$$

If tan A is unity and $b = 0$, the line runs through the origin at 45°

The longitude and latitude of a particular spot on a line are usually called the *co-ordinates* of the point. It is useful to use a mathematical *adjective* to describe co-ordinates. If we call x any distance measured horizontally from the origin, and y any distance measured vertically from the origin, the co-ordinates of a point P are called x_p, y_p. The

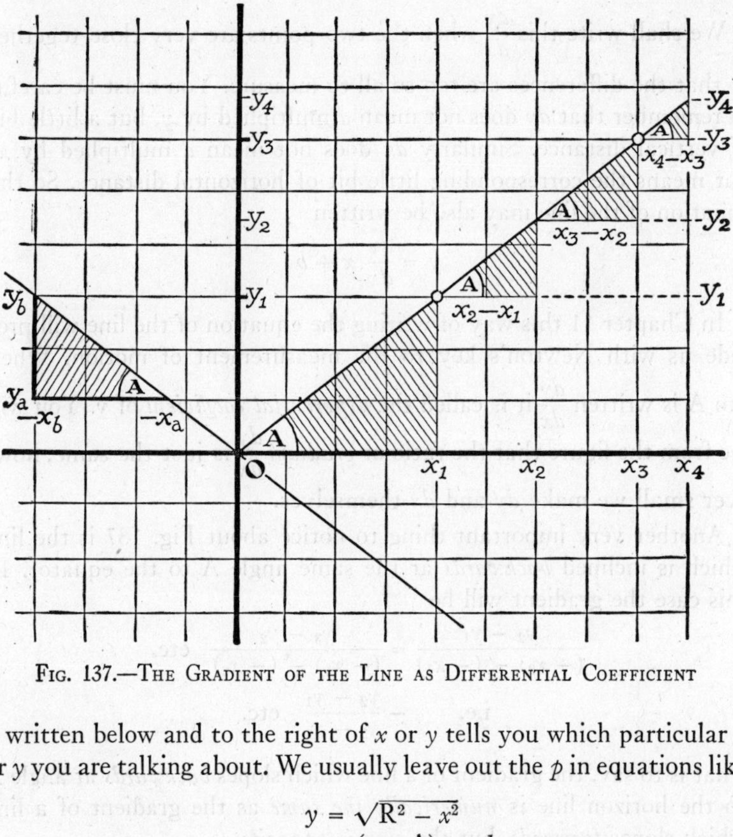

FIG. 137.—THE GRADIENT OF THE LINE AS DIFFERENTIAL COEFFICIENT

p written below and to the right of x or y tells you which particular x or y you are talking about. We usually leave out the p in equations like

$$y = \sqrt{R^2 - x^2}$$

$$\text{or} \qquad y = (\tan A)x + b$$

The reason is that we take it for granted that the y we are talking about is the y corresponding with the x we are talking about. Since all right-angled triangles enclosed by parts of the same line and parallels of longitude and latitude are similar, you will see from Fig. 137 that

$$\frac{y_2 - y_1}{x_2 - x_1} = \tan A = \frac{y_3 - y_2}{x_3 - x_2} = \frac{y_4 - y_3}{x_4 - x_3}$$

That is to say, for any two points on the line, the gradient is the difference between the y co-ordinates divided by the difference between the x co-ordinates, or

$$\tan A = \frac{\text{diff. } y}{\text{diff. } x}$$

We shall write this $\frac{dy}{dx}$ when the two points are very close together so that the differences are too small to measure. You must be careful to remember that dy does not mean d multiplied by y, but a little bit of vertical distance. Similarly dx does not mean d multiplied by x, but means the corresponding little bit of horizontal distance. So the equation of the line may also be written

$$y = \frac{dy}{dx}.x + b$$

In Chapter 11 this way of writing the equation of the line will provide us with Newton's key to the measurement of motion. When tan A is written $\frac{dy}{dx}$ it is called the *differential coefficient* of y. You will see from the figure that the ratio or *gradient* $\frac{dy}{dx}$ is just the same, however small we make dy and dx themselves.

Another very important thing to notice about Fig. 137 is the line which is inclined *backwards* at the same angle A to the equator. In this case the gradient will be

$$\frac{y_2 - y_1}{(-x_2) - (-x_1)} = \frac{y_3 - y_2}{(-x_3) - (-x_2)} \quad \text{etc.}$$

$$\text{i.e.} \qquad -\frac{y_2 - y_1}{x_2 - x_1} \quad \text{etc.}$$

That is to say, the gradient of a line which slopes *backwards* at angle A to the horizon line is *numerically the same* as the gradient of a line which slopes *forwards*, but the *sign is opposite*.

GUNPOWDER PLOTTING.—We have called the new geometry Reformation geometry to draw attention to the social context in which it arose. We have seen that the geometry of René Descartes included something which Euclid's geometry left out. It tells you the *position* a figure occupies in space. We shall now see that it found a place for something else which Euclid left out. It can take *time* into account. In both respects it stands in close relation to the great intellectual changes associated with the Protestant Reformation, though Descartes, like Erasmus, who laid the foundations of Protestant biblical scholarship and advanced many liberal doctrines of a later period, died without actually renouncing the Roman faith.

The Reformation was not carried through by biblical scholarship alone. Europe was ravaged with wars in which artillery played an increasingly important part. It was the age of gunpowder plots, when military success depended on exploiting a new technique. When cannon was first introduced in the thirteenth century its effects were chiefly directed to destroying the morale of the enemy. By the sixteenth

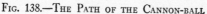

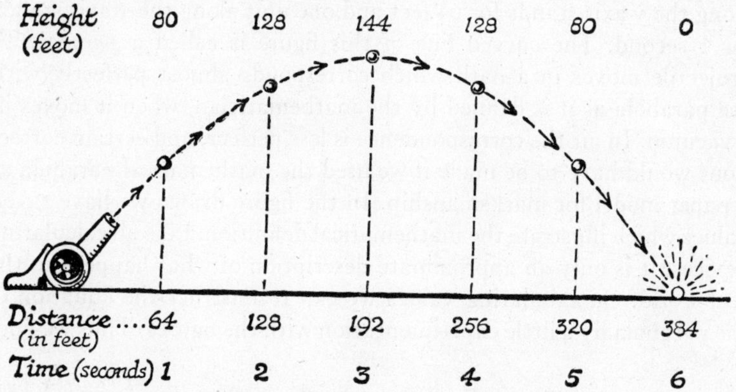

FIG. 138.—THE PATH OF THE CANNON-BALL

century it was being used as an effective weapon of destruction. How to tilt the cannon so that the missile would hit a particular place, and how to sight the distance, had enlisted mathematical ingenuity in the art of warfare.

Fig. 138 is a scale diagram of the fundamental problem. It shows the progress of the cannon-ball, vertically and horizontally. If convenient in drawing, the scale of the vertical height need not be the same as the scale of the horizontal distance. You will see that each position of the moving cannon-ball, like each position of the moving ship, has two co-ordinates, the horizontal distance $(+x)$ to the right of the cannon corresponding with the longitude east, and the vertical distance upward from the ground $(+y)$ corresponding with the latitude north. The difference between the scale diagram of the cannon-ball and an ordinary map is that we have put into it something we do not include in a map. Maps are made for different ships travelling at different speeds. So they take no account of time. They are only concerned with showing us the position of the ship. In the scale diagram of the cannon-ball we have shown the time which elapses between the firing of the cannon and the instant when the ball passes the horizontal distances corresponding with degrees of longitude. So we can equally give the co-ordinates of any point in the progress of the projectile as:

(*a*) vertical height = $+ y$, horizontal distance = $+ x$
(*b*) vertical height = $+ y$, time since firing = $+ x$

In other words, we can use our Cartesian framework to represent the passage of time as in Fig. 139, where one unit of measurement along the y axis stands for 64 feet and one unit along the x axis stands for 1 second. The curved line of this figure is called a *parabola.* A projectile moves in a path which corresponds almost perfectly with the parabola as it is defined by the mathematician, when it moves in a vacuum. In air the correspondence is less perfect, and certain corrections would have to be made if we used the mathematical parabola as a paper model for marksmanship. In the figure drawn we have taken values which illustrate the mathematical definition. Like all calculating devices, it is only an approximate description of what happens in the real world. On tabulating values we can reconstruct the equation of the parabola by a little experimentation with the figures. Thus we find:

x	y	$\frac{3x}{2}$	x^2	$\frac{x^2}{4}$	$\left(\frac{3x}{2} - \frac{x^2}{4}\right)$
0	0	0	0	0	0
1	$1\frac{1}{4}$	$1\frac{1}{2}$	1	$\frac{1}{4}$	$1\frac{1}{4}$
2	2	3	4	1	2
3	$2\frac{1}{4}$	$4\frac{1}{2}$	9	$2\frac{1}{4}$	$2\frac{1}{4}$
4	2	6	16	4	2
5	$1\frac{1}{4}$	$7\frac{1}{2}$	25	$6\frac{1}{4}$	$1\frac{1}{4}$
6	0	9	36	9	0

The equation of the descending parabola drawn in this way is

$$y = ax^2 + bx + c$$

In the example taken, as the table shows, $a = -\frac{1}{4}$, $b = \frac{3}{2}$, and $c = 0$. Since one y unit represents 64 feet, the value of y calculated from this equation must be multiplied by 64 to get the correct answer in *feet.* By shifting the origin of measurement we get a much simpler equation. Fig. 140 is drawn so that the origin is the turning-point 192 feet from the cannon, and y is the vertical distance

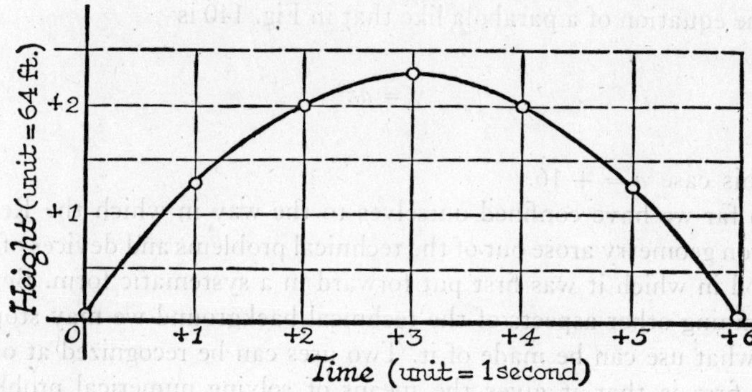

FIG. 139.—PUTTING TIME INTO GEOMETRY

downwards from the highest point (144 feet) of the curve in Fig. 138. Distance (y) is measured in feet, and time (x) is measured in so many seconds before ($-x$) or after ($+x$) the cannon-ball is at its highest point. We then have:

x	y		
-3	144	=	$(-3)^2 \times 16$
-2	64	=	$(-2)^2 \times 16$
-1	16	=	$(-1)^2 \times 16$
0	0	=	$0^2 \times 16$
$+1$	16	=	$(+1)^2 \times 16$
$+2$	64	=	$(+2)^2 \times 16$
$+3$	144	=	$(+3)^2 \times 16$

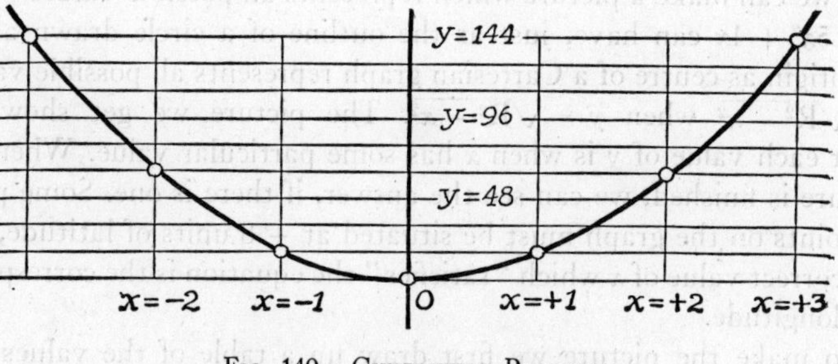

FIG. 140.—GUNPOWDER PLOTTING

The curve called the "parabola"

The *Cartesian Equation of the Parabola* when drawn like this is:

$$y = ax^2$$

In this figure $a = 16$.

So the equation of a parabola like that in Fig. 140 is

$$y = ax^2$$

In this case $a = +16$.

So far we have confined ourselves to the way in which the Reformation geometry arose out of the technical problems and devices of the period in which it was first put forward in a systematic form. Before examining other aspects of the technical background we may stop to ask what use can be made of it. Two uses can be recognized at once. The first is that it gives the means of solving numerical problems which can be stated in the form of an equation, even when we cannot find any direct algebraical rules for the solution.

For instance, here is an equation which we have not yet found a way of solving:

$$x^3 - 5x^2 + 4x - 8 = 0$$

or

$$x^3 - 5x^2 + 4x = 8$$

On the left-hand side of this equation we have a set of quantities of which we do not know the values. Standing by themselves they may amount to anything, according to the proper number which is represented by x. The right-hand side of the equation tells us that the correct proper number or numbers which x stands for must be such that the total of $x^3 - 5x^2 + 4x$ is 8. If we call the total $(x^3 - 5x^2 + 4x)$ "y" we can make a picture which represents all possible values which $x^3 - 5x^2 + 4x$ can have, just as the outline of a circle drawn about the origin as centre of a Cartesian graph represents all possible values of $\sqrt{R^2 - x^2}$ when $y = \sqrt{R^2 - x^2}$. The picture we get shows us what each value of y is when x has some particular value. When the picture is finished, we can see the answer, if there is one. Some point or points on the graph must be situated at $+8$ units of latitude, and the correct value of x which "satisfies" the equation is the corresponding longitude.

To make the picture we first draw up a table of the values of y corresponding with a lot of different values of x, going on till some of our values of y are larger and others smaller than the value which y has according to the equation $y = 8$. Here is a table of this sort:

x	x^3	$-5x^2$	$4x$	y co-ordinate $(x^3 - 5x^2 + 4x)$
	x co-ordinate			
-2	-8	-20	-8	-36
$-1\frac{1}{2}$	$-\frac{27}{8}$	$-\frac{45}{4}$	-6	$-20\frac{5}{8}$
-1	-1	-5	-4	-10
$-\frac{1}{2}$	$-\frac{1}{8}$	$-\frac{5}{4}$	-2	$-3\frac{3}{8}$
0	0	0	0	0
$\frac{1}{2}$	$\frac{1}{8}$	$-\frac{5}{4}$	2	$\frac{7}{8}$
1	1	-5	4	0
$1\frac{1}{2}$	$\frac{27}{8}$	$-\frac{45}{4}$	6	$-1\frac{7}{8}$
2	8	-20	8	-4
$2\frac{1}{2}$	$\frac{125}{8}$	$-\frac{125}{4}$	10	$-5\frac{5}{8}$
3	27	-45	12	-6
$3\frac{1}{2}$	$\frac{343}{8}$	$-\frac{245}{4}$	14	$-4\frac{3}{8}$
4	64	-80	16	0
$4\frac{1}{2}$	$\frac{729}{8}$	$-\frac{405}{4}$	18	$7\frac{7}{8}$
5	125	-125	20	20

Having done this, we now dot in points like the small circles in Fig. 141, whose co-ordinates are x (extreme left-hand column) and y (extreme right-hand column) in the table. This is called *plotting* the curve. Join these points with a curved line running smoothly between them.

The curve shows the values of x corresponding with

$$y = x^3 - 5x^2 + 4x$$

The equation tells us that

$$8 = x^3 - 5x^2 + 4x$$

So we draw across the graph a line whose vertical height is 8, ($y = 8$). The horizontal distance of the point or points where this line cuts the curve is the value or values of x which satisfy the equation. The accuracy of the result depends on how well you draw the curve, how finely graduated the graph paper is, and the scale you choose. You will see that x lies between 4·5 and 4·75, and it is very much nearer to the former than to the latter. With trouble you can get as much accuracy as you need for whatever you happen to be calculating.

A numerical application is seen in Fig. 142. If we want approximate values for squares, square roots, cube roots, etc., we can make a suitable graph, e.g. $y = x^2$, $y = x^3$. Square roots may be found from the parabola

$$y = x^2$$

which is the same thing as $x = \pm\sqrt{y}$

Having drawn the curve, you merely have to read off the x co-ordinate

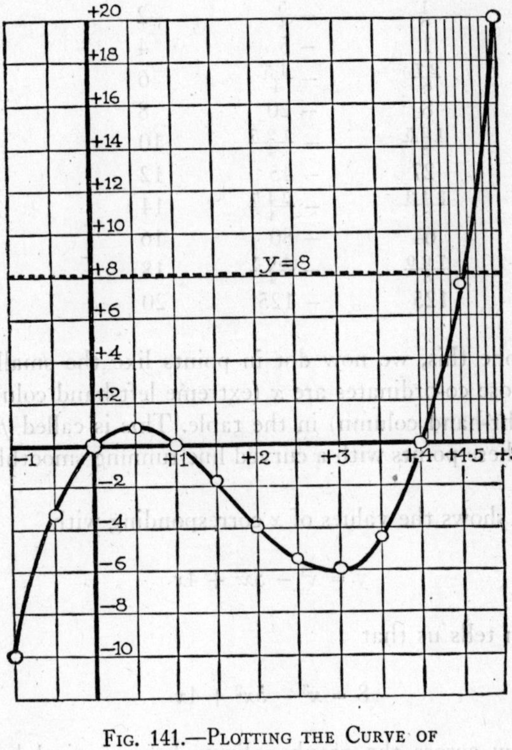

FIG. 141.—PLOTTING THE CURVE OF $x^3 - 5x^2 + 4x = y$

of a point whose y co-ordinate is the number whose square root is required.

A second way in which the Reformation geometry is useful is that it suggests the kind of numerical rules or laws which connect physical, biological, and social changes which can be expressed by numbers. Here are some illustrations.

The stretching of a string or a piece of elastic is shown in Fig. 143. The experiment can be carried out in a few minutes. The spring in this case was a piece of thick valve tubing, suspended by a nail knocked into the leg of a kitchen table with a foot-rule having divisions of $\frac{1}{10}$ inch fixed below with drawing-pins or a couple of screws. The scale pan was the top of a cigarette tin attached by four holes, which can be made with a hammer and nail. Weights from a

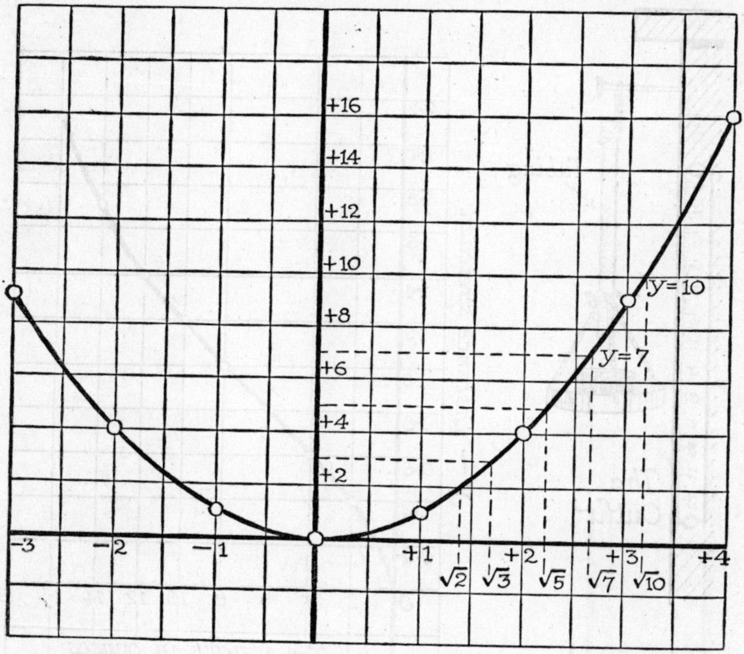

FIG. 142.—GRAPHICAL METHOD FOR FINDING SQUARE ROOTS

kitchen scale were used. The graph is made from the following observations:

x (weight in ounces)	Level of Pan (inches)	y (distance stretched, inches)
0	3·0	0·0
2	3·4	0·4
4	3·6	0·6
6	3·8	0·8
8	4·0	1·0
10	4·2	1·2
12	4·4	1·4
14	4·7	1·7
16	5·1	2·1

From such a graph you can read off the distances which correspond with any weight if you want to calibrate (i.e. mark off a scale of weights on) a spring balance. You will notice that from $x = 2$ to $x = 12$ the graph is a straight line. Within this range the addition of

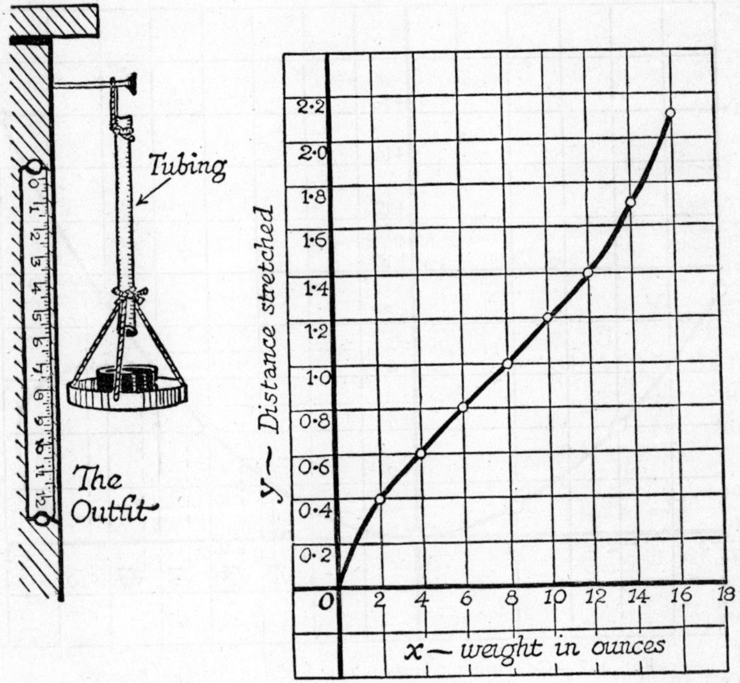

FIG. 143.—THE LAW OF THE SPRING BALANCE

2 ounces to the pan (diff. $x = 2$) produces an extension of 0·2 inch (diff. $y = 0 \cdot 2$). Now the equation of a line is

$$y = \frac{\text{diff. } y}{\text{diff. } x}\, x + a$$

So the equation of this graph in the range where it runs straight is

$$y = (0 \cdot 1)\, x + a$$

You can find a by putting in the corresponding values of x and y

for any point between $x = 4$ and $x = 12$, e.g. when $x = 10$, $y = 1{\cdot}2$, so that:

$$1{\cdot}2 = (0{\cdot}1)\ 10 + a$$
$$\therefore \quad a = 0{\cdot}2$$

In full, the equation of the graph is, therefore:

$$y = (0{\cdot}1)\ x + 0{\cdot}2$$

This means that I can mark off scale divisions to make a weighing machine which weighs pretty accurately between 4 and 12 ounces with the same spring. Thus the mark corresponding with a weight of $4\frac{3}{4}$ ounces will be $(0{\cdot}1)\ (4{\cdot}75) + 0{\cdot}2 = 0{\cdot}675$ inch, or twenty-seven fortieths of an inch from the zero mark. The rule or "law" which connects the weight used with the amount which a spring stretches was discovered by Hooke, the inventor of the watch-spring. Hooke was a scientist who, like many of Newton's contemporaries, devoted much of his time to perfecting a clock which would be accurate enough to keep Greenwich time at sea and thus provide a simple means of finding longitude. That was one of the chief reasons why discovering correct laws of motion was important.

You will notice that if we made our x and y measurements start from zero marks corresponding with the length of the spring when a two-ounce weight was attached, as by using a scale pan 2 ounces heavier, the values of y corresponding with $x = 2, 4, 6$, etc., would be $0{\cdot}2$, $0{\cdot}4$, $0{\cdot}6$, etc., and the equation which would describe the stretching due to weights up to 10 ounces with good accuracy would be $y = (0{\cdot}1)x$ or $x = 10y$ (weight in ounces added = ten times stretch from zero mark in inches). The way in which Hooke's law is usually stated is

$$W = kl$$

This is equivalent to $x = 10y$ if $k = 10$. In any particular experiment the value which k has depends on the units of weight (e.g. if weight were measured in pounds it would be $\frac{10}{16}$ in this experiment), and also on the thickness and material of the spring. Hooke's rule is fairly accurate over a long range for metal springs. For india-rubber it works well within certain limits, and gives very bad results when large differences in weight are compared. This is true of all physical laws. A scientific law is an approximate truth, and can only be used with safety when we know the limits within which it works sufficiently well for our requirements.

Another important characteristic of a scientific law is worth noticing here. To make the fullest use of Hooke's rule we need to know how the value of *k* depends on the thickness of the spring and how it depends on the materials. Taking some standard material, we plot graphs for springs of different thickness, getting different values of *k*. So if we now plot different values of *k* for different thicknesses of springs of a particular material, we can get the connexion between the two in the form of a simple rule. By finding *k* for springs of the same thickness made of different materials we can make a table showing the ratios of the value of *k* for springs of different materials to the value of *k* for springs of some material used as a standard. With the equation connecting *k* with thickness for the standard material and such a table of relative values of *k* for springs of the same thickness we can calculate the stretching power of a weight, if we know the thickness of the spring and what it is made of. A typical physical law contains an abstract number or *constant* like *k*, which can be split up into a "dimensional" factor (thickness in this case) and a "specific factor" (depending on the quality of the material). So to say, as some people do, that physical laws are only about quantities is merely true of the way in which they are written down in a textbook. When we actually use them we have to replace the abstract numbers which occur in them by proper numbers appropriate to qualities of real objects.

Before the coming of the Reformation geometry, mathematics had been used to study the courses of the stars, the bending and reflection of light rays, and simple problems of mechanical poise like the principle of the lever. Being based on Euclid's geometry, it was mainly preoccupied with space. Science was still chiefly concerned with the shapes of things. It was anatomical rather than physiological. The map geometry of Descartes is not limited to shapes. It can be applied to connexions between all sorts of quantities. Just as we can make the longitude and latitude of a map correspond with time and space measurements in the graph of the projectile, or space and heaviness, as in the last example, there is no reason why either of the co-ordinates of a graph should stand for a measurement of distance. The next illustration of a simple quantitative law is Newton's Law of Cooling (Fig. 144). Along the *y* axis the graph records the temperature of a saucepan of boiling water allowed to cool at room temperature, and protected from draughts. The *x* co-ordinates of a point represent the number of minutes which have elapsed since the water was put to cool. All you require for the experiment is a thermometer, a saucepan, water, a stove, and a clock. The shape of the curve is not like any one which we have yet met. Later in the chapter (Fig. 154) we shall give

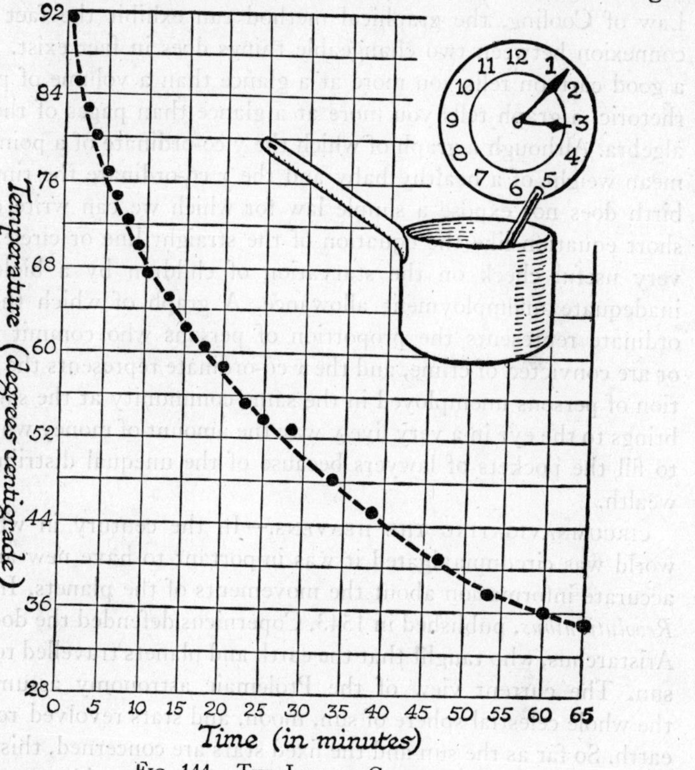

FIG. 144.—THE LAW OF COOLING

Graph of cooling of water in a 1-pint saucepan between 92° C. and 33° C. The room temperature was 17° C.

the equation which yields a curve like it. You may remember that 10^{-1} stands for $\frac{1}{10}$ and 10^{-2} stands for $\frac{1}{10^2}$ on the paper abacus which extends as far as you like both ways. If not, look up Chapter 7, p. 294. The curve in Fig. 154, representing $y = 2^x$, is the mirror image of the one shown in Fig. 144. The equation which describes the cooling of the water in the saucepan is

$$y = a^{-cx} + b$$

or

$$T = a^{-ct} + T_0$$

where T is temperature and t is time, and T_0 is the temperature of the surrounding air.

Even when the curve obtained by joining a set of points in a graph fails to suggest a simple numerical rule like Hooke's law or Newton's Law of Cooling, the graphical method can exhibit the fact that a connexion between two changeable things does in fact exist. Just as a good cartoon tells you more at a glance than a volume of political rhetoric, a graph tells you more at a glance than pages of rhetorical algebra. Although a graph of which the y co-ordinate of a point is the mean weight of a healthy baby and the x co-ordinate the time since birth does not expose a simple law for which we can write down a short equation like the equation of the straight line or circle, it is a very useful check on the starvation of children by a biologically inadequate unemployment allowance. A graph of which the y co-ordinate represents the proportion of persons who commit suicide, or are convicted of crime, and the x co-ordinate represents the proportion of persons unemployed in the same community at the same time brings to the eye in a very lively way the amount of money which goes to fill the pockets of lawyers because of the unequal distribution of wealth.

CIRCUMNAVIGATING THE HEAVENS.—In the century in which the world was circumnavigated it was important to have new and more accurate information about the movements of the planets. In the *De Revolutionibus*, published in 1543, Copernicus defended the doctrine of Aristarchus, who taught that the earth and planets travelled round the sun. The current view of the Ptolemaic astronomy assumed that the whole celestial sphere of sun, moon, and stars revolved round the earth. So far as the sun and the fixed stars are concerned, this alternative was equally plausible in the light of all the evidence available. Difficulty only arose in accounting for the position of the planets which were used in determining longitude before the chronometer was perfected. The observations of Tycho Brahe, a Danish astronomer, in the half-century which followed the death of Copernicus established a simple rule for finding the position of the planets. Their motion becomes easy to calculate if we assume that the earth and the other planets of the solar system follow an *elliptical* track round the sun.

An ellipse is a figure like the section of a football bladder. When the bladder is completely collapsed, the section is two lines pressed close together. When it is thoroughly blown up it becomes practically a circle. A mathematical definition of the ellipse can be got from the way in which it can be drawn. The method shown in Fig. 145 is very much like the sand-tracing of Fig. 18. Instead of one fixed peg, two are necessary, and a closed loop of cord instead of a single piece is used, as in the top of Fig. 145 (*a*) and (*b*), which shows how to draw the

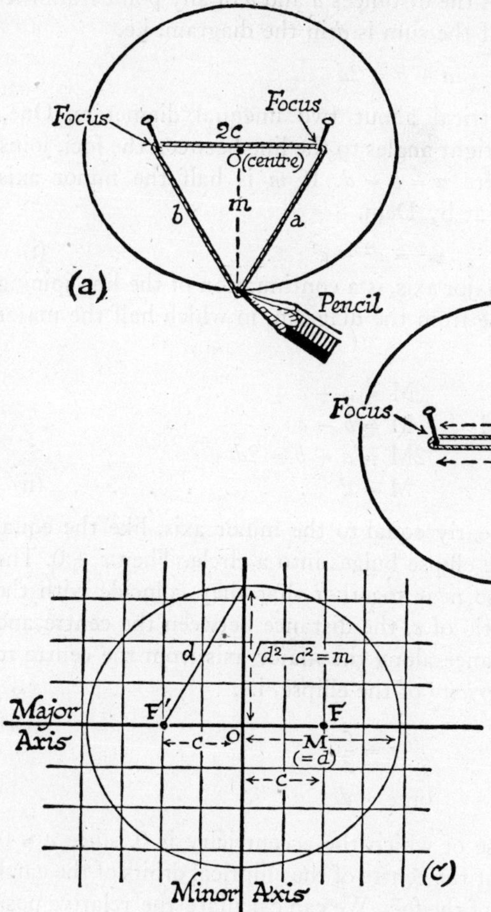

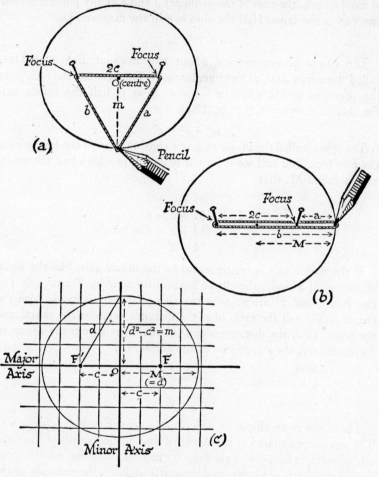

FIG. 145.—THE ELLIPSE

ellipse on paper with two pins and a loop of cotton, instead of cord and pegs. The two points where the pegs (or pins) are driven in are called the *foci* of the ellipse marked F and F′ in the lower figure. They are fixed 2*c* units of length apart. The mid-point *c* units from each focus, marked 0, is called the centre. If the two foci are so near that they cannot be distinguished, the curve is indistinguishable from a circle. If they are so far apart that the cord is stretched tight between them the ellipse is practically flattened into a line. Since the loop is of fixed length, the sum of the distances a and b of any point from the two foci is the same. Half the sum is d in the diagram, i.e.

$$a + b = 2d$$

The ellipse is symmetrical about two unequal diameters. One, called the minor *axis*, at right angles to the line between the foci, joins the opposite points where $a = b = d$. If m is half the minor axis Fig. 145(c) shows you that by Dem. 8

$$m^2 = d^2 - c^2 \quad . \quad . \quad . \quad . \quad . \quad . \quad (i)$$

The other, called the major axis, is a continuation of the line joining the two foci. You will see from the diagram, in which half the major axis is called M, that

$$\begin{aligned} M &= a + c \\ \text{and} \qquad M &= b - c \\ \therefore \qquad 2M &= a + b = 2d \\ M &= d \quad . \quad . \quad . \quad . \quad . \quad . \quad . \quad (ii) \end{aligned}$$

If the major axis is nearly equal to the minor axis, like the equal diameters of a circle, the ellipse bulges into a circle. Then $c = 0$. The two foci F and F′ are so near together that they coincide with the centre 0. We call the ratio of c, the distance between the centre and the focus, to d, the distance along the major axis from the centre to the boundary, the *eccentricity* of the ellipse, i.e.

$$e = \frac{c}{d}.$$

$$\text{or } c = de$$

The circle is an ellipse of which the eccentricity is 0, since $c = 0$. The sun is not situated at the centre of the elliptical orbits of the earth and planets. It is at one of the foci. We can calculate the relative position of the earth or planets and the sun if we know the equation of the ellipse. In Chapter 6 we spoke of the radius of the moon's orbit as if it were a circle. This is quite good enough for a first approximation, since, as you may now see, the eccentricity is small. Taking the greatest (b) and least (a) earth distances of the moon as 251,947 and 225,719 miles, half the major axis, i.e. $M = \frac{1}{2}(a + b)$, is 238,833 miles. Since $a + c = M = b - c$ and $c = de = Me$, it follows that

$$e = (b - a) \div 2M$$

So the eccentricity of the moon's orbit is

$$\tfrac{1}{2}(251{,}947 - 225{,}719) \div 238{,}833 = 0\cdot055.$$

In getting the equation of the ellipse we shall find it better to rewrite (i) as

$$m^2 = d^2 - (de)^2 = d^2(1 - e^2)$$
$$= M^2(1 - e^2) \quad . \quad . \quad . \quad . \quad . \quad . \quad . \quad \text{(iii)}$$

From which we get for m (half the minor axis of the moon's orbit)

$$238{,}833\sqrt{1 - (0\cdot055)^2} = 238{,}470 \text{ miles.}$$

If you find the way in which we get the equation is a little complicated, read first Appendix 2. From Fig. 146 you will see that if P is any

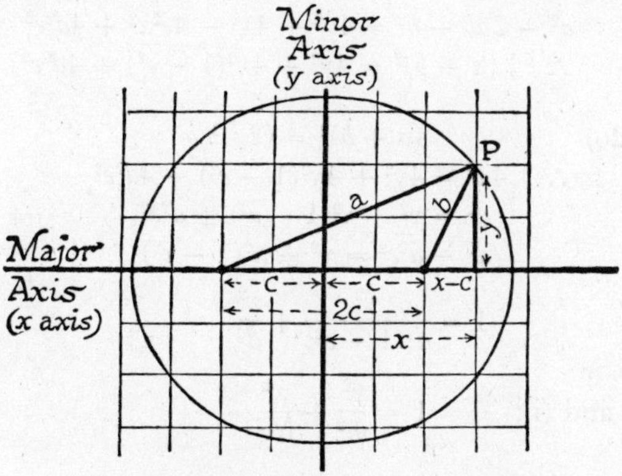

Fig. 146.—The Equation of the Ellipse

$$\frac{x^2}{M^2} + \frac{y^2}{m^2} = 1$$

point on the boundary, its vertical height y and its horizontal distance from the centre x, from the two right-angled triangles whose hypotenuses are the lines joining P to the two foci, by Dem. 8,

$$a^2 = y^2 + (x + c)^2 = y^2 + x^2 + 2cx + c^2 \quad . \quad . \quad \text{(iv)}$$
$$b^2 = y^2 + (x - c)^2 = y^2 + x^2 - 2cx + c^2 \quad . \quad . \quad \text{(v)}$$

Adding the left-hand side of (iv) to the left-hand side of (v) and the right-hand side of (iv) to the right-hand side of (v), we get

$$a^2 + b^2 = 2y^2 + 2x^2 + 2c^2$$
$$= 2y^2 + 2x^2 + 2d^2e^2 \quad . \quad . \quad . \quad . \quad \text{(vi)}$$

Subtract (v) from (iv):

$$a^2 - b^2 = 4cx = 4dex$$

By Dem. 4

$$a^2 - b^2 = (a + b)(a - b)$$
$$\therefore \quad (a + b)(a - b) = 4dex$$
$$2d(a - b) = 4dex$$
$$a - b = 2ex$$
$$\therefore \quad (a - b)^2 = 4e^2x^2$$

or
$$a^2 - 2ab + b^2 = 4e^2x^2 \quad . \quad . \quad . \quad . \quad \text{(vii)}$$

Take (vii) from (vi):

$$2ab = 2y^2 + 2x^2 - 4e^2x^2 + 2d^2e^2 \quad . \quad . \quad . \quad . \text{(viii)}$$

Add (viii) and (vi):

$$a^2 + 2ab + b^2 = 4y^2 + 4x^2 - 4e^2x^2 + 4d^2e^2$$
$$\therefore \quad (a + b)^2 = 4y^2 + 4x^2(1 - e^2) + 4d^2e^2$$

But (p. 426)
$$(a + b)^2 = (2d)^2$$
$$\therefore \quad 4d^2 = 4y^2 + 4x^2(1 - e^2) + 4d^2e^2$$
$$d^2 = y^2 + x^2(1 - e^2) + d^2e^2$$
$$d^2 - d^2e^2 = y^2 + x^2(1 - e^2)$$
$$1 = \frac{y^2}{d^2(1 - e^2)} + \frac{x^2}{d^2}$$

From (ii) and (iii)
$$1 = \frac{y^2}{m^2} + \frac{x^2}{\mathrm{M}^2}$$

This is the Cartesian Equation of the Ellipse. It tells you how to find the distance y parallel to the minor axis ($2m$) of a point whose horizontal distance along the major axis (2M) is x. To use it you need to know the values of m and M for the particular ellipse. In the case of the moon's orbit

$$m = 238{,}470 \text{ miles}$$
$$\mathrm{M} = 238{,}833 \text{ miles}$$

From a centre situated a distance $c = \mathrm{M}e$ ($= 238{,}833 \times 0{\cdot}055$ miles) from the earth as focus the equation of the moon's orbit is therefore:

$$1 = \frac{y^2}{(238{,}470)^2} + \frac{x^2}{(238{,}833)^2}$$

or
$$y = \frac{238{,}470}{238{,}833} \sqrt{(238{,}833)^2 - x^2}$$

By a method which is too long to explain here it is comparatively easy to plot a graph showing the relative distances of the earth and any planet from the sun (making the distance of the earth from the sun the unit of measurement) from continuous observations of its right ascension and declination over a long period. When you have done this you can test whether the figure of a planet's track is an ellipse with the sun as its focus by first measuring its greatest width. This will be the major axis, if it is an ellipse. The width of the figure in the line at right angles to its greatest width drawn through the mid-point will be its minor axis. Since you know the equation connecting y with x for an ellipse, of which the major and minor axes are known, you can now calculate successive values of y for different values of x, dotting in the points corresponding with each pair. If the path is actually an ellipse, these points will lie very close to the graph based on direct observations. Kepler had to try a very large number of figures before he found that the ellipse fitted best, and gave the quietus to Plato's doctrine that the heavenly bodies move in circles because the circle is the most perfect figure.

THE ENFRANCHISEMENT OF THE OPERATIVE CLASS.—In the static figures of Euclid's geometry we only meet with angles not greater than four right angles (360°). It may have occurred to you that when we introduced the *radian* or wheelwright's measure of the angle we made room for angles as big as we like to make them. When the Reformation geometry came into use people were becoming familiar with two instruments which impress this possibility on the imagination vividly. One was the mariner's compass. The other was the clock.

Fig. 147 will help you to see how these two inventions liberated the angle from the strait-jacket in which the timeless static figures of Greek geometry had imprisoned it. First look at the clock. The time is ten o'clock, or, in modern language, 22.00. What is the angle A degrees or a radians between the hands? Your first impulse is to say 60°, or $\frac{1}{3}\pi$. Now suppose we prevent the hour hand from moving. In an hour's time the hands will be in exactly the same position, but the long hand will have revolved through 360°. So the angle is now $360° + A$, or, in radians, $2\pi + a$. If we wait another hour, the gap between the two hands is again 60° in the geometry of timeless figures. But when we have put time into geometry it is $2(360°) + A$, or $4\pi + a$ radians. An hour later the hands will be in the same position, but the big hand will have revolved through another 2π radians, or 360°. The angle is now $3(360°) + A$, or $6\pi + a$. So you see the static angle of $\frac{2}{3}$ of a right angle (60° or $\pi/3$ radians) in the geometry of antiquity is equivalent to $\pm 60°$ or $n(360°) \pm 60°$, $\{n(2\pi) \pm \pi/3 \text{ rad}\}$, n being 0, 1, 2, 3, etc. That is not all the story. If we turn back the minute hand an hour, still keeping the hour hand fixed, we have taken away 360°, four right angles, or 2π radians, and so far as Euclid is concerned we are back to the same angle. So $A - 360°$ or $a - 2\pi$ is the same thing as A or a in Euclid's geometry. Similarly

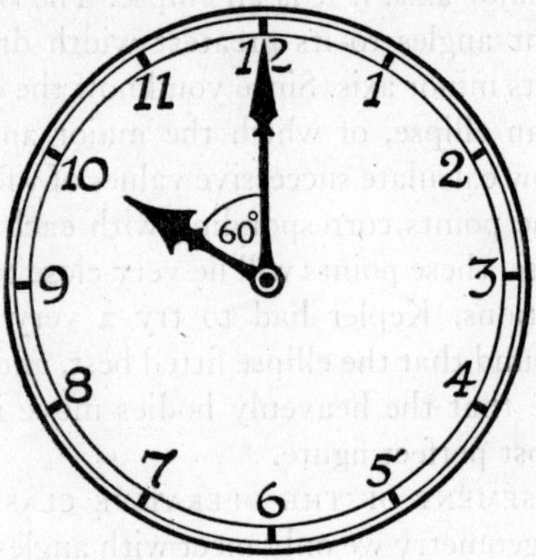

FIG. 147

$A - n(360°)$ and $a - 2n\pi$, where n is any whole number, look just the same so far as Euclid's geometry is concerned. So

$$\begin{aligned} &\text{A (in Euclid's geometry)} = A - n(360°) \\ \text{or} \quad &n(360°) - A = -A \\ \text{and} \quad &2n\pi - a = -a \end{aligned}$$

Of course, we do not need to stop the hour hand to show that the angle has many alibis when we use it to describe the motion of the spoke of a wheel which is turning round, instead of using it to describe the gape of a pillar which we are putting (or failing to put) in an upright position. Even if we do not stop the hour hand, the same Euclidean angle is seen on the face of the clock in the same position every twelve hours or twice a day. Once we put time into geometry, we have to ask how many times one edge has turned round an axis before it got into the position in which it happens to be when we are looking at it. If you are locating a point due N.E., i.e. 45° or $\pi/4$ radians from the northerly direction, and have set the compass, you can turn the compass round through 360° or 2π radians as often as you like, clockwise or anti-clockwise, and you always find the same Euclidean angle between the pointer and the N.E. mark on the scale.

So far the issue is straightforward. Now comes a novel result, if you are going to face all that is involved in the fact that a Euclidean angle has many alibis. We have said

$$\text{Greek A} = \text{Modern } \{n(360°) + \text{A}\}$$
$$\text{and} \quad -\text{A} = n(360°) - \text{A}$$
$$\text{or} \quad a = 2n\pi + a$$
$$\text{and} \quad -a = 2n\pi - a$$

Why should we not go a step further and say

$$\tan \text{A} = \tan (360° + \text{A})$$
$$\text{or} \quad \tan \alpha = \tan (2n\pi + a)?$$

In Euclid's geometry we define the sine, cosine, or tangent of an angle as the ratio of two sides of a right-angled triangle, and since no angle of a right-angled triangle drawn on a flat surface can be greater than 90°, Euclid's geometry can only show us how to use the sine, cosine, or tangent as a way of measuring angles which do not exceed 90°. However, we have also seen in Chapter 8, p. 388, that sin (180° – A) and cos (180° – A) can be treated for purposes of calculation as if they were respectively sin A and – cos A. Thus, if sin 30° = $\frac{1}{2}$, sin 150° = $\frac{1}{2}$; and if cos 60° = $\frac{1}{2}$, cos 120° = – $\frac{1}{2}$. The failure of Euclid's geometry to give us a picture of what we do when we carry out calculations according to these rules is due to a limitation which we have already recognized. In Euclid's timeless geometry an angle is a fixed and ready-made quantity. In Reformation geometry it has a history. It is generated by the movement of a line about the x axis, having a direction of movement represented by the negative sign if clockwise, and the positive sign if anti-clockwise. We saw on page 388 that there is nothing absurd about sin 150°, if we define a sine as the relation between a chord and an arc. Likewise there is nothing absurd in saying that the angle 210° (180° + 30°), or the angle 150° (180° – 30°), can be measured by the tangent method, if we go back to our original definition of the tangent (p. 126) as *gradient.*

In Fig. 148 a track drawn for clearness with a gradient of 1 in 2 passes under a tunnel. The x axis along which the horizontal distance of any point on it is measured crosses the y axis along which the vertical height of any point on the track is measured under the tunnel. So the position of the tunnel corresponds with the origin of reference in

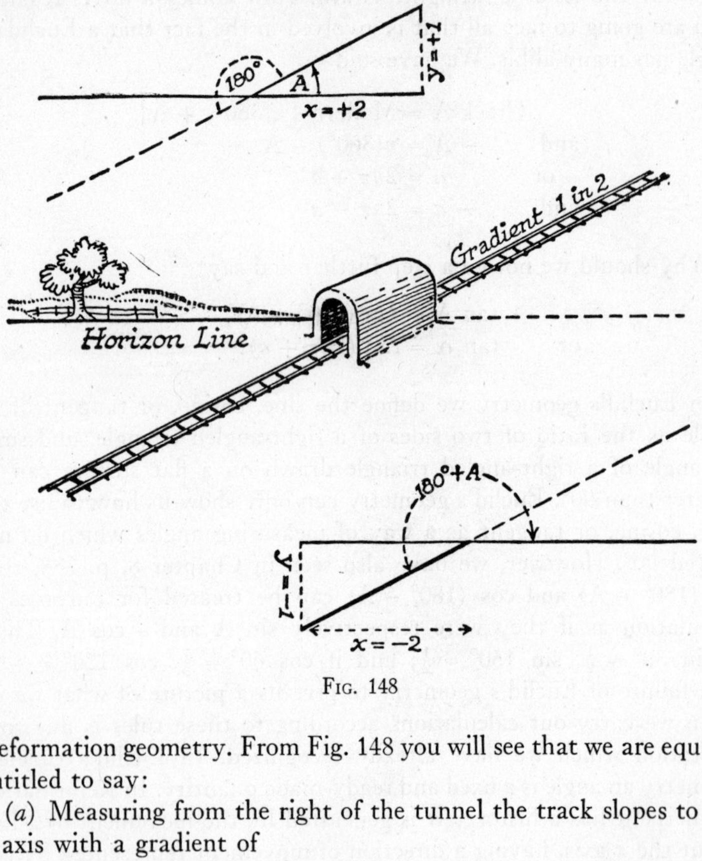

FIG. 148

Reformation geometry. From Fig. 148 you will see that we are equally entitled to say:

(*a*) Measuring from the right of the tunnel the track slopes to the x axis with a gradient of

$$\frac{+y}{+x}$$

(*b*) Measuring to the left of the tunnel the track slopes at 180° + A to the x axis with a gradient of

$$\frac{-y}{-x}$$

But the ratio $$\frac{-y}{-x} = \frac{+y}{+x}$$

So if we use the tangent of A to mean the slope of the track, Cartesian geometry can define it by the ratio of the x and y co-ordinates of any point to the right or left of the origin. Thus

$$\tan A = \tan (180° + A)$$

There is a simple advantage in extending our definition of the

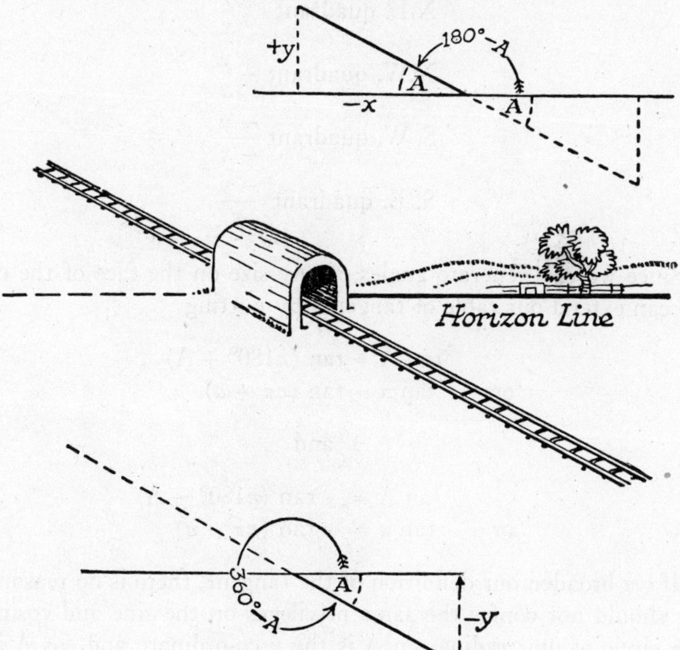

FIG. 149

tangent in this way. The tangent of the Euclidean triangle does not distinguish between the gradient of a line sloping backwards at an angle A to the axis like the track in Fig. 149, and a line which slopes at an angle A forwards like the single track in Fig. 148. In Cartesian geometry the track in Fig. 149 slopes at an angle (180° – A) to the x axis above the tunnel and (360° – A) below the tunnel. Its gradient is not $\frac{y}{x}$, but $+y \div -x$, or, what is the same thing, $-y \div +x$.

So in the Reformation geometry

$$\tan (180° - A) \text{ or } \tan (360° - A) = -\tan A$$

So if tan 45° = 1, tan 135° = tan (180° − 45°) = − 1, and tan 225° = tan (180° + 45°) = + 1. Thus the numerical values of the tangents of the angles repeat themselves in each quadrant (N.E., N.W., S.W., S.E.) if the compass and the signs change from

$$\text{N.E. quadrant } \frac{y}{x}$$

$$\text{N.W. quadrant } -\frac{y}{x}$$

$$\text{S.W. quadrant } \frac{-y}{-x}$$

$$\text{S.E. quadrant } \frac{-y}{x}$$

Since we can generate angles of any size on the face of the clock, we can extend our table of tangents by putting

$$\tan A = \tan (n180° + A)$$

or

$$\tan a = \tan (n\pi + a)$$

and

$$\tan A = -\tan (n180° - A)$$

or

$$\tan a = -\tan (n\pi - a)$$

If we broaden our definition of the tangent, there is no reason why we should not confer the same privileges on the sine and cosine. In the circle of unit radius, sin A is the y co-ordinate and cos A is the x co-ordinate (see Fig. 129, Chapter 8) of the point where the radius cuts the circle (Fig. 150). So the numerical values of sines and cosines repeat themselves and the signs change according to the rule—

Quadrant	sine	cosine	tangent
N.E.	+	+	+
N.W.	+	−	−
S.W.	−	−	+
S.E.	−	+	−

We can also extend our tables of sines and cosines further by using the equations

$$\sin A = \sin(180° - A) = -\sin (180° + A)$$
$$\cos A = -\cos (180° \pm A)$$

From Fig. 151 we can also see that the tables could be extended by using the formulae:

$$\sin(90° + A) = +\cos A$$
$$\tan(90° + A) = \frac{-1}{\tan A}$$
$$\cos(90° + A) = -\sin A$$

There is now no objection to taking the further step of recognizing

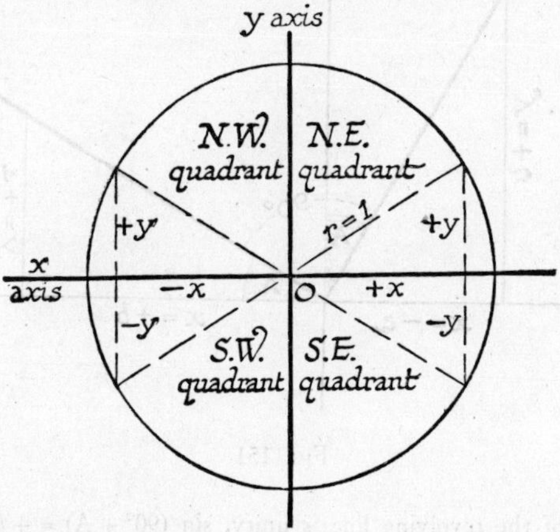

FIG. 150.—EXTENDING THE TABLES OF ANGLE RATIOS

ANGLES 180° − A, 540° − A, etc. sine y cosine $-x$	ANGLES A, A + 360°, etc. sine y cosine x
ANGLES 180° + A, 540° + A, etc. sine $-y$ cosine $-x$	ANGLES − A, 360° − A, etc. sine $-y$ cosine x

that 360° − A is A measured below the x axis, and has the same position as −A. So

$$\sin(360° - A) = -\sin A$$
$$\cos(360° - A) = \cos A$$
$$\tan(360° - A) = -\tan A$$

You will now rightly ask what is the point of extending our tables of sines, cosines, and tangents beyond 90°. The answer is seen at a glance in Fig. 152. As they stand, the figures of timeless geometry are only suitable as models of the way in which the size of something increases or diminishes to a certain limit. It required great ingenuity to make them stand for the very large class of quantities which continually revert to the same value. This class of quantities is very great and very significant. The displacement of the vibrating string of a violin and the ups and downs of unemployment figures in successive trade cycles under capitalism are two familiar illustrations of y quan-

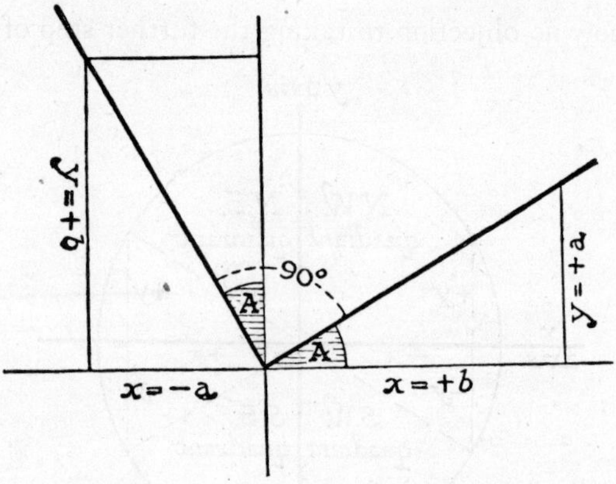

FIG. 151

If the length of the revolving line is unity, $\sin(90° + A) = +b = +\cos A$, and $\cos(90° + A) = -a = -\sin A$.

$$\tan A = +a \div +b = \frac{a}{b}$$

$$\tan(90° + A) = +b \div -a = -\frac{1}{\tan A}$$

tities which vary *periodically* with time measurements represented along the x axis.

The curve in Fig. 152 represents the equation

$$y = \cos x$$

The curve of the equation $y = \sin x$ is exactly like it, except that we should begin at the origin ($x = 0°$) half-way up the crest of a wave instead of at the top of it. You can plot for yourself

$$y = \sin x$$

By plotting $y = 2 \cos \frac{1}{2}x$ or $y = \frac{1}{2} \cos 2x$, you can discover for yourself that a more general type of equation gives a curve just like the foregoing, except in so far as interchanging 2 and $\frac{1}{2}$ make it flatter or steeper. The more general form is

$$y = a \cos bx$$
$$y = a \sin bx$$

These equations are the parent of the mathematics of wave motion, now one of the most important applications of mathematics to the

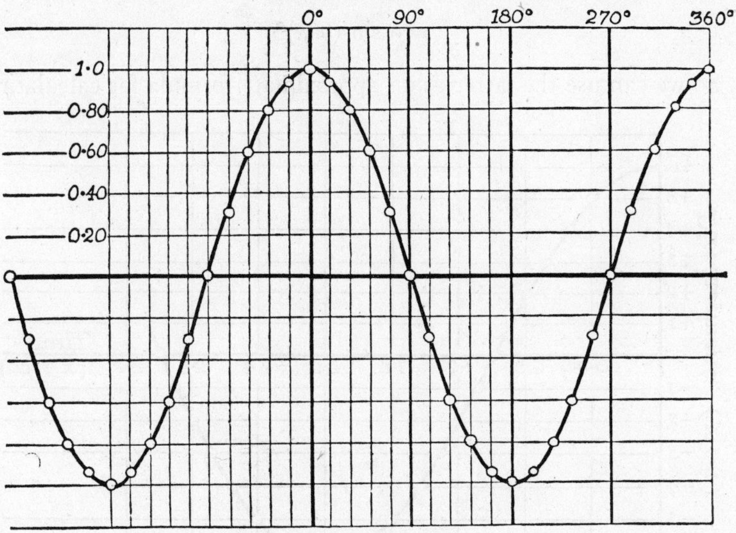

FIG. 152.—GRAPH OF
$y = \cos x$

real world. The discovery of a simple way of representing wave-like or periodic movement has made it possible to interpret measurements of the spectrum and the discharge of electricity in gases. Without it we should not be able to make calculations about alternating currents.

We shall come back to the discussion of "wave motion" later. Here you must be content with a glimpse of something which may often have puzzled you. You have heard or read in books on popular science that light travels in waves, and "wave-lengths" in the age of radio are familiar realities of everyday life. So you have probably wondered what physicists mean when they talk about waves. The next figure (Fig. 153) shows you the answer to your question. It is a graph of the table given at the beginning of the chapter to illustrate the use of "+" and "−" for describing the position of the pendulum at different instants of time. Along the y axis we have put the displacements, along the x axis we have recorded the time which has elapsed since the observations in the table on p. 401 started. The curve of the pendulum is very much like the curve whose general equation is

$$y = a \cos bx$$

If you make a table and dot in the points you will find that the curve in Fig. 153 runs very close to

$$y = 6 \sin (90x)^\circ$$

So we can use the latter as an approximate formula for calculating

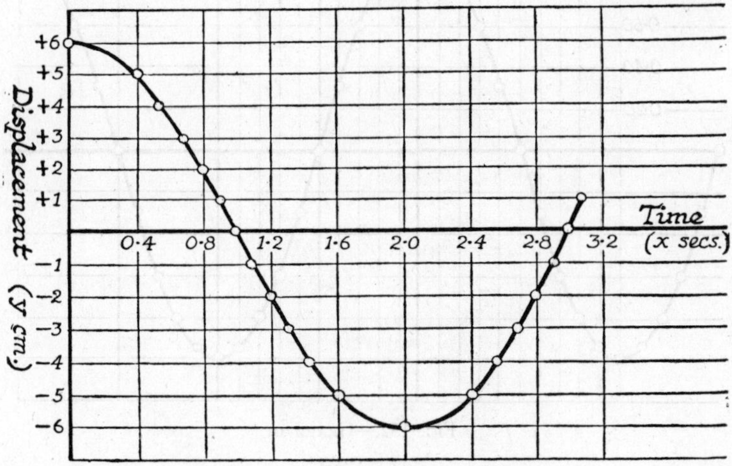

FIG. 153

where the pendulum is at any particular time. All the physicist means when he talks about waves of light or sound or electricity is that he calculates with the aid of equations which can be represented by wave-like curves such as the one in Fig. 152. You have dispersed one of the mystifying things in modern language by liberating the operators "sin" and "cos" from the Euclidean figures in which they could only work with angles between 0° and 90°, or 0^r and $(\frac{1}{2}\pi)^r$.

There is another class of operators which gained new opportunities for usefulness in the Reformation geometry. The abacus stands for a White Settler policy. It allows the operator n in the phrase a^n to work with whole numbers, but sets up a colour bar which prevents n from doing skilled work with fractions. Fig. 154 shows you that

x may do good work as a fractional number in the curve whose equation is:

$$y = 2^x$$

You already know what 2^x means when x is a whole number,

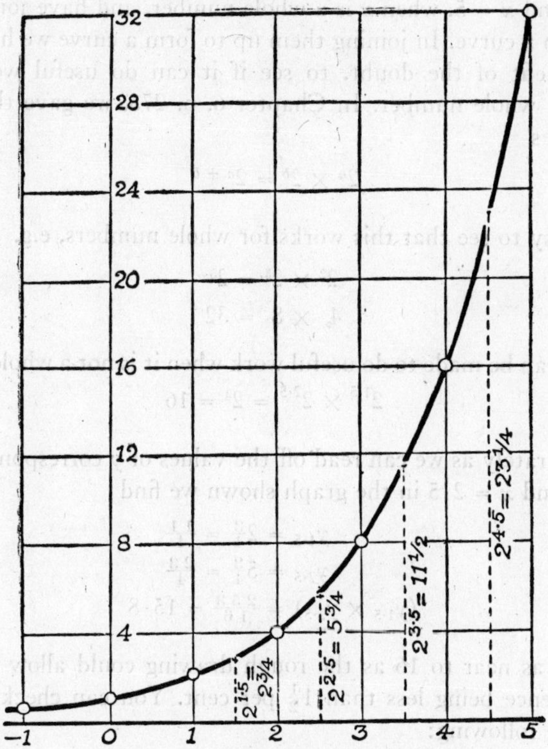

FIG. 154.—THE CURVE WHOSE EQUATION IS
$y = 2^x$

negative or positive (see pages 208 and 294). Neither the figures of Euclid nor the counting-frame can give you a model in which x can stand for a fraction. Indeed, when you are first taught that it can do so you may feel uneasy, like South Africans who say that natives cannot be taught to read and write, in spite of the fact that they could see Xosa and Zulu students working at sums in the integral calculus if they took the precaution of visiting Fort Hare College in the Ciskei. The way to see whether a native can learn what we can learn is to teach him, as the South African Labour Movement would do if it were a really progressive party. Reformation geometry does for the operator x in 2^x what a really progressive party would do for the Bantu. It gives it the opportunity of doing skilled work.

In Fig. 154 we have plotted all the values of $y = 2^x$ between $x = -1$ and $x = 5$, when x is a whole number, and have joined them up to form a curve. In joining them up to form a curve we have given x the benefit of the doubt, to see if it can do useful work when it is not a whole number. In Chapter 6, p. 273, we gave the rule of Archimedes

$$2^a \times 2^b = 2^{a+b}$$

It is easy to see that this works for whole numbers, e.g.

$$2^2 \times 2^3 = 2^5$$
$$4 \times 8 = 32$$

So if x can be made to do useful work when it is not a whole number,

$$2^{1\cdot5} \times 2^{2\cdot5} = 2^4 = 16$$

As accurately as we can read off the values of y corresponding with $x = 1\cdot5$ and $x = 2\cdot5$ in the graph shown we find

$$y_{1\cdot5} = 2\tfrac{3}{4} = \tfrac{11}{4}$$
$$y_{2\cdot5} = 5\tfrac{3}{4} = \tfrac{23}{4}$$

So $$(y_{1\cdot5} \times y_{2\cdot5}) = \tfrac{253}{16} = 15\cdot8$$

This is as near to 16 as the rough drawing could allow us to get, the difference being less than $1\tfrac{1}{2}$ per cent. You can check from the graph the following:

	Measured (approximate) Value		Theoretical Value
$2^{1\cdot5} \times 2^{3\cdot5}$	$\tfrac{11}{4} \times \tfrac{23}{2}$	31·6	32
$2^{1\cdot5} \times 2^{4\cdot5}$	$\tfrac{11}{4} \times \tfrac{93}{4}$	63·9	64
$2^{2\cdot5} \times 2^{3\cdot5}$	$\tfrac{23}{4} \times \tfrac{23}{2}$	66·1	64
$2^{2\cdot5} \times 2^{4\cdot5}$	$\tfrac{23}{4} \times \tfrac{93}{4}$	134	128
$2^{3\cdot5} \times 2^{4\cdot5}$	$\tfrac{23}{2} \times \tfrac{93}{4}$	267	256

The graph of Fig. 154 was drawn on very cheap (penny exercise book) squared paper, and so the measurements cannot be correct within much less than 5 per cent. When multiplied they might well be out by as much as 10 per cent. You can probably get much better results yourself. What we have given here is sufficient to show you that x can do just as good work as we can reasonably expect when it is allowed to do skilled work with fractions in the industry represented by 2^x. In the next chapter we shall see that liberating the operator x from the restriction of working only with whole numbers leads to the greatest time-saving device which has been invented in the history of calculation. The operation a^x, like $\sin x$ or $\cos x$, plays a most important part in the measurement of alternating currents, when we have put it to work on jobs which the fetters of Euclid and the colour-bar laws of the counting-frame prevented it from doing.

THE MEANING OF THE VERB $f(\ \ )$.—It will help you later if we break off the narrative at this point to introduce a small point in the grammar of size. You are well aware that the verb *to do* in English can stand for almost any other verb, as when the Victorian parent tells the old-fashioned child, "Do as you are bid." The corresponding universal verb which stands for any operator in mathematics is written $f(\ \ )$ or $\phi(\ \ )$. It means, "Look up the corresponding value of . . . in a table." Thus the sentence

$$y = f(x)$$

means, "Look up the corresponding value of y in a table which gives the values of x," i.e. x is the departure column which corresponds with y the arrival column in the time-table we make when we plot a graph.

In the grammar of everyday speech we learn some rules which are true of all or nearly all verbs. For instance, the gerundial form of English verbs end in *ing*. Thus *socializing* agriculture under a socialist Government and *nationalizing* the mines under a capitalist Government illustrate the same grammatical rule, though they are very different things. In the same way there are certain rules which apply to all operators or large families of operators in mathematics. One rule which applies to all curves which are smooth and do not have any sharp angles is very important in connexion with the discovery of series which choke off for $\sin x$, $\cos x$, 2^x, etc.

The rule is not difficult to grasp, if you first familiarize yourself, by drawing them, with the shape of curves whose equations are:

$$(a)\ y = x,\ y = x^3,\ y = x^5, \text{ etc.}$$
$$(b)\ y = x^2,\ y = x^4,\ y = x^6, \text{ etc.}$$

We have already studied the graph of

$$y = ax^2$$

The shape of graphs corresponding with $y = x^4$, $y = x^6$, etc., is similar, except in so far as they become steeper. By the sign rule

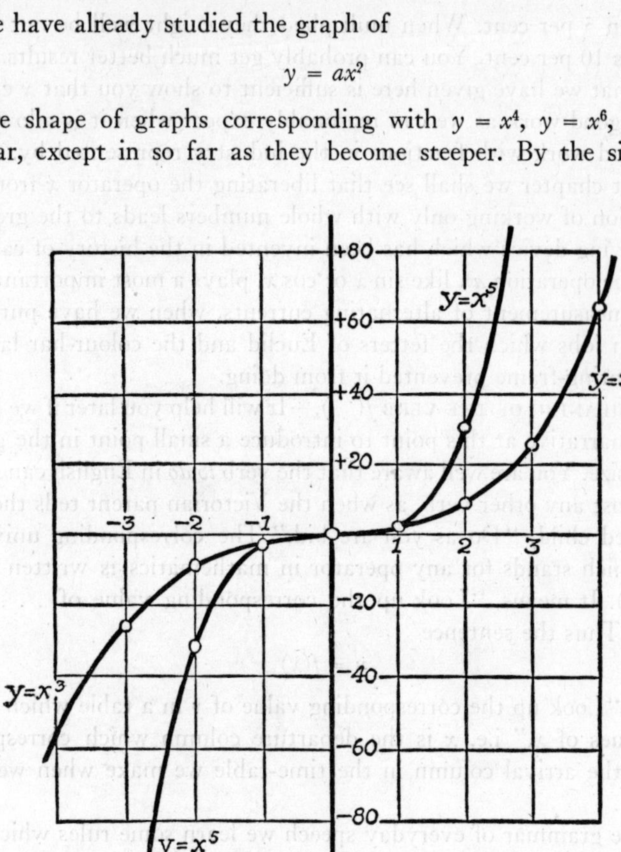

FIG. 155.—GRAPHS OF
$y = x^3$ and $y = x^5$

$(-x)(-x)(-x)\ldots(-x)$ to m terms is x^m, when m is even. So the graph of $y = x^m$, when m is even, is always U-shaped, y being positive whether x is positive or negative. The graphs of $y = x^m$, when m is an odd number, are illustrated in Fig. 155. They all cross the origin downwards to the left and upwards to the right, because $(-x)(-x)\ldots(-x)$ to m factors, if m is odd, is $-x^m$. So y is negative when x is negative. The graphs of $y = -x^3$, $y = -x^5$, etc., are of the same shape, crossing the origin downwards to the right and upwards to the left. To distinguish curves representing even and odd powers we may write their equations respectively as $y = x^{2n}$ and $y = x^{2n+1}$. Thus if $n = 1$, $x^{2n} = x^2$, and $x^{2n+1} = x^3$. If $n = 2$, $x^{2n} = x^4$, and $x^{2n+1} = x^5$.

The next two figures show curves whose equations belong to the family:

$$y = ax^{2n} + bx^{2n+1}$$

You will notice that for large values of x in Fig. 156 (compare

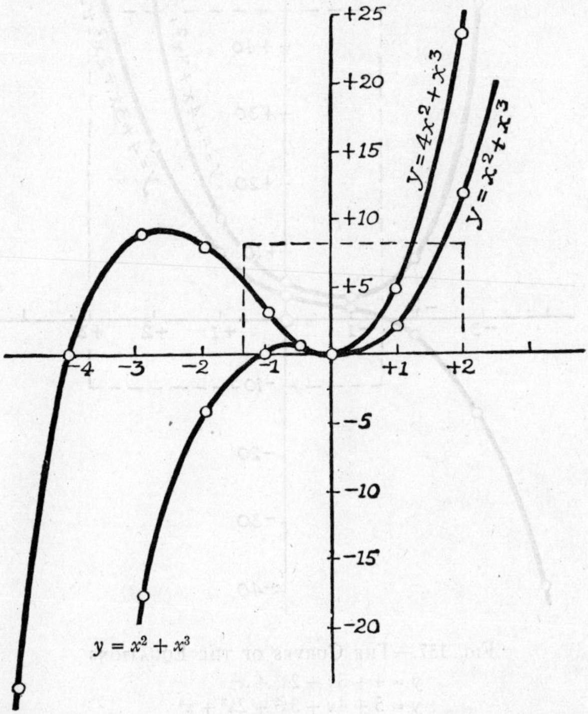

FIG. 156

with Fig. 155) the curve becomes like that of $y = bx^m$, when m is odd, i.e.

$$y = bx^{2n+1}$$

This is as we should expect. Thus when $x = 2$, x^3 is only twice x^2. But, when $x = 8$, x^3 is eight times x^2. For small values of x the shape of the curve is more like that of

$$y = ax^{2n}$$

This again is common sense. When $x = 1$, $x^2 = 1 = x^3$. When $x = \frac{1}{4}$, $x^2 = \frac{1}{16}$, and x^3 is $\frac{1}{64}$, i.e. x^2 is four times as large as x^3. So we see that in the neighbourhood of the origin ($x = 0 = y$) the lower power (x^{2n}) is the chief thing which affects the shape of the

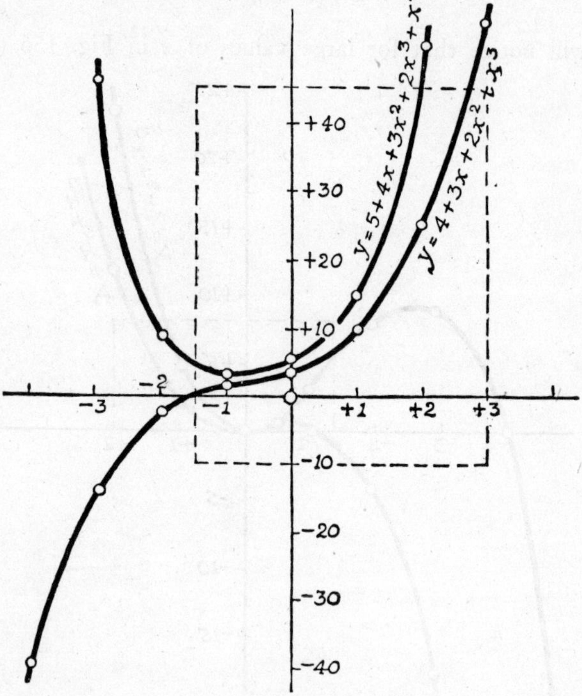

FIG. 157.—THE CURVES OF THE EQUATIONS
$y = 4 + 3x + 2x^2 + x^3$
$y = 5 + 4x + 3x^2 + 2x^3 + x^4$

curve, and when x is large the higher power (x^{2n+1}) is the chief thing which affects the shape of the curve.

Fig. 156 shows you another thing. You can make the region of the curve in which the lower power predominates larger if you make a large compared with b in the graph of

$$y = ax^{2n} \pm bx^{2n+1}$$

In both graphs n is 1. In one (the lower curve) $a = 1 = b$, and the U-shaped part of the curve is barely recognizable. In the other a is four times b, and there is quite a large region in which the curve has the U-shape of $y = x^2$, the lower power. In the next figure (157) we have made y a little more complicated. There are two graphs:

$$y = 4 + 3x + 2x^2 + x^3$$
$$y = 5 + 4x + 3x^2 + 2x^3 + x^4$$

When you have plotted these curves for yourself, compare them with Fig. 154, which shows the graph of

$$y = a^x$$

You will then see that within the rectangular area marked off by straight lines parallel to the x and y axes the curve of Fig. 154 is very much like the shape of the curves in Fig. 157. In fact, by giving a suitable values different from its value ($a = 2$) in Fig. 154, you could use either of these curves as an approximate way of reading off values of a^x within certain limits.

If you now turn to Figs. 158 and 159 you will see the graphs of

$$y = 6x - x^3$$
$$y = 4 - 5x^2 + x^4$$

These equations have been built up by using only odd or only even powers. In the neighbourhood of the origin, they are *periodic* or wave-like. They approximate to the curves whose equations are

$$y = a \sin bx$$
$$y = a \cos bx$$

The important point to notice about the second curve is that by putting in a higher power of x we have added another half-period to the curve. All the smooth curves which we have drawn can be represented as members of a single family,

$$y = a + bx + cx^2 + dx^3 + ex^4 + fx^5 \quad \text{and so on}$$

or to use the general verb

$$f(x) = a + bx + cx^2 + dx^3 + ex^4 + fx^5 \quad \text{and so on}$$

They differ in the numerical values and signs of the numbers a, b, c, etc., which are called the *constants* of the equation. Thus the values

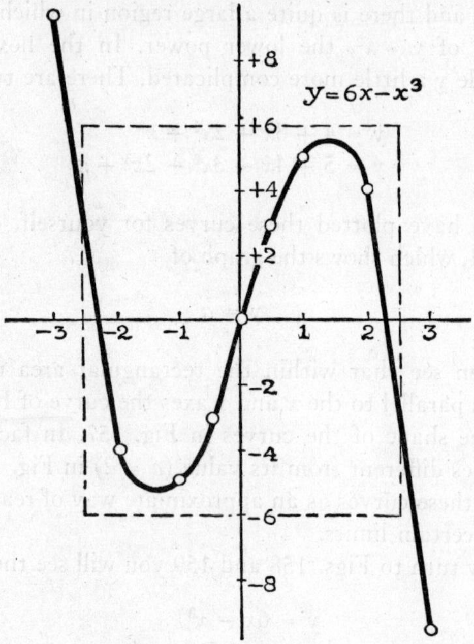

FIG. 158.—THE CURVE WHOSE EQUATION IS

$$y = 6x - x^3$$

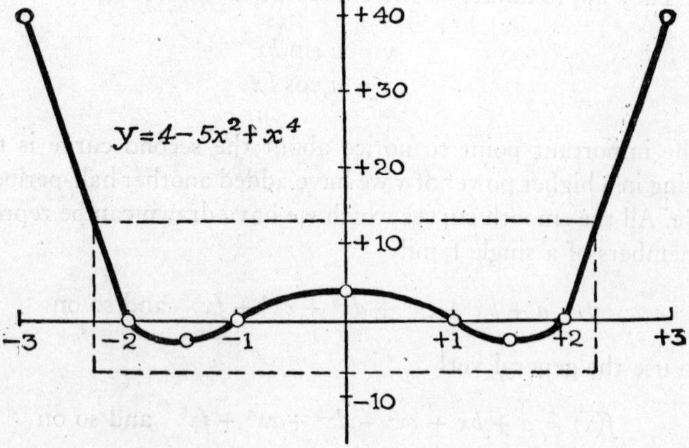

FIG. 159.—THE CURVE WHOSE EQUATION IS

$$y = 4 - 5x^2 + x^4$$

of the constants are $b = 6$, $d = -1$, and $a = 0 = c = e$, etc., in the graph of

$$y = 6x - x^3$$

What we have seen justifies the suspicion that by using enough powers of x ($x, x^2 \ldots x^5, x^6 \ldots x^{16} \ldots$) we can build up a curve as near as we like to curves such as

$$y = a^x$$
$$\text{or} \quad y = \sin x$$

This is the principle we shall use later to get for $\sin x$ and a^x series which choke off like a recurring decimal.

MAP GEOMETRY FOR AEROPLANE AND SUBMARINE.—Euclid devoted some space to the geometry of solid figures. Apollonius adapted Euclid's geometry of solid figures to the study of curves. You may recall the fact that we gave a reason for omitting any account of Euclid's "solid geometry" from Chapter 4. The reason was that solid figures are much more easy to visualize and measure by later methods. In describing the Reformation geometry so far we have seen how the flat projection maps of the Great Navigations paved the way for a new method of studying flat figures. Flat projection maps are good enough for ships which move on the sea. Nowadays we have submarines that move at different *depths* and aeroplanes that move at different heights above the surface of the sea. So a longitude (E.–W.) and latitude (N.–S.) method of describing the movement of modern means of communication does not meet all the requirements of transport. The Reformation geometry can be adapted to the needs of submarine and aeroplane without much difficulty, so that the Cartesian method can describe solid space as well as figures drawn on a flat surface.

All that is needed is to go back to the world centre in the Gulf of Guinea, anchor the ship, drop a plumb-line vertically downwards, and hoist a mast vertically upwards with the flag of the Parliament of Man to remind us that civilized people regard modern warfare as a degenerate branch of piracy. Mast and plumb-line stand for the z axis of the aeroplane's height and the submarine's depth. Every point in solid space is now represented by a z parallel of height and depth, as well as an x parallel of longitude and a y parallel of latitude. A flat figure is represented by an equation in which the value of y is found by tabulating all the values x can have. A solid figure is represented by an equation in which the value of z is found by tabulating all the different values both x and y can have. In other words, it is an equation which gives the z co-ordinate of height and depth corresponding to

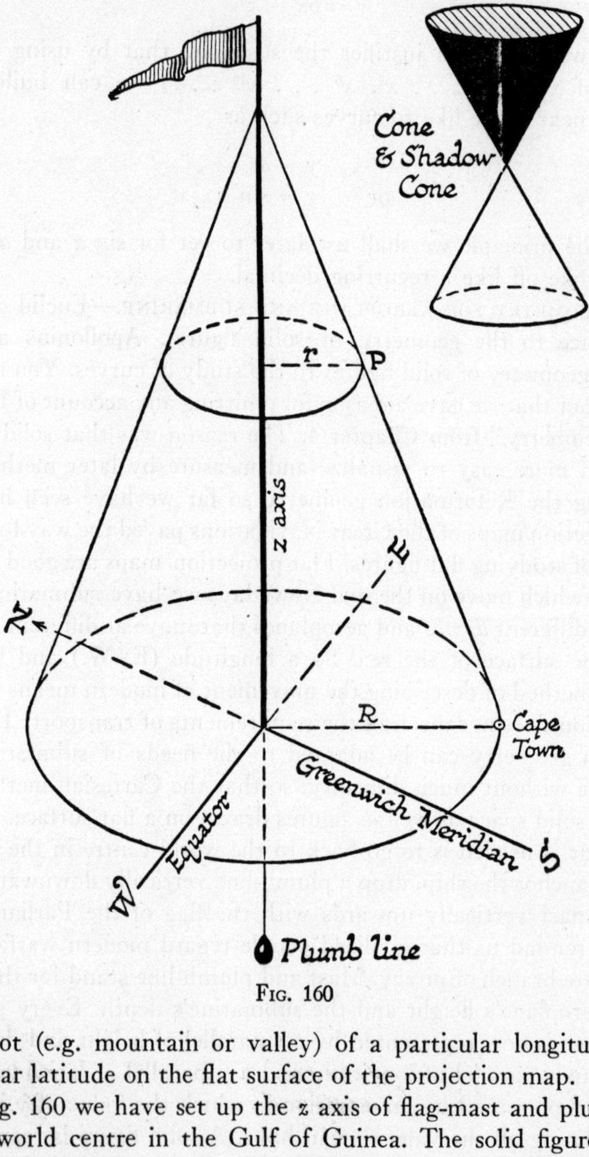

Fig. 160

each spot (e.g. mountain or valley) of a particular longitude or a particular latitude on the flat surface of the projection map.

In Fig. 160 we have set up the z axis of flag-mast and plumb-line at the world centre in the Gulf of Guinea. The solid figure whose equation we shall give to illustrate the Cartesian method is the cone.

If the centre of its circular base (radius R) lies on the surface of the Gulf of Guinea at Lat. 0°, Long. 0°, any slice parallel to the surface of the sea is also bounded by a circle. Every vertical half-slice through the axis of the cone is a right-angled triangle. At P, drawn about half-way on the upward ascent from the circular base to the apex of the cone, the horizontal displacement is r and the vertical displacement is z. We already know the connexion between the vertical and horizontal co-ordinates of a point on a straight line when x is the horizontal and y the vertical displacement. It is the equation

$$y = ax + b$$

If we call the vertical displacement z instead of y and the horizontal displacement r instead of x, we can write this

$$z = ar + b$$

$$\text{or} \quad z - b = ar$$

We also know that if R is the distance of the boundary of a circle from the world centre, the connexion between R, x (longitude), and y (latitude) on a flat map (footnote, p. 406) is the equation

$$R^2 = x^2 + y^2$$

A similar connexion will apply to any circle lying parallel to the sea-surface with its centre directly above the world centre in the Gulf of Guinea. We can therefore write

$$r^2 = x^2 + y^2$$

$$\text{or} \quad a^2r^2 = a^2(x^2 + y^2)$$

But we have seen that $a^2r^2 = (z - b)^2$

$$\therefore \quad a^2(x^2 + y^2) = (z - b)^2$$

To use this equation for calculation we need to know what a and b are. When $z = h$, the height of the cone, $r = 0$; so if

$$z = ar + b$$

$$b = h$$

When $z = 0$, $r = R$, the radius of the base; so

$$0 = aR + b$$

$$\therefore \quad a = -\frac{b}{R}$$

$$= -\frac{h}{R}$$

Thus we can rewrite

$$a^2(x^2 + y^2) = (z - b)^2$$

in the form

$$\frac{h^2}{R^2}(x^2 + y^2) = (z - h)^2$$

or

$$h^2x^2 + h^2y^2 = R^2(z - h)^2$$

To see how this equation can be used, suppose a wasp is crawling up outside the canvas of a conical tent 40 feet high, with a base 40 feet in diameter (i.e. R = 20 feet). How high from the ground will the wasp be when it crawls through a hole 6 feet east of the tent pole ($x = 6$) and 8 feet south of it ($y = -8$)? The equation tells us:

$$40^2(36 + 64) = 20^2(z - 40)^2$$
$$40^2 \times 10^2 = 20^2(z - 40)^2$$

Taking the square root of both sides, we get

$$400 = \pm 20(z - 40)$$
$$20 = \pm (z - 40)$$
$$\therefore \quad 20 = z - 40$$
$$\text{or} \quad 20 = -z + 40$$
$$z = 60 \text{ or } 20$$

The reason why we get two answers is that, properly speaking, the equation of the cone is the equation of the cone and its shadow cone or mirror image (Fig. 160). The answer 60 feet upwards from the base of the cone means 60 – 40, or 20 feet upwards from the apex of the shadow cone. We shall return again to the simplicity of the Cartesian method as compared with Euclid's treatment of solid figures in Chapter 10.

DIFFERENT KINDS OF MAPS.—Once the fruitfulness of representing the position of a point in a framework of co-ordinates was recognized, the possibility of devising different kinds of map geometry suggested itself. One kind, which is especially useful for solid figures, called spherical co-ordinates, is essentially the method of the globe as opposed to the flat map. One method sometimes suitable for flat curves is based on the mariner's compass, and is called the method of polar co-ordinates. Instead of describing position by vertical and horizontal displacements like the parallels of longitude and latitude on a projection map (Mercator projection), we can say where something is by giving the length of the line (r) joining it to the world centre and the angle (a) which this line makes with the equator.

This leads to very simple equations of closed curves like the circle and the ellipse. The circle is a figure in which r, the distance from the centre to any point on the boundary, is always the same whatever the

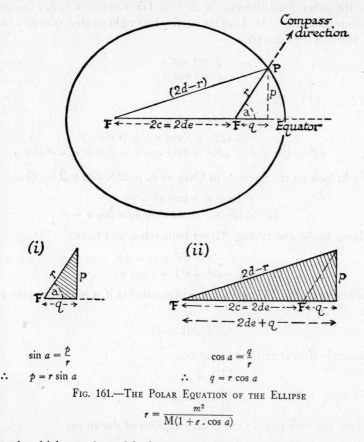

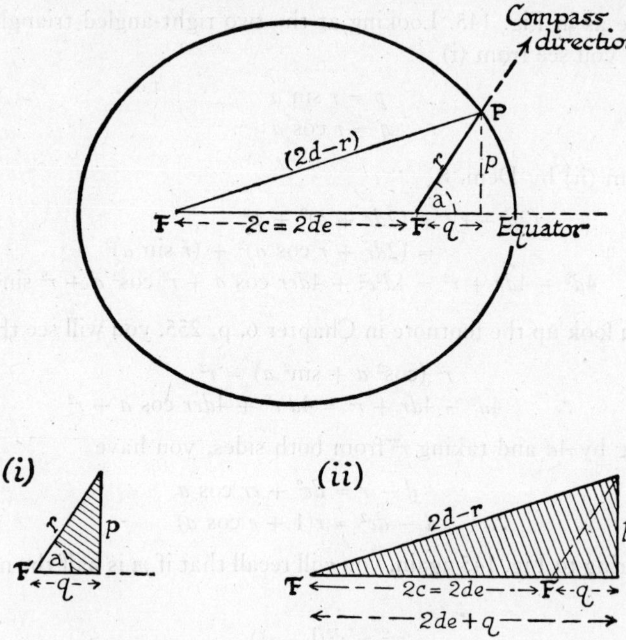

$\sin a = \frac{p}{r}$ $\qquad\qquad$ $\cos a = \frac{q}{r}$

$\therefore \quad p = r \sin a$ $\qquad\qquad$ $\therefore \quad q = r \cos a$

FIG. 161.—THE POLAR EQUATION OF THE ELLIPSE

$$r = \frac{m^2}{M(1 + e \,.\, \cos a)}$$

angle which r makes with the equator. So if c is a constant quantity, the *polar* equation of the circle is simply

$$r = c$$

A straight line makes the same angle with the equator or parallels of latitude everywhere, so, if it goes through the origin, its polar equation is simply

$$a = c$$

In Fig. 161 the distance (r) from one focus is one of the polar co-ordinates, and the equatorial angle (a) of the line joining the same focus to a point P on the boundary is the other polar co-ordinate. Since the sum of the focal distances of a point on the boundary is constant ($2d$), the other focal distance is $2d - r$. The constants c, d, e mean the same as in Fig. 145. Looking at the two right-angled triangles in Fig. 161 you see from (i)

$$p = r \sin a$$
$$q = r \cos a$$

Also from (ii) by Dem. 8

$$(2d - r)^2 = (2de + q)^2 + p^2$$
$$= (2de + r \cos a)^2 + (r \sin a)^2$$
$$\therefore \quad 4d^2 - 4dr + r^2 = 4d^2e^2 + 4der \cos a + r^2 \cos^2 a + r^2 \sin^2 a$$

If you look up the footnote in Chapter 6, p. 255, you will see that

$$r^2 (\cos^2 a + \sin^2 a) = r^2$$
$$\therefore \quad 4d^2 - 4dr + r^2 = 4d^2e^2 + 4der \cos a + r^2$$

Dividing by $4d$ and taking r^2 from both sides, you have

$$d - r = de^2 + er \cos a$$
$$\therefore \quad d - de^2 = r(1 + e \cos a)$$

Referring to Fig. 145 again, you will recall that if m is half the minor axis

$$m^2 = d^2(1 - e^2)$$

Similarly if M is half the major axis

$$M = d$$
$$\frac{m^2}{M} = d - de^2$$

So we can now put for the polar equation of the ellipse

$$\frac{m^2}{M} = r(1 + e \cos a)$$

$$\text{or} \quad r = \frac{m^2}{M(1 + e \cos a)}$$

Another way of representing the position of a point is by means of the kind of maps which geographers call Flamsteed or Mollweide projection maps, and mathematicians call curvilinear co-ordinates. The meridians of longitude on the curved surface of the globe are not parallel like the circles of latitude. They converge at the poles. The

Mercator projection map in which the meridians of longitude are represented by parallel straight lines distorts the relative sizes of the continents and oceans, making countries like Greenland which lie far north of the equator appear to be much larger than they actually

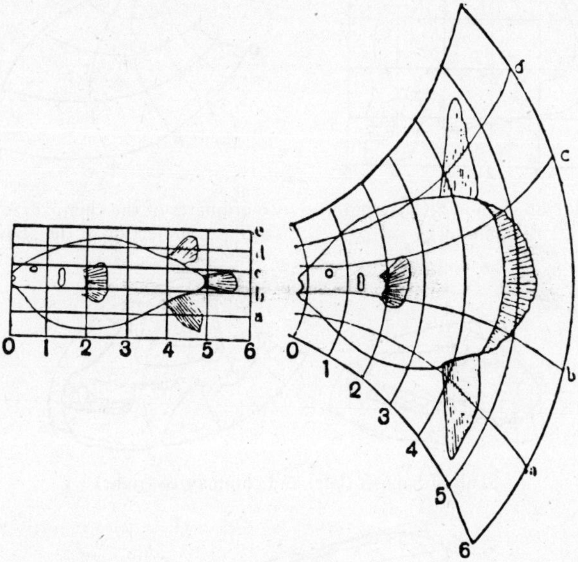

Fig. 162

On the left is a typical species of the genus Diodon. On the right, says Professor D'Arcy Thompson, "I have deformed its vertical co-ordinates into a system of concentric circles and its horizontal co-ordinates into a system of curves which approximately and provisionally are made to resemble a system of hyperbolas. The old outline transformed in its integrity to the new network appears as a manifest representation of the closely allied but very different-looking sunfish Orthagoriscus."

are. Maps like the Flamsteed projection map, in which the meridians are represented by curved lines converging towards the poles, correct this distortion. A very suggestive application of curvilinear co-ordinates in Fig. 162 is taken from a book *Growth and Form* by Professor D'Arcy Thompson, who is one of the most learned men in the English-speaking world. A skull or body of one species drawn in a framework of curvilinear co-ordinates looks exactly like the skull or body of another species drawn in a Cartesian framework. The use of this method may provide a clue to the laws of growth in the evolution of species.

LIMITATIONS OF THE REFORMATION GEOMETRY.—Throughout our studics wc have kept before us the fact that the application of mathematics to the real world only gives us an approximate description of

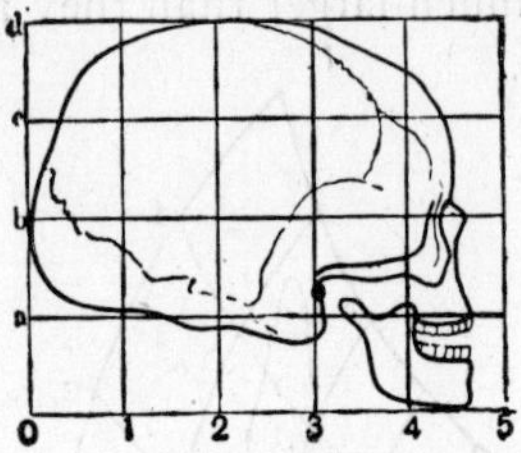

Human skull in a Cartesian framework

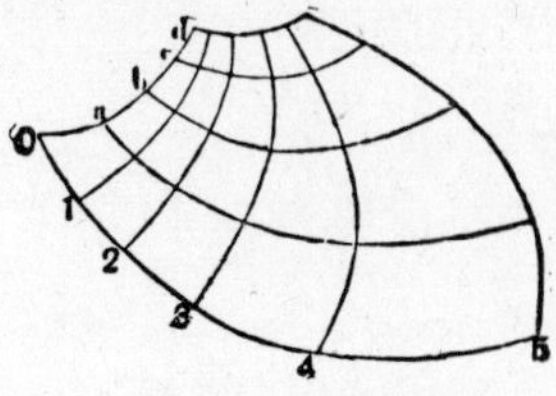

Co-ordinates of the chimpanzee's skull as a projection of the above

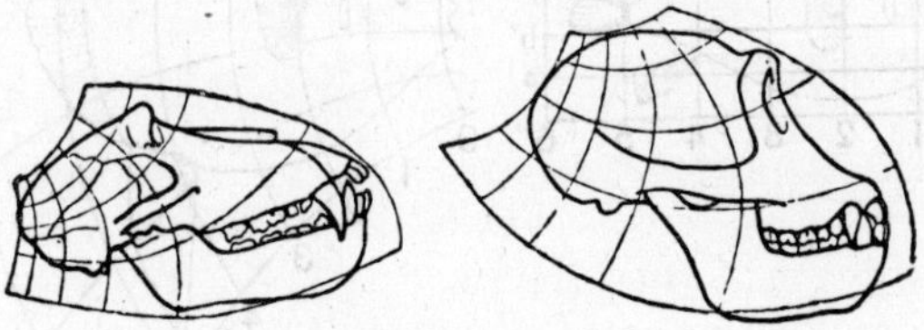

Skull of baboon (left) and chimpanzee (right)

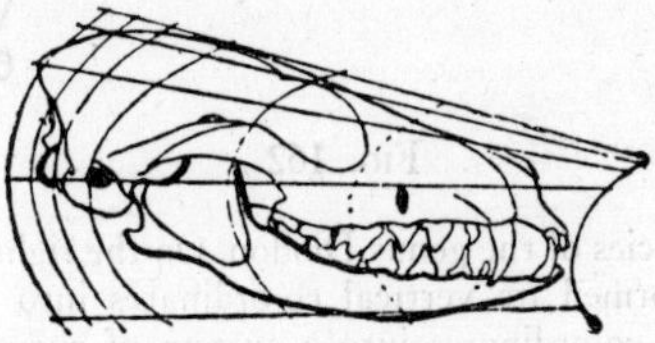

Skull of dog

FIG. 162A

the things we see, hear, and handle. We saw that Euclid left time out of geometry, and we have seen how Descartes put time into geometry. Does this mean that the Reformation geometry has at last given us a perfect description of the world? The answer is No. Reformation geometry has left out something just as Greek geometry left out something. To see what that something is, go back to the pendulum. It is only a half-truth to say that the swing of the pendulum can be correctly described by an equation like

$$y = a \cos bx$$

The reason why it is a half-truth is that the curve which represents this equation extends as far as we like to the left and to the right. That is to say, if x stands for time, the equation tells us that the pendulum has been swinging from all eternity before our observations began. When we draw the curve starting at some particular time, we bring in something which is not in the mathematical form of the curve, just as we reject one answer in the equation of the cone because we are only using one of two cones which the equation of the cone describes.

In contrast with the mathematics of the Greeks, the mathematics of the Reformation was dynamic. It took time into account. In contrast with the requirements of a mathematics which would be necessary to deal with the whole range of modern knowledge Reformation mathematics is *non-historical.* It does not take fully into account the historic past. It arose in the age of merchant enterprise, when ships were using astronomy to steer on the high seas. For astronomical purposes the historic past is unimportant because the characteristics of the universe of stars change so little during a period which affects man's social needs. So we can use the same principles for calculating when an eclipse *did* and when an eclipse *will* occur. Modern physics, modern chemistry, and modern biology are immensely preoccupied with problems of growth and decay. The historic past is becoming the all-important issue in natural science. In the twilight of mercantile culture, the future of the human reason depends more and more on understanding human relationships in the light of historic experience. We are beginning to see that a mathematics which allows us to move is not enough. We need a mathematics which can concern itself with whence we came and whither we are going.

Exercises on Chapter 9

In all these exercises on graphs, in case you have not already realized it in reading the text, the following point is very important to remember. If we are using a graph to represent the *shape* of a geometrical figure correctly, we must always use the same unit of measurement for x and y. Thus $r^2 = x^2 + y^2$ is only the equation of a circle if x and y are both measured in the same units, e.g. centimetres or inches. If we are merely using a graph to solve an equation, our units need not be the same length. Thus if y is very large compared with x, it may be convenient to make one unit of x 1 centimetre, and one unit of y 0·01 centimetre, and all that matters is that we remember that a given distance measured along one axis has a different value from a given distance measured along the other axis. Of course, in graphs which represent physical laws the same applies, since we please ourselves what units we use.

Before you attempt any of the succeeding examples, show that the circle is the figure which corresponds with the equation

$$y = \sqrt{25 - x^2}$$

To do this make a table of all values of y corresponding with values of x between -5 and $+5$ in steps of $\frac{1}{2}$, using a table of square roots. Thus when $x = -4\frac{1}{2}$

$$\begin{aligned} y &= \sqrt{25 - (\tfrac{9}{2})^2} \\ &= \tfrac{1}{2}\sqrt{19} = \pm\tfrac{1}{2}(4\cdot36) \\ &= \pm 2\cdot18 \end{aligned}$$

Mark on your graph the two points which are $\pm 2\cdot18$ units measured along the y axis and $-4\frac{1}{2}$ along the x axis. If you use 1 centimetre as the unit and graph paper divided by lines 0·1 centimetre apart, y will be two large and practically two small divisions. Do the same for all the other values tabulated, and draw a line running smoothly between the points.

1. An elevator in a sixty-storey building makes the following journeys, starting at the lowest floor: up twenty storeys, down four, up eight, down three, down seventeen, up ten, down one, up five, up eleven, down twenty-four. Where is it at the end of this period?

2. Draw a graph of a circle with radius 4 centimetres, (*a*) with its centre at the origin, (*b*) with its centre at the point $x = 2$, $y = 3$. What is the Cartesian equation in each case?

3. Show that the angle which the tangent to a circle at any point makes with the x axis is $-\frac{x_r}{y_r}$, when x_r and y_r are the co-ordinates of the point.

From the figure you have just drawn see whether you can show that when a positive angle a is measured in radians $\sin a$ is less than a and $\tan a$ is greater than a.

4. If x is any length measured in inches and y is the same length measured in feet, then

$$12y = x$$

Plot a 5-point graph connecting inches and feet. Read off from the graph how many inches there are in $1\frac{3}{4}$ feet, 3·6 feet, and 4·1 feet.

5. Make similar graphs for converting centimetres into inches, pounds into dollars, and pints into pounds of water.

6. Draw the graph $y = 3x + 4$, then draw at sight (i.e. without making a table)

$$3y = 5x + 6 \left(\text{i.e. } y = \frac{5x}{3} + 2\right)$$

$$y = 32x + 40$$

7. On the Fahrenheit scale water freezes at 32° and boils at 212°. On the Centigrade scale it boils at 100° and freezes at 0°. Show that the formula for converting degrees Centigrade into degrees Fahrenheit is

$$F = \frac{9C}{5} + 32$$

Draw the graph of this equation, and from the graph read off the Centigrade equivalent of normal blood temperature (98·4° F.).

8. If two straight lines are described by the equations

$$(a)\ y = x + 3$$
$$(b)\ y = \sqrt{3}x + 2$$

at what angles are they inclined to the x axis?

9. If a set of straight lines are described by the equations

$$y = mx + 1$$
$$y = mx + 2$$
$$y = mx + 3 \quad \text{etc.}$$

what do you know about these straight lines?

10. What does the quantity C represent graphically in the equation $y = mx + C$?

11. What would be the equation of a straight line drawn parallel to the x axis?

12. Mr. Evans sets out for a walk. He walks 3 miles in the first hour, $2\frac{1}{2}$ miles in the next, 2 miles in the next hour. He rests for three-quarters of an hour and then goes on at a uniform rate of $2\frac{1}{2}$ miles an hour for 3 hours. Find from a graph the distance walked by Mr. Evans in $1\frac{1}{2}$ hours, $3\frac{1}{2}$ hours, and $5\frac{1}{2}$ hours.

Mr. Davies starts from the same point 2 hours later than Mr. Evans, and cycles at a uniform rate of 6 miles per hour. Show Mr. Davies's journey on the graph you have just drawn and read off the distance from the start when Mr. Davies overtakes Mr. Evans.

13. Plot the straight lines

$$2y + 3x = 31$$
$$3y + 2x = 39$$

on the same graph. Read off from your graph what must be the values of x and y so that both equations shall be true at the same time. Turn back to Chapter 7, p. 316 *et seq.*, and you will see that you have found a graphical method for solving problems involving two simultaneous equations.

14. Solve the problems in Example 14, Chapter 7, graphically, and compare your solutions with those you have obtained previously.

15. Draw a careful graph of $y = x^2$, taking values of x between -10 and 10 and making the y unit equal to the x unit. Use your graph:

(*a*) to make a table of the square roots of all the numbers from 1 to 100;

(*b*) to make a table of the squares of all the numbers from 1 to 100.

16. Make graphs connecting

(*a*) the area of an equilateral triangle with its base;

(*b*) the area of an isosceles triangle with base angles of 45° with its base;

(*c*) the area of a right-angled triangle with one angle of 30° with its base.

17. For the length of a pendulum in centimetres and the number of seconds per complete swing, the following values were found:

seconds	0·7	0·8	0·9	0·5	0·6	0·4
length	49	64	81	25	36	16

Check this with a button, a piece of cotton, and a watch, taking the average of ten complete swings in each case. Draw the graph. What is its equation?

18. Find the formula connecting area (y) and radius (x) of a circle by drawing a graph based on the area obtained by counting squares (Japanese method on p. 259). Having satisfied yourself that the correct formula is

$$y = cx^2$$

read off from the graph what c is.

19. Solve the following simultaneous equations graphically:

(*a*) $xy = 0$, $3x + 4y = 12$ (*b*) $x^2 + y^2 = 25$, $x + y = 7$ (*c*) $(x - y)^2 = 1$, $(3x - 5y)^2 = 1$

20. Find the curves of which the equations are:

$$y = \pm \tfrac{5}{4}\sqrt{16 - x^2}$$
$$y = \pm \tfrac{4}{7}\sqrt{49 - x^2}$$

To what measurement in the figure do the numbers refer?

21. Graph the Cartesian and polar equations of the ellipse whose major axis is 3 and minor axis 2 units of length.

22. Using the formulae for sin (A + B), cos (A + B) given on p. 254, put sin 180° = sin (90° + 90°), cos 180° = cos (90° + 90°), sin 270° = sin (180° + 90°), etc. Hence show

(*a*) sin 180° = 0, sin 270° = – 1, sin 360° = 0
(*b*) cos 180° = – 1, cos 270° = 0, cos 360° = + 1

Substituting these values show that

sin (90°+A) = +cos A, cos (90°+A) = –sin A, tan (90°+A) = –cot A
sin(180°+A) = –sin A, cos(180°+A) = –cos A, tan(180°+A) = +tan A
sin(270°+A) = –cos A, cos(270°+A) = +sin A, tan(270°+A) = –cot A
sin(360°+A) = +sin A, cos(360°+A) = +cos A, tan(360°+A) = +tan A

23. Using the formulae for sin (A – B), cos (A – B) in Chapter 10, p. 464 and 466, show that

sin (90°–A) = +cos A, cos (90°–A) = +sin A, tan (90°–A) = +cot A
sin(180°–A) = +sin A, cos(180°–A) = –cos A, tan(180°–A) = –tan A
sin(270°–A) = –cos A, cos(270°–A) = –sin A, tan(270°–A) = +cot A
sin(360°–A) = –sin A, cos(360°–A) = +cos A, tan(360°–A) = –tan A

24. Using a diagram interpret the meaning of the following and check your results by putting sin $(-A) = \sin(0 - A)$, etc.:

$\sin(-A) = -\sin A \qquad \cos(-A) = \cos A \qquad \tan(-A) = -\tan A$

25. $\sin 130° = \sin(2n \times 90° - 50°)$ [where $n = 1$]
$= \sin(180° - 50°)$
$= \sin 50°$

Alternatively

$$\sin 130° = \sin(\overline{2n+1} \times 90° + 40°) \text{ [where } n = 0\text{]}$$
$$= \cos 40°$$
$$= \sin 50°$$

In the same way find by two alternative methods the values of:

$\tan 210° \qquad \sin 230° \qquad \cos 300°$
$\tan 120° \qquad \sin 150° \qquad \cos 100°$

26. Solve the following quadratic equations by the method on p. 418 and check by p. 325

(i) $5x^2 + 2x = 7$
(ii) $8x^2 - 2x - 3 = 0$
(iii) $5x^2 - x - 6 = 0$

27. Graph sin x and tan x for $x = 0°, 30°, 45°, 60°, 90°$. From your graph read off the approximate values of:

$\sin 15° \qquad \sin 35° \qquad \sin 75°$
$\tan 15° \qquad \tan 35° \qquad \tan 75°$

and compare with the tables.

28. Draw a graph of $y = x^3$ and from your graph construct a table of the cubes and cube roots of the numbers 1 to 20.

29. Draw graphs of

$2^x \qquad 1{\cdot}5^x \qquad 3^x \qquad 1{\cdot}1^x$

From your graphs read off the values of

$2^{3\cdot5} \qquad (1{\cdot}5)^{1\cdot5} \qquad 3^{2\cdot5} \qquad (1{\cdot}1)^{0\cdot5}$

30. Draw the graphs of

$y = x^4 \qquad y = x^5 \qquad y = x^6 \qquad y = x^7$

31. Draw the graphs of

$$xy = 4 \qquad \text{and} \qquad x^2 - y^2 = 8$$

This curve is called an hyperbola.

32. Make a figure to show that the equation of the sphere, when the centre is at the origin, is

$$x^2 + y^2 + z^2 = r^2$$

33. Find, using the tables, the sin, cosine, and tangent of the following angles: – 20°, – 108°, 400°, – 500°.

34. Make a graph to connect the amount (y) to which £100 or \$100 grows in x years at 2, $2\frac{1}{2}$, 3, $3\frac{1}{2}$, 4, 5 per cent (a) at simple interest, (b) at compound interest.

THINGS TO MEMORIZE

1. The Equation of the Circle

$$r^2 = (x - a)^2 + (y - b)^2$$

2. The Equation of the Straight Line

$$y = (\tan A)\, x + b$$

3. The Equation of the Parabola

$$y = ax^2$$

4. The Equation of the Ellipse

$$\frac{x^2}{M^2} + \frac{y^2}{m^2} = 1$$

5. $\sin(-\theta) = -\sin\theta$ $\qquad$ $\cos(-\theta) = \cos\theta$
$\sin(90° - \theta) = \cos\theta$ $\qquad$ $\cos(90° - \theta) = \sin\theta$
$\sin(90° + \theta) = \cos\theta$ $\qquad$ $\cos(90° + \theta) = -\sin\theta$
$\sin(180° - \theta) = \sin\theta$ $\qquad$ $\cos(180° - \theta) = -\cos\theta$
$\sin(180° + \theta) = -\sin\theta$ $\qquad$ $\cos(180° + \theta) = -\cos\theta$

6. $\sin(n\pi + (-1)^n\alpha) = \sin\alpha$

$$\cos(2n\pi \perp \alpha) = \cos\alpha$$

$$\tan(n\pi + \alpha) = \tan\alpha$$

$$\sin\left[\frac{2n+1}{2}\pi \pm \alpha\right] = (-1)^n\cos\alpha \quad \text{etc.}$$

It is very important to be familiar with the values of general angles, but they are most easily recalled, not by memorizing the formulae, but by visualizing a diagram.

Note that in the last two sections, 5 and 6, the Greek letters α and θ have been used to represent angles. This is a common mathematical practice, like using x for an unknown quantity in an equation, or a, b, c for known quantities.

CHAPTER X

The Collectivization of Arithmetic

OR

HOW LOGARITHMS WERE DISCOVERED

FIFTEEN hundred years earlier the Alexandrian culture had foreshadowed the three great developments in the mathematical awakening which accompanied the rise of the Protestant democracies. The cartography of Ptolemy and the curves of Apollonius embodied the essential features of Cartesian geometry dealt with in the preceding chapter. The mensuration of the circle by Archimedes and Theon's device for taking square roots anticipated two fundamental operations which will be used in a later chapter on the infinitesimal calculus. Archimedes also stumbled on the principle which underlies logarithms. We shall now turn our attention to the invention of logarithms and the new impetus which it gave to the study of series. By comparison with such calculations as had been undertaken by the Alexandrian mathematicians the tasks which arose from the expansion of trade and improved technique in navigation during the fifteenth century made exorbitant demands upon the *Rechenmeister*, and compelled the search for more compact and less laborious algorithms than those which we learn in our childhood from the Arab schoolmasters of Western civilization. The outcome was an immense step forward towards the socialization of arithmetic.

If you compare the algorithms for multiplying two numbers (e.g. 324 × 245) and adding the same two numbers, you will see that the number of operations involved in multiplication is always greater than the number of operations involved in adding them (unless, of course, one of the numbers lies between 1 and 10, or is a simple multiple of 10), e.g.

324	324
245	245
569 (one operation)	648
	1296
	1620
	79,380 (four operations)

With very big numbers the discrepancy between the amount of labour involved in multiplication (or division) as compared with addition (or subtraction) becomes greater and greater. So it is a very big economy of effort if we can reduce all multiplication to the addition of two numbers. This is what the invention of logarithms achieved for us. To quote the 1631 edition of *Logarithmall Arithmetike* by Briggs, who first compiled the tables which are now used: "Logarithmes are numbers invented for the more easie working of questions in arithmetike and geometrie . . . by them all troublesome multiplications and divisions are avoided and performed only by addition instead of multiplication and by subtraction instead of division. The curious and laborious extraction of roots are also performed with great ease. . . . In a word, all questions not only in Arithmetike and Geometrie but in Astronomie also are thereby most plainely and easily answered. . . ."

The possibility of adding numbers which can be looked up in tables compiled "for ever," as Napier remarks, instead of carrying out a lengthy process of multiplication, was suggested in two ways which were quite independent at first. Later on we shall see how they can be linked together by making use of the "imaginary number" i or $\sqrt{-1}$. The first arose in connexion with the preparation of trigonometrical tables for use in navigation. The second was closely connected with the laborious calculation involved in reckoning compound interest upon investments.

During the latter part of the sixteenth century Denmark became an important centre of research in problems connected with navigation. In Denmark the epoch-making researches of Tycho Brahe the astronomer were carried out. Two Danish mathematicians, Wittich (1584) and Clavius (whose work *de Astrolabio* was published in 1593), suggested the use of trigonometrical tables for shortening calculations. In Chapter 6, p. 254, you will find the expression

$$\sin (A + B) = \sin A \cos B + \sin B \cos A \quad . \quad . \quad (i)$$

A corresponding expression for the sine of the difference between two angles can be got by a similar construction (Fig. 164)

$$\sin (A - B) = \sin A \cos B - \sin B \cos A \quad . \quad . \quad (ii)$$

Adding the two expressions on the right of (i) and (ii) and the two expressions on the left of (i) and (ii), we get

$$\sin (A + B) + \sin (A - B) = 2 \sin A \cos B$$

$$\text{or} \qquad \sin A \cos B = \tfrac{1}{2} \sin (A + B) + \tfrac{1}{2} \sin (A - B)$$

This equation can be used to substitute the socialized information of the sine and cosine tables for the individual labour of multiplying two numbers. Thus, to multiply

$$0{\cdot}17365 \times 0{\cdot}99027$$

we look up the tables and find

$$\sin 10° = 0{\cdot}17365$$
$$\cos 8° = 0{\cdot}99027$$

Our formula tells that

$$\sin 10°.\cos 8° = \tfrac{1}{2}(\sin 18° + \sin 2°)$$

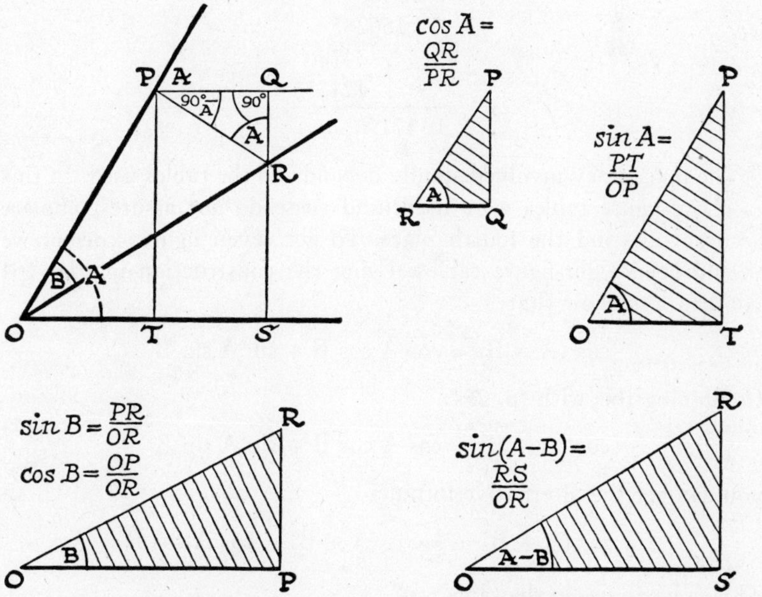

FIG. 164.—THE SINE OF THE DIFFERENCE BETWEEN TWO ANGLES

CONSTRUCTION.—Angle POT = A; ∠POR = B; ∠ROS = (A – B). Draw PT perp. to OS, PQ perp. to PT, PR perp. to OP, and QS through R perp. to PQ.

DEMONSTRATION.—$\sin(A - B) = \frac{RS}{OR} = \frac{QS}{OR} - \frac{QR}{OR} = \frac{PT}{OR} - \frac{QR}{OR}$

$$= \frac{PT.OP}{OP.OR} - \frac{QR.PR}{PR.OR}$$

$$= \underline{\sin A \cos B - \cos A \sin B}$$

The tables tell us that

$$\sin 18^\circ = 0\cdot 30902$$
$$\sin 2^\circ = 0\cdot 03490$$
$$\sin 18^\circ + \sin 2^\circ = 0\cdot 34392$$
$$\tfrac{1}{2}(\sin 18^\circ + \sin 2^\circ) = 0\cdot 17196$$

Thus, correct to five decimal places,

$$0\cdot 17365 \times 0\cdot 99027 = 0\cdot 17196$$

You will see that this is correct to the fifth place by multiplying out as follows:

$$\begin{array}{l} 0\cdot 17365 \\ \underline{0\cdot 99027} \\ 0\cdot 156285 \\ \quad\;\; 156285 \\ \qquad\quad 34730 \\ \qquad\quad \underline{121555} \\ 0\cdot 17196\ldots \end{array}$$

The inaccuracy involved simply depends on the tables used. In this case five-figure tables were used, and these do not assure complete accuracy beyond the fourth place. To get seven figures correct we should need eight-figure tables. Using the construction in Fig. 164 you can also show that

$$\cos(A - B) = \cos A \cos B + \sin A \sin B$$

Combining this with (p. 254)

$$\cos(A + B) = \cos A \cos B - \sin A \sin B$$

you can get the alternative formula

$$\tfrac{1}{2}\cos(A + B) + \tfrac{1}{2}\cos(A - B) = \cos A \cos B$$

This you can use in the same way.

This device probably suggested to Napier, who is usually called the inventor of logarithms, a simple method for multiplying the sines of angles by a process of straightforward addition. Napier's discovery was eagerly welcomed by Tycho Brahe and Kepler. It was translated from its Latin edition in the year (1614) of its first publication by Edward Wright, a Cambridge mathematician, who had already written in 1599 a book entitled *Certaine Errors in Navigation detected and corrected.*

However, it rarely if ever happens in the history of science that a great discovery is made singly. The same social context which demanded quicker methods for calculating the position of the stars in the heavens called for quicker ways of calculating the wealth which accumulated through voyages which could not have been made without the use of astronomy to find the ship's position at sea. One line which led to the discovery of logarithms was the preparation of tables for calculating interest. The calculation of compound interest is a practical application of the use of geometric series. If r is the rate of interest per pound invested, £1 in one year grows to £$(1 + r)$. For instance, if r is 5 per cent ($\frac{5}{100}$), £1 grows to £1·05. At the end of the second year every £1 invested at the end of the first year will be worth £1·05. If no interest is paid on the first year £1·05 will be invested at the beginning of the second year for every £1 invested at the beginning of the first year. So the original £1 will have grown to £1·05 × 1·05 or £$(1{\cdot}05)^2$ at the end of the second year. Similarly it will be £$(1{\cdot}05)^3$ at the end of the third year. So we may tabulate the rate of growth of £1 in the following way:

At the end of					
0	1	2	3	4	years
1	$(1 + r)$	$(1 + r)^2$	$(1 + r)^3$	$(1 + r)^4$	

The series above is an arithmetic and the series below a geometric series. If we wish to calculate compound interest to quarter years we must extend the table, using *fractional* powers thus:

0	$\frac{1}{4}$	$\frac{1}{2}$	$\frac{3}{4}$	1	$1\frac{1}{4}$	$1\frac{1}{2}$	$1\frac{3}{4}$	etc.
1	$(1 + r)^{\frac{1}{4}}$	$(1 + r)^{\frac{1}{2}}$	$(1 + r)^{\frac{3}{4}}$	$(1 + r)$	$(1 + r)^{\frac{5}{4}}$	$(1 + r)^{\frac{3}{2}}$	$(1 + r)^{\frac{7}{4}}$	

To get the value of £156, which has been accumulating compound interest at 3 per cent for $2\frac{3}{4}$ years, all we have to do is to multiply thus:

$$£156 \times (1{\cdot}03)^{2\frac{3}{4}} = £156 \times (1{\cdot}03)^{\frac{11}{4}}$$

Stevinus, to whom we have already referred on more than one occasion, published tables like this for calculations in commercial arithmetic.

If we make the rate of interest 100 per cent (i.e. $r = 1$), the two rows of series given above correspond with the x co-ordinates and y co-ordinates in the graph on p. 439, since $(1 + r) = 2$ when $r = 1$. We have seen how to read off approximate values of y corresponding with the quarter days, i.e. $x = \frac{1}{4}, \frac{1}{2}$, etc., from the graph. We must now examine the meaning of a *fractional* power more closely. The fundamental principle of the logarithm table was understood by

Archimedes. Let us retrace our steps to this discovery, putting down any geometric series underneath its generating series of the first n natural numbers, e.g.

1	2	3	4	5	6	7
2^1	2^2	2^3	2^4	2^5	2^6	2^7
2	4	8	16	32	64	128

Following Napier we shall now call the numbers in the upper or arithmetic series *logarithms* and the numbers in the bottom or geometric series *antilogarithms*. The principle of Archimedes is that if we want to multiply any two numbers in the bottom series we add the corresponding numbers in the top series and look for the corresponding number in the bottom series. One way of writing this rule is

$$a^m \times a^n = a^{m+n}$$

$$\text{e.g.} \qquad 2^3 \times 2^4 = 2^7$$

$$(8 \times 16 = 128)$$

The operator "*log*" written in front of a number means, "Look up in the table the power to which a has to be raised to give the number." "*Antilog*" written in front of a number means, "Look up in the table the value of the base when raised to the power represented by the number." Thus, if

$$p = a^m$$

$$m = \log_a p$$

$$p = \text{antilog}_a\, m$$

We can thus write the rule for multiplication in an alternative form, putting:

$$q = a^n \quad \text{so that} \quad n = \log_a q$$

$$p \times q = a^{m+n} \quad \text{so that} \quad m + n = \log_a (p \times q)$$

$$\text{or} \qquad p \times q = \text{antilog}_a\, (m + n)$$

$$= \text{antilog}_a\, (\log_a p + \log_a q)$$

The particular numerical example given in the new symbols would read:

$$8 \times 16 = \text{antilog}_2\, (\log_2 8 + \log_2 16)$$

$$= \text{antilog}_2\, (3 + 4)$$

$$= \text{antilog}_2\, 7$$

The last step means, "Look up the number in the bottom row of antilogarithms corresponding with 7 in the top rows of logarithms." On looking it up, we find that it is 128.

Of course, a table like this is of no use for multiplication unless we can fill it up so as to include all the numbers which we might wish to multiply. We started by using the operator x in a^x to mean multiplying x a's together. Then we noticed that we could look at the connexion between x and a in another way. As we go from right to left in the series, one step downwards in the x numbers means that the number in the bottom column has to be divided by a. Thus if $2^4 = 16$, $2^3 = 16 \div 2$. So we found that if a is the basis of the positional notation, a^n is the value of each bead in the $(n + 1)$th column of the abacus. Thus a^0 corresponds with the value of a bead in the units column, i.e. for any value of a

$$a^0 = 1$$

The power one less than 0 is -1, so

$$a^{-1} = \frac{a^0}{a^1} = \frac{1}{a}$$

Similarly, $$a^{-2} = \frac{1}{a} \div a = \frac{1}{a^2}$$

And generally $$a^{-n} = \frac{1}{a^n}$$

Thus a^n corresponds with the value of a bead in the nth column to the left of the units and a^{-n} corresponds with the value of a bead in the nth column to the right of the units, i.e. with the value of a figure which occupies the nth decimal place. We can thus write down the following logarithms and antilogarithms based on the geometric progression 3^n:

Log	-3	-2	-1	0	1	2	3	4
	3^{-3}	3^{-2}	3^{-1}	3^0	3^1	3^2	3^3	3^4
Antilog	$0{\cdot}\dot{0}3\dot{7}$	$0{\cdot}\dot{1}$	$0{\cdot}\dot{3}$	1	3	9	27	81

On drawing a graph with these numbers as points ($y = 3^x$ or $y = \text{antilog}_3\, x$) we can measure the length of y corresponding with any particular value of x, whether x is a fraction or a whole number. We then find that the rule of Archimedes still holds good even when m and n are fractions in the equation

$$a^m \times a^n = a^{m+n}$$

To test the rule arithmetically we need some way of defining a^n or

a^m when m or n are not whole numbers. If the rule of Archimedes holds good:

$$\sqrt[2]{a^1} = \sqrt[2]{a^{\frac{1}{2}+\frac{1}{2}}} = \sqrt[2]{a^{\frac{1}{2}} \times a^{\frac{1}{2}}} = a^{\frac{1}{2}}$$

$$\text{i.e.} \quad a^{\frac{1}{2}} = \sqrt[2]{a}$$

Similarly,

$$\sqrt[3]{a^1} = \sqrt[3]{a^{\frac{1}{3}+\frac{1}{3}+\frac{1}{3}}} = \sqrt[3]{a^{\frac{1}{3}} \times a^{\frac{1}{3}} \times a^{\frac{1}{3}}} = a^{\frac{1}{3}}$$

$$\text{i.e.} \quad a^{\frac{1}{3}} = \sqrt[3]{a}$$

So in general $\quad a^{\frac{1}{n}} = \sqrt[n]{a}$

Thus $3^{2\cdot5}$ means

$$3^{2+\frac{1}{2}} = 3^2 \times 3^{\frac{1}{2}} = 9\sqrt{3}$$

Similarly $2^{\frac{4}{3}}$ means

$$2^{1+\frac{1}{3}} = 2^1 \times 2^{\frac{1}{3}} = 2\sqrt[3]{2}$$

A quantity like $2^{\frac{4}{3}}$ or $3^{\frac{5}{2}}$, or in general $a^{\frac{m}{n}}$, can be translated in another way, using the fact that

$$\sqrt[2]{a} \times \sqrt[2]{b} = \sqrt[2]{ab}$$

$$\text{or} \quad \sqrt[3]{a} \times \sqrt[3]{b} = \sqrt[3]{ab} \quad \text{etc.}$$

Thus we may put

$$3^{2\cdot5} = 3^{\frac{5}{2}} = 3^2 \times \sqrt{3} = \sqrt{3^4}\ \sqrt{3} = \sqrt{3^5}$$

$$2^{\frac{4}{3}} = 2\sqrt[3]{2} = \sqrt[3]{2^3} \times \sqrt[3]{2} = \sqrt[3]{2^4}$$

So that the rule is

$$a^{\frac{p}{q}} = \sqrt[q]{a^p}$$

The two rules which we have given for fractional and negative powers were first stated by Oresmus in a book called *Algorismus Proportionum*, published about A.D. 1350. It took the human race a thousand years to bridge the gulf between the rule of Archimedes and the next stage in the evolution of the logarithm table. You need not be discouraged if it takes you a few hours or days to get accustomed to the use of a fractional or negative power.

We can now extend a table of logarithms as far as we like. Thus for logarithms based on the geometric series 2^n, we can draw up a table like this which is correct to three decimal places.

$n = \log_2 N$	$N = (\text{antilog}_2\, n)$	
0	1	1·000
0·5	$\sqrt{2}$	1·414
1·0	2	2·000
1·5	$\sqrt{2^3}$	2·828
2·0	4	4·000
2·5	$\sqrt{2^5}$	5·657
3·0	8	8·000
3·5	$\sqrt{2^7}$	11·314
4·0	16	16·000
etc.	etc.	

Logarithms are the numbers of the arithmetical generating series n of a geometric series a^n. To distinguish logarithms corresponding with terms in one geometric series from logarithms corresponding with terms in another geometric series we call a the base of the series, and write a as a mathematical adjective in the bottom right-hand corner to indicate what logarithm tables we are using, as in:

$$\log_2 2{\cdot}828 = 1{\cdot}5$$

$$\text{or} \quad \text{antilog}_2\,(1{\cdot}5) = 2{\cdot}828$$

Of course we can go on filling up this table as far as we need. Thus we can put

n	$\text{antilog}_2\, n$
0·25 ($\frac{1}{4}$)	$\sqrt[4]{2}$
0·75 ($\frac{3}{4}$)	$\sqrt[4]{2^3}$
etc.	etc.

Once we have got such a table we can use it to multiply numbers in this way. Suppose we wish to multiply 2·828 by 5·657. The table tells us that

$$\log_2 2{\cdot}828 = 1{\cdot}5 \quad \text{or} \quad 2^{1\cdot5} = 2{\cdot}828$$

$$\log_2 5{\cdot}657 = 2{\cdot}5 \quad \text{or} \quad 2^{2\cdot5} = 5{\cdot}657$$

The rule of Archimedes tells us that

$$2{\cdot}828 \times 5{\cdot}657 = 2^{1\cdot5} \times 2^{2\cdot5} = 2^{1\cdot5 + 2\cdot5} = 2^4$$

So the number we are looking for is the number whose logarithm is 4, i.e.

$$\begin{aligned}\text{antilog}_2\, 4 &= \text{antilog}_2\,(1\cdot 5 + 2\cdot 5)\\ &= \text{antilog}_2\,(\log 2\cdot 828 + \log 5\cdot 657)\end{aligned}$$

The table shows that antilog₂ 4 is 16. To check this multiply out:

$$\begin{array}{r} 2\cdot 828\\ 5\cdot 657\\ \hline 14\cdot 140\\ 1\cdot 6968\\ 14140\\ 19796\\ \hline 15\cdot 997996 \end{array} = 16 \text{ to four significant figures}$$

The discrepancy is 2 in 16,000, an error of little more than 1 in 10,000. Of course, a better result could be obtained by using a table in which the figures are given correct to five, seven, nine, or more decimal places. The rule for multiplication with logarithms may be stated briefly thus: "To multiply two numbers find these numbers in the column of antilogs, add the corresponding numbers in the column of logs, and find the number corresponding with the result in the column of antilogs."

The possibility of making such a table was hinted at in several sixteenth-century works on commercial arithmetic. Stifel realized its usefulness. It was suggested again by Simon Jacob, and within a few years of publication of Napier's logarithms of sines, Jobst Bürgi, of Prague, published *Tables of Arithmetical and Geometrical Progressions* to simplify calculations by applying the principle of logarithmic multiplication. Bürgi's table was essentially like the one which we have just given, except that the base was 1·0001. This number was chosen for a reason which will be explained later. Although Bürgi's table was mentioned by Kepler as a useful device for astronomical calculations, its origin is not directly connected with the need for ready-reckoning in navigation like Napier's logarithms of sines. It simply carried the use of the compound-interest tables of Stevinus a stage further.

Neither Napier nor Bürgi, who discovered logarithms independently within a few years of one another, used either of the two base numbers for which modern tables are computed. We have seen that in trigonometry two units for measuring angles are used. In working out practical problems we still stick to the Babylonian degree. For theoretical purposes we use the radian because the size of the radian is connected in a very simple way with the size of the circumference of the circle. The advantage of the radian will be seen more clearly later on. As with the angle, so with logarithms we use two sets of tables, one for practical convenience, one because logarithms so calculated have relatively simple mathematical peculiarities. The latter are called *natural* logarithms. In trigonometry, as we shall see, modern tables are first calculated in radians and then changed to degrees for practical use by using the equation

$$1 \text{ radian} = \frac{180}{\pi} \text{ degrees}$$

There is a simple rule by which logarithms calculated for one base can be converted into logarithms calculated to another. It depends on the fact that $(n^a)^b = n^{ab}$, e.g. $8^3 = (2^3)^3 = 2^9$, as you can see by multiplying. The rule is demonstrated as follows. Suppose we have calculated a table of logarithms and antilogarithms to the base 2. On looking over the table we find $\log_2 10 = 3 \cdot 322$, or in other words $2^{3 \cdot 322} = 10$. So if

$$M = 10^m \quad \text{i.e.} \quad m = \log_{10} M$$
$$M = 2^{3 \cdot 322 m} \quad \text{i.e.} \quad 3 \cdot 322\, m = \log_2 M$$
$$\therefore \quad 3 \cdot 322 \log_{10} M = \log_2 M$$
$$\text{or} \quad \log_{10} M = \frac{\log_2 M}{\log_2 10}$$

We may write out the rule in more general terms:

$$\log_a M = \frac{\log_b M}{\log_b a}$$

For instance, $\log_2 8 = 3$, whence

$$\log_{10} 8 = \frac{3}{3 \cdot 322} = 0 \cdot 903$$

For practical purposes the base of logarithmic tables is 10, because 10 is the base of our numerical system. This fact simplifies the calculation of logarithmic tables for the following reason. If the base is 10 the fundamental numbers in the tables are the two series:

Log	– 2	– 1	0	1	2	3	4	etc.
Antilog	0·01	0·1	1	10	100	1,000	10,000	

So $\log_{10} 1 = 0$, $\log_{10} 10 = 1$, and $\log_{10} \sqrt{10} = \log_{10} 10^{\frac{1}{2}} = 0{\cdot}50$. The square root of 10 (to three decimals) is $3{\cdot}162$. So we can write

$$\log_{10} 3{\cdot}162 = 0{\cdot}500$$

Now $$31{\cdot}62 = 3{\cdot}162 \times 10$$

So
$$\begin{aligned} \log_{10} 31{\cdot}62 &= \log_{10} (3{\cdot}162 \times 10) \\ &= \log_{10} 3{\cdot}162 + \log_{10} 10 \\ &= 0{\cdot}500 + 1 \\ &= 1{\cdot}5 \end{aligned}$$

Likewise
$$\begin{aligned} \log_{10} 316{\cdot}2 &= \log_{10} (3{\cdot}162 \times 100) \\ &= \log_{10} 3{\cdot}162 + \log_{10} 100 \\ &= 0{\cdot}500 + 2 \\ &= 2{\cdot}5 \end{aligned}$$

So shifting the decimal place in a number does not alter the value to the right of the decimal place in its logarithm, and the number to the left of the decimal place can be written down by common sense. Since $10^0 = 1$ and $10^1 = 10$, the number to the left of the decimal place in the logarithm is 0 for all numbers between 1 and 10. Since $10^1 = 10$ and $10^2 = 100$, it is 1 for numbers between 10 and 100. Since $10^2 = 100$ and $10^3 = 1{,}000$, it is 2 for numbers between 100 and 1,000. Similarly, 1 put in front of the fractional part of a number whose antilogarithm we are looking for means, "Multiply the antilogarithm of the fractional part by 10"; 2 in front means, "Multiply the antilogarithm of the fractional part by 100," and so on. This means that if we have the logarithms of all numbers between 1 and 10 in suitable intervals we have all we need for multiplying. For instance, we may want to multiply $1{\cdot}536$ by 77. The tables tell us that

$$\log_{10} 1{\cdot}536 = 0{\cdot}1864$$
$$\log_{10} 7{\cdot}7 = 0{\cdot}8865$$

Hence $$\log_{10} 77 = 1{\cdot}8865$$

So
$$\begin{aligned} 1{\cdot}536 \times 77 &= \text{antilog}_{10} (0{\cdot}1864 + 1{\cdot}8865) \\ &= \text{antilog}_{10} 2{\cdot}0729 \\ &= 100 \times \text{antilog}_{10} 0{\cdot}0729 \\ &= 100 \times 1{\cdot}183 \\ &= 118{\cdot}3 \end{aligned}$$

The result, as you will see by multiplying, is correct to four significant figures (first decimal place), and that is all you can expect since we have only used four-figure tables.

The first logarithms calculated to the base 10 were published by Briggs in collaboration with Napier. Briggs gave the logarithms of all numbers from 1 to 1,000 correct to fourteen decimal places. A little later (1628) Adrian Vlacq, in Holland, published logarithms from 1 to 100,000 correct to ten decimal places. To use logarithms we only require one table, giving in one column n (= log N) and in the other N (= antilog n). It is more convenient in working with logarithms to have separate tables of numbers equally spaced with corresponding logarithms and antilogarithms, so as to be able to look up whichever is required more quickly. A table in which the left-hand column gives numbers (N) in equivalent intervals and the right-hand column gives their logarithms (log N) is called a table of logarithms. A table in which the left-hand column gives numbers (n) in equivalent intervals and the right-hand column gives the corresponding antilogarithms (antilog n) is called a table of antilogarithms. The tables of Bürgi were tables of antilogarithms in this sense. The tables of Briggs were tables of logarithms. To construct a table of logarithms we have to start by making a table of antilogarithms. You can make a rough table of logarithms by an approximate method in this way. First we have

$$1 = 10^0$$
$$\log_{10} 1 = 0$$

Next we find by multiplication

$$2^{10} = 1{,}024$$

which differs from 1,000 by $2\frac{1}{2}$ per cent,

$$2^{10} = 10^3 \text{ approximately}$$
$$2 = \sqrt[10]{10^3} \text{ approximately}$$
$$= 10^{\frac{3}{10}} = 10^{0\cdot 3} \text{ approximately}$$
$$\log_{10} 2 = 0\cdot 3 \text{ approximately}$$

Similarly by multiplication

$$3^9 = 19{,}683$$
$$= 20{,}000 \text{ approximately}$$
$$= 2 \times 10{,}000 \text{ approximately}$$
$$= 10^{0\cdot 3} \times 10^4 \text{ approximately}$$
$$= 10^{4\cdot 3} \text{ approximately}$$
$$3 = \sqrt[9]{10^{4\cdot 3}} \text{ approximately}$$
$$= 10^{\frac{4\cdot 3}{9}} = 10^{0\cdot 48}$$
$$\log_{10} 3 = 0\cdot 48 \text{ approximately}$$

Now $4 = 2^2 = 10^{0\cdot 3} \times 10^{0\cdot 3}$ approximately

$= 10^{0\cdot 6}$ approximately

$\log_{10} 4 = 0\cdot 6$ approximately

Similarly $2 \times 5 = 10$

$\therefore \log_{10} 2 + \log_{10} 5 = \log_{10} 10 = 1$

$\therefore \log_{10} 5 = 1 - 0\cdot 30$ approximately

$= 0\cdot 70$ approximately

$6 = 2 \times 3 = 10^{0\cdot 3} \times 10^{0\cdot 48}$ approximately

$= 10^{0\cdot 78}$ approximately

$\log_{10} 6 = 0\cdot 78$ approximately

$7^2 = 49 = 5 \times 10$ approximately

$\log_{10} (7 \times 7) = \log_{10} 7 + \log_{10} 7 = \log_{10} 5 + \log_{10} 10$

$\therefore 2 \log_{10} 7 = 1\cdot 70$ approximately

$\therefore \log_{10} 7 = 0\cdot 85$ approximately

$8 = 2^3 = (10^{0\cdot 3})^3 = 10^{0\cdot 9}$ approximately

$\therefore \log_{10} 8 = 0\cdot 90$ approximately

$9 = 3^2 = (10^{0\cdot 48})^2 = 10^{0\cdot 96}$ approximately

$\log_{10} 9 = 0\cdot 96$

So we now have the following rough table of logarithms:

N	$\log_{10}$ N	N	$\log_{10}$ N
1	0	10	1·00
2	0·30	20	1·30
3	0·48	30	1·48
4	0·60	40	1·60
5	0·70	50	1·70
6	0·78	60	1·78
7	0·85	70	1·85
8	0·90	80	1·90
9	0·96	90	1·96
		100	2·00
antilog$_{10}n$	n	*antilog*$_{10}n$	n

You can test this rough table as follows:

$$6 \times 8 = \text{antilog}_{10} (\log_{10} 6 + \log_{10} 8)$$
$$= \text{antilog}_{10} (0\cdot 78 + 0\cdot 90)$$
$$= \text{antilog}_{10} (1\cdot 68)$$

The antilog of 1·68 lies between 40 and 50. The number 1·68 corresponds with $\frac{8}{10}$ or $\frac{4}{5}$ of the interval between 1·60, the logarithm of 40, and 1·70, the logarithm of 50. Taking as the antilog of 1·68 the number corresponding with four-fifths or eight-tenths of the interval between 40 and 50, we get 48, the correct result. You may also use this rough table to familiarize yourself with the use of logarithms for division or the "curious and laborious extraction of the roots." Combining the rule given by Oresmus for a negative power with the rule of Archimedes, we get

$$\frac{10^n}{10^m} = 10^n \times 10^{-m}$$

$$\frac{10^n}{10^m} = 10^{n-m}$$

If $$10^n = N, \log_{10} N = n$$

$$10^m = M, \log_{10} M = m$$

$$\therefore \quad \frac{N}{M} = 10^{n-m} \text{ and } \log_{10} \frac{N}{M} = n - m$$

$$\therefore \quad \log_{10} \frac{N}{M} = \log_{10} N - \log_{10} M$$

or $$\frac{N}{M} = \text{antilog}_{10} (\log_{10} N - \log_{10} M)$$

Suppose we want to find $20 \div 5$. We put

$$20 \div 5 = \text{antilog}_{10} (\log_{10} 20 - \log_{10} 5)$$

Looking up the rough table of logarithms given above, we find that

$$20 \div 5 = \text{antilog}_{10} (1 \cdot 30 - 0 \cdot 70)$$
$$= \text{antilog}_{10} (0 \cdot 60)$$
$$= 4$$

The extraction of a root depends on the rule

$$\sqrt[n]{10} = 10^{\frac{1}{n}}$$

So if $$N = 10^m$$

$$m = \log_{10} N$$

Likewise $$\sqrt[n]{N} = N^{\frac{1}{n}} = 10^{\frac{m}{n}}$$

$$\log_{10} \sqrt[n]{N} = \frac{m}{n}$$

$$\log_{10} \sqrt[n]{N} = \frac{1}{n} \log_{10} N$$

If we want to find the cube root of 8, we put

$$\sqrt[3]{8} = \text{antilog}_{10} (\tfrac{1}{3} \log_{10} 8)$$

From this rough table we get

$$\begin{aligned}\sqrt[3]{8} &= \text{antilog}_{10} \left(\frac{0\cdot 90}{3}\right)\\ &= \text{antilog}_{10}\, 0\cdot 30\\ &= 2\end{aligned}$$

You will be able to deduce the analogous rule

$$N^n = \text{antilog}_{10} (n \log_{10} N)$$

Test this by finding 2^3 from the rough table.

The four rules which you have now learned for performing multiplication, division, the extraction of roots, and raising a number to any power were among the "marvellous things relating to these numbers" recorded by Stifel. Stifel put arithmetic and geometric series side by side, as we did on p. 273 and noted that:

(*a*) Addition of terms in the arithmetic series corresponds with multiplication of the terms in the geometric series.

(*b*) Subtraction of terms in the arithmetic series corresponds with division of terms in the geometric series.

(*c*) Multiplication of a term in the arithmetic series by a constant corresponds with raising a term in the geometric series to a given power.

(*d*) Division of a term in the arithmetic series by a constant corresponds with extracting a given root of a term in the geometric series.

Having got so far, it seems a great pity that Luther's convert spent so much time in arithmetical calculations to prove that Pope Leo X was the Beast of the Apocalypse, instead of undertaking the socially useful task of compiling tables like those of Bürgi or Briggs.

In constructing an accurate table of logarithms Briggs began by making a table of antilogarithms, using the equations

$$10^{\frac{p}{q}} = \sqrt[q]{10^p}$$

$$\log_{10} \sqrt[q]{10^p} = \frac{p}{q}$$

$$\text{or} \quad \text{antilog}_{10} \frac{p}{q} = \sqrt[q]{10^p}$$

We thus get:

$n = \log_{10} N$	$N = \text{antilog}_{10}\, n$
$1 \cdot 000$	$10 \cdot 0000$, $(10 \cdot 0)$
$0 \cdot 875$, $(\frac{7}{8})$	$7 \cdot 4989$, $(\sqrt[8]{10^7})$
$0 \cdot 750$, $(\frac{3}{4})$	$5 \cdot 6234$, $(\sqrt[4]{10^3})$
$0 \cdot 625$, $(\frac{5}{8})$	$4 \cdot 2170$, $(\sqrt[8]{10^5})$
$0 \cdot 500$, $(\frac{1}{2})$	$3 \cdot 1623$, $(\sqrt{10})$
$0 \cdot 375$, $(\frac{3}{8})$	$2 \cdot 3714$, $(\sqrt[8]{10^3})$
$0 \cdot 250$, $(\frac{1}{4})$	$1 \cdot 7783$, $(\sqrt[4]{10})$
$0 \cdot 125$, $(\frac{1}{8})$	$1 \cdot 3335$, $(\sqrt[8]{10})$
$0 \cdot 000$	$1 \cdot 0000$, $(1 \cdot 0)$

By extracting higher roots we can make the intervals between the numbers (n) in the left-hand column as small as we like. To get a table of logarithms, i.e. a table with numbers (N) equally spaced for reference in the left-hand column and their logarithms in the right-hand column, Briggs made use of the rule which was first recognized by Stifel. Put down any arithmetic series (logs) starting with unity, and a geometric series (antilogs) starting with the base of the series, e.g.

1	2	3	4	5	. . .	arithmetic series (logs)
2	4	8	16	32	. . .	geometric series (antilogs)

You may recall (p. 159) that the arithmetic mean of two numbers a and b is $\frac{1}{2}(a + b)$, and the geometric mean between two numbers A and B is $\sqrt{AB}$. If you take any three consecutive numbers in the top row, the middle one is the arithmetic mean of the other two. Thus, if 2, 3, 4 are the numbers chosen $3 = \frac{1}{2}(2 + 4)$. Similarly, for any three consecutive numbers in the bottom series the middle one is the geometric mean of the other two. Thus, if 4, 8, 16 are the numbers, $8 = \sqrt{64} = \sqrt{4 \times 16}$. This is also true if we reduce the interval of the arithmetic series to give fractional steps, as

$$2,\ 2 \cdot 5,\ 3$$
$$4,\ 2^{2 \cdot 5},\ 8$$

The middle term in the bottom row is $2^{2 \cdot 5} = \sqrt[2]{2^5}$ and the geometric mean of the other two is $\sqrt{4 \times 8} = \sqrt{32} = \sqrt[2]{2^5}$.

Briggs used this fact to convert an antilogarithm table, i.e. one in which the logarithms are given in equal intervals in the left-hand column, into a logarithm table, i.e. one in which the antilogarithms are given in equal intervals in the left-hand column. The process, which is laborious, will be illustrated by successive approximation to the value of $\log_{10} 5$, as in the table which follows.

$N = \text{antilog}_{10}\, n$		$n = \log_{10} N$	
$A = 1$		a	$= 0{\cdot}000$
$B = 10$		b	$= 1{\cdot}000$
$C = \sqrt{AB}$	$= 3{\cdot}162277$	$c = \frac{1}{2}(a + b)$	$= 0{\cdot}500$
$D = \sqrt{BC}$	$= 5{\cdot}623413$	$d = \frac{1}{2}(b + c)$	$= 0{\cdot}750$
$E = \sqrt{CD}$	$= 4{\cdot}216964$	$e = \frac{1}{2}(c + d)$	$= 0{\cdot}625$
$F = \sqrt{DE}$	$= 4{\cdot}869674$	$f = \frac{1}{2}(d + e)$	$= 0{\cdot}6875$
$G = \sqrt{DF}$	$= 5{\cdot}232991$	$g = \frac{1}{2}(d + f)$	$= 0{\cdot}71875$
$H = \sqrt{FG}$	$= 5{\cdot}048065$	$h = \frac{1}{2}(f + g)$	$= 0{\cdot}703125$
$I = \sqrt{FH}$	$= 4{\cdot}958067$	$i = \frac{1}{2}(f + h)$	$= 0{\cdot}6953125$
$J = \sqrt{HI}$	$= 5{\cdot}002865$	$j = \frac{1}{2}(h + i)$	$= 0{\cdot}6992187$

There is no reason to carry on this process till the result is correct to the fourteenth decimal place to illustrate the method which Briggs used. You can work out a few of the results yourself, and then make up sums which you can do by means of the table at the end of the book, testing the results by direct multiplication, etc. You will then realize what the serious business of the social culture to which the Protestant Reformation gave birth owed to the industry and common sense of men like Briggs and Vlacq.

In a previous chapter we have seen that the admirable proposal of Stevinus for introducing a decimal system of weights and measures in conformity with the material needs of the new mercantile democracies received little attention and produced no immediate response. The ideological leaders of the movement were too busy arguing about the perseverance of the saints and the Real Presence. Napier's logarithms barely escaped obscurity for a similar reason. The enthusiasm with which they were taken up by the mathematicians of the time was largely due to the practical common sense of Edward Wright and the immense labour which Briggs devoted to the subject. In the year of publication Briggs wrote to Bishop Usher that "he never saw book which pleased me better or made more wonder." Usher was amusing himself with another branch of arithmetic. At the conclusion of years of painstaking research upon the genealogies of the Old Testament canon he finally succeeded in establishing, to quote Professor Bury's words, that man was created by the "Trinity on October 23rd B.C. 4004 at nine o'clock in the morning." Napier indulged a similar taste. At college he was "moved in admiration against the blindness of papists that could not most evidently see their seven hilled citie of Rome painted and there so lively by St. John as the mother of all spiritual whoredome. . . . From thenceforward I determined with myself by the assistance of God's spirit to employ my study and diligence to search out the remanent mysteries of that holy booke, as to this hour praised be the Lord I have bin doing at all such times as convenientlie I might have occasion." Fortunately he was a quick worker, and completed for publication the *Plaine Discoverie of the whole Revelation of St. John* in 1594. In the same year Tycho Brahe was delighted to hear, from a young Scot who visited him, first news of a great simplification in the art of calculation. It seems the fate of a revolutionary epoch to fling up live lava and dead ashes in about equal amounts. To lay the foundations of the classless society in which there is abundance for everybody and poverty for none we shall need to make the most of the lessons of man's past history. It is easy to find excuses for Stifel or Napier. It is more difficult to understand why some well-meaning socialists should weary us with tiresome disputations about the Hegelian dialectic.

SERIES FOR MAKING TABLES.—The first tables of logarithms contained inaccuracies which were noticed and corrected from time to time. The labour expended in constructing them was stupendous. Not unnaturally it stimulated the search for more congenial methods of calculating them. This search gave a new impetus to the study of what mathematicians call *infinite series*. At the beginning of this book we used the recurring decimal $0 \cdot \dot{1}$ to illustrate a series which never grows beyond a certain limiting value however many terms we continue to add. Later we were able to show that any geometric series with a fractional base less than unity has the convenient characteristic of choking off in this way (p. 231, 22, 23). The invention of logarithms was followed by the discovery of a large family of series which do the same thing.

The example with which we shall start is the binomial series for a fractional power. If you refer back to Chapter 7, p. 329, you will recall that:

$$(a + b)^n = a^n + na^{n-1}b + \frac{n(n-1)}{2!}a^{n-2}b^2 + \frac{n(n-1)(n-2)}{3!}a^{n-3}b^3 \ \ldots$$

If n is a positive whole number the series on the right contains $(n+1)$ terms. We have now found an intelligible meaning for n when n is not positive, and when it is a fraction. This raises the question: Does the binomial theorem still work when we put negative and fractional numbers in the place of n? The answer is that it does often work. It leads to series which go on for ever like a recurring decimal, and such series choke off like a geometric series with a fractional base if a and b have certain values. To show that this is so, we shall use the binomial theorem to find two quantities which we have already required in order to construct the trigonometrical table on p. 243. The first is $\sqrt{\frac{3}{4}}$, which may be written

$$(1 - \tfrac{1}{4})^{\frac{1}{2}}$$

The other is $\sqrt{2}$, which may be written

$$\sqrt{2} = (\tfrac{1}{2})^{-\frac{1}{2}}$$
$$= (1 - \tfrac{1}{2})^{-\frac{1}{2}}$$

In both these expressions a is 1, so the binomial series simplifies to the form

$$(1 - b)^n = 1 + n(-b) + \frac{n(n-1)(-b)^2}{2!} + \frac{n(n-1)(n-2)(-b)^3}{3!} \ldots$$
$$= 1 - nb + \frac{n(n-1)b^2}{2!} - \frac{n(n-1)(n-2)b^3}{3!} + \ldots$$

To use the binomial theorem to get a series for $\sqrt{\frac{3}{4}}$ and $\sqrt{2}$ we need first to tabulate the values of the binomial coefficients for $n = \frac{1}{2}$, (0·5) and $-\frac{1}{2}$, (– 0·5). Thus when

$$n = \tfrac{1}{2}$$
$$\frac{n(n-1)}{2!} = \frac{\frac{1}{2}(\frac{1}{2}-1)}{2}$$
$$= -\tfrac{1}{8}$$
$$= -0{\cdot}125$$

When

$$n = -\tfrac{1}{2}$$
$$\frac{n(n-1)}{2!} = \frac{-\frac{1}{2}(-\frac{1}{2}-1)}{2}$$
$$= +\tfrac{3}{8}$$
$$= +0{\cdot}375$$

So we have

$B_1 =$	n	$+0\cdot5$	$-0\cdot5$
$B_2 =$	$\frac{n(n-1)}{2!}$	$-0\cdot125$	$+0\cdot375$
$B_3 =$	$\frac{n(n-1)(n-2)}{3!}$	$+0\cdot0625$	$-0\cdot3125$
$B_4 =$	$\frac{n(n-1)(n-2)(n-3)}{4!}$	$-0\cdot0390625$	$+0\cdot2734375$
	B_5	$+0\cdot02734375$	$-0\cdot24609375$
	B_6	$-0\cdot0205078125$	$+0\cdot2255859375$
	B_7	$+0\cdot01611328125$	$-0\cdot20947265625$
	B_8	$-0\cdot013092041016$	$+0\cdot196380615234$
	B_9	$+0\cdot010910034180$	$-0\cdot185470581054$
	B_{10}	$-0\cdot009273529053$	$+0\cdot176197052001$
	B_{11}	$+0\cdot008008956909$	$-0\cdot168188095092$
	B_{12}	$-0\cdot007007837295$	$+0\cdot161180257797$

To get $\sqrt{\frac{3}{4}}$ we want $(1+b)^n$, where $b = -\frac{1}{4}$ and $n = \frac{1}{2}$. So the binomial series is

$$1 - 0\cdot5(\tfrac{1}{4}) - 0\cdot125(\tfrac{1}{16}) - 0\cdot0625(\tfrac{1}{64}) - 0\cdot0390625(\tfrac{1}{256}) - 0\cdot02734375(\tfrac{1}{1024}) \ldots$$

If we take the first two terms of this series we have

$$1 - \tfrac{1}{8} = 0\cdot875$$

We can tabulate the values we get by taking the sum of the first few terms thus:

Term	Sum
1	1
2	0·875
3	0·8671875
4	0·8662109375
5	0·866058349609375
6	0·866031646728515625
7	0·8660266399383544922

However many terms we take, the sum of this series never grows smaller than 0·866025, which is the value of $\sqrt{\frac{3}{4}}$ correct to six decimals. We only need to take the sum of the first seven terms of the series to get $\sqrt{\frac{3}{4}}$ for making a five-figure table of sines or cosines (see table in Chapter 6, p. 243).

The series for $\sqrt{2}$ does not choke off so quickly. By now you will probably remember that the correct value to four figures is 1·414. The binomial series is obtained by putting $b = -\frac{1}{2}$ and $n = -\frac{1}{2}$ in the expression

$$(1 - b)^n = 1 + (-0 \cdot 5)\,(-\tfrac{1}{2}) + (0 \cdot 375)\,(-\tfrac{1}{2})^2 + (-0 \cdot 3125)\,(-\tfrac{1}{2})^3 \ldots$$

Tabulating as in the preceding illustration the sum of the first few terms, and giving the answer correct to four figures only, we have

Term	Sum
1	1
2	1·250
3	1·344
4	1·383
5	1·400
6	1·408
7	1·411
8	1·413
9	1·414

The series never grows as large as 1·4143 however many terms we go on adding.

As an additional check on the use of the binomial series for negative powers the following result will be used later to get an unlimited series for π. We may write in the form

$$(1 + x)^{-1}$$

the expression

$$\frac{1}{1 + x}$$

By direct division we get

$$\begin{array}{r l}
1 + x)\ 1\ (1 - x + x^2 - x^3 + x^4 - x^5 \ldots & \\
\underline{1 + x} & \\
- x & \\
\underline{- x - x^2} & \\
x^2 & \\
\underline{x^2 + x^3} & \\
- x^3 & \\
\underline{- x^3 - x^4} & \\
x^4 & \\
\underline{x^4 + x^5} & \\
- x^5 \ldots &
\end{array}$$

By using the binomial series we get

$$(1+x)^{-1} = 1 + (-1)x + \frac{(-1)(-1-1)x^2}{2} + \frac{(-1)(-1-1)(-1-2)x^3}{3.2}$$
$$+ \frac{(-1)(-1-1)(-1-2)(-1-3)x^4}{4.3.2} \cdots$$
$$= \underline{1 - x + x^2 - x^3 + x^4 \; . \; . \; .}$$

The result is therefore the same as the one which we get by direct division.

You will naturally ask how we know when such series do eventually choke off. The first mathematicians who used series of unlimited length did not bother themselves to find a satisfactory test to decide when a series of unlimited length chokes off and when it does not. They were content to use them because they found that they led to useful results. It is very comforting to recall the curious mistakes which some of the most eminent mathematicians of the seventeenth century made before such tests were discovered. A series which puzzled Leibniz, whose immense contributions to mathematics will be dealt with later was the foregoing, when $x = 1$:

$$1 - 1 + 1 - 1 + 1 - 1 + 1 - 1 \; . \; . \; .$$

This is the geometric series $(-1)^n$, where n can have successively the values 0, 1, 2, 3, and so on, as long as we care to continue. The sum of the first n terms would be

Term	Sum
1	1
2	0
3	1
4	0
5	1
6	0
7	1
etc.	etc.

This does not choke off. Leibniz argued that the sum of the series is $\frac{1}{2}$, since $2^{-1} = 0{\cdot}5$. Actually it has no limiting value. So $(1+1)^{-1}$ cannot be represented in this way. It was left till the nineteenth century to find satisfactory tests for deciding whether series of unlimited length approach a limiting value like the limiting value $\frac{1}{9}$ for the series

$$0{\cdot}1 + 0{\cdot}01 + 0{\cdot}001 + 0{\cdot}0001 \; . \; . \; .$$

You will find it easier to forgive Leibniz when you know that a seventeenth-century mathematician deduced irrefutable evidence for the creation of the world out of nothing by divine providence from the behaviour of this series.

The simplest test which helps us to decide whether an unlimited series chokes off is to compare it with one like the above, which is known to do so. This test can be used to show that the binomial series in the expression

$$(1+b)^n = 1 + nb + \frac{n(n-1)b^2}{2\,!} + \frac{n(n-1)\,(n-2)b^3}{3\,!} \;.\;\;.\;\;.$$

does so, as long as b is between -1 and $+1$.

You can see how this test works on the series

$$1 + x + \frac{x^2}{2\,!} + \frac{x^3}{3\,!} + \frac{x^4}{4\,!} + \;.\;\;.\;\;.$$

The reason why this series chokes off depends on the factor $r\,!$ in the denominator of the $(r+1)$th term, which we shall call t^r. Now $t_{r+1} = x^{r+1}/(r+1)\,! = t_r \times \{x/(r+1)\}$, (see p. 221), and there eventually comes a time when r is bigger than $10x$, however big x is. After this stage each term is less than one-tenth of the term before. We already know that a series in which every term is exactly one-tenth of the preceding term is a recurring decimal fraction like 0.1, which has a limiting value of $\frac{1}{9}$, or $0\cdot\dot{7}$, which has a limiting value of $\frac{7}{9}$. If a series in which every term is exactly a tenth of the one before cannot grow beyond a certain size, a series in which every term is less than a tenth of the one before cannot grow beyond a certain size. So a series is always "convergent," as the mathematicians say; or, to use our own metaphor, a series which chokes off, provided that m_r is less than x^r, (any fixed x), when it belongs to the family

$$1 + m_1 + \frac{m_2}{2\,!} + \frac{m_3}{3\,!} + \frac{m_4}{4\,!} \;\;.\;\;.\;\;.$$

When the numerator is a very small fraction in a series of this family a highly accurate result can be got by taking only a few terms. For instance, if we want to find the fifth power of $1\cdot0001$, the base of Bürgi's tables, we can put

$$(1\cdot0001)^5 = (1 + 0\cdot0001)^5$$
$$= 1 + 5(0\cdot0001) + \frac{5.4}{2.1}(0\cdot0001)^2 + \frac{5.4.3}{3.2.1}(0\cdot0001)^3 \;\;.\;\;.\;\;.$$

This belongs to the family because $m_6 = m_7 = \;.\;\;.\;\;. = 0$.

The sum of the first two terms is $1\cdot0005$, of the first three terms

1·0005001, of the first four terms 1·00050010001. The successive terms of the series are always less than a thousandth of the preceding one. So the result is correct to ten decimals, even if we only take the first three terms of the series.

One series of this family is of immense importance in modern mathematics. It leads us to the pronoun e, which was mentioned on p. 81, and is the base of what are called "natural" logarithms. The best modern logarithm tables are calculated to more than twenty figures. For such precision the labour involved in using the method of Briggs would be almost superhuman. It is enormously reduced by first calculating "natural" logarithms to the base e and then using the rule

$$\log_{10} a = \frac{\log_e a}{\log_e 10}$$

This series, which leads to e, is called the exponential series. The exponential series is

$$1 + x + \frac{x^2}{2!} + \frac{x^3}{3!} + \frac{x^4}{4!} + \frac{x^5}{5!} \quad \text{and so on}$$

If $x = 1$, its value is "e", i.e.

$$e = 1 + 1 + \frac{1}{2!} + \frac{1}{3!} + \frac{1}{4!} + \frac{1}{5!} \ldots$$

After the tenth term every other is less than a tenth of its predecessor. So adding it on introduces another correct figure beyond the last correct decimal place of the sum of the terms which go before it. However many terms we take, it does not get bigger than 2·7182818285 correct to ten decimals. The result obtained is correct to five figures if we only add nine terms. Like π, it cannot be expressed by a single number. There are many ways in which the useful characteristic of this series can be deduced. One depends on the binomial theorem. We shall approach it by the method of experiment. The reason why this series is so useful is because the quantity e can be raised to any power by a simple rule (see Appendix 3).

This rule is $$(e)^x = 1 + x + \frac{x^2}{2!} + \frac{x^3}{3!} + \frac{x^4}{4!} \ldots$$

For instance $e^{\frac{1}{5}} = (2{\cdot}71828 \ldots)^{\frac{1}{5}}$ is

$$1 + \frac{1}{5} + \frac{1}{25} \cdot \frac{1}{2!} + \frac{1}{125} \cdot \frac{1}{3!} + \frac{1}{625} \cdot \frac{1}{4!} \ldots$$

You will see for yourself how rapidly this chokes off by adding the first n terms where n is 1, 2, 3, 4, 5, viz. 1, 1·2, 1·$\dot{2}\dot{2}$, 1·221$\dot{3}$, 1·2213$\dot{9}$. The addition of a new term in this case never affects the new correct decimal place given by the preceding term. So we have only to take six terms of the exponential series to get the fifth root of 2·71828 . . . correct to six figures. It is an immense saving of effort to calculate logarithms by using the exponential series. Later on we shall meet another series, which reduces the work still more. It is called the *logarithmic* series, and we shall use it to get a "convergent" series for π.

The exponential series was suggested by the binomial series, such as

$$(1 + x)^2 = 1 + 2x + x^2$$
$$(1 + x)^3 = 1 + 3x + 3x^2 + x^3$$
$$(1 + x)^4 = 1 + 4x + 6x^2 + 4x^3 + x^4$$

When x is very small in such expressions, x^2, x^3, etc., will always be very much smaller than x in descending order of size; if, for example,

$$x = \frac{1}{100} = (0 \cdot 01) \qquad x^2 = \frac{1}{10000} = (0 \cdot 0001)$$
$$x^3 = 0 \cdot 000001 \qquad x^4 = 0 \cdot 00000001 \quad \text{etc.}$$

So we get a very good first approximation when x is very small, if we take

$$(1 + x)^2 = 1 + 2x$$
$$(1 + x)^3 = 1 + 3x$$
$$(1 + x)^4 = 1 + 4x$$

How good the answer is depends on how small x is and how big n is in the general expression

$$(1 + x)^n = 1 + nx \text{ (approximately)}$$

For instance, if x is 0·1 $(1 + x)^2 = (1 \cdot 1)^2 = 1 \cdot 21$, and the first approximation $1 + 2x$ gives 1·2, which is less than 1 per cent too small. You will find it helpful to check for yourself the following results for $(1 + x)^n$:

x	n	$(1+x)^n$	$1 + nx$	Percentage Error
0·1	2	1·21	1·2	0·8
0·1	3	1·331	1·3	2·3
0·1	4	1·4641	1·4	4·4
0·01	2	1·0201	1·02	0·01
0·01	3	1·030301	1·03	0·03
0·01	4	1·04060401	1·04	0·06

You see from this that if x is the same, the error involved in using the approximate formula is always greater for higher than for lower powers, e.g. the error in finding $(1 + x)^4$ is nearly six times as large as the error in finding $(1 + x)^2$, when x is $0 \cdot 1$. However, by making x ten times smaller ($x = 0 \cdot 01$) the error in using the formula $1 + nx$ for $(1 + x)^4$ is less than one-tenth the error in using it for $(1 + x)^2$, when x is $0 \cdot 1$ in the latter expression.

In using $1 + nx$ as a first approximation for $(1 + x)^n$, what we have done is to neglect as a trivial quantity every power of x which does not occur in the expression within the brackets. Let us now do the same with

$$\left(1 + x + \frac{x^2}{2\,!}\right)^n$$

We now get, when we put $n = 2$,

$$\left(1 + x + \frac{x^2}{2\,!}\right)^2 = 1 + x + \frac{x^2}{2\,!} + x + x^2 + \left[\frac{x^3}{2\,!}\right] + \frac{x^2}{2\,!} + \left[\frac{x^3}{2\,!} + \frac{x^4}{4}\right]$$

If we reject all terms involving powers of x which are higher than those in the original expression we get

$$1 + 2x + x^2(\tfrac{1}{2} + 1 + \tfrac{1}{2}) = 1 + 2x + 2x^2 = 1 + 2x + \frac{(2x)^2}{2\,!}$$

Do the same with the expression

$$\left(1 + x + \frac{x^2}{2\,!}\right)^3$$

You will find that when you reject all powers of x above x^2 this can be reduced to

$$1 + 3x + \frac{(3x)^2}{2\,!}$$

Similarly the approximate formula for

$$\left(1 + x + \frac{x^2}{2\,!}\right)^4$$

$$1 + 4x + \frac{(4x)^2}{2\,!}$$

So in general if we reject again all powers of x which are above those enclosed by the brackets we get a second approximation formula

$$\left(1 + x + \frac{x^2}{2!}\right)^n = 1 + nx + \frac{(nx)^2}{2!} \cdot \cdot \cdot$$

The agreement between the expressions on the right and left of this equation is much closer than for

$$(1 + x)^n = 1 + nx$$

This you will see by multiplying out when $x = 0 \cdot 1$. We then have

$$\left\{1 + 0 \cdot 1 + \frac{(0 \cdot 1)^2}{2!}\right\}^2 = (1 \cdot 105)^2 = 1 \cdot 221025$$

Substituting $0 \cdot 1$ for x in the approximate formula, we get

$$1 + 2x + \frac{(2x)^2}{2!} = 1 \cdot 22$$

The result is less than $0 \cdot 1$ per cent too small. We can tabulate for this approximation a set of numerical values similar to those in the last table thus:

x	n	$\left(1+x+\frac{x^2}{2!}\right)^n$	$1 + nx + \frac{(nx)^2}{2!}$	Percentage Error
0·1	2	1·221025	1·22	0·1
0·1	3	1·349232625	1·345	0·3
0·1	4	1·49090205	1·48	0·7
0·01	2	1·0202010025	1·0202	0·0001
0·01	3	1·0304540226	1·03045	0·0004
0·01	4	1·0408100855	1·0408	0·001

This encourages us to go on looking for a better approximation of the same kind for raising a number to any required power. You will find, if you multiply out:

$$\begin{aligned}\left(1 + x + \frac{x^2}{2!} + \frac{x^3}{3!}\right)^2 = 1 &+ x + \frac{x^2}{2!} + \frac{x^3}{3!} \\ &+ x + x^2 + \frac{x^3}{2!} + \left[\frac{x^4}{3!}\right] \\ &+ \frac{x^2}{2!} + \frac{x^3}{2!} + \left[\frac{x^4}{2!\,2!} + \frac{x^5}{2!\,3!}\right] \\ &+ \frac{x^3}{3!} + \left[\frac{x^4}{3!} + \frac{x^5}{3!\,2!} + \frac{x^6}{3!\,3!}\right]\end{aligned}$$

If you reject all powers of x higher than x^3, you will get

$$1 + 2x + 2x^2 + \frac{4x^3}{3} = 1 + 2x + \frac{(2x)^2}{2!} + \frac{(2x)^3}{3!}$$

Similarly, when x is small you will get the approximate results

$$\left(1 + x + \frac{x^2}{2!} + \frac{x^3}{3!}\right)^3 = 1 + 3x + \frac{(3x)^2}{2!} + \frac{(3x)^3}{3!}$$

$$\left(1 + x + \frac{x^2}{2!} + \frac{x^3}{3!}\right)^4 = 1 + 4x + \frac{(4x)^2}{2!} + \frac{(4x)^3}{3!}$$

Or more generally

$$\left(1 + x + \frac{x^2}{2!} + \frac{x^3}{3!}\right)^n = 1 + nx + \frac{(nx)^2}{2!} + \frac{(nx)^3}{3!}$$

If you tabulate the numerical results of applying this approximate formula, as we have previously done, you will get the following results:

x	n	$\left(1 + x + \frac{x^2}{2!} + \frac{x^3}{3!}\right)^n$	$1 + nx + \frac{(nx)^2}{2!} + \frac{(nx)^3}{3!}$	Percentage Error
0·1	2	1·22139336	1·221$\dot{3}$	0·005
0·1	3	1·34984323	1·3495	0·025
0·1	4	1·49180174	1·490$\dot{6}$	0·076
0·01	2	1·0202013392	1·020201$\dot{3}$	0·0000006
0·01	3	1·0304545327	1·0304545	0·000003
0·01	4	1·0408107725	1·040810$\dot{6}$	0·00001

You may now suspect what you can find out for yourself by multiplication; that is to say, if we reject the terms above x^4 as trivial compared with x^4, x^3, x^2, when x is smaller than 1:

$$\left(1 + x + \frac{x^2}{2!} + \frac{x^3}{3!} + \frac{x^4}{4!}\right)^n \quad 1 + nx + \frac{(nx)^2}{2!} + \frac{(nx)^3}{3!} + \frac{(nx)^4}{4!}$$

On tabulating the numerical results which we get from this approximate formula, we find:

x	n	$\left(1 + x + \frac{x^2}{2!} + \frac{x^3}{3!} + \frac{x^4}{4!}\right)^n$	$1 + nx + \frac{(nx)^2}{2!} + \frac{(nx)^3}{3!} + \frac{(nx)^4}{4!}$	Percentage Error
0·1	2	1·22140257	1·2214	0·0002
0·1	3	1·34985850	1·3498375	0·0015
0·1	4	1·49182424	1·4917$\dot{3}$	0·006
0·01	2	1·020201340025	1·02020134	0·0000000025
0·01	3	1·030454533951	1·03045453375	0·00000002
0·01	4	1·040810774189	1·04081077$\dot{3}$	0·00000009

You will thus see that we get better and better agreement every time we add a new term $\frac{x^r}{r!}$ to the left and $\frac{(nx)^r}{r!}$ to the right in the expression

$$\left(1 + x + \frac{x^2}{2!} + \frac{x^3}{3!} + \frac{x^4}{4!} \ldots\right)^n = 1 + nx + \frac{(nx)^2}{2!} + \frac{(nx)^3}{3!} + \frac{(nx)^4}{4!} \ldots$$

So you would not be surprised to find that if we add enough terms of this kind we can make x as near to 1 as we like and still get a good result. If $x = 1$ in the unlimited exponential series

$$1 + x + \frac{x^2}{2!} + \frac{x^3}{3!} \ldots$$

the series becomes $1 + 1 + \frac{1}{2!} + \frac{1}{3!} + \frac{1}{4!} \ldots$

This series, as we have already noticed, cannot grow beyond a certain limiting value, which is 2·71828 correct to six figures. So if the result holds good when $x = 1$,

$$(2{\cdot}71828 \ldots)^n = 1 + n + \frac{n^2}{2!} + \frac{n^3}{3!} + \frac{n^4}{4!} \ldots$$

That the correspondence can be made as close as we need by adding enough decimals on the left and new terms of the type $\frac{x^r}{r!}$ on the right is illustrated in the following way. Take only two terms, i.e.

$$(1 + x) = (1 + 1) = 2$$

Then

$$(1 + x)^2 = 2^2 = 4$$

$$(1 + 2x) = 3$$

The difference between $(1 + x)^2$ and $1 + 2x$ is 25 per cent. Proceeding in the same way, we may draw up a table like this:

Correct Value of	Total	Approximate Value	Total	Percentage Error
$(1+1)^2$	4	$1+2$	3	25
$\left(1+1+\frac{1}{2!}\right)^2$	6·25	$1+2+\frac{2^2}{2!}$	5	20
$\left(1+1+\frac{1}{2!}+\frac{1}{3!}\right)^2$	7·1	$1+2+\frac{2^2}{2!}+\frac{2^3}{3!}$	$6{\cdot}\dot{3}$	11
$\left(1+1+\frac{1}{2!}+\frac{1}{3!}+\frac{1}{4!}\right)^2$	7·33507	$1+2+\frac{2^2}{2!}+\frac{2^3}{3!}+\frac{2^4}{4!}$	7	4·6
$\left(1+1+\frac{1}{2!}+\frac{1}{3!}+\frac{1}{4!}+\frac{1}{5!}\right)^2$	7·38028	$1+2+\frac{2^2}{2!}+\frac{2^3}{3!}+\frac{2^4}{4!}+\frac{2^5}{5!}$	$7{\cdot}2\dot{6}$	1·5

The conclusion to which we are led is that if

$$e = 1 + 1 + \frac{1}{2!} + \frac{1}{3!} + \frac{1}{4!} + \frac{1}{5!} \quad \text{and so on,}$$

$$e^x = 1 + x + \frac{x^2}{2!} + \frac{x^3}{3!} + \frac{x^4}{4!} + \frac{x^5}{5!} \quad \text{and so on.}$$

You can test this for a fractional power by putting $x = \frac{1}{2}$ and adding the first six terms of the exponential series:

$$e^{\frac{1}{2}} = \sqrt{2 \cdot 71828 \; . \; . \; .} = 1 \cdot 649 \text{ (correct to three decimals)}$$

$$1 + \frac{1}{2} + \frac{1}{2^2 2!} + \frac{1}{2^3 3!} + \frac{1}{2^4 4!} + \frac{1}{2^5 5!} + \; . \; . \; .$$

$$= 1 + 0 \cdot 5 + 0 \cdot 125 + 0 \cdot 02083 + 0 \cdot 00260 + 0 \cdot 00026 \; . \; . \; .$$

$$= 1 \cdot 649 \text{ (correct to three decimals)}$$

To test it for negative powers put $x = -1$. On adding the first eight terms of the exponential series we get:

$$e^{-1} = \frac{1}{2 \cdot 71828 \; . \; . \; .} = 0 \cdot 368 \text{ (correct to three decimals)}$$

$$1 - 1 + \frac{1}{2!} - \frac{1}{3!} + \frac{1}{4!} - \frac{1}{5!} + \frac{1}{6!} - \frac{1}{7!} \; . \; . \; .$$

$$= (1 - 1) + \tfrac{1}{2}(1 - \tfrac{1}{3}) + \tfrac{1}{24}(1 - \tfrac{1}{5}) + \tfrac{1}{720}(1 - \tfrac{1}{7}) \; . \; . \; .$$

$$= 0 + \tfrac{1}{3} + \tfrac{1}{30} + \tfrac{1}{840} \; . \; . \; .$$

$$= 0 \cdot 368 \text{ (correct to three decimals)}$$

In calculating logarithms for any base other than e by the original methods we have first to go on extracting square roots or cube roots repeatedly to get a table of antilogarithms. If we wish to get the eighth root of 10, we have to take the square root successively three times. To get the sixth root we have to take the square root of the cube root, or *vice versa*. There are no algorithms for getting an odd root other than the cube root. We can get any root of e by substituting a fraction for x, and the higher roots of e are easier to calculate than the lower ones, because they choke off more quickly. You may see this from the calculation of $\sqrt[5]{e}$ or $e^{\frac{1}{5}}$, which has been given already. The first logarithms to the base e were published by Speidell in A.D. 1619. The ease with which it is possible to get any root of e is only one of many interesting characteristics which this extraordinary number possesses. For instance, it is closely connected with an unlimited series which represent π.

It also helps us to get an unlimited series for the sine and cosine of an angle, thus simplifying the construction of accurate tables of angle ratios for use in astronomy, surveying, and navigation.

THE USE OF THE IMAGINARY NUMBER.—The most interesting, and at first surprising, thing about the mathematical pronoun e is that it is closely connected with quantities met with in trigonometry. In tabulating logarithms for the sines of angles Napier set out to find how the length of the half chord varies (see Fig. 129) as it moves along the diameter of a circle in steps equivalent to equal strips of the circumference. In a circle of unit radius (p. 389) the half chord is the sine of the angle enclosed by an arc. The practical problem was to connect with the length of the half chord quantities whose addition corresponds to the multiplication of sines. In the language of modern mathematics this was equivalent to calculating the logarithms of sines to the base $e^{-1} = (0 \cdot 368 \ldots)$. Napier was not acquainted with the series which we have just given, and the reason why e is connected with the behaviour of sines did not become clear until the first really important use of the imaginary i was discovered by de Moivre.

Towards the middle of the sixteenth century the Reformation movement was gaining strength in France, as socialism was gaining strength in Germany and Austria in the closing years of the nineteenth and opening years of the twentieth century. Then came the terror of St. Bartholomew in August 1572. Intellectual reaction reigned supreme, as in Germany and Austria to-day. Even men like Descartes, who never severed their allegiance to the old regime, sought sanctuary in Holland, England, and their colonies. So it came to pass that the intellectual life of the rising Protestant democracies was enriched by absorbing the finest flower of French intellect in the seventeenth century. It may be that Soviet Russia is going to enrich herself at the expense of a decaying social order in the same way. No doubt England, Holland, and their American colonies were not ideal countries to live in. The important thing was that the new social order could find a use, and give opportunities, for real intellectual work, just as Soviet Russia can absorb engineering technique while capitalist countries are restricting production and checking expenditure on research, unless it promotes the extermination of the human species. Among the Huguenot exiles who settled in England during the seventeenth century were the parents of de Moivre. We pronounce his name in the English way, because we can be justly proud that there was once a time when our own country was leading the advance of mankind towards the commonwealth of knowledge.

De Moivre discovered a new field of calculating devices by using the mathematical gerund i or $\sqrt{-1}$ as Diophantus had used the mathematical gerund "$-a$." What is called de Moivre's theorem started a new chapter in modern algebra just as the *law of signs* started a new chapter in the algebra of antiquity. The fundamental rules for using $\sqrt{-1}$ in calculation are simply based on the law of signs itself. Thus if:

$$\begin{aligned} i &= \sqrt{-1} \\ i^2 &= (\sqrt{-1})^2 = -1 \\ i^3 &= (\sqrt{-1})^2 \times i = -i \\ i^4 &= (\sqrt{-1})^3 \times i = -i^2 = +1 \\ i^5 &= (\sqrt{-1})^4 \times i = +i \\ &\text{etc.} \end{aligned}$$

so we have:

i	i^2	i^3	i^4	i^5	i^6	i^7	i^8	i^9	. .
$+i$	-1	$-i$	$+1$	$+i$	-1	$-i$	$+1$	$+i$	. .

The rule which bears the name of de Moivre (de Moivre's theorem) like the binomial theorem of Omar Khayyám, is a rule for raising a quantity to some power represented by the operator n written in the top right-hand corner. It is:

$$(\cos a + i \sin a)^n = \cos na + i \sin na$$

Do not bother at present about the *meaning* of this. The meaning of a rule in mathematics is either a statement about its consistency with other rules, or a statement about how it can be used. First satisfy yourself that it is consistent with what you know already about sines and cosines, negative quantities, square roots, and powers. One thing which you will need to remember is the demonstration which is given in Chapter 6, p. 255:

$$\cos^2 a + \sin^2 a = 1$$
$$\text{or} \qquad \sin^2 a = 1 - \cos^2 a$$

Bearing this in mind, apply the customary laws of multiplication to

$$(\cos a + i \sin a)^2$$

We then have

$$\begin{array}{l} \cos a + i \sin a \\ \underline{\cos a + i \sin a} \\ \cos^2 a + i \cos a \sin a \\ \qquad\quad \underline{+\, i \cos a \sin a + i^2 \sin^2 a} \\ \cos^2 a + 2i \cos a \sin a + i^2 \sin^2 a \end{array}$$

Now we already know that

$$\sin 2a = \sin (a + a)$$
$$= 2 \sin a \cos a \quad \text{(p. 255)}$$
$$\therefore \quad 2i \cos a \sin a = i \sin 2a$$

So we may rewrite the result obtained as

$$\cos^2 a + i \sin 2a + i^2 \sin^2 a$$

And since $i = \sqrt{-1}$ this is also the same as:

$$\cos^2 a - \sin^2 a + i \sin 2a$$

But we also know (see p. 255) that

$$\cos 2a = \cos (a + a)$$
$$= \cos^2 a - \sin^2 a$$

So we can now write:

$$(\cos a + i \sin a)^2 = \underline{\cos 2a + i \sin 2a}$$

We see then that the theorem works for squaring. By multiplying out you get:

$$(\cos a + i \sin a)^3 = \cos^3 a + 3i \sin a \cos^2 a$$
$$+ 3i^2 \sin^2 a \cos a + i^3 \sin^3 a$$
$$= \cos^3 a + 3i \sin a \cos^2 a - 3 \sin^2 a \cos a - i \sin^3 a$$

By applying the rules given on p. 254 we find that

$$\cos 3a = \cos (2a + a)$$
$$= \cos 2a \cos a - \sin 2a \sin a$$
$$= \cos a (\cos^2 a - \sin^2 a) - \sin a (2 \sin a \cos a)$$
$$= \cos^3 a - 3 \sin^2 a \cos a$$

In the same way

$$\sin 3a = \sin (2a + a)$$
$$= \sin a \cos 2a + \cos a \sin 2a$$
$$= \sin a (\cos^2 a - \sin^2 a) + \cos a (2 \sin a \cos a)$$
$$= 3 \cos^2 a \sin a - \sin^3 a$$

So we may now put:

$$(\cos a + i \sin a)^3 = \cos^3 a + 3i \sin a \cos^2 a - 3 \sin^2 a \cos a - i \sin^3 a$$
$$= (\cos^3 a - 3 \sin^2 a \cos a) + i\,(3 \cos^2 a \sin a - \sin^3 a)$$
$$= \underline{\cos 3a + i \sin 3a}$$

Thus the theorem also works for cubes, and in the same way we arrive at:

$$(\cos a + i \sin a)^4 = \cos 4a + i \sin 4a$$
$$(\cos a + i \sin a)^5 = \cos 5a + i \sin 5a$$

The rule which is known as de Moivre's theorem is equally true for fractional powers and negative powers. Thus we can see that

$$(\cos a + i \sin a)^{-n} = \frac{1}{\cos na + i \sin na}$$
$$= \frac{\cos na - i \sin na}{\cos na - i \sin na} \cdot \frac{1}{\cos na + i \sin na}$$

Now we know (Dem. 4, p. 142) that

$$(a + b)\,(a - b) = a^2 - b^2$$

$$\therefore\ (\cos na - i \sin na)\,(\cos na + i \sin na) = \cos^2 na - i^2 \sin^2 na$$
$$= \cos^2 na + \sin^2 na$$
$$= 1$$

Hence

$$\frac{\cos na - i \sin na}{(\cos na - i \sin na)\,(\cos na + i \sin na)} = \cos na - i \sin na$$

For fractional powers de Moivre's theorem is found to be consistent with the rules we have already learned by putting $a = \frac{b}{n}$, thus:

$$\left(\cos \frac{b}{n} + i \sin \frac{b}{n}\right)^n = \cos n\frac{b}{n} + i \sin n\frac{b}{n}$$
$$= \cos b + i \sin b$$

But we must now be careful, because

$$\left(\cos \frac{b + 2\pi}{n} + i \sin \frac{b + 2\pi}{n}\right)^n = \cos (b + 2\pi) + i \sin (b + 2\pi)$$
$$= \cos b + i \sin b$$

and you can easily verify that

$$\cos \frac{b}{n} + i \sin \frac{b}{n} \text{ and } \cos \frac{b + 2\pi}{n} + i \sin \frac{b + 2\pi}{n}$$

are not the same. So we can only say that *one of the values of* $\sqrt[n]{\cos b + i \sin b}$ *or* $(\cos b + i \sin b)^{1/n}$ *is* $\cos \frac{b}{n} + i \sin \frac{b}{n}$.

If n is a whole number there are also $n - 1$ other values

$$\cos \frac{b + 2r\pi}{n} + i \sin \frac{b + 2r\pi}{n}$$

where $$r = 1, 2, 3, \ldots \text{ up to } n - 1.$$

In one of Dickens's novels the charity boy asks, when he comes to the end of the alphabet, whether it is worth going through so much to get so little. The same question may occur to you. So we shall now proceed to show how the theorem of de Moivre can be used to shorten the work of constructing a table of trigonometrical ratios. To make this clear, it will be helpful if we retrace our steps. We have already seen that

$$\cos 3a = \cos^3 a - 3 \sin^2 a \cos a$$

We may also write this as

$$\begin{aligned} \cos 3a &= \cos^3 a - 3 \cos a\,(1 - \cos^2 a) \\ &= \cos^3 a - 3 \cos a + 3 \cos^3 a \\ &= 4 \cos^3 a - 3 \cos a \end{aligned}$$

The same result which we used to illustrate the truth of de Moivre's rule can naturally be obtained by applying it. Thus if

$$\begin{aligned} x &= \cos a + i \sin a \\ x^{-1} &= (\cos a + i \sin a)^{-1} \\ \therefore \quad \frac{1}{x} &= \cos a - i \sin a \\ \therefore \quad x + \frac{1}{x} &= 2 \cos a \\ \text{and} \quad x - \frac{1}{x} &= 2i \sin a \end{aligned}$$

Likewise we may put

$$\begin{aligned} x^n &= \cos na + i \sin na \\ \frac{1}{x^n} &= \cos na - i \sin na \\ \therefore \quad x^n + \frac{1}{x^n} &= 2 \cos na \\ \text{and} \quad x^n - \frac{1}{x^n} &= 2i \sin na \end{aligned}$$

We thus see that if $x + \frac{1}{x} = 2 \cos a$

$$x^n + \frac{1}{x^n} = 2 \cos na$$

So if we wish to find cos $3a$, knowing cos a, we may put

$$2\cos 3a = x^3 + \frac{1}{x^3}$$

$$\therefore \quad 2\cos a = x + \frac{1}{x}$$

$$\therefore \quad (2\cos a)^3 = \left(x + \frac{1}{x}\right)^3$$

$$\therefore \quad 8\cos^3 a = x^3 + 3x^2\cdot\frac{1}{x} + 3x\cdot\frac{1}{x^2} + \frac{1}{x^3}$$

$$= \left(x^3 + \frac{1}{x^3}\right) + 3\left(x + \frac{1}{x}\right)$$

$$= 2\cos 3a + 6\cos a$$

$$\therefore \quad 4\cos^3 a = \cos 3a + 3\cos a$$

$$\text{or} \quad \cos 3a = 4\cos^3 a - 3\cos a$$

This is the same result as we have already used. To convince yourself that the *imaginary* quantities may be used for calculation you can now put

$$(2\cos a)^6 = \left(x + \frac{1}{x}\right)^6$$

$$64\cos^6 a = x^6 + 6x^5\cdot\frac{1}{x} + 15x^4\cdot\frac{1}{x^2} + 20x^3\cdot\frac{1}{x^3} + 15x^2\cdot\frac{1}{x^4} + 6x\cdot\frac{1}{x^5} + \frac{1}{x^6}$$

$$= \left(x^6 + \frac{1}{x^6}\right) + 6\left(x^4 + \frac{1}{x^4}\right) + 15\left(x^2 + \frac{1}{x^2}\right) + 20$$

$$= 2\cos 6a + 12\cos 4a + 30\cos 2a + 20$$

$$\cos 6a = 32\cos^6 a - 6\cos 4a - 15\cos 2a - 10$$

You can check this from two values of cos a which you know already, i.e. (a) cos 90° = 0; (b) cos 60° = $\frac{1}{2}$. So

$$(a) \quad \cos 540^\circ = 32\cos^6 90^\circ - 6\cos 360^\circ - 15\cos 180^\circ - 10$$

$$\therefore \quad \cos(360 + 180)^\circ = 0 - 6(1) - 15(-1) - 10$$

$$\therefore \quad \cos 180^\circ = -1$$

$$(b) \quad \cos 360^\circ = 32\cos^6 60^\circ - 6\cos 240^\circ - 15\cos 120^\circ - 10$$

$$= 32\cos^6 60^\circ - 6\cos(180 + 60)^\circ - 15\cos(180 - 60)^\circ - 10$$

$$= 32\left(\tfrac{1}{64}\right) + 6\left(\tfrac{1}{2}\right) + 15\left(\tfrac{1}{2}\right) - 10$$

$$= 1$$

Having now reason to hope that we may make $\sqrt{-1}$ or i do the sort of work which can be checked by actual calculations, we shall use it to derive the two series from which we can obtain the sine or cosine of any angle to any degree of accuracy required. We have seen how the study of trigonometry in connexion with the preparation of astronomical tables for navigation prompted the search for quick methods of calculation, and how the discovery of logarithms led on to the study of unlimited series such as the exponential series. A crowning achievement which followed the Great Navigations was the further discovery that the exponential series has a simple relation to the theorem of de Moivre. The result of this discovery was a further simplification of the labour entailed in socializing the fruits of Greek geometry in the tables of angle ratios which are used to find the position of a ship at sea or to construct an ordnance map. To see the connexion between the exponential series and the theorem of de Moivre, first put

$$x = \cos 1 + i \sin 1$$

This is the same as making $a = 1$ in the original expression of de Moivre's rule, and if we now use a like n for *any* number

$$x^a = \cos a + i \sin a \qquad \text{(i)}$$

$$\text{and} \qquad x^{-a} = \cos a - i \sin a$$

As before, we may put $\quad x^a - x^{-a} = 2i \sin a$

We can also represent x as some power of e, thus

$$x = e^y$$

$$\text{or} \qquad y = \log_e x \qquad \text{(ii)}$$

Using the exponential series, we have:

$$x^a = e^{ay} = 1 + ay + \frac{a^2y^2}{2!} + \frac{a^3y^3}{3!} + \frac{a^4y^4}{4!} \ldots$$

$$x^{-a} = e^{-ay} = 1 - ay + \frac{a^2y^2}{2!} - \frac{a^3y^3}{3!} + \frac{a^4y^4}{4!} \ldots$$

Subtracting the lower from the upper, we get

$$x^a - x^{-a} = 2ay + 2\frac{a^3y^3}{3!} + 2\frac{a^5y^5}{5!} + 2\frac{a^7y^7}{7!} \ldots$$

This may also be written

$$2i \sin a = 2ya + 2\frac{y^3a^3}{3!} + 2\frac{y^5a^5}{5!} \ldots$$

$$\therefore \quad \frac{i \sin a}{a} = y + \frac{y^3a^2}{3!} + \frac{y^5a^4}{5!} \ldots \qquad \text{(iii)}$$

Since a is any angle, this equation is true when a is so small that we can neglect any term multiplied by a, i.e.

$$y + \frac{y^3a^2}{3!} + \frac{y^5a^4}{5!} + \frac{y^7a^6}{7!} \ . \ . \ . = y$$

We have also seen that if a stands for *radians* (see Chapter 6, p. 264) when a is very small:

$$\frac{\sin a}{a} = 1$$

$$\therefore \quad \frac{i \sin a}{a} = i$$

So when a is very small one side of equation (iii) reduces to i and the other side to y. We thus find that

$$i = y$$

$$\therefore \quad x = e^i$$

$$\therefore \quad x^a = e^{ia}$$

Putting in the value of x^a in (i), this means that if a is measured in radians:

$$e^{ia} = \cos a + i \sin a$$

But since $i^2 = -1$, $i^3 = -i$, $i^4 = +1$, etc.

$$e^{ia} = 1 + ia - \frac{a^2}{2!} - \frac{ia^3}{3!} + \frac{a^4}{4!} + \frac{ia^5}{5!} - \frac{a^6}{6!}$$

$$\therefore \cos a + i \sin a = \left(1 - \frac{a^2}{2!} + \frac{a^4}{4!} - \frac{a^6}{6!} \ . \ . \ . \right) + i\left(a - \frac{a^3}{3!} + \frac{a^5}{5!} \ . \ . \ . \right)$$

Do not now make the same mistake as those who confuse people with price indices in which all sorts of quantities are mixed up indiscriminately till the final result of their cerebrations is a state of muddle which faithfully reflects the system of which they are the hired apologists. To take the next step, remember that real mathematicians do not jumble up numbers which stand for one sort of thing with numbers which stand for another sort of thing. The man who did not go to church (p. 403) after he left the inn called "The Turtle and Toasting Fork" taught us that quantities which have i in front of them do not represent the same sort of measurements as quantities which have not. In the Reformation geometry they represent measurements in a different direction. So just as we say that if

a pears and b ponies = 30 pears and 2 ponies

$$a = 30$$

and $\quad b = 2$

we must also say that if

$$\cos a + i \sin a = p + iq$$
$$p = \cos a$$
$$q = \sin a$$

We now do the same thing with the equation

$$\cos a + i \sin a = \left(1 - \frac{a^2}{2!} + \frac{a^4}{4!} \cdot \cdot \cdot\right) + i\left(a - \frac{a^3}{3!} + \frac{a^5}{5!} \cdot \cdot \cdot\right)$$

From which we conclude that if a is measured in *radians:*

$$\cos a = 1 - \frac{a^2}{2!} + \frac{a^4}{4!} - \frac{a^6}{6!} + \frac{a^8}{8!} \cdot \cdot \cdot$$
$$\sin a = a - \frac{a^3}{3!} + \frac{a^5}{5!} - \frac{a^7}{7!} \cdot \cdot \cdot$$

This means that you can calculate the cosine or sine of 1, 0·5, 0·1, etc., radians directly by substituting 1, 0·5, 0·1, etc., for a in the unlimited series given above. You will see that they must choke off quickly if a is less than 1. To assure yourself that this result is trustworthy turn back to Chapter 6, p. 246, and you will find that by using Euclid's geometry we obtained the values

$$\cos 15° = 0\cdot 966$$
$$\sin 15° = 0\cdot 259$$

To use the series given we have to convert 15° into radians, thus:

$$15° = \frac{1}{6}(90°) = \frac{1}{6}\left(\frac{\pi}{2}\right) \text{ radians}$$

If we take $\pi = 3\cdot 1416$, $15° = 0\cdot 2618$ radians

So putting $a = 0\cdot 2618$ we have

$$a^2 = 0\cdot 0685$$
$$a^3 = 0\cdot 0179$$
$$a^4 = 0\cdot 005$$
etc.

Thus $$\cos 15° = 1 - \frac{0\cdot 0685}{2} + \frac{0\cdot 005}{24} \cdot \cdot \cdot$$

$$\sin 15° = 0\cdot 2618 - \frac{0\cdot 0179}{6} \cdot \cdot \cdot$$

These series choke off so rapidly that we only need to take the first two terms to get

$$\cos 15^\circ = 0{\cdot}966$$
$$\sin 15^\circ = 0{\cdot}259$$

VECTOR ANALYSIS.—You can now see that the *imaginary* number i is anything but a mere figment of the imagination. With its help we can make tables from which we can calculate the latitude and longitude of an ocean liner. The calculation of alternating currents on which modern lighting and power depend also employs the equation

$$e^{ia} = \cos a + i \sin a$$

Since the time of de Moivre a new branch of mathematics called *Vector Analysis* has been developed, especially in connection with the study of the electrical phenomena which were first discovered by Faraday in the earlier part of the nineteenth century. A *vector* is a quantity which is understood to have a definite direction from some fixed point, as well as a definite distance from it. Temperatures, forces, magnetic and electrical attractions, and the like can be represented by distances. Consequently the flow of heat, forces tending to propel a body in a particular direction, magnetic and electrical fields can all be represented by vectors. The use of vectors illustrates a feature of great interest in the history of mathematics. The rules of geometry and algebra were invented so long ago that we are apt to forget that they were invented to deal with real objects in the world of social experience. The rules of vector algebra have been drawn up to fit the requirements of measuring new phenomena in the world of social experience. So it is less easy to conceal the fact that they are nothing more than grammatical conventions which are used because they are suitable to the needs of socially organized mankind.

Chapter 1 introduced a small tank with an automatic siphon to illustrate the fact that adding two to two in the real world does not always give us four. For the figure on p. 33 the laws of elementary arithmetic would not help us to find how much the tank contains when a measured quantity of water is added to what is there already. If we continue to use the sign + to mean addition in the physical sense, we should have to make different laws, such as

$$2 + 2 = 2$$
$$3 + 1 = 2$$

In vector analysis laws of addition, subtraction, and multiplication are made to fit the way in which mechanical forces interact. As this branch of mathematics has developed mainly in connexion with physical problems, it is not possible to indicate its scope without recourse to technical illustrations. However, the basic principles can

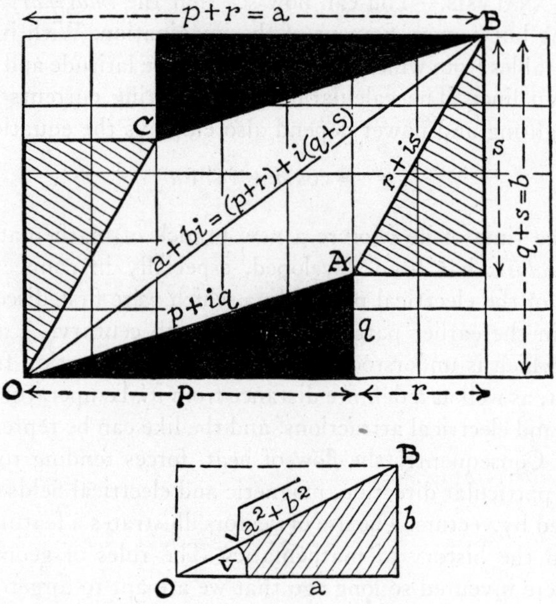

FIG. 165.—THE ADDITION OF TWO VECTORS

be illustrated in a general way by what is called vector addition. In Fig. 165 OA is a vector which represents movement along a measured distance from the point O in the direction shown. OC is another vector representing a measured distance in a more northerly direction from the same fixed point. Adding the vector OA to the vector OC means finding the distance and direction from the fixed point O if we first execute the movement represented by the vector OA and proceeding from A move along AB, which is equivalent in distance and compass reading to the vector OC, or alternatively movement from O to C followed by movement from C to B equivalent in distance and compass reading to OA. This is written with the old sign, though it carries a new meaning. Thus:

$$OA + OC = OB$$

The vector OB, which stands for the result of adding a day's march represented by the vector OC to a walking tour which began with the vector OA or *vice versa*, stands for our final distance and direction from the place where we started. The numerical value of OB, which includes its length, the distance of B from O, and its direction, the angle which OB makes with the base line running east and west, is itself the result of adding a day's march so many units of length east to a day's march so many units north, or *vice versa*. From the illustration given in Fig. 133 we have found that multiplying a distance x units by i is equivalent to a distance x units measured in a direction at right angles to the original distance. To distinguish b units of measurement due north from a units of measurement due east, we use i as a label in front of the former, so that we write

$$\text{OB} = a + ib$$

In the same way, if OA is equivalent to q units due north and p units due east, we put

$$\text{OA} = p + iq$$

Also, if OC is s units due north and r units due east,

$$\text{OC} = r + is$$

You will now see from the upper diagram that

$$a = p + r$$
$$b = q + s$$

From the lower figure you will see that the distance represented by the vector OB is

$$\sqrt{a^2 + b^2}$$

The angle V, which stands for the direction of the vector, is the angle whose tangent is $\frac{b}{a}$. This can be found from tables of tangents, provided we know b and a. Thus the principle of vector addition is that if we go hiking and change our direction every day, we deduce the final direction and distance from the place where we started by adding separately all the northerly bearings and all the easterly bearings. For this the imaginary i is merely used as a label to warn us against making the same confusion as political economists.

Having defined a process of vector addition to correspond with the physical act of walking a certain distance in one direction and a certain distance in another direction, we can go on from this to define other operations in which i is used in the same way as de Moivre used it. This leads to some very valuable short cuts in physical measurement. Such operations have been designed to fit the results of experimental observations, and they are appropriate to the kind of phenomena which suggested them. However exact science becomes it is necessarily more than a mere collection of symbols. What the scientist investigates decides the rules which the symbols have to obey.

Exercises on Chapter 10

HOW TO USE LOGARITHM TABLES

There are a few details of method to note when using logarithm tables. Any number whatever can be written as the product of a number between 1 and 10 and 10 raised to some power.

For example, 9,876 can be written as $9 \cdot 876 \times 10^3$. Now we know that the logarithm of any number between 1 and 10 is a positive fraction, and we can write down the logarithm of 10^3 as 3. It is easy to see that the logarithm of any number consists of a whole number which can be written down by inspection and a fractional part which is the same for all numbers having the same digits in the same order.

Thus

$$\begin{aligned} \log 9 \cdot 876 &= 0 \cdot 9946 \\ \log 98 \cdot 76 &= \log 10 + \log 9 \cdot 876 \\ &= 1 \cdot 9946 \\ \log 987 \cdot 6 &= \log 10^2 + \log 9 \cdot 876 \\ &= 2 \cdot 9946 \\ &\text{etc.} \end{aligned}$$

and

$$\begin{aligned} \log 0 \cdot 9876 &= \log 10^{-1} \times \log 9 \cdot 876 \\ &= -1 + 0 \cdot 9946 \\ \log 0 \cdot 09876 &= \log 10^{-2} \times \log 9 \cdot 876 \\ &= -2 + 0 \cdot 9946 \end{aligned}$$

The last two logarithms are written as follows:

$$\log 0\cdot 9876 = \bar{1}\cdot 9946$$
$$\log 0\cdot 09876 = \bar{2}\cdot 9946$$

This is simply a device for making calculations easier. For example:

$$\begin{aligned}\log \frac{182\cdot 3}{0\cdot 021} &= \log 182\cdot 3 - \log 0\cdot 021\\ &= 2\cdot 2608 - (\bar{2}\cdot 3222)\\ &= 2 + 0\cdot 2608 - (-2 + 0\cdot 3222)\\ &= 2 + 0\cdot 2608 + 2 - 0\cdot 3222\\ &= 4 - 0\cdot 0614\\ &= 3\cdot 9386\end{aligned}$$

$$\therefore \qquad \frac{182\cdot 3}{0\cdot 021} = 8682$$

The positive fractional part of the logarithm is called the *mantissa*, and the integral part, which may be positive or negative, is called the *characteristic*.

To find the logarithm of 9·876 in the table the procedure is as follows. At the left-hand side of the table is a column of double figures beginning with 10. We look down this till we find 98. Looking at the top of the page we see columns headed by the numbers 0 to 9, so that we look along the line beginning 98 till we come to the column headed 7. The number given in this place is 9,943, and this is the mantissa of the logarithm of 9·87. To take into account the last figure, 6, we look at the right-hand side of the table, where there is a set of columns with the numbers 1 to 9 at the top. The numbers in these columns indicate what has to be added to the logarithm to take account of the fourth figure in the given number. In the present case we have found the right mantissa for 9·870, and we want to know how much to add on for 9·876. Looking along the line from 98 we see at the extreme right hand under the column headed 6 the number 3. So that the required mantissa is 0·9943 + 0·0003, i.e. 0·9946.

When the logarithm is known, the number of which it is the logarithm can be found by reversing the above process. For example, we can find the number whose logarithm is 2·6276. Considering first the mantissa 0·6276, we can find from either a table of logarithms or a table of antilogarithms that the digits corresponding with it are 4,242.

The characteristic 2 tells us that the number lies between 100 and 1,000. Therefore the number required is 424·2.

1. Multiply the following numbers:

(*a*) by using the formula

$$\sin A \cos B = \tfrac{1}{2}\sin (A + B) + \tfrac{1}{2}\sin (A - B)$$

(*b*) by using the formula

$$\cos A \cos B = \tfrac{1}{2}\cos (A + B) + \tfrac{1}{2}\cos (A - B)$$

(*c*) by using logarithm tables

(i) $2 \cdot 738 \times 1504$ (iii) $5 \cdot 412 \times 368$

(ii) $8 \cdot 726 \times 3471$ (iv) $2 \cdot 1505 \times 46 \cdot 12$

Check your results by ordinary multiplication.

2. Calculate the following by logarithms:

$(78 \cdot 91)^2$ $(1 \cdot 003)^3$

$\sqrt{68990 \cdot 3} \div 0 \cdot 0271$ $\sqrt[3]{0 \cdot 0731}$

$9 \cdot 437 \div 484$

$$\frac{\sqrt{273} \times (1 \cdot 1)^3}{0 \cdot 48}$$

3. Find the tenth root of 1,024, the eighth root of 6,561, and the eighth root of $25\frac{161}{256}$ by logarithms, and check your results by multiplication.

4. Plot the curve $y = \log_{10} x$

5. Do not forget that logarithms are a device for doing multiplication and division rapidly. There is no simple way of finding the value of $\log (a + b)$, so that if, for example, you want to calculate $\sqrt{1 \cdot 01} - \sqrt[3]{1 \cdot 01}$, each term must be calculated separately.

Find the value of

(i) $(23 \cdot 91)^3 + (48 \cdot 24)^3$

(ii) $\sqrt[4]{1001} - \sqrt[3]{101}$

(iii) $$\frac{(0 \cdot 4573)^2}{(0 \cdot 5436)^2 - (0 \cdot 3276)^2}$$

6. Calculate the following, using log tables:

(i) Find the compound interest on £1,000 in 6 years at 4 per cent per annum.

(ii) How long will it take a sum of money to double itself at 10 per cent per annum.

(iii) Find the compound interest on £400 for $5\frac{1}{2}$ years at $3\frac{1}{2}$ per cent per annum, payable half-yearly.

7. Taking e as $2 \cdot 718$, calculate the following:

$$\log_e 1 \cdot 001 \qquad \log_e \sqrt{2}, \qquad \log_e 3789$$

8. In an experiment the following values were obtained for two variables x and y:

x	1·70	2·24	2·89	4·08	5·63	6·80
y	320	411	491	671	903	1,050
x	8·42	12·4	16·3	19·0	24·3	
y	1,270	1,780	2,250	2,520	3,180	

Plot two graphs, one showing x and y, and the other $\log x$ and $\log y$. From the second show that the relation between $\log x$ and $\log y$ is approximately described by the equation

$$\log y = 0 \cdot 876 \log x + 2 \cdot 299$$

From this write down an equation connecting x and y.

9. Write down the binomial expansion of $(1 + 0 \cdot 05)^{-4}$. Find its value by taking the first five terms. Show that the error involved is less than $0 \cdot 0000163$.

10. Using the "infinite" series for $\sin a$ and $\cos a$, find the values of $\sin 1°$ and $\cos 1°$. How many terms do you need to get the values of $\sin 1°$ and $\cos 1°$ given in four-figure tables?

11. Using the "infinite" series for $\sin na$ and $\cos na$ and the values just obtained for $\sin 1°$ and $\cos 1°$, make a table of the sines and cosines of 1°, 2°, 3°, 4°, 5°, and compare with the values given in the tables.

THINGS TO MEMORIZE

$\sin A \cos B = \frac{1}{2}\sin(A+B) + \frac{1}{2}\sin(A-B)$

$\cos A \cos B = \frac{1}{2}\cos(A+B) + \frac{1}{2}\cos(A-B)$

$\log_{10} 100 = 2$

$\log_{10} 10 = 1$

$\log_{10} 1 = 0$

$\log_{10} 0{\cdot}1 = -1$

$\log_{10} 0{\cdot}01 = -2$

$e = 1 + 1 + \frac{1}{2!} + \frac{1}{3!} + \frac{1}{4!} + \frac{1}{5!} + \ldots$

$(\cos a + i \sin a)^n = \cos na + i \sin na$

$\sin 3A = 3 \sin A - 4 \sin^3 A$ (p. 496)

$\cos 3A = 4 \cos^3 A - 3 \cos A$

$\sin a \text{ (radians)} = a - \frac{a^3}{3!} + \frac{a^5}{5!} - \frac{a^7}{7!} \ldots$

$\cos a \text{ (radians)} = 1 - \frac{a^2}{2!} + \frac{a^4}{4!} - \frac{a^6}{6!} \ldots$

CHAPTER XI

The Arithmetic of Growth and Shape

OR

WHAT THE CALCULUS IS ABOUT

THE invention of logarithms and the introduction of the Reformation geometry coincided in the opening years of the seventeenth century. Two technical developments which forced themselves on the attention of mathematicians during the ensuing period paved the way for advance in the science of mechanics and new methods of calculation necessary for further advance. One of these was progress in the use of artillery. The other was improvement in the construction of clocks. When a Spanish king retired from the intrigues of European politics to end his years designing them, clocks had all the novelty of the racing car and the autogyro in our generation.

We commonly divide the mechanical problems arising in connection with solid objects into two groups. One, called *statics*, deals with how one weight balances another when both are at rest. The problems of stress in designing a building are among the principal applications of the mechanics of rest. In contrast to architectural mechanics, or *statics*, *dynamics* is the study of moving bodies. The world of classical antiquity produced architectural achievements and feats of irrigation hardly inferior to anything which our own civilization has constructed. In Alexandria, which was in close touch with the technical problems arising out of large-scale building construction and irrigation, the basic principles of statical mechanics for both solid bodies and liquids were taught in much the same way as we teach them today. Such machinery as was used till the fall of the Roman Empire included little more than devices for using the bodily energy of the slave, the soldier, the horse, or the ox. For designing primitive machinery like the catapult or the pump, the statical mechanics of Archimedes was sufficient. The introduction of explosives and of clocks driven by weights or (later on) by springs, laid the foundations of the modern age which exploits energy derived from sources other than the metabolism of human beings or beasts of burden. Although isolated inventors among the Chinese and Alexandrians, like Hero, who made a model steam-turbine, recognized the possibility of constructing machines driven without the muscular activity of living beings, the energetic basis of ancient civilization rested primarily upon the institution of slavery mitigated more or less by the use of beasts of burden. At the beginning of the sixteenth century civilization stands on the threshold of an advance which was destined to eclipse every constructive achievement from the dawn of Nilotic civilization to the circumnavigation of the terrestrial globe. At the very moment when the greed of competitive mercantile enterprise was initiating the infamies of the slave trade, human inventiveness had discovered the means of creating a society which could guarantee leisure and security without slavery. The birth of dynamics, or the mechanics of motion, signalizes the great cultural dichotomy which separates the slave civilizations of the past from men and women who are now becoming historically conscious of their part in planning human life on earth in accordance with common human needs.

While the laws of planetary motion were being studied by Tycho Brahe and Kepler at the end of the sixteenth century, the clock was becoming an instrument of increasing importance, and experiments directed to improve its mechanism were exposing the laws of terrestrial movement. Acceleration, or gathering speed, something so easy to grasp in these days when we hear automobiles changing gear on a hill, was quite a new experience which had not impressed itself on the imagination of men and women accustomed to the relatively slow and jerky movements of vehicles drawn by horse or ox against the friction of rough roads. Galileo (1564–1642), who discovered the principle that successive swings of a pendulum occupy the same time, also showed that compact and comparatively heavy bodies of different sizes and densities fall to the earth simultaneously, gathering speed at the same rate, if they start from the same place. Galileo revolutionized mechanics by introducing the principle that the pulling power which a body exerts by its weight may be measured by its power to increase the rate at which another body moves. Huyghens (1629–1695), who first adapted the pendulum to the clock, studied the laws of collision of elastic bodies and the principle of centrifugal motion which he used to make clocks keep correct time in different latitudes.* As compared with any which went before, the century which followed the Great Navigations was obsessed with the problem of motion. The crowning

* The earth's centrifugal pull is different at different latitudes, and hence a pendulum does not swing exactly at the same rate at the equator and the poles.

achievement, which came at the end of the seventeenth century, was Newton's Law of Universal Gravitation, which linked together the path of the planets, the path of the cannon-ball, and the principle of centrifugal motion. Galileo's principle of terrestrial gravitation made it possible to show why a cannon-ball projected at an angle to the horizon follows a curved path at approximately constant horizontal speed owing to the combined action of the initial explosion and the pull which makes bodies gather speed as they fall to the earth. The possibility that all material bodies exert a pull on one another proportional to their masses like the pull of a weight at the end of a string when we swing it round in a circle suggested itself to several of Newton's contemporaries as the explanation of Kepler's laws. Newton was able to show that the curved path of a body moving at constant speed will be an ellipse if the pull towards one of the foci of the ellipse measured by its power to impart motion is inversely proportional to the square of its distance from that focus. This demonstration linked together the facts of terrestrial motion with the motion of the planets in elliptical orbits, their sizes, and their distances from the sun as focus.

So soon as mathematicians began to concern themselves with the problems of motion, they found themselves severely handicapped by the Arabic algebra, which derived its principles from classical geometry. They were forced to devise a new instrument of calculation, based on the Reformation geometry. This new algebra is usually called the Infinitesimal Calculus. Though it was first devised to deal with the geometry of motion, it can also be applied to other kinds of calculation, such as constructing a table of logarithms or getting a value for π. From a geometrical point of view, it is primarily concerned with two problems (Fig. 166). One branch, called the Differential Calculus, is a means of finding how steep a curve is at any point. Thus the curve shown in the figure begins with a very gradual slope, then becomes very steep, and finally flattens out till it hardly slopes at all. What is called a *differential coefficient* is nothing more than a formula for finding how much a curve slopes at a particular point if we know the co-ordinates of the point. The other branch, called the *Integral Calculus*, is primarily concerned with finding the area enclosed between a portion of the curve (AC in the diagram), the corresponding points on the x axis (B and D), and two lines called "ordinates" parallel to the y axis (AB and CD). What is called an *integral* is simply the formula for finding such an area if we know the x co-ordinates (OB and

OD) of A and C. The Differential and Integral Calculus both employ similar methods, because the area enclosed between two ordinates of a curve itself depends on how much the boundary slopes.

Since the calculus was devised to deal with problems of motion, it is not easy to see the point of it without first asking how measuring slopes and areas comes into the study of movement. So before seeing

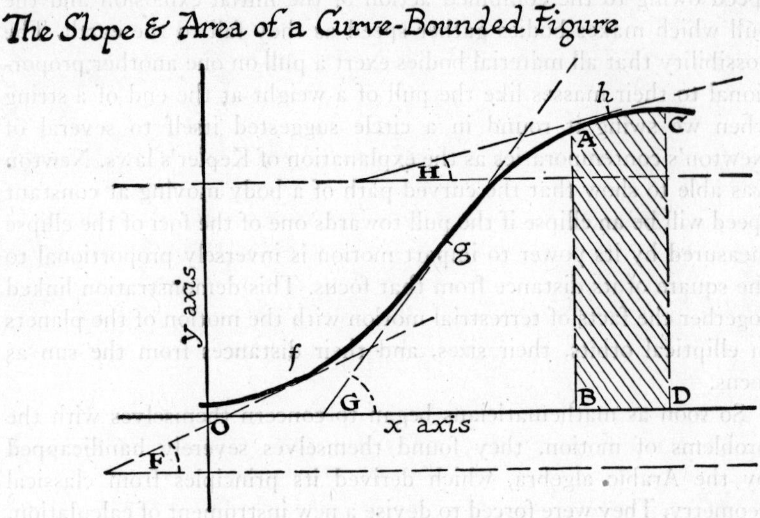

FIG. 166

The slope of the curve is first relatively flat at *f*. It becomes steeper in the middle at *g* as *x* increases. Finally it becomes flatter at *h*. At any point the steepness is indicated by the size of the angle which the tangent to the curve makes with the *x* axis or with any line parallel to it.

how we can use it to do other things we must spend a little effort in trying to see how the speed of the ship is represented in the map geometry of the great navigations.

GRAPHICAL REPRESENTATION OF SPEED AND ACCELERATION.—In using the old algebra to describe moving things, we do not find ourselves in any difficulties provided things move in a straight line at uniform speed. Problems of that kind only occur in textbooks. They do not happen in real life. Indeed, we have only to look a little more closely at textbook problems to see how very roughly they can represent real happenings. Such a problem, taken from a textbook, was given to illustrate a simple equation in Chapter 7. We were told that one train (A) travelling at 50 miles per hour left London on a 400-mile journey to Edinburgh at one o'clock and another train (B) travelling at 25 miles per hour by the same route left Edinburgh at four o'clock. Taking the problem at its face value we might plot along the *y* axis,

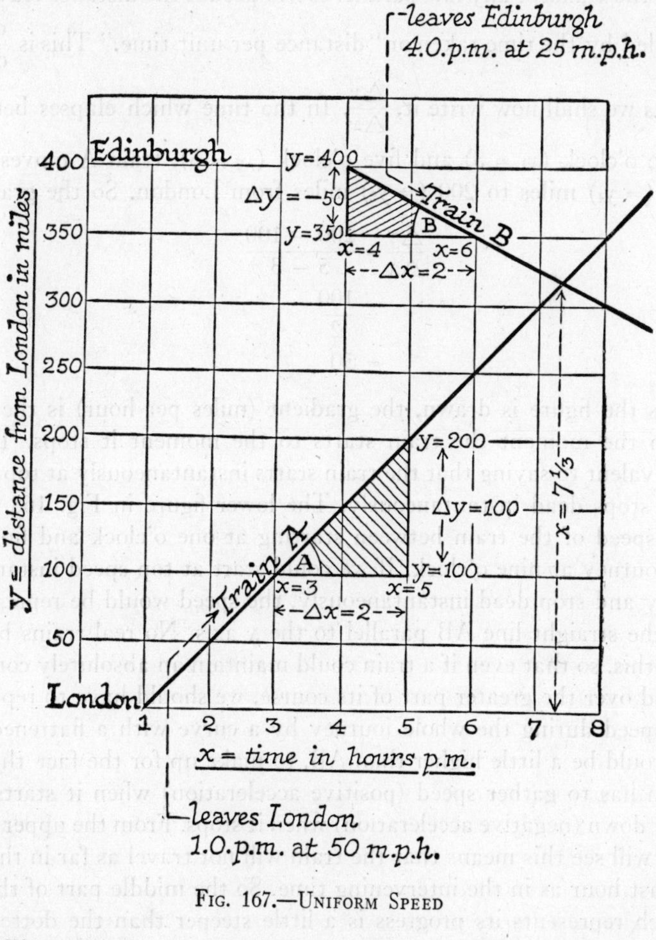

FIG. 167.—UNIFORM SPEED

as in Fig. 167, the distance from London in miles, and along the *x* axis the time in hours p.m. on the day when this improbable event took place. The progress of the two trains would then be represented by two straight lines crossing where $x = 7\frac{1}{3}$ (7.20 p.m.), the result obtained by solving the equation. If you now look at the next figure you will see why this problem could only exist in a book and could never arise in a signal box.

First re-examine the original graph. If we take any two points on the line which represents the progress of train A, its speed, as given in the problem, corresponds with the gradient which the line makes with the x-axis or any line parallel to it. Speed is the distance traversed divided by the time taken or "distance per unit time." This is $\frac{\text{diff. } y}{\text{diff. } x}$, or, as we shall now write it, $\frac{\Delta y}{\Delta x}$. In the time which elapses between three o'clock ($x_1 = 3$) and five o'clock ($x_2 = 5$), train A moves from 100 ($= y_1$) miles to 200 ($= y_2$) miles from London. So the gradient,

$$\frac{\Delta y}{\Delta x} = \frac{200 - 100}{5 - 3}$$
$$= \frac{100}{2}$$
$$= 50$$

As the figure is drawn, the gradient (miles per hour) is the same from the moment the train starts to the moment it stops. This is equivalent to saying that the train starts instantaneously at top speed and stops dead instantaneously. The lower figure in Fig. 168 shows the speed of the train between starting at one o'clock and finishing its journey at nine o'clock. If we could start at top speed instantaneously and stop dead instantaneously, the speed would be represented by the straight line AB parallel to the x axis. No real trains behave like this, so that even if a train could maintain an absolutely constant speed over the greater part of its course, we should have to represent its speed during the whole journey by a curve with a flattened top. It would be a little higher than AB, to make up for the fact that the train has to gather speed (positive acceleration) when it starts, and slow down (negative acceleration) when it stops. From the upper figure you will see this means that the train will not travel as far in the first or last hour as in the intervening time. So the middle part of the line which represents its progress is a little steeper than the dotted line corresponding with its path in Fig. 167.

Thus the use of the simple equation depends upon two assumptions. The first is that a train can move at a constant speed (speedometer-pointer stationary) over the greater part of its course. The second is that the journey is so long that the time taken to start up and slow down does not appreciably affect our calculations. Actually the time wasted in starting up or slowing down means that if the train does the

400 miles in exactly eight hours, it must travel at something over 50 miles an hour, however small the excess, during part of the journey. Hence the two lines in Fig. 167 need not cross at exactly 7.20 p.m.

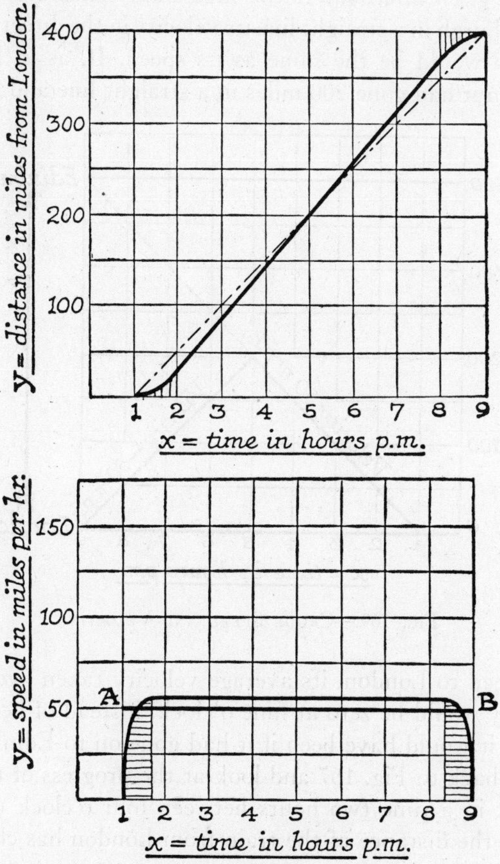

Owing to the scale on which they are drawn, the ascending and descending limbs are less oblique than they should be.

FIG. 168.—SPEED AND ACCELERATION

When the journey is a long one the error arising from the second assumption may well be too small to bother about.

In real life few things move at a constant speed in a straight line, and even when they go straight over a long distance, they change direction eventually. In the new algebra of motion we can take account of direction as well as speed just as in real life the route chosen is as important as the distance which a motor-bicycle is capable of covering in a given time. So we distinguish between crude speed and useful speed, which is called velocity. Crude speed is simply the total distance divided by the time taken, irrespective of the direction taken. Velocity is speed in a *given direction.* If the first train continued its journey towards Edinburgh in a straight line its velocity in the direction London to Edinburgh would be the same as its speed. If, as in Fig. 169, it reversed when it had gone 200 miles in a straight line and returned at

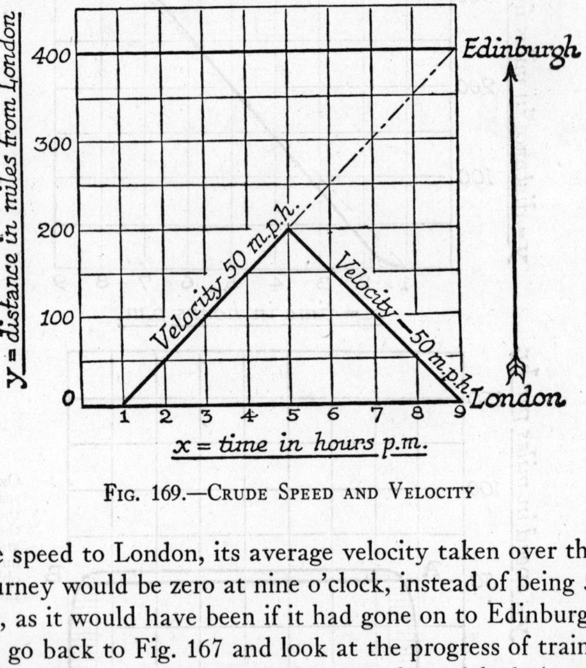

FIG. 169.—CRUDE SPEED AND VELOCITY

the same speed to London, its average velocity taken over the whole of its journey would be zero at nine o'clock, instead of being 50 miles per hour, as it would have been if it had gone on to Edinburgh.

If you go back to Fig. 167 and look at the progress of train B, you will see that in a time two hours between four o'clock ($x_1 = 4$) and six ($x_2 = 6$), the distance of the train from London has changed from $y_1 = 400$ to $y_2 = 350$ miles. So if we write, as before $\frac{\Delta y}{\Delta x} = \frac{y_2 - y_1}{x_2 - x_1}$

$$\frac{\Delta y}{\Delta x} = \frac{350 - 400}{6 - 4}$$

$$= -\frac{50}{2}$$

$$= -25$$

Thus the gradient in the graph of distance (measured along a straight line) plotted against time represents not the crude speed, but speed in a particular direction, i.e. *velocity*. Train A moves with a velocity of + 50 miles per hour, i.e. a speed of 50 miles per hour away from

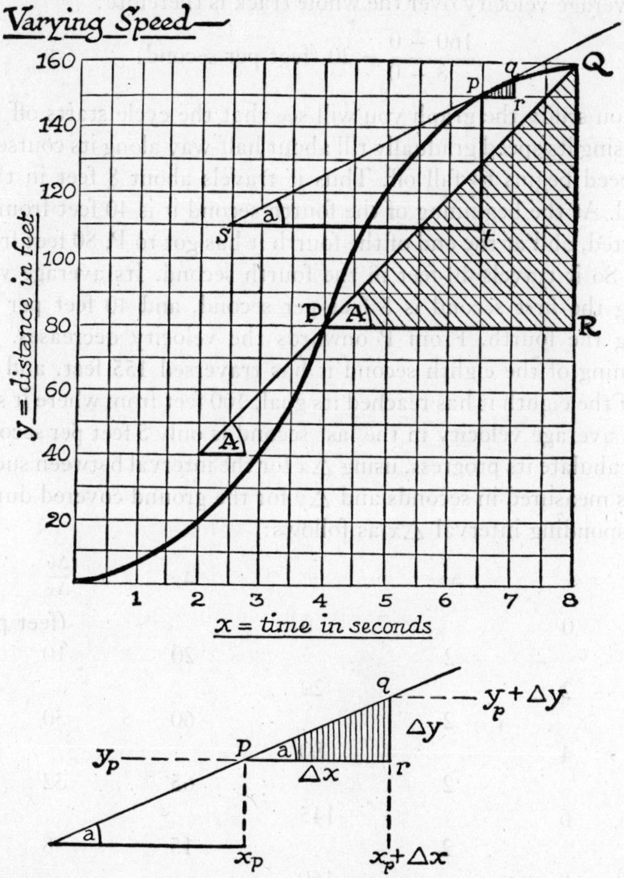

FIG. 170

sp is drawn *roughly* to represent the tangent to the curve at *p*.

London when the distance is measured *from* London. Train B moves with a velocity of – 25 miles per hour, i.e. with a speed of 25 miles per hour, distance being measured *towards* London.

The next figure (Fig. 170) represents something more like motion as we see it in the real world. The curve shows the distance which a motor-cycle travels in a short trial, timed with a stop-watch over a straight track of 160 feet. The direction remains the same. So the speed and the velocity are equivalent. The entire trial from the time of starting ($x = 0$) to the time of stopping ($x = 8$) occupies 8 seconds. The average velocity over the whole track is therefore:

$$\frac{160 - 0}{8 - 0} = 20 \text{ (feet per second)}$$

If you study the graph you will see that the cycle starts off slowly, increasing its speed gradually till about half-way along its course, when the speed begins to fall off. Thus it travels about 8 feet in the first second. At the beginning of the fourth second it is 40 feet from where it started, and at the end of the fourth it has got to P, 80 feet from the start. So it travels 40 feet in the fourth second. Its average velocity during the first second is 8 feet per second, and 40 feet per second during the fourth. From P onwards the velocity decreases. At the beginning of the eighth second it has traversed 155 feet, and by the end of the eighth it has reached its goal, 160 feet from where it started. So its average velocity in the last second is only 5 feet per second. We may tabulate its progress, using Δx for the interval between successive stages measured in seconds and Δy for the ground covered during the corresponding interval Δx as follows:

x	Δx	y	Δy	$\frac{\Delta y}{\Delta x}$
0		0		(feet per sec.)
	2		20	10
2		20		
	2		60	30
4		80		
	2		65	32
6		145		
	2		15	8
8		160		

Suppose now that we have observed the track of a cyclist who started some distance behind the beginning of the trial course and ended some distance beyond. He would not have to accelerate or slow down. He would be able to keep the pointer-reading of his speedometer at practically the same place throughout the course. The graph which recorded his progress would then be a straight line. On converting seconds to hours and feet to miles, the gradient of the line would be equivalent to the speedometer-reading. The average velocity between two points like P and Q in the graph of Fig. 170 is also the gradient of the straight line joining them. PR is the interval of time (Δx), and QR is the distance (Δy) traversed, the gradient

$$\frac{\Delta y}{\Delta x} = \frac{\text{QR}}{\text{PR}} = \tan \text{A}$$

If two points in the course are very close together, as are the y co-ordinates of p and q, the curved line joining them is difficult to distinguish from a straight line, and the pointer of the speedometer will not shift appreciably during the interval represented by the difference between the x co-ordinates of q and p. When p and q are very close together, so that we cannot distinguish them, the line passing through them becomes the tangent at the point $p = q$, and the gradient of this line corresponds with the speedometer-reading at the instant represented by the x co-ordinate of p or at the distance from the start represented by the y co-ordinate of p. However small we make the triangle pqr, or, in other words, however near together p and q are, the angle a between pq and pr remains a perfectly definite quantity, being the angle which the tangent to the curve makes with the x axis or any line parallel to it.

In a speed graph like this one, i.e. a graph in which distances are measured off along the y axis and time along the x axis, we can always determine the speedometer-reading at any point p, whose x co-ordinate is x_p and y co-ordinate y_p, i.e. when the moving object has traversed a distance y_p in a time x_p. All we have to do is to draw the tangent to the curve at p, read off the angle which the tangent makes with any line parallel to the x axis, and look up the tangent of this angle in tables. In this instance we do not need tables. From the larger triangle we can see that the gradient

$$\tan a = \frac{pt}{st}$$

Now pt corresponds with 4 divisions along y, i.e. 40 feet, and st from $x = 2\cdot4$ to $x = 6\cdot5$ corresponds with approximately $4\cdot1$ divisions along x, so that the velocity at p is approximately

$$40 \div 4\cdot1 = 9\cdot8 \text{ feet per second}$$

This result would correspond closely with the speedometer reading, if the tangent were very accurately drawn. We could get a more rough-and-ready measure of the velocity at p (i.e. $6\frac{1}{2}$ seconds, or 150 feet from the beginning of the trial) by taking the average velocity between two points close to p, e.g. the average velocity between the points on the course passed 6 and 7 seconds after the trial started. Here is a table of approximate speeds constructed in this way:

x	Δx	y	Δy	$\frac{\Delta y}{\Delta x}$	Approximate speed at $x =$
0		0			
	1		8	8	0·5
1		8			
	1		12	12	1·5
2		20			
	1		22	22	2·5
3		42			
	1		38	38	3·5
4		80			
	1		43	43	4·5
5		123			
	1		22	22	5·5
6		145			
	1		10	10	6·5
7		155			
	1		5	5	7·5
8		160			

From this table we see that if we take the average velocity between the beginning and the end of the seventh second as the speedometer-reading (in feet per second) when the stop-watch reading is $6\frac{1}{2}$ seconds, the result, 10 feet per second, is 2 per cent more than the previous estimate, partly because the tangent was drawn roughly, and partly because the speed does not change uniformly between the end of the sixth and the end of the seventh second. The tangent method is equivalent to taking two points with its x co-ordinates x_p and $(x_p + \Delta x)$ and its y co-ordinates y_p and $(y_p + \Delta y)$ so close together that Δx and Δy are too small to measure. The gradient (lower figure in Fig. 170) is:

$$\frac{\Delta y}{\Delta x} = \tan a$$

When Δy and Δx are immeasurably small we write the ratio (pronounced as dee-wy-by-dee-eks)

$$\frac{dy}{dx}$$

This ratio is called the *differential coefficient of y with respect to x*.

It corresponds with velocity or *distance per unit time* when the quantity measured along the *x* axis is time, and the quantity measured along the *y* axis is distance in a straight line. However, it may stand for any rate of change, e.g. the swelling of a tyre produced by the stroke of the pump. If we plotted the length of a bar of iron along *y* and the temperature along *x*, our graph would represent the expansion or

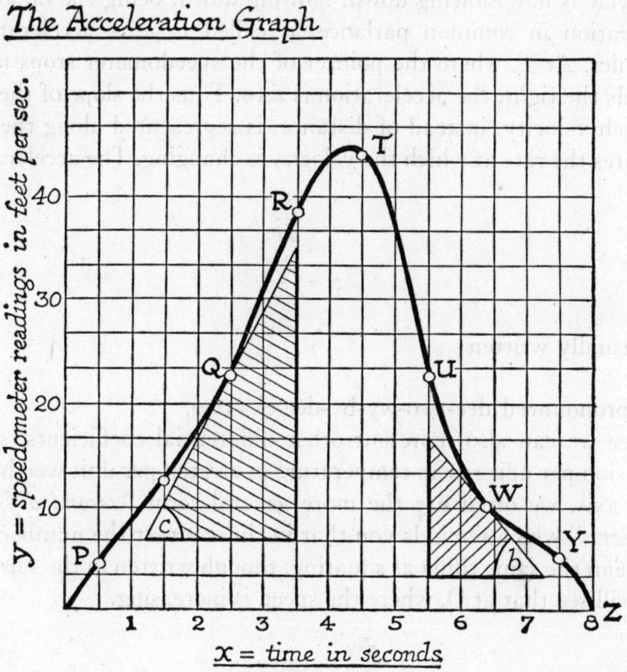

FIG. 171

increased length per degree of the bar as the temperature increases or diminishes. If we plotted the length of a spring along *y* and the weight attached to it along *x* as in Fig. 143, our graph would represent the stretching of the spring or increased length per unit load as the attached weight is increased or diminished.

We are now in a position to measure acceleration or the rate at which a moving body gathers (or loses) velocity. In the next illustration (Fig. 171) the divisions on the *x* axis are half-seconds as in the previous one, but the divisions on the *y* axis measure the speedometer-readings at successive instants. It is based on the approximate speedometer-readings of the last table given. To distinguish measurement along the y axis in this graph from the preceding, we might call it the v axis, v standing for velocity. The curve shown is steep from P to Q and Q to R, where the velocity is still increasing. The pointer of the speedometer is moving towards the right. The cycle is *accelerating*. At T the curve flattens out momentarily, and thereafter the velocity decreases. The cycle is now slowing down. Slowing down, being the opposite of acceleration in common parlance, is called *negative* acceleration in dynamics. At T, where the pointer of the speedometer stops moving towards the right, the acceleration is zero. Thus the slope of the graph in which velocity, instead of distance, is represented along the y axis measures the rate at which the velocity is changing. The acceleration is

$$\frac{dv}{dx}$$

where

$$v = \frac{dy}{dx}$$

It is usually written

$$\frac{d^2y}{dx^2}$$

and pronounced dee-two-wy-by-dee-eks-two.

Since we can also represent other differential coefficients, such as expansion per unit rise in temperature or stretch per unit weight along the y axis, we often use the more general term "*second differential coefficient*," which reminds you that in this context the number 2 does not mean the same thing as squaring, though written in the same way. You will see that at Q, where the speed is increasing,

$$\frac{d^2y}{dx^2} = \tan c$$

while at W, where it is diminishing

$$\frac{d^2y}{dx^2} = -\tan b$$

DIFFERENTIATION.—So far we have only shown how to find the differential coefficient by means of a geometrical construction. The accuracy of our result by this method depends on our draughtsmanship. Even with the best draughtmanship, big inaccuracies are inevitable when the curve is steep. The first person who appears to have realized that there is no need to rely on draughtsmanship was Isaac Barrow, the teacher of Newton. We can illustrate the method he introduced by the path of the cannon-ball, which is reproduced in Figs. 172–4.

In Fig. 172 the average velocity of the ball in the upward direction between the points P and Q is measured by the tangent of the angle A, on substituting the appropriate units of measurement. If the unit of time (x) is one second and of distance (y) 64 feet, the equation of the curve as drawn is:

$$y = \frac{3x}{2} - \frac{1x^2}{4}$$

If, as in Fig. 173, we want to find the velocity upwards at any point P (x co-ordinate x_p), after a time x from the moment when the gun

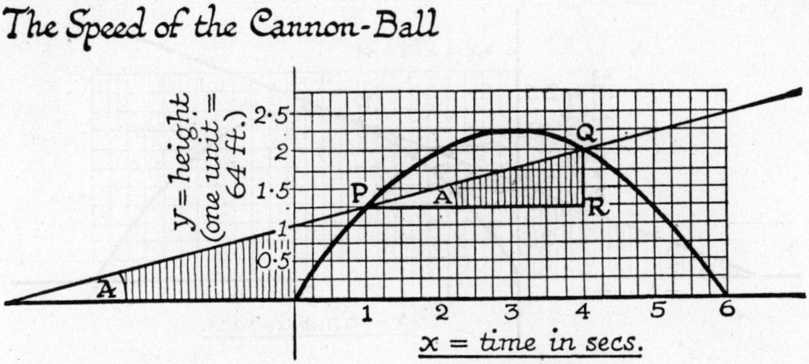

FIG. 172.—VELOCITY OF THE CANNON-BALL

is fired, we set about it in this way. Returning to Fig. 172 we see that

$$\tan A = \frac{QR}{PR}$$

$$= \frac{y_q - y_p}{x_q - x_p}$$

If we represent the interval between x_q and x_p as dx (i.e. $x_q = x_p + dx$), we can write

$$y_p = \tfrac{3}{2}\, x_p - \tfrac{1}{4}\, x_p{}^2$$

$$y_q = \tfrac{3}{2}\,(x_p + dx) - \tfrac{1}{4}\,(x_p + dx)^2$$

$$= \frac{3}{2}\, x_p + \frac{3}{2}\, dx - \frac{x_p{}^2}{4} - \frac{x_p\, dx}{2} - \frac{(dx)^2}{4}$$

$$= \left(\frac{3}{2}\, x_p - \frac{x_p{}^2}{4}\right) + \left\{\frac{3}{2}\, dx - \frac{1}{2}\, x_p\, dx - \frac{1}{4}\,(dx)^2\right\}$$

$$\therefore \quad y_q - y_p = \tfrac{3}{2}\, dx - \tfrac{1}{2}\, x_p\, dx - \tfrac{1}{4}(dx)^2$$

$$\frac{y_q - y_p}{dx} = \frac{3}{2} - \frac{1}{2}\, x_p - \frac{1}{4}\, dx$$

When P and Q are so close as to be indistinguishable (Fig. 173), dx is too small to be measured, so

$$\frac{dy}{dx} = \frac{3}{2} - \frac{x}{2}$$

If you look at Fig. 173 you will see that x_p, the x co-ordinate of P, is in this case $2\frac{1}{4}$. So that at P:

$$\frac{dy}{dx} = \frac{3}{2} - \frac{9}{8}$$
$$= 0 \cdot 375$$

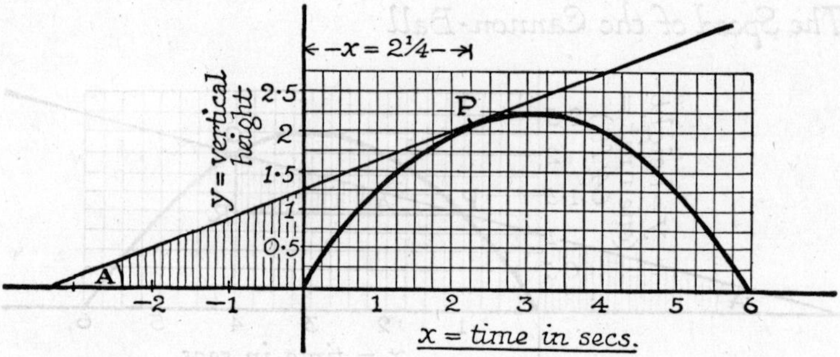

FIG. 173

With a protractor we find that the angle A is $20\frac{1}{2}°$ to the nearest half-degree. The tables of tangents give

$$\tan 20\tfrac{1}{2}° = 0 \cdot 374$$

Each unit along x is one second, so this measures the velocity per second in the particular units of length chosen for y. In the figure the unit of y is 64 feet. So in feet per second

$$v = 64 \times 0 \cdot 375$$
$$= 24 \text{ feet per second}$$

It will help us to see a more general rule for differentiating, i.e. finding tangents, if we put down the values of y and its differential coefficient in a similar form, thus

$$y = \tfrac{3}{2}x^1 - \tfrac{1}{4}x^2$$
$$\frac{dy}{dx} = \frac{3}{2} - \frac{1}{4}(2x)$$

The symbol p may be left out, as it was only put in to distinguish

x_p from x_q when P and Q were far apart. Since $x^0 = 1$, whatever value we give to x, the last equation may be written

$$\frac{dy}{dx} = \frac{3x^0}{2} - \frac{1(2x^1)}{4}$$

Before exposing the rule suggested by the similarity between y and $\frac{dy}{dx}$ when written out in this way, we may draw two practical conclusions from the expression we have got. First, we can use it to find the precise instant at which the cannon-ball reaches the highest point in its path. This will be when it stops moving upwards, and has not yet begun to

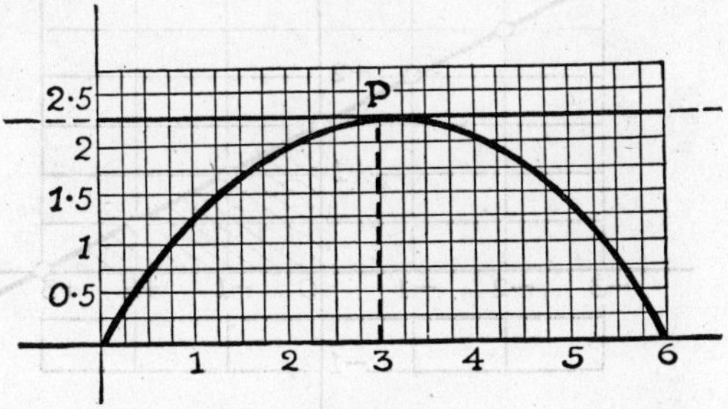

FIG. 174

move downwards. At this point it is moving horizontally in the air for the moment. Its upward velocity, which is changing from positive to negative, will be zero. The tangent to the curve (Fig. 174) will be parallel to the x axis, to which its angle of slope will therefore be zero, i.e.

$$\frac{dy}{dx} = 0$$

$$\therefore \quad \frac{3}{2} - \frac{1x}{2} = 0$$

$$\therefore \quad x = 3$$

That is to say, the cannon-ball reaches its maximum height 3 seconds after the explosion. Its height at this instant can be found by putting $x = 3$ in the original equation:

$$y = \frac{3x}{2} - \frac{x^2}{4}$$

$$\therefore \quad y = \frac{3(3)}{2} - \frac{(9)}{4}$$

$$= 2\tfrac{1}{4} \text{ (}v\text{-units)}$$

The unit of measurement along the y axis is 64 feet. So the height in feet is

$$2\tfrac{1}{4} \times 64 = 144 \text{ feet}$$

We can also use the equation for the differential coefficient to find

The Downward Acceleration of the Cannon-Ball —

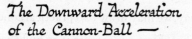

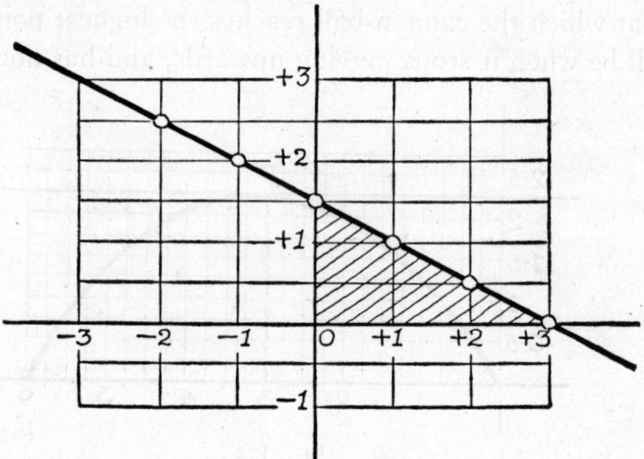

Fig. 175

Along the x axis the units represent time in seconds. Along the y axis the units represent speed, i.e. distance per second, measured vertically upwards. One y unit corresponds with 64 feet per second. The line slopes from right to left upward and the sign of the gradient is therefore negative. That is to say, the ball *looses* speed upwards, i.e. gains speed towards the earth. The gradient as seen from the shaded area is

$$\frac{(0 - 1\cdot 5) \text{ units of } y}{(3 - 0) \text{ units of } x} \quad \text{or} \quad -\frac{1\cdot 5 \times 64 \text{ feet per second}}{3 \text{ seconds}}$$

i.e. − 32 ft. per second per second

the acceleration of the cannon-ball downwards. In Fig. 175 we have plotted the graph of

$$v = \frac{3}{2} - \frac{x}{2}$$

As before, measurements along the x axis represent seconds, and measurements along the y axis represent corresponding values of $v = \dfrac{dy}{dx}$. The graph is a straight line, the slope of which represents the rate at which the velocity of the cannon-ball changes in the direction vertically upwards. The slope of the line is the second differential coefficient. As the legend beneath the graph shows you

$$\frac{d^2y}{dx^2} = \frac{-1\cdot 5}{3} \text{ (}y\text{-units per second per second)}$$

$$= -32 \text{ feet per second per second}$$

That is to say, throughout its whole path the cannon-ball is always losing (negative sign) speed in the upward direction and therefore gaining speed earthwards at the same rate. Galileo showed that all bodies falling near the earth gather speed downwards at a rate approximately equivalent to 32 feet per second in one second if there is no matter to obstruct their progress. In a vacuum the feather and the coin fall at the same rate. The tendency of the feather to float is due to the large surface which it offers to frictional resistance with the air. The cigar shape of the modern projectile, in contrast with the old-fashioned cannon-ball, and the streamlines of a modern car are designed to reduce the resistance of the air through which they move.

The differential calculus can be used for a great variety of calculations besides the mechanical problems in connexion with which it was invented. To apply it correctly to the sort of problems involved in the mechanics of movement it is very important to remember that acceleration does not merely mean speeding up or slowing down, as we use the word in everyday speech. In mechanics acceleration means change in velocity, and velocity always means speed measured in a particular direction along a *straight line*. If a thing moves in a straight line, its velocity is its speed with the appropriate sign attached to indicate which way it is going. If it does not move in a straight line its average speed between two points on its path must always be greater than its average velocity. Thus if a train moves straight from A to B in an hour its velocity along the direction AB is + AB miles per hour and along the direction BA, – AB miles per hour. Its speed is AB miles per hour either way. If it goes by a roundabout path, e.g. straight from A to C and straight from C to B, its speed is (AC + CB) miles per hour (total distance ÷ time) but its velocity measured in the direction AB is still AB miles per hour. The reason for making this distinction lies in the universal experience of inertia. When a train stops suddenly we have to exert a pull to prevent ourselves from lurching forwards. When we turn a corner suddenly we have to bend inwards to prevent ourselves from going straight on while the bicycle turns. A pull has to be exerted to stop a thing from moving onwards straight ahead, as well as to make it move faster or more slowly in the direction in which it is going. If we measure force or pulling power by the motion it imparts to things, we are therefore just as much concerned with the direction *in* which they move as the distance *through* which they move. When anything moves with constant speed (i.e. distance per unit time) in a circle, its direction is changing all the time. It would fly off at a tangent if it were not held to the centre by the steady pull which your finger exerts when you swing a stone at the end of a cord. Cut the cord and the stone flies on along the straight line grazing its circular path at the point where it was when the cord was cut. All the while your finger is there you are bending it inwards, giving it motion towards the centre. This is what is meant in mechanics by saying that it has an acceleration towards the centre. Though there is no speeding up or slowing down in the ordinary sense, there is a continuous change in velocity. It lies outside our scope to go into details about measuring the way in which the velocity of a thing changes when it moves in a curved path.

In this chapter we shall chiefly use the infinitesimal calculus to solve numerical problems which do not depend on understanding mechanics. The most valuable applications outside mechanics can only be understood if you will persevere in studying the rules for getting the slope of different sorts of curves. Before getting into deeper waters a simple illustration of its use to solve a class of problems to which ordinary algebra does not apply may therefore help you to face the necessary hard work. Finding the height of the cannon-ball when it is furthest off the ground is an example of finding the greatest value which some measurement may have, when we know some general expression which includes all the possible measurements, and problems of this kind are not confined to motion. For instance, you might be asked to make an oblong run to hold the greatest number of poultry with a roll of wire netting 200 yards long. Your problem then is to make a rectangular figure with the greatest area (ground space for the fowls) when the total length of the four sides is fixed.

If all four sides measure 200 yards, two adjacent sides measure 100 yards. So if x is the length of one side, its neighbour is $(100 - x)$ yards, and if you know x you know the shape of the figure which is to have the greatest area y. The value of y is $x(100 - x)$ or $100x - x^2$. Your problem is to find the value of x which makes y a maximum. One way of solving it is to draw a graph of the parabola

$$y = 100x - x^2$$

You can then measure off the x co-ordinate corresponding to the highest point of the curve. The other is to save yourself the trouble of drawing it by applying the rule that y must have its greatest value, when

$$\frac{dy}{dx} = 0$$

As in the example of the cannon-ball,

$$\begin{aligned} \Delta y &= 100\,(x + \Delta x) - (x + \Delta x)^2 - (100\,x - x^2) \\ &= 100\,\Delta x - 2x\Delta x - (\Delta x)^2 \end{aligned}$$

$$\therefore \quad \frac{\Delta y}{\Delta x} = 100 - 2x - \Delta x$$

When $\triangle x$ is too small to matter this is $100-2x$, and when $100-2x=0$, $x = 50$. So the area is greatest when one side is 50 yards long. The other is then 100 – 50 or 50 yards, and the shape of the figure is that of a square. You can check the result with a table. Thus if both sides are equivalent the area is 2,500 sq. yards. If one side is twenty yards longer than the other, the area is 60×40, or 2,400 sq. yards. If one side is 40 yards longer than the other, the area is 70×30 or 2,100 sq. yards. If one side is 99 yards longer than the other, the area is $99 \cdot 5 \times 0 \cdot 5$ or $49 \cdot 75$ sq. yards.

METHODS OF DIFFERENTIATION.—You have now grasped the fundamental utility of the differential calculus. It resides in the fact that the gradient of the tangent to the curve measures the rate of change of the quantity represented by measurements along the *y axis* for unit change in the quantity represented by measurements along the *x axis*, and y is greatest or least when the gradient is zero. It happens that the last example depends on the same type of curve (*parabola*) as the cannon-ball. To solve any problem of finding the greatest or least value of some measurement consistent with the limits set, you need to know how to find the gradient of the tangent to a curve of any shape.

Finding this gradient for any curve whose equation is known, or, as we shall now say, *differentiating y with respect to x*, depends on understanding the natural history of curves. Curves can be classified in families and genera and species, like families, genera, and species of insects or mammals. The most primitive species is the straight line

$$y = ax + b$$

As we have already seen, the differential coefficient is a (= tan A), which is the same for every value of x since it does not contain x. In mathematical language it is a *constant* as opposed to a *variable* quantity. So we may write (see p. 409)

$$\frac{dy}{dx} = a$$

when $$y = ax + b$$

Another simple species which we have met is the curve represented by

$$y = ax^2$$

Applying the method of Barrow's triangle, we get

$$\frac{dy}{dx} = \frac{ax_q^2 - ax_p^2}{dx}$$
$$= a.\frac{(x_p + dx)^2 - x_p^2}{dx}$$
$$= a.\frac{x_p^2 + 2x_p dx + (dx)^2 - x_p^2}{dx}$$
$$= 2ax_p + a.dx$$
$$= 2ax \text{ (when } dx \text{ is too small to matter)}$$

The last results we have obtained illustrate a rule which applies to a larger genus including the straight line and the parabola, as the genus Felis includes the cat and the tiger. The genus is

$$y = ax^n$$

The rule is $$\frac{dy}{dx} = anx^{n-1}$$

Thus we may rewrite the equation of the line

$$y = ax$$

in the form $$y = ax^1$$

whence $$\frac{dy}{dx} = ax^0$$
$$= a$$

The rule is easily seen to be true by using the binomial theorem. Thus

$$y_q = a(x_p + dx)^n$$
$$= a\left(x_p^n + n.x_p^{n-1}dx + \frac{n(n-1)x_p^{n-2}}{2!}(dx)^2 \ . \ . \ .\right)$$

and $$y_p = ax_p^n$$

$$\therefore y_q - y_p = a(n.x_p^{n-1}dx + \frac{n(n-1)}{2!}x_p^{n-2}(dx)^2 + \frac{n(n-1)(n-2)}{3!}x_p^{n-3}(dx)^3 \ . \ . \ .)$$

$$\therefore \frac{y_q - y_p}{dx} = a\left(n.x_p^{n-1} + \frac{n(n-1)x_p^{n-2}}{2!}dx + \frac{n(n-1)(n-2)x_p^{n-3}}{3!}(dx)^2 \ . \ . \ .\right)$$

When P = Q and dx becomes indefinitely small, we can leave out all the terms which contain dx. So when

$$y = ax^n$$

$$\frac{dy}{dx} = a.n.x^{n-1}$$

For instance, if the curve corresponds with the equation

$$y = ax^5$$

$$\frac{dy}{dx} = 5a.x^4$$

If the curve is

$$y = 12x^6$$

$$\frac{dy}{dx} = 72x^5$$

If the curve is

$$y = ax^{-3} = \left(\frac{a}{x^3}\right)$$

$$\frac{dy}{dx} = -\ 3ax^{-4}$$

$$= -\ \frac{3a}{x^4}$$

A particular species of this genus is

$$y = a$$

This is the equation of a straight line like AB in Fig. 168 parallel to the x axis at a distance a units along y. Since the equation may be written

$$y = ax^0$$

$$\frac{dy}{dx} = 0$$

This simply means that the value of y does not grow as x grows. Since

$$\frac{dy}{dx} = a$$

when

$$y = ax + b$$

the second differential coefficient of y is $\frac{dy'}{dx}$ where $y' = a$, i.e.

$$\frac{d^2y}{dx^2} = 0$$

This simply means that if the velocity is constant there is no acceleration.

Just as cats and tigers, both of the genus Felis, and dogs and jackals, both of the genus Canis, are all examples of the larger group *Carnivora*, so all the curves whose equations have been dealt with are examples of the larger class

$$y = A + Bx + Cx^2 + Dx^3 \ldots$$

To find the tangent of any curve which represents an equation of this kind (see p. 445), when suitable values are given to the constants, A, B, C, D, etc., all we have to do is to differentiate each term separately. As before, putting $y_q = y_p + dx$, we have

$$y_q = A + B(x_p + dx) + C(x_p + dx)^2 + D(x_p + dx)^3 \ldots$$
$$y_p = A + Bx_p + Cx_p^2 + Dx_p^3 \ldots$$
$$\therefore \quad \frac{y_q - y_p}{dx} = \frac{B.(x_p + dx) - Bx_p}{dx} + \frac{C.(x_p + dx)^2 - Cx_p^2}{dx} + \frac{D.(x_p + dx)^3 - Dx_p^3}{dx} \ldots$$
$$\frac{dy}{dx} = B + 2Cx + 3Dx^2 \ldots$$

This result can be used to differentiate a large number of expressions. Take first the family

$$y = b + a^x$$

One curve with such an equation is shown in Fig. 154, in Chapter 9, where $a = 2$ and $b = 0$, i.e.

$$y = 2^x$$

We may change the form of the previous expression by putting

$$a = e^c$$
$$\log_e a = c$$

So the general equation becomes

$$y = b + e^{cx}$$

Now e^{cx} is an expression of the same large class as the power series

$$Ax^0 + Bx^1 + Cx^2 + Dx^3 \ldots$$

In the last chapter we saw that it is the unlimited series

$$1 + cx + \frac{c^2x^2}{2!} + \frac{c^3x^3}{3!} + \frac{c^4x^4}{4!} \ldots$$

So we can put for y

$$(b + 1)x^0 + cx^1 + \frac{c^2x^2}{2!} + \frac{c^3x^3}{3!} \ldots$$

The value of $\frac{dy}{dx}$ is got by differentiating successive terms separately, thus:

$$\begin{aligned}\frac{dy}{dx} &= 0 + c + \frac{2c^2x}{2!} + \frac{3c^3x^2}{3!} + \frac{4c^4x^3}{4!} \cdots \\ &= c\left(1 + cx + \frac{c^2x^2}{2!} + \frac{c^3x^3}{3!} \cdots\right) \\ &= c(e^{cx}) \\ &= (\log_e a)a^x\end{aligned}$$

So if

$$\begin{aligned}y &= b + a^x \\ \frac{dy}{dx} &= (\log_e a) \,.\, a^x\end{aligned}$$

If $b = 0$ and $a = e$, $\log_e a = 1$. Then $y = e^x$ and

$$\frac{dy}{dx} = e^x = y$$

This is one of the many remarkable characteristics which make the pronoun e such an important item in the vocabulary of mathematics. It means that the slope at any point is equivalent to the number of units represented by its y co-ordinate.

A still larger class of curves, which includes both the last two examples, is represented by the general equation:

$$y = e^{cx+d} + b$$

Since the constant b disappears in differentiation, as before, we need only bother about the simpler form of it, namely

$$y = e^{cx+d}$$

Applying the rule of Archimedes, we may write this

$$y = (e^{cx})\ (e^d)$$

As d stands for a fixed number, e^d also stands for a fixed number, which we will write for short

$$\mathrm{D} = e^d$$

$$\text{i.e.}\quad y = \mathrm{D} \,.\, e^{cx}$$

$$\begin{aligned}\therefore \quad y &= \mathrm{D}\left(1 + cx + \frac{c^2x^2}{2!} + \frac{c^3x^3}{3!} + \frac{c^4x^4}{4!} \cdots\right) \\ &= \mathrm{D} + \mathrm{D}cx + \frac{\mathrm{D}c^2x^2}{2!} + \frac{\mathrm{D}c^3x^3}{3!} + \frac{\mathrm{D}c^4x^4}{4!} \cdots\end{aligned}$$

$$\therefore \frac{dy}{dx} = 0 + Dc + Dc^2x + \frac{Dc^3x^2}{2!} + \frac{Dc^4x^3}{3!} \ldots$$

$$= Dc\left(1 + cx + \frac{c^2x^2}{2!} + \frac{c^3x^3}{3!} \ldots\right)$$

$$= Dc . e^{cx}$$

$$= c . (e^d)\ (e^{cx})$$

$$= c . e^{cx+d}$$

We can write the expression

$$y = a^x + b$$

alternatively as:

$$y - b = \text{antilog}_a\ x$$

We can also write in two ways the equation of another species of an allied genus of curves, namely

$$y = \log_e x$$

$$\text{or} \quad e^y = x$$

Remembering that $\frac{dy}{dx}$ is the *ratio* of two sides in Barrow's triangle, we can put

$$\frac{dy}{dx} = \frac{1}{\left(\frac{dx}{dy}\right)}$$

We have found that $\frac{dy}{dx} = e^x$ when $y = e^x$. The result when we interchange all the symbols is

$$\frac{dx}{dy} = e^y$$

when $x = e^y$. So we get

$$\frac{dy}{dx} = \frac{1}{e^y}$$

$$= \frac{1}{x}$$

This means that the slope of the curve is inversely proportional to x. The curve gets flatter and flatter while x gets bigger as in the curve in Fig. 176, which belongs to the allied species

$$y = \log_{10} x$$

If you turn back to p. 473 you will see that

$$\log_{10} x = \frac{\log_e x}{\log_e 10}$$

$$= \frac{\log_e x}{2\cdot 303}$$

$$\therefore \quad 2\cdot 303y = \log_e x$$

or $$e^{2\cdot 303y} = x$$

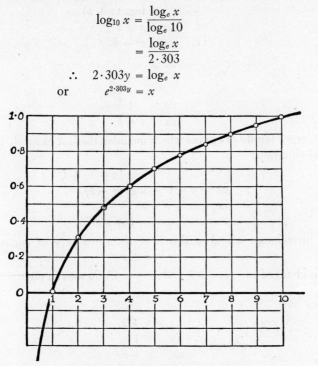

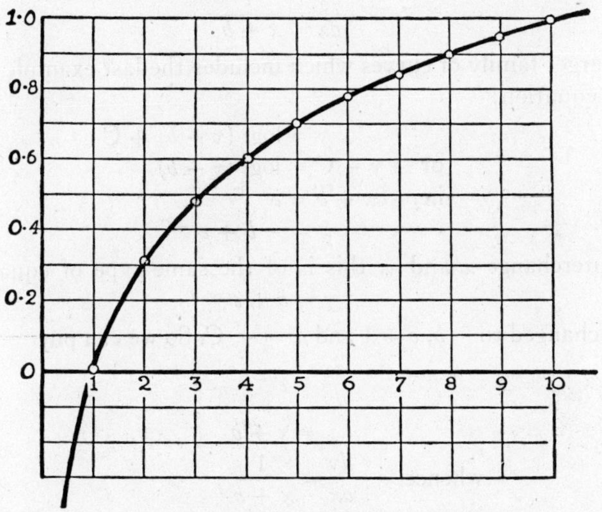

FIG. 176.—THE GRAPH OF $y = \log_{10} x$

The differential coefficient is, as before,

$$\frac{1}{\left(\frac{dx}{dy}\right)}$$

We have seen that when $y = e^{cx} + b$

$$\frac{dy}{dx} = c(e^{cx})$$

So if $x = e^{2\cdot 303y} + 0$ $$\frac{dx}{dy} = 2\cdot 303e^{2\cdot 303y}$$

$$\frac{dy}{dx} = \frac{1}{2\cdot 303x}$$

So when $$y = \log_{10} x$$

$$\frac{dy}{dx} = \frac{1}{x\,.\log_e 10}$$

Another important species of the same genus is

$$y = \log_e (x + b)$$

$$\text{or} \quad e^y = x + b$$

$$\text{i.e.} \quad x = e^y - b$$

$$\therefore \quad \frac{dx}{dy} = e^y$$

$$= x + b$$

$$\therefore \quad \frac{dy}{dx} = \frac{1}{x + b}.$$

A still larger family of curves which includes the last example has the general equation:

$$y = \log_e (x + b) + C$$

$$\text{or} \quad y - C = \log_e (x + b)$$

$$\text{i.e.} \quad x + b = e^{y-C}$$

$$x = -b + e^{y-C}$$

If we interchange x and y, this is of the same type of equation as

$$y = b + e^{cx+d}$$

but b is changed to $-b$, $c = 1$ and $d = -$ C. So we can put

$$\frac{dx}{dy} = e^{y-C}$$

$$= x + b$$

$$\text{whence} \quad \frac{dy}{dx} = \frac{1}{x + b}$$

If the equation of the curve is

$$y = a \log_e (x + b) + C$$

$$\therefore \quad \log_e (x + b) = \frac{y - C}{a}$$

$$\text{or} \quad x + b = e^{\frac{y-c}{a}}$$

$$\therefore \quad x = e^{\frac{y-c}{a}} - b$$

$$\frac{dx}{dy} = \frac{1}{a} e^{\frac{y-c}{a}} = \frac{x + b}{a}$$

$$\therefore \quad \frac{dy}{dx} = \frac{a}{x + b}$$

The last family which we need examine is represented by

$$y = \sin x$$

$$\text{and} \quad y = \cos x$$

There are several ways of getting the differential coefficients of these curves. To avoid confusion we shall write the coefficients

$$\frac{d}{dx}(\sin x)$$

$$\text{and} \quad \frac{d}{dx}(\cos x)$$

The first is based on the fact that, when the unit of x stands for 1 *radian*, (see p. 502),

$$\sin x = x - \frac{x^3}{3!} + \frac{x^5}{5!} - \frac{x^7}{7!} \cdots$$

$$\cos x = 1 - \frac{x^2}{2!} + \frac{x^4}{4!} - \frac{x^6}{6!} \cdots$$

These, like e^x, belong to the large family

$$y = Ax^0 + Bx^1 + Cx^2 + Dx^3 \cdots$$

So we can put

$$\frac{d}{dx}(\sin x) = 1 - \frac{3x^2}{3!} + \frac{5x^4}{5!} - \frac{7x^6}{7!} \cdots$$

$$= 1 - \frac{x^2}{2!} + \frac{x^4}{4!} - \frac{x^6}{6!} \cdots$$

$$= \underline{\cos x}$$

$$\text{and} \quad \frac{d}{dx}(\cos x) = 0 - \frac{2x^1}{2!} + \frac{4x^3}{4!} - \frac{6x^5}{6!} \cdots$$

$$= -x + \frac{x^3}{3!} - \frac{x^5}{5!} \cdots$$

$$= \underline{-\sin x}$$

You will easily see from this that

$$\frac{d^2 \sin x}{dx^2} = \frac{d \cos x}{dx}$$

$$= \underline{-\sin x}$$

$$\text{Similarly} \quad \frac{d^2 \cos x}{dx^2} = \underline{-\cos x}$$

We can get the same result by a method which is based on elementary trigonometry without using unlimited series, using the equations given on p. 254. Thus:

$$\sin(x + dx) = \sin x \cos dx + \cos x \sin dx$$

and (when x is measured in radians)

$$\frac{\sin dx}{dx} = 1$$

Hence we may put

$$\frac{dy}{dx} = \frac{\sin (x + dx) - \sin x}{dx}.$$

in the form $$\frac{\sin x \cos dx + \cos x \sin dx - \sin x}{dx}$$

$$= \frac{\sin x \cos dx - \sin x + \cos x \sin dx}{dx}$$

When dx becomes indefinitely small

$$\cos dx = 1$$
$$\sin x \cos dx - \sin x = 0$$

So this reduces to $$\frac{dy}{dx} = \cos x . \frac{\sin dx}{dx}$$

$$= \cos x$$

You will have no difficulty in differentiating sin ax, cos ax, by dealing with the unlimited series

$$\sin ax = ax - \frac{(ax)^3}{3!} + \frac{(ax)^5}{5!} \ . \ . \ .$$

or $$\cos ax = 1 - \frac{(ax)^2}{2!} + \frac{(ax)^4}{4!} \ . \ . \ .$$

The method is essentially the same as for e^{cx} which has been given already. Thus you will find that

$$\frac{d^2}{dx^2} (\sin ax) = - a^2 \sin ax$$

If we put $a = \sqrt{b}$ this is equivalent to

$$\frac{d^2 (\sin \sqrt{b} x)}{dx^2} = - b \sin (\sqrt{b} . x)$$

Fig. 177 shows you that the curves of $y = \sin x$, $y = - \sin x$, $y = \cos x$, $y = - \cos x$, all represent periodic or wave-like motion. The results obtained for the gradients of the curves

$$y = \sin x$$
$$y = \cos x$$

mean that if a measurement, e.g. the horizontal displacement of the pendulum, varies *periodically* with the time, its speed and acceleration also vary periodically with the time. They provide us with a dramatic illustration of the way in which the new algebra of Newton's generation linked together the new machines with the established mechanics of bodies at rest. The name of Robert Hooke, a friend of Newton, and apparently the first person to notice the cellular structure of living

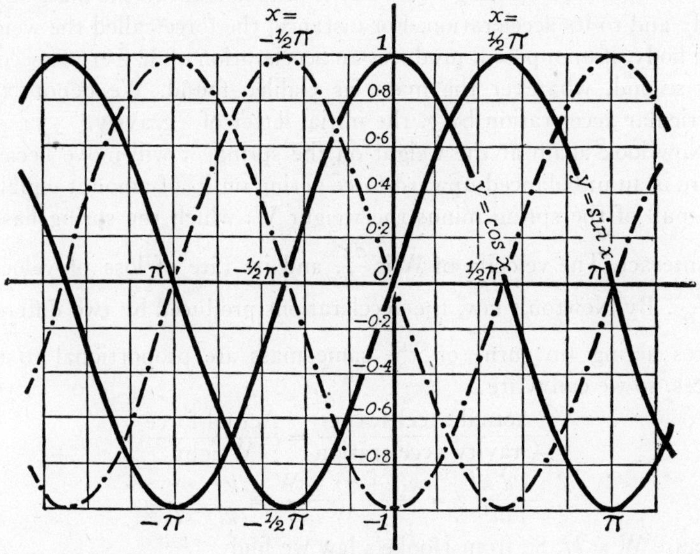

FIG. 177.—THE GRAPHS OF
$y = \sin x$, $y = -\sin x$, $y = \cos x$, and $y = -\cos x$

bodies as seen under the newly-invented microscope, is also associated with the law of the stretched spring. It will not surprise you to learn that the properties of stretched springs attracted the attention of scientists when the clock occupied the centre of interest among contemporary inventions. Hooke's law of the stretched spring, represented in Fig. 143, tells us that the ratio of the weight (W) suspended at the end of the spring to the distance (l) through which it is stretched is constant. This may be written

$$W = kl$$

The weight which the elastic force of the spring can support depends on the amount it is stretched. So if the spring is now extended an amount x beyond the stretch l necessary to support the weight W, it could really support a weight $k(l + x)$, or $W + kx$. So the forces acting on the weight W are not balanced, and the old statical method of comparing balanced forces at rest now fails us. Newton came to our rescue with another way of measuring forces. He took the resistance to change of velocity, or inertia, of moving matter as the basis of his system of mechanics, and his law is that the unbalanced part, or resultant, of forces acting on a body is proportional to the mass of the body and to its acceleration. For instance, the force called the weight of a body, if unopposed, produces an acceleration of 32 feet per second per second, whatever the mass, as Galileo found. We denote this particular acceleration by g, the initial letter of "gravity."

Now look again at the weight on the spring, it will move because there is an unbalanced upward force acting on it, of amount equal to the pull of the spring minus the weight W, which the spring has to counteract. The velocity of W is $\frac{dx}{dt}$, and its rate of loss of velocity $-\frac{d^2x}{dt^2}$. By Newton's law, the accelerations produced by two different forces acting (in turn) on the same mass are proportional to the forces, so we can write

$$\frac{\text{Actual acceleration}}{\text{Gravity acceleration}} = \frac{\text{Actual force}}{\text{Weight}}$$

or

$$-\frac{d^2x}{dt^2}\Big/ g = \frac{k(l+x) - W}{W} = \frac{kx}{kl} = \frac{x}{l}$$

because $W = kl$. So from Hooke's law we find

$$\frac{d^2x}{dt^2} = -\frac{g}{l}x$$

This type of equation is called a differential equation. To solve it we need to find something which when differentiated twice is always itself multiplied by the same constant and has its sign changed. We have learned

that if $\quad y = \sin ax \quad$ then $\quad \frac{d^2y}{dx^2} = -a^2 \sin ax$

So if $\quad x = \sin\left(\sqrt{\frac{g}{l}}\right)t \quad$ then $\quad \frac{d^2x}{dt^2} = -\frac{g}{l}\sin\left(\sqrt{\frac{g}{l}}\right)t$

i.e.

$$\frac{d^2x}{dt^2} = -\frac{g}{l}x$$

A solution of the equation is therefore

$$x = \sin(\sqrt{g/l})t$$

This means that if we plot *time* along the x-axis and extra *distance stretched* (x) along the y-axis we should trace out a curve like that shown in Fig. 177. If you envisage what actually does happen, by trying to imagine a succession of cinematographic images as in Fig. 178, you will realize that this is approximately correct. By putting in Newton's dynamical definition of the force which the spring exerts against the weight applied to its end we find that the weight at the end of the spring oscillates about its point of equilibrium with periodic motion. In common parlance, it "bobs" up and down.

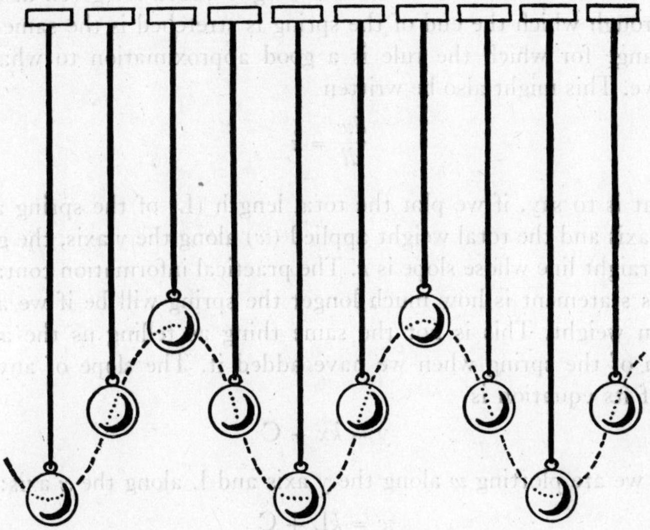

FIG. 178.—CINEMATOGRAPHIC IMAGES OF A WEIGHT OSCILLATING UP AND DOWN AT THE END OF AN ELASTIC CORD

Before passing on to the method of the integral calculus, we shall find it useful to tabulate the results of this section thus:

y	$\frac{dy}{dx}$
$ax^n + b$	nax^{n-1}
$a^x + b$	$(\log_e a)a^x$
$a \log_e (x + b) + c$	$\frac{a}{x + b}$
$\sin (ax + b)$	$a \cos (ax + b)$
$\cos (ax + b)$	$- a \sin (ax + b)$

DIFFERENTIAL EQUATIONS.—You will notice that $x = \sin t(\sqrt{g/l})$ and $x = \cos t(\sqrt{g/l})$ are both possible solutions of the simple differential equation which represents a first approximation to the periodic motion of a weight attached to the end of a spring. The two curves only differ in where they cut the horizontal axis, that is to say, the value of l when $t = 0$. We need to know this in order to choose which answer to use. The answer to a differential equation is not a number, but a family of numbers. Which member of the family we choose for practical use depends on the information supplied by the practical problem. To see this, consider the form in which we have written Hooke's law. The law tells us that the amount of weight added for given distance (l) through which the end of the spring is stretched is the same over the range for which the rule is a good approximation to what we observe. This might also be written

$$\frac{dw}{dl} = k$$

That is to say, if we plot the total length (L) of the spring along the x axis and the total weight applied (w) along the y axis, the graph is a straight line whose slope is k. The practical information contained in this statement is how much longer the spring will be if we add a certain weight. This is not the same thing as telling us the actual length of the spring when we have added it. The slope of any line is k, if its equation is

$$y = kx + C$$

or, as we are plotting w along the y axis and L along the x axis:

$$w = k\text{L} + C$$

When we write Hooke's law in this form we can use it to find the actual length of the spring when a given weight is added, provided we already know its length when some other weight is suspended from it. Suppose a spring stretches one-tenth of an inch per ounce. We can write the equation of the spring as:

$$w = 10\text{L} + C$$

If we are told that it is 9 inches long when a weight of 3 ounces is attached,

$$3 = (10)9 + C$$
$$C = -87$$

So the equation becomes

$$w = 10\text{L} - 87$$

We can now calculate the length of the spring when any weight is attached. For example, if 13 ounces is the weight,

$$13 = 10\text{L} - 87$$

So the length will be 10 inches.

The form in which we give the result of a differential equation must always contain a constant like C in the last equation if it is to be of any practical use for calculation. The equations which are used in modern science chiefly belong to the type which we have just discussed. The method used in solving them is very much like what schoolmasters call "cooking" the result. We have to know the sort of answer from which the equation could be built up, and adjust it accordingly. Here are some very simple examples of differential equations which we shall meet in the next section.

(*a*) To find *y*, if $\dfrac{dy}{dx} = x^n$

We know that if
$$y = ax^n + b$$
$$\frac{dy}{dx} = nax^{n-1}$$

So if
$$y = ax^{n+1} + b$$
$$\frac{dy}{dx} = (n+1)ax^{(n+1)-1}$$
$$= (n+1)ax^n$$

This is equivalent to x^n, if
$$a = \frac{1}{n+1}$$

So the solution is
$$y = \frac{1}{n+1}x^{n+1} + b$$

(*b*) To find *y*, if $\dfrac{dy}{dx} = b + cx + dx^2 + ex^3 \ . \ . \ .$

We know that if
$$y = \text{A} + \text{B}x + \text{C}x^2 + \text{D}x^3 \ . \ . \ .$$
$$\frac{dy}{dx} = \text{B} + 2\text{C}x + 3\text{D}x^2 \ . \ . \ .$$

So if
$$\frac{dy}{dx} = b + cx + dx^2 \ . \ . \ .$$
$$y = a + bx + \frac{cx^2}{2} + \frac{dx^3}{3} \ . \ . \ .$$

(*c*) To find y, if $\frac{dy}{dx} = \frac{a}{x+b}$

The solution of this is given in the previous table, i.e.

$$a \log_e (x + b) + C$$

(*d*) To find y, if $\frac{d^2y}{dx^2} = ky$

We know that if $y = e^{cx+b}$

$$\frac{dy}{dx} = c . e^{cx+b}$$

and $\frac{d^2y}{dx^2} = c^2 e^{cx+b}$

So if we put $k = c^2$, i.e.

$$c = \sqrt{k}$$

and $y = e^{\sqrt{k}.x+b}$

$$\frac{d^2}{dx^2}(e^{\sqrt{k}.x+b}) = k . e^{\sqrt{k}.x+b}$$

Since $\sqrt{k}$ can be negative or positive

$$y = e^{+\sqrt{k}.x+b}$$

or $e^{-\sqrt{k}.x+b}$

INTEGRATION.—The respective claims of Newton and his continental contemporary Leibniz to be regarded as the author of the infinitesimal calculus have given rise to considerable discussion in which national sentiment has played no small part. Such controversies reflect a narrowly individualistic outlook on the history of science. Nobody invented the calculus. It was the co-operative product of a group of men. If any event must be singled out as the beginning of the differential calculus, credit would seem to be due pre-eminently to Barrow, who was Newton's teacher. If any event need be singled out as the beginning of the integral calculus, it was the recognition that the determination of an area is the same thing as solving a differential equation, and the credit for this step is mainly due to Leibniz, who also introduced the *dx* symbolism. Newton's main contribution was to show how differential equations could be used to interpret the observed truths of mechanics, astronomy, and optics, and so to emphasize the extraordinary usefulness of the new methods.

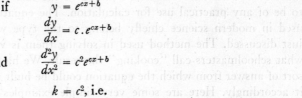

The problem of finding a tangent to a curve was not a new one when Barrow proposed the "differential triangle." Neither was the method of finding an area by the differential rectangle a new one when Leibniz made his own contribution to the problem. It was being used independently by the Japanese about the same time, and Wallis, who was one of Newton's teachers, used it to find a series for π. The essential feature of his method has already been given in Chapter 6,

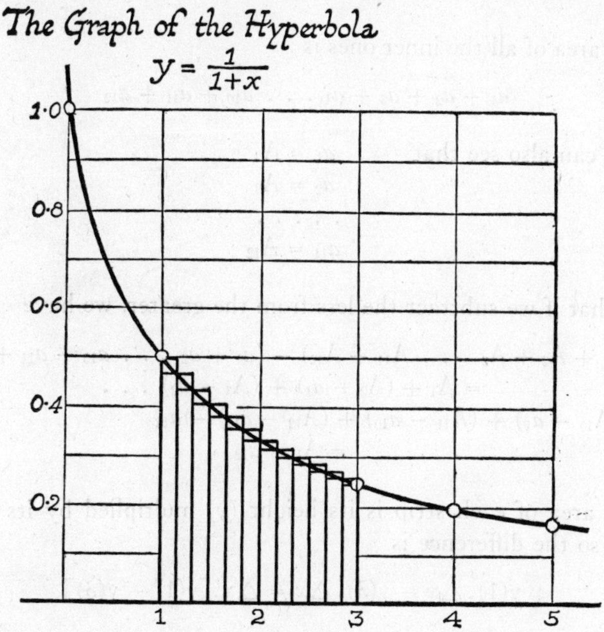

FIG. 179

Note that the hyperbola has two separate portions. Part of one shown here slopes closer and closer to the x axis, as x increases and indefinitely close to a line whose x co-ordinate is -1 parallel to the y axis.

p. 260. If the reader will read once more what was said earlier about the Japanese method for getting π, there will be no need to labour the point. Integration has already been defined as finding the area enclosed between a portion of a curve, two lines parallel to the y-axis drawn through its extremities, and the part of the x-axis which they cut ($x = 1$ to $x = 3$ in Fig. 179). The area marked off in Fig. 179 is divided into rectangular strips of width Δx just as we divided the area of the quarter circle into rectangular strips of the same width on p. 259. It lies between the sum of the inner and outer rectangles which differ by the small rectangular blocks shown in the picture.

If you look carefully at the picture, you will see that there are twelve outer rectangles (A_1, A_2, etc.) with their right-hand corners lying above the curve, and twelve inner rectangles (a_1, a_2, etc.) with their left-hand corners below the curve. The area of all the outer ones is

$$A_1 + A_2 + A_3 + A_4 \ . \ . \ . \ A_{10} + A_{11} + A_{12}$$

The area of all the inner ones is

$$a_1 + a_2 + a_3 + a_4 \ . \ . \ . \ a_{10} + a_{11} + a_{12}$$

You can also see that

$$a_1 = A_2$$
$$a_2 = A_3$$
$$. \ . \ . \ . \ .$$
$$a_{11} = A_{12}$$

So that if we subtract the less from the greater, we have

$$(A_1 + A_2 + A_3 \ . \ . \ . \ A_{11} + A_{12}) - (a_1 + a_2 \ . \ . \ . \ a_{10} + a_{11} + a_{12})$$
$$= A_1 + (A_2 - a_1) + (A_3 - a_2) \ . \ . \ .$$
$$+ (A_{10} - a_9) + (A_{11} - a_{10}) + (A_{12} - a_{11}) - a_{12}$$
$$= A_1 - a_{12}$$

The area of each strip is its height (y) multiplied by its breadth ($\triangle x$), so the difference is

$$y(1) . \triangle x - y(3) . \triangle x = \triangle x . [y(1) - y(3)]$$

where $y(x)$ is written for the value of y corresponding to x.

This means that if we took the area marked off as the sum of the areas of all the larger (outer) rectangular strips, the result would be too big by a quantity about one-half of

$$\triangle x . [y(1) - y(3)]$$

This source of error continually diminishes as we increase the number of strips by making $\triangle x$ the width of each strip smaller. If we make $\triangle x = dx$ too small to measure, the error will also be too small to measure. If we use the symbol introduced on p. 262, the area will then be

$$\sum_{x=1}^{x=3} y . dx \quad \text{or} \quad \sum_{x=1}^{x=3} \frac{1}{1 + x} . dx$$

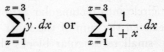

In the integral calculus this is usually written with a different symbol, as

$$\int_1^3 y.dx \quad \text{or} \quad \int_1^3 \frac{1}{1+x}.dx$$

It is then called "the integral of y from one to three."

Just as we can get a rough value for the differential coefficient by drawing the tangent with a ruler and measuring the angle it makes with the x axis with a protractor, we can get a good approximation for an area like the one we are considering by measuring the heights (y_1 to y_n) of the n outer rectangles, and multiplying their sum by the width of the strip $\triangle x$. In the diagram $n = 12$; $\triangle x = 1/6$. The result will be too big by a quantity roughly equivalent to

$$\tfrac{1}{2}(y_1 - y_{n+1})\triangle x$$

We need not actually measure the height of each rectangle if we know the equation of the curve, which in this figure is

$$y = \frac{1}{1+x}$$

So if we start by dividing one unit along x into six divisions ($\triangle x = 1/6$), to find the area enclosed between $x = 1$ and $x = 3$, the first value of y is obtained by substituting 1 for x in the equation. The second is found by substituting $1\frac{1}{6}$, the third by substituting $1\frac{1}{3}$, and so on, till $x = 2\frac{5}{6}$. So y_1 to y_n have the successive values,

$$\tfrac{1}{2},\ \tfrac{6}{13},\ \ldots\ \tfrac{6}{23}$$

The area of all the outer rectangles will be

$$\tfrac{1}{6}\left\{\tfrac{1}{2} + \tfrac{6}{13}\ \ldots + \tfrac{6}{23}\right\} = 0{\cdot}714^*$$

This will be too big by about

$$\tfrac{1}{2}\cdot\tfrac{1}{6}(y_1 - y_{n+1})$$

To get y_{n+1} we have to substitute $x = 3$ in the equation of the curve. So the excess which we have to subtract is roughly

$$\tfrac{1}{12}\left\{\tfrac{1}{2} - \tfrac{1}{4}\right\} = 0{\cdot}021$$

* To check this result quickly write the terms in the form

$$\tfrac{1}{12}\ \tfrac{1}{13}\ \tfrac{1}{14}\ldots\tfrac{1}{23}$$

Then read off the values from the table of reciprocals.

The result, which is 0·693, cannot be out by more than this amount. So we can make the error as small as we like by making Δx as small as we can.

Real progress in the integral calculus began when Leibniz showed

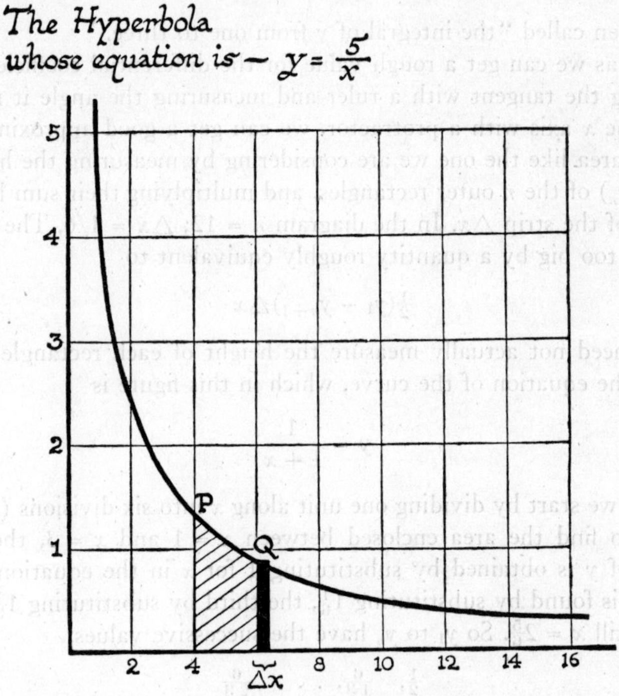

FIG. 180

how to find a simple formula for the sum, when Δx is so small (dx) that we can neglect

$$\tfrac{1}{2}dx(y_1 - y_{n+1})$$

Since there are still ignorant people who produce average measurements of the brain capacity of natives in backward regions as a reason for withholding educational opportunities from them, it is worth while remembering that the cranial capacity of Leibniz, like that of Anatole France, was lower than the average figure for any aboriginal population.

To get over the labour of successive approximation, such as we used in Chapter 6 on p. 261 to find π, Leibniz introduced motion into the measurement of area. You will see how he did it in Fig. 180, where the area which we have to find is the shaded portion bounded above by the portion of the curve PQ, and below by the part of the x-axis between $x = 4$ and $x = 6$. With the symbol we shall now employ, the area shaded is

$$\int_4^6 y \, . \, dx \quad \text{or} \quad \int_4^6 \frac{5}{x} \, . \, dx$$

First, imagine the y ordinate as a piece of sooty elastic stretched between P and $x = 4$, with a sliding loop round the curve at one end and around the x-axis at the other. As we push it along till one end is at Q and the other at $x = 6$, it will trace out the shaded area in the figure. Now let it move a very short distance $\triangle x$ further along, and mark off a rectangular strip of area $\triangle A$ like the one which is black in the figure. Then

$$\triangle A = y \, . \, \triangle x$$

$$\text{or} \qquad \frac{\triangle A}{\triangle x} = y \text{ very nearly}$$

If $\triangle x$ becomes indefinitely small this may be written

$$\frac{dA}{dx} = y \text{ exactly}$$

That is to say, the rate at which the area is growing as x increases at any particular point along the x-axis is measured by the y ordinate at the same point.

This is a differential equation which we have already met, as we see at once when we write it out in full thus:

$$\frac{dA}{dx} = \frac{5}{x}$$

To solve it we have to find an expression which gives $\frac{5}{x}$ when differentiated. We already know that the differential coefficient of

$$C + a \log_e (x + b)$$

is

$$\frac{a}{x + b}$$

If we put $a = 5$, $b = 0$,

$$\frac{a}{x + b} = \frac{5}{x}$$

and

$$a \, . \log_e (x + b) = 5 \log_e x$$

So the solution is

$$A = C + 5 \log_e x$$

To use this we only have to remember that the area was zero when the elastic joined P to $x = 4$, i.e.

$$5 \log_e 4 + C = 0$$
$$C = -5 \log_e 4$$

The area traced out as the elastic slides along to any other point x_q on the x-axis is

$$5 \log_e x_q - 5 \log_e 4$$

In this case we are considering the area between $x = 4$ and $x = 6$ so it is

$$5 \log_e 6 - 5 \log_e 4$$
$$5 (\log_e 6 - \log_e 4)$$
$$5 \log_e \tfrac{6}{4}$$

or

$$5 \log_e \frac{3}{2}$$

In the same way we can now find the area marked off in Fig. 179, i.e.

$$\int_1^3 \frac{1}{1+x} dx$$

From the table already given, we know that

$$\frac{dA}{dx} = \frac{1}{1+x}$$

when

$$A = \log_e (1 + x) + C$$

Starting from $x = 1$ when the area is zero

$$\log_e (1 + 1) + C = 0$$
$$C = -\log_e 2$$

$$\therefore \int_1^3 \frac{1}{1+x} . dx = \log_e 4 - \log_e 2$$
$$= \log_e \tfrac{4}{2}$$
$$= \log_e 2$$

The tables give $\log_{10} 2 = 0 \cdot 301$, and $\log_e 2 = \log_e 10 . \log_{10} 2 = 2 \cdot 303 \log_{10} 2$. So the result is $0 \cdot 693$ correct to the same number of decimals as the approximate answer already obtained.

We can now draw up tables for finding areas of this kind by using the results of the last section in exactly the same way. We know that if

$$\frac{dA}{dx} = ax^n$$

$$A = \frac{a}{n+1} \cdot x^{n+1} + C$$

$$\therefore \quad \int_p^q ax^n dx = \frac{a}{n+1} \cdot q^{n+1} - \frac{a}{n+1} \cdot p^{n+1}$$

$$= \frac{a}{n+1}(q^{n+1} - p^{n+1})$$

We also know that if

$$\frac{dA}{dx} = \cos x$$

$$A = \sin x + C$$

$$\therefore \quad \int_p^q \cos x . dx = \sin q - \sin p$$

Another item for such a table follows from the fact that the differential coefficient of $b + ae^{cx}$ is $ac . e^{cx}$. Putting $a = \frac{1}{c}$, we get

$$\frac{d}{dx}(b + \frac{1}{c}e^{cx}) = e^{cx}$$

So if

$$\frac{dA}{dx} = e^{cx}$$

$$A = \frac{1}{c} . e^{cx} + b$$

Hence we have

$$\int_p^q e^{cx} . dx = \frac{1}{c}(e^{cq} - e^{cp})$$

A short table for finding areas might therefore be made like this:

y	$\int_p^q y . dx$
$\frac{a}{b+x}$	$a . \log_e\left(\frac{b+q}{b+p}\right)$
ax^n	$\frac{a}{n+1}(q^{n+1} - p^{n+1})$
$\cos ax$	$\frac{1}{a}(\sin aq - \sin ap)$
e^{cx}	$\frac{1}{c}(e^{cq} - e^{cp})$

THE USEFULNESS OF INTEGRATION.—So far we have not explained why we should want to measure an area like that marked off in Figs. 166, 179, and 180. The integral calculus attained its greatest usefulness when coal as a source of energy supplanted human labour and that of the beast of burden. In the age of Newton and Leibniz one of the uses to which it was put was the discovery of series like those which we have studied in the last chapter. The first important application

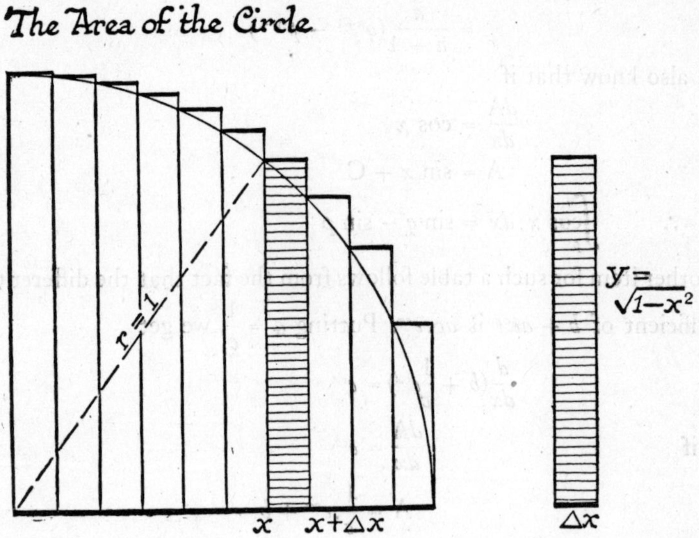

FIG. 181

of the method of integration was finding a value for π as an unlimited series which chokes off. We have already touched on the method which Wallis used to get a rough value for π in Chapter 6, p. 266. In Fig. 181 the area of the quarter circle of unit radius ($r = 1$) is inscribed in a sequence of rectangular strips of area $y.\ \Delta x$. As you will see from Chapter 6, p. 260, $y = \sqrt{1 - x^2}$. The moving ordinate y slides from $x = 0$ to $x = r = 1$, as it traces out the area in question. When the number of strips is made as large as possible and Δx becomes a width dx too small to measure,

$$A = \int_0^r y\,.\,dx$$

$$= \int_0^r \sqrt{1 - x^2}\,.\,dx$$

We can find the value of this (see Chapter 7, p. 329) by using the binomial theorem, thus:

$$\begin{aligned}\sqrt{1-x^2} &= (1-x^2)^{\frac{1}{2}}\\ &= 1 - 0{\cdot}5x^2 - 0{\cdot}125x^4 - 0{\cdot}0625x^6\\ &\quad - 0{\cdot}0390625x^8 - 0{\cdot}02734375x^{10} \ldots\end{aligned}$$

So we have to find A when

$$\frac{dA}{dx} = 1 - 0{\cdot}5x^2 - 0{\cdot}125x^4 \ldots$$

We know that if

$$\frac{dA}{dx} = b + cx + dx^2 + ex^3 + fx^4 \ldots$$

$$A = a + bx + \frac{cx^2}{2} + \frac{dx^3}{3} + \frac{ex^4}{4} \ldots$$

If we put $b = 1$, $c = 0$, $d = -0{\cdot}5$, $e = 0$, $f = -0{\cdot}125$, etc., in the former, we get the binomial series for $\sqrt{1-x^2}$ given above. So the result of integrating $(1-x^2)^{\frac{1}{2}}$ is

$$A = a + x - \frac{0{\cdot}5x^3}{3} - \frac{0{\cdot}125x^5}{5} - \frac{0{\cdot}0625x^7}{7} - \frac{0{\cdot}0390625x^9}{9} - \frac{0{\cdot}02734375x^{11}}{11} \ldots$$

To find a, we have to recall the fact that the moving ordinate starts at $x = 0$. So that the area $A = 0$ when $x = 0$. Thus

$$0 = a + 0 - 0 - 0 \ldots$$

$$\text{i.e.}\quad a = 0$$

To get the area of the quarter circle of unit radius we have now to find the value of A when $x = r = 1$. Thus:

$$A = 1 - \frac{0{\cdot}5}{3} - \frac{0{\cdot}125}{5} - \frac{0{\cdot}0625}{7} - \frac{0{\cdot}0390625}{9} - \frac{0{\cdot}02734375}{11} \ldots$$

The area (A) of the quarter circle of unit radius is $\frac{\pi}{4}$. So we can put for π the unlimited series

$$4\left(1 - \frac{0{\cdot}5}{3} - \frac{0{\cdot}125}{5} - \frac{0{\cdot}0625}{7} \ldots\right)$$

If we take the first six terms in this series we get

$$4(0 \cdot 7926 \ldots)$$
$$= 3 \cdot 17$$

This series chokes off rather slowly. However many terms we include, it never grows smaller than 3·14159. So the value of π correct to four decimals is 3·1416. There are many other series for π, some of which choke off very rapidly. One series for π depends on the use of a most valuable device for constructing tables of logarithms.

We have already seen how to integrate

$$\int_p^q \frac{1}{1+x} . dx$$

If $p = 0$, the value of this integral is $\log_e (1 + q)$. It is also possible to find a value for such an area by a method similar to the one which we have just used for the circle, since we may write it (see p. 485)

$$\int_p^q (1 - x + x^2 - x^3 \ . \ . \ .) . dx$$

If the differential coefficient of A is the series

$$1 - x + x^2 - x^3 \ldots$$

we have $$A = a + x - \frac{x^2}{2} + \frac{x^3}{3} - \frac{x^4}{4} + \frac{x^5}{5} \ldots$$

If we are taking the area between $x = 0$, $(p = 0)$ and $x = q$, $A = 0$ when $x = 0$. Hence $a = 0$, and

$$\int_0^q \frac{1}{1+x} . dx = q - \frac{q^2}{2} + \frac{q^3}{3} - \frac{q^4}{4} + \frac{q^5}{5} \ldots$$

Thus we get the *logarithmic series*

$$\log_e (1 + q) = q - \frac{q^2}{2} + \frac{q^3}{3} - \frac{q^4}{4} + \frac{q^5}{5} \ldots$$

This series chokes off, provided q is not greater than 1. So we can use it to calculate logarithms for the base e for as many numbers as we like between 1 and 2. To get $\log_e (1 \cdot 25)$ we put

$$\log_e(1 + 0 \cdot 25) = 0 \cdot 25 - \frac{(0 \cdot 25)^2}{2} + \frac{(0 \cdot 25)^3}{3} - \frac{(0 \cdot 25)^4}{4} \ldots$$

This boils down to a series which chokes off fairly quickly, viz.:

$$\tfrac{1}{4}(1 - \tfrac{1}{8}) + \tfrac{1}{64}(\tfrac{1}{3} - \tfrac{1}{16}) + \tfrac{1}{1024}(\tfrac{1}{5} - \tfrac{1}{24}) \ldots$$

Similarly to get $\log_e 2$, we have

$$\begin{aligned}\log_e (1 + 1) &= 1 - \tfrac{1}{2} + \tfrac{1}{3} - \tfrac{1}{4} + \tfrac{1}{5} - \tfrac{1}{6} \ldots \\ &= \tfrac{1}{2} + \tfrac{1}{12} + \tfrac{1}{30} + \tfrac{1}{56} + \tfrac{1}{90} + \tfrac{1}{132} \ldots\end{aligned}$$

The logarithmic series, besides being useful to calculate logarithms, also leads to another method for calculating π. We have to introduce the imaginary $\sqrt{-1}$. To get series for $\cos a$ and $\sin a$, when a is measured in radians, we have already used the equation

$$e^{ia} = \cos a + i \sin a$$

$$\therefore \quad \frac{1}{\cos a} \cdot e^{ia} = 1 + \frac{i \sin a}{\cos a}$$

$$= 1 + i \tan a$$

$$\therefore \quad \log_e \frac{e^{ia}}{\cos a} = \log_e (1 + i \tan a)$$

$$\therefore \quad \log_e e^{ia} - \log_e \cos a = \log_e (1 + i \tan a)$$

Looking back to p. 477 you will recall the rule for finding the logarithm of a number raised to any power, i.e.

$$\log_e e^{ia} = ia \log_e e$$

Since the logarithm of the base is always 1, ($e^1 = e \ldots \log_e e = 1$)

$$\log_e e^{ia} = ia$$

Hence

$$ia - \log_e \cos a = \log_e (1 + i \tan a)$$

Using the logarithmic series, we put $q = i \tan a$:

$$\log_e (1 + i \tan a) = i \tan a - \frac{i^2 \tan^2 a}{2} + \frac{i^3 \tan^3 a}{3} - \frac{i^4 \tan^4 a}{4} + \frac{i^5 \tan^5 a}{5} \ldots$$

Putting in the numerical values for the powers of i, we get

$$\log_e (1 + i \tan a) = i \tan a + \frac{\tan^2 a}{2} - \frac{i \tan^3 a}{3} - \frac{\tan^4 a}{4} + \frac{i \tan^5 a}{5} + \frac{\tan^6 a}{6} \ldots$$

$$ia - \log_e \cos a = \left(i \tan a - \frac{i \tan^3 a}{3} + \frac{i \tan^5 a}{5} \ldots\right) + \left(\frac{\tan^2 a}{2} - \frac{\tan^4 a}{4} + \frac{\tan^6 a}{6} \ldots\right)$$

Remembering the rule about pears and ponies, we have

$$ia = i \tan a - \frac{i \tan^3 a}{3} + \frac{i \tan^5 a}{5} \ . \ . \ .$$

$$\therefore \qquad a = \tan a - \frac{\tan^3 a}{3} + \frac{\tan^5 a}{5} - \frac{\tan^7 a}{7} \ . \ . \ .$$

We can use this series to get π in several ways. We learned at the Bridge of Asses that tan $(\frac{1}{4}\pi)$ radians (i.e. tan 45°) = 1. So if $a = \frac{1}{4}\pi$, we have

$$\frac{\pi}{4} = 1 - \frac{1}{3} + \frac{1}{5} - \frac{1}{7} + \frac{1}{9} \ . \ . \ .$$
$$= 1 - (\tfrac{1}{3} - \tfrac{1}{5}) - (\tfrac{1}{7} - \tfrac{1}{9}) - (\tfrac{1}{11} - \tfrac{1}{13})$$
$$= 1 - 2(\tfrac{1}{15} + \tfrac{1}{63} + \tfrac{1}{143} + \tfrac{1}{255} \ . \ . \ .)$$

This series chokes off very slowly, and we can get a much more convenient form by using other values of tan a. For instance, tan 30°, i.e.

$\tan \frac{\pi}{6} = \frac{1}{\sqrt{3}}$. Hence if $a = \frac{\pi}{6}$

$$\frac{\pi}{6} = \frac{1}{\sqrt{3}} - \left(\frac{1}{\sqrt{3}}\right)^3 \cdot \frac{1}{3} + \left(\frac{1}{\sqrt{3}}\right)^5 \cdot \frac{1}{5} - \left(\frac{1}{\sqrt{3}}\right)^7 \cdot \frac{1}{7}$$
$$+ \left(\frac{1}{\sqrt{3}}\right)^9 \cdot \frac{1}{9} - \left(\frac{1}{\sqrt{3}}\right)^{11} \cdot \frac{1}{11}$$
$$= \frac{1}{\sqrt{3}}\left(1 - \frac{1}{9}\right) + \left(\frac{1}{\sqrt{3}}\right)^5 \left(\frac{1}{5} - \frac{1}{21}\right) + \left(\frac{1}{\sqrt{3}}\right)^9 \left(\frac{1}{9} - \frac{1}{33}\right) \ . \ . \ .$$
$$= \frac{1}{\sqrt{3}}\left(\frac{8}{9}\right) + \frac{1}{9\sqrt{3}}\left(\frac{16}{105}\right) + \frac{1}{81\sqrt{3}}\left(\frac{24}{297}\right) \ . \ . \ .$$
$$= \sqrt{3}\left\{\frac{8}{27} + \frac{16}{27 \times 105} + \frac{24}{243 \times 297} \ . \ . \ .\right\}$$
$$\therefore \quad \pi = 3 \cdot 14 \ . \ . \ .$$

When written in this way you will see that successive terms get smaller more rapidly than those of the series $1 + \frac{1}{9} + (\frac{1}{9})^2 + (\frac{1}{9})^3$. So the last result is certainly correct to two decimal places.

The methods of the integral calculus are specially helpful in solving problems concerning the measurement of solid figures. That is why so little has been said about them so far. In this connexion the fundamental device which we use is of very great antiquity. Archimedes, who found a value for π based on dividing the circle into a large number of approximately triangular strips, asserts that Democritus gave the correct value for the volume of a pyramid by regarding it as the sum of a large number of slices. It is quite probable that the father of Greek materialism derived his method from the Egyptians. A papyrus now in Moscow appears to show that the Egyptians possessed a correct formula for the volume of the pyramid and the area of a sphere about 1800 B.C. Perhaps the brilliant achievements of the Alexandrians owe a great deal more to the survivals of Egyptian mensuration than our habit of writing history as a succession of biographical studies is apt

The Area & Volume of the Sphere

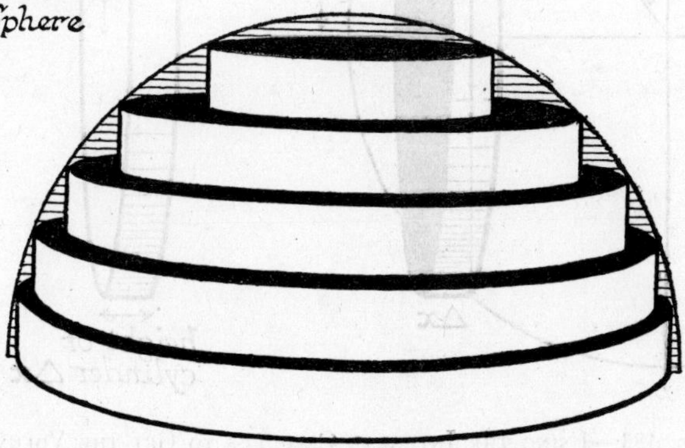

FIG. 182

to disclose. How the area and volume of solid figures like cones, pyramids, spheres, or ellipsoids can be found by applying the integral calculus may be illustrated by finding the volume of the figure which is of greatest interest in the study of astronomy. If we want to find the volume or area of a sphere we split it up into an immensely large number of parallel slices, and notice that each slice is very nearly the same as a slice of a cone (a different cone for each slice), so that the area or volume of the two slices is almost the same. For finding the volume, but not the area, we can simplify further, using cylindrical slices (see Fig. 182) just as a circle can be looked upon as the sum of an immensely large number of rectangles (Fig. 181). The volume of a solid figure which has the same cross-section everywhere is the product of the area of the cross-section and the height. Hence the volume of a cylinder is $\pi r^2 h$. To get the volume of the sphere (Fig. 183) we proceed as if a series of flat cylindrical slices are placed end to end along the x axis, each flat cylinder being Δx units in *height* when put to stand on its base. The radius of each cylinder will correspond with the y ordinate

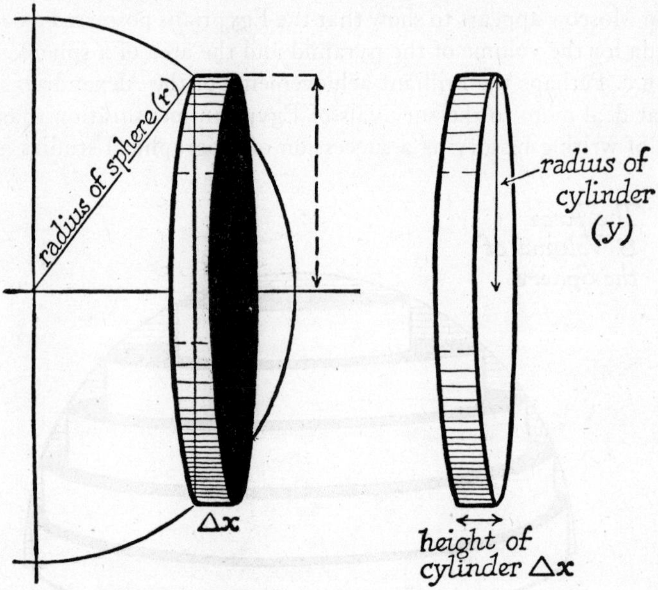

FIG. 183.—USING THE INTEGRAL CALCULUS TO GET THE VOLUME OF THE SPHERE

of the circular cross-section of the sphere. If the radius of the sphere is r, the radius of each cylinder, y, will be given by the equation

$$y^2 = r^2 - x^2$$

The volume of each slice is

$$\pi y^2 \Delta x$$
$$= \pi(r^2 - x^2)\Delta x$$

The volume of the half sphere will be the sum of all the cylinders when Δx becomes indefinitely small, i.e.

$$\int_0^r \pi(r^2 - x^2)dx$$

For the volume of the half sphere we therefore need to solve the differential equation

$$\frac{dV}{dx} = \pi r^2 - \pi x^2$$

The solution of such an equation has been given as:

$$V = a + \pi r^2 x - \frac{\pi x^3}{3}$$

Since we are only considering the volume to the right of $x = 0$, $V = 0$ when $x = 0$, and therefore $a = 0$. Hence the value of the integral is obtained by putting r for x in

$$\pi r^2 x - \frac{\pi x^3}{3}$$

i.e.

$$V = \pi r^3 - \frac{\pi r^3}{3}$$

$$= \frac{2\pi r^3}{3}$$

The volume of the whole sphere will be twice this volume, i.e.

$$\tfrac{4}{3}\pi r^3$$

Thus the volume of the earth is approximately $\frac{4}{3} \times \frac{22}{7} \times (4{,}000)^3$ cubic miles. This is roughly 268,000,000,000 cubic miles.

MATHEMATICAL INTEGRATION AND SOCIAL EFFICIENCY.—As we have seen in the last chapter, the study of series as calculating devices became an issue of great practical importance in the social context from which the integral calculus in its modern form arose. So far the illustrations which we have given to show its use have been confined to the discovery of series and to problems of mensuration. The utility of the integral calculus for measurements in physical science did not come into its own until the period of power production. The explosion of the cannon and the ticking of the clock were the tocsin of a new phase in the organization of man's social life. Before the seventeenth century closed another technical development reflected increased use of metals. Progress in *mining* paved the way for the industrial revolution which introduced in the sphere of production extensive use of machinery independent of human or animal sources of energy. The integral calculus provided the mathematical tool for calculating the efficiency of the new machinery. If we made the fullest use of our present scientific knowledge, we could draw up an inventory of all the sources of power available for planning an age of plenty and leisure for everybody. At present, economists have too little training in real science to realize the futility of trivial disputations about usury and salesmanship carried on in much the same temper as the theological quibbles of the fourteenth century.

With the advent of coal as a source of power, the Newtonian conception of force began to play a less prominent role in physical science. At the beginning of the industrial revolution those who controlled industry were interested in getting the maximum efficiency out of the machine. Chemistry was providing new opportunities for the manufacturer. Biology linked to chemistry reflected the absorbing interest of the period in the problem of combustion. The dominating issue of the time was how the chemical nature of fuel or foodstuffs is connected with the work which the non-living or living machine can carry out. The phenomena of friction, as illustrated by Count Rumford's experiments on the boring of cannon, came into prominence. A new word, *energy*, or capacity for doing work, became increasingly important in the vocabulary of science. The methods of the integral calculus became the basis of the new physics and chemistry of energetics (or *thermodynamics*), just as the differential calculus had provided the means of studying mechanical motion *per se* in the preceding century.

In Newtonian physics the *work* done by a falling weight is measured by the product of the force exerted by the weight and the distance through which it falls ($W = Fl$). If the weight descends through a small distance dl, the small amount of work done is

$$dW = F \cdot dl$$

Remembering that Newtonian force is the product of the mass (m) moved and the acceleration produced $\left(\frac{d^2l}{dt^2} \text{ or } \frac{dv}{dt}\text{, where } v \text{ is the velocity at a given instant}\right)$, we may put

$$dW = m \cdot \frac{dv}{dt} \cdot dl$$

If we multiply both sides by $dl \div dl$ ($= 1$),

$$dW = m \cdot \frac{dl}{dt} \cdot \frac{dv}{dl} \cdot dl$$

$$= mv \cdot dv$$

So in starting with a velocity 0 when $l = 0$ and moving till the velocity is V, when the distance fallen is L, the work done is

$$\int_0^V mv\,.\,dv = \tfrac{1}{2}mV^2$$

The quantity $\frac{1}{2}mV^2$ is called the Kinetic Energy of *m*, when it has speed V.

If the weight fell in a vacuum its acceleration would be approximately 32 feet per second. The work done by falling through a distance L would therefore be $32m$L, i.e.

$$32mL = \tfrac{1}{2}mV^2$$

Suppose that it does not fall in a vacuum, and that as it falls it makes the wheel of the old-fashioned weight-driven clock spin round quickly. According to the Newtonian view, the clock wheel has all the sluggishness of matter, or inertia, which resists change of movement. The weight will have to bring the *mass* of each particle of the wheel up to a certain velocity. If we call the total mass of the weight and wheel M_2 and the average value of the square of the speed of all the particles of the weight and wheel V_2^2, we do not find that $\frac{1}{2}M_2V_2^2$ is equivalent to $32m$L, the work done by the falling weight in getting the wheel to move. It is actually less, just as the acceleration of the weight is less when descending in air than it is when it descends in a vacuum. Something else has come in. Heat is produced as well as motion. The more the heat produced, the more is motion slowed down. Newtonian mathematics could only help us to calculate the speed of a machine if the wheel moved very slowly (like the wheels of the weight-driven clock), and was very well greased, so that very little heat was produced. Before the fullest use could be made of it, new experimental information about the way in which heat is produced had to be found out.

At the beginning of the eighteenth century physical science acquired a new tool, the thermometer. A unit of heat was adopted by general agreement. This is the amount of heat required to raise a fixed quantity of some particular form of matter from one level of temperature to another (one gram of water one degree centigrade in the international system). At the end of the eighteenth century and in the opening years of the nineteenth, when the process of combustion was the absorbing topic of practical interest, three discoveries led to the adoption of *energy* as a common basis of measurement in the physical sciences, chemistry, and biology. There is a constant ratio between the amount of heat produced in combustion and the amount of any particular substance burned. There is a constant ratio between the amount of foodstuffs consumed and the amount of bodily heat which is generated by an animal. There is also a constant ratio between the amount of heat generated by friction and the amount of work done by moving against this friction. So much matter is equivalent to so much heat, so much mechanical work to so much heat; therefore so much matter represents the possibility of so much work. The invention of the steam-engine meant that dead matter acquired *potential energy* or the possibility of doing work which need no longer be done by men working under conditions of slavery. In real life we never get *all* the potential energy out of matter in the form of equivalent units of mechanical work. There is always a certain amount of heat produced. The pre-eminent technological problem of the machine age was designing machines so as to get as much work out of them as possible. To know how efficient a machine is we need to be able to calculate how much potential energy is wasted. The solution of this problem gave the methods of the integral calculus much greater practical importance than its inventors could have realized.

The simplest illustration of how the integral calculus can help us to calculate how much work a machine can do, if none of its store of energy is wasted, is provided by the machine of the Newtonian age. For simplicity we will assume that the spring of the clock obeys Hooke's Law faithfully, as in Fig. 184. The spring in Fig. 184 extends $0 \cdot 6$ inches (x) per 10 pound weight (y) applied, i.e.

$$y = \frac{10x}{0 \cdot 6}$$
$$= 16 \cdot 7x$$

Suppose when it is stretched $1 \cdot 6$ inches we stretch it further till it is $2 \cdot 1$ inches longer than its non-stretched length. If it is stretched through a distance dx, the work done is the Force, y (measured in pounds weight), multiplied by the distance through which it is applied, i.e.

$$y \, . \, dx$$

Between $x = 1 \cdot 6$ and $x = 2 \cdot 1$ the work done will be the sum of all the rectangular strips, i.e.

$$\int_{1\cdot 6}^{2\cdot 1} y \, . \, dx = \int_{1\cdot 6}^{2\cdot 1} 16 \cdot 7x \, . \, dx$$

This means solving $\frac{dA}{dx} = 16 \cdot 7x$

i.e. $A = \frac{16 \cdot 7x^2}{2} + C$

When $x = 1 \cdot 6$, $A = 0$

$$C = -\frac{16 \cdot 7}{2}(1 \cdot 6)^2$$

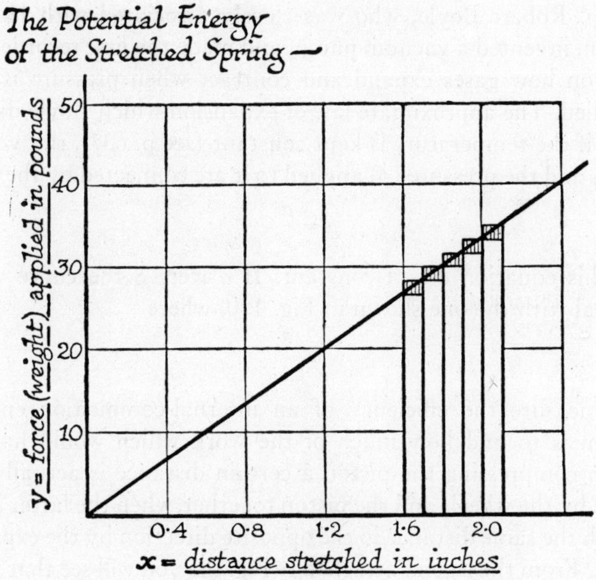

FIG. 184

So the total work which could be done in stretching the spring from $1 \cdot 6$ to $2 \cdot 1$ inches is

$$\frac{16 \cdot 7}{2}\left\{(2 \cdot 1)^2 - (1 \cdot 6)^2\right\}$$
$$= 15 \cdot 4 \text{ pound-weight-inches.}$$

We call this quantity the amount by which the *potential energy* of the spring is *increased* when it is stretched from $1 \cdot 6$ to $2 \cdot 1$ inches. The *efficiency* of a machine driven by a spring is measured by how much mechanical work the wheels can be made to perform as the potential energy is decreased by a given amount, i.e. the ratio of the work which we get out of it when it is wound up to the work we put into winding it.

Efficiency in the age of the internal-combustion engine depends on using the elastic power of a gas instead of the elastic power of a spring. The theory of the combustion engine depends on the law of elasticity of gases. By the end of the seventeenth century the technical problems of mining had already attracted the attention of physicists. Among the technical problems which arise in sinking shafts, pumping and ventilation are of great importance. The pump came in for its share of attention when the scientific study of mechanics began to develop. Robert Boyle, who was closely associated with Hooke and Newton, invented a vacuum pump, and made the first recorded experiments on how gases expand and contract when pressure is reduced or applied. The approximate law of expansion which Boyle discovered is that if the temperature is kept constant (see p. 637), the volume (v) of a gas and the pressure (p) applied to it are connected by the equation

$$p = \frac{a}{v}$$

In this equation a is a constant. If a were 5 the curve would be identical with the one shown in Fig. 180, where

$$y = \frac{5}{x}$$

To measure the efficiency of an internal-combustion engine our problem is to find how much of the work which would have to be done in compressing the piston a certain distance is actually accomplished by the wheels and the piston together, when the latter is pushed through the same distance in the opposite direction by the expansion of the gas. From the legend attached to Fig. 185 you will see that if the gas is compressed from a volume v_1 to a volume v_2 this is the same thing as

$$-\int_{v_1}^{v_2} p\,.\,dv$$

$$= -\int_{v_1}^{v_2} \frac{a}{v}\,.\,dv$$

If v is measured along the x axis this is the integral

$$-\int_{v_1}^{v_2} \frac{a}{x}\,.\,dx$$

$$= a\,.\log_e \frac{v_1}{v_2}$$

The value of this is obtained from tables of logarithms.

MATHEMATICS IN THE NEWTONIAN AGE—When allowance has been made for the fabulous dimensions which Newton's achievements have assumed, the outstanding fact about his contribution is the success with which he was able to use the new methods resulting from the union of algebra and geometry. Progress with the new methods was less rapid than it might have been if those who understood the new

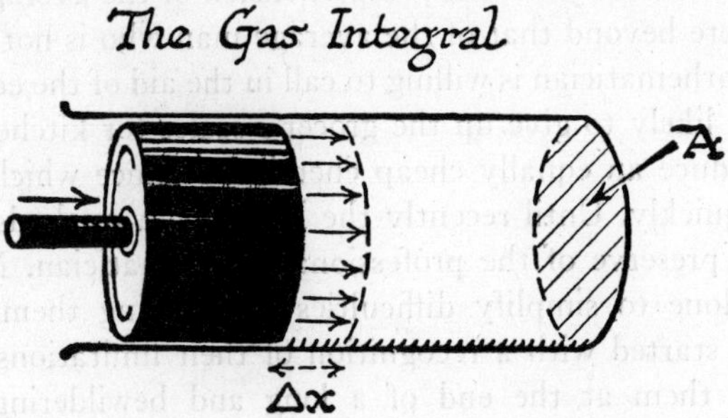

FIG. 185

If a vessel of height x has the same area in cross-section (A) throughout like a cylinder its volume is $A \, . \, x$. If the piston is pushed through a distance Δx the decrease in volume of the gas inside the piston is therefore $A \, . \, \Delta x$. Pressure is measured in the mechanics of gases by the force applied to unit area, and Work is measured by the product of the force applied into the distance traversed, i.e.

$$F = p \, . \, A$$

and

$$W = F \, . \, D$$

If the piston is pushed through a distance Δx without loss of energy by friction, the work done is therefore $F \, . \, \Delta x$. This may be written also $p \, . \, A \, . \, \Delta x$. The small change of volume which is represented by $- A \, . \, \Delta x$ may be written Δv, and the small amount of work done in changing it ΔW, so that:

$$\Delta W = - p \, . \, \Delta v$$

technique had benefited from the fate of the *Sand Reckoner* and the algebra of Theon and Diophantus. The intellectual leaders in the Newtonian period did not realize that every intellectual advance raises a constructive problem in education. Newton himself devoted much of his energy to devising long-winded demonstrations in Euclidean geometry instead of trying to make his own methods intelligible to his contemporaries. One result of this was that conspicuous progress in Newtonian mechanics did not take place in his own country during the century which followed the publication of the *Principia*.

Nowadays we constantly hear about the limitations of Newton's mechanics and of the mathematical methods which he used. When we recognize clearly what these limitations are, the plain fact is that the Newtonian methods remain, and will for long remain, the basis of calculation in natural science. For certain purposes other methods yield results which are more in accordance with the facts. When they do, they do so at the cost of immense intellectual labour with a technique which will remain beyond the comprehension of the average scientist, and still more beyond that of the average man who is not a scientist, until the mathematician is willing to call in the aid of the educationist. We are not likely to give up the grocer's scales for kitchen use until we can produce an equally cheap chemical balance which will come to rest as quickly. Until recently the Newtonian methods were very largely the preserve of the professional mathematician. Much more might be done to simplify difficulties in grasping them and using them if we started with a recognition of their limitations instead of discovering them at the end of a long and bewildering course of mechanics in which perfectly smooth balls roll down perfectly rigid planes and wheels spin round their unlubricated axles without any friction whatsoever. Nothing would do more to promote a rapid advance in human understanding than an annual conference between schoolboys, schoolmasters, and elderly scientists. The scientists should be compelled to attend under pain of losing their pension rights.

Exercises on Chapter 11

1. Use the series for $\log_e (1 + x)$ to find $\log_e 10$, $\log_e 2$, $\log_e 3$, $\log_e 4$, $\log_e 5$.

Hence make a table of $\log_{10} 2$, $\log_{10} 3$, $\log_{10} 4$, $\log_{10} 5$.

2. Find π by infinite series correct to 3 places of decimals by two different methods.

3. Draw very accurately the graph of

$$y = \tfrac{1}{5}x^2$$

Measure its slope at three points corresponding with three different values of x, and, using a table of tangents, compare your measurements with the values calculated by substituting the appropriate numbers in the differential coefficient $\frac{2x}{5}$.

Find by counting squares the area enclosed by the curve, the x axis, and the y ordinates at the points $x = 5$ and $x = 10$, and compare this with the area calculated from the integral

$$\int_5^{10} \tfrac{1}{5}x^2 . dx = \left[\frac{x^3}{15}\right]_5^{10} = \left[\frac{10^3}{15} - \frac{5^3}{15}\right]$$

4. Draw the graph of $y = \sqrt{36 - x^2}$.

Find $\frac{dy}{dx}$ when $x = 1, 2, -2$.

Draw the tangents and compare with the results obtained by differentiation.

5. In the same way draw the graph of $y = \frac{1}{x}$ between $x = 0$ and $x = 4$, and find $\frac{dy}{dx}$ when $x = 1, 2$.

6. Find from first principles (i.e. by applying the methods of p. 534) $\frac{dy}{dx}$ when $y = x + \frac{1}{x}$.

7. Write down $\frac{dy}{dx}$ when

$$y = x^{3\cdot 6},\ 5\sqrt{x},\ x^{-1\frac{1}{2}},\ \sqrt{x^7},\ \frac{3}{\sqrt[3]{x^{-\frac{1}{3}}}}$$

8. What is $\frac{dy}{dx}$ when

$$y = x^5 - 5x^3 + 5x^2 - 4x + 3$$

9. If $pv = k$, k being a constant, show that

$$\frac{dp}{dv} = -\frac{p}{v}$$

10. Find the turning points of the curve $y = x^3 - 3x$ and plot the curve, showing these points.

11. Find the greatest possible volume of a cylindrical parcel when the length and girth together must not be more than 6 feet.

12. In a dynamo x is the weight of the armature and y the weight of the rest. The cost of running (c) is given by

$$c = 10x + 3y$$

The power is proportional to xy. If the cost is fixed, find the relation between x and y so as to obtain the maximum power.

13. If the boundary of a rectangle is of fixed length 2L, one side may be written x and the adjacent side is $(L - x)$. If the area is a, $a = x(L - x)$. This is a maximum when $\frac{da}{dx} = 0$. Hence show that the square is the rectangle of fixed perimeter having the greatest area.

Prove that the greatest rectangle that can be inscribed in a circle is a square.

14. Write down the values of y corresponding with the following values of $\frac{dy}{dx}$:

(i) $4x^3$ (ii) $\frac{3}{x}$ (iii) $\frac{x^n}{4}$

(iv) $\sqrt{x}$ (v) $3x^2 + 2x + 1$

15. What values of y correspond with the following values of $\frac{d^2y}{dx^2}$?

(i) $2x$ (ii) 5 (iii) $\sqrt{x}$

16. If $\frac{dp}{dv} = \frac{-700}{v^{2\cdot 4}}$ and $p = 18\cdot 95$ when v is 20, express p as a function of v.

17. Write down the values of $\frac{dy}{dx}$ when y has the values

(i) $\cos a^2x$ (ii) $4 \sin 3x$ (iii) $a \sin nx + b \cos nx$

18. Draw a graph of $y = \tan x$ from $x = 0$ to $x = 1\cdot 2$. Show by the method of p. 540 that when $y = \tan x$, $\frac{dy}{dx} = \sec^2 x$. Verify this from your graph (see also p. 156).

19. Draw the graph of $y = e^x$, making the y unit one-tenth the x unit. At any point P on the curve, draw PM perpendicular to the axis, meeting it at M. Take a point T one x unit to the left of M.

Show that PT is a tangent to the curve at P.

20. Find by the method of p. 551 the area bounded by $y = 4x + 3$, the x axis, and the y ordinates at the points (i) $x = 4$, $x = 8$, (ii) $x = 2$, $x = 10$, (iii) $x = 5$, $x = 6$.

21. Find the area bounded by $y = 2x^2 + 3x + 1$, $y = 0$, $x = 3$, $x = 7$.

22. Write down the values of the following integrals and check by differentiation before substituting numbers for x:

(i) $\int_2^7 (2x^2)dx$ (ii) $\int_{-1}^1 (ax^2 + bx + c)dx$ (iii) $\int_1^8 \frac{1}{\sqrt[3]{x}}dx$

(iv) $\int_{-3}^5 7dx$ (v) $\int_1^2 \left(x + \frac{1}{x^2}\right)dx$

23. In surveying, the area of a plot bounded by a closed curve is sometimes found by Simpson's rule. The rule is: Divide the area into an even number of strips of equal width by an odd number of ordinates; the area is approximately

$$\tfrac{1}{3}.\text{Width of a strip} \times \{ \text{sum of extreme ordinates} + \text{twice sum of other odd ordinates} + 4 \text{ times sum of even ordinates} \}$$

Assuming that the curve bounding the area can be described by a curve of the type $y = p + qx = rx^2 + sx^3$, see whether you can justify Simpson's rule as an approximation to the area.

Find the area bounded by $y = 0$, $x = 2$, $x = 10$, and the curve $y = x^4$

(*a*) by Simpson's rule using three ordinates
(*b*) by Simpson's rule using nine ordinates
(*c*) by integration

24. Find the area bounded by $y = x^3 - 6x^2 + 9x + 5$, the x axis, and the maximum and minimum ordinates.

25. The speed v of a body at the end of t seconds is given by

$$v = u + at$$

Show that the distance travelled in t seconds is

$$ut + \tfrac{1}{2}at^2$$

26. Find the work done in the expansion of a quantity of steam at 4,000 lb. per square foot pressure from 2 cubic feet to 8 cubic feet. Volume and pressure are connected by the equation

$$pv^{0 \cdot 9} = \text{K (constant)}$$

27. Find the volume of a cone with radius 5 inches, height 12 inches.

28. In a sphere of radius 12 inches find the volume of a slice contained between two parallel planes distant 3 inches and 6 inches from the centre.

29. Find $\int_0^{\pi} \sin x dx \qquad \int_0^{\frac{\pi}{2}} \cos x dx$

30. Write down

(i) $\int_0^{\frac{\pi}{2}} \sin 2x dx$ (ii) $\int_{-\frac{\pi}{2}}^{\frac{\pi}{2}} \cos 2x dx$ (iii) $\int_0^{\pi} x \sin x dx$

31. Sometimes a function of x can be recognized as the product of two simpler ones, e.g. $y = x^2 \log x$.

Suppose y can be put in the form uv, where u and v are each simpler functions of x. When u becomes $u + \triangle u$ and v becomes $v + \triangle v$, y becomes $y + \triangle y$; hence show that $\frac{dy}{dx} = u\frac{dv}{dx} + v\frac{du}{dx}$.

Check this formula by differentiating x^7 and x^5 in the ordinary way, and then by representing them in the form

$$x^7 = x^5 \times x^2 \text{ and } x^5 = x^7 \times x^{-2}$$

In this way differentiate

(i) $x \sin x$ (ii) $\cos x \tan x$ (iii) $(2x^2 + x + 3)(x + 1)$

first as a product and then by multiplying out.

32. By using the same method as in the previous example, show that if $y = \frac{u}{v}$ when u and v are functions of x, and v is not zero,

$$\frac{dy}{dx} = \frac{v\frac{du}{dx} - u\frac{dv}{dx}}{v^2}$$

Differentiate (i) $\dfrac{x}{x+1}$ (ii) $\dfrac{\sin x}{x}$ (iii) $\dfrac{1}{\cos x}$ (iv) $\tan x$

33. Sometimes a function of x (e.g. $\cos^2 x$) can be recognized as a function of a simpler function (in this case $\cos x$) of x. Show that if y is a function of u and u is a simpler function of x, $\dfrac{dy}{dx} = \dfrac{dy}{du}\cdot\dfrac{du}{dx}$.

This can be used to differentiate expressions like the following:

$$\begin{aligned} y &= \cos^2 x \\ \frac{dy}{dx} &= \frac{d(\cos^2 x)}{d\cos x}\cdot\frac{d\cos x}{dx} \\ &= 2\cos x \times (-\sin x) \\ &= -2\sin x\cos x \end{aligned}$$

Check this formula by using it to differentiate $\log_e x^3$ written as a function of x^3 and $\log_e x^3$ written as $3\log_e x$.

In this way differentiate

(i) $\sqrt{\sin x}$ (iii) $\sin(ax+b)$

(ii) $(ax+b)^n$ (iv) $\log_e(ax^2+bx+c)$

34. If $y = \text{A}\cos x + \text{B}\sin x$, show that $\dfrac{d^2y}{dx^2} + y = 0$.

35. Solve the following equations

(i) $\dfrac{d^2y}{dx^2} + 4y = 0$ (ii) $\dfrac{d^2y}{dx^2} - 4y = 0$

Find y in terms of x in each case if $y = 5$ and $\dfrac{dy}{dx} = 4$ when $x = 0$

THINGS TO MEMORIZE

1.

y	$\dfrac{dy}{dx}$
$ax^n + b$	nax^{n-1}
$a^x + b$	$(\log_e a)a^x$
$a\log_e(x+b) + c$	$\dfrac{a}{x+b}$
$\sin(ax+b)$	$a\cos(ax+b)$
$\cos(ax+b)$	$-a\sin(ax+b)$
e^x	e^x

2.

y	$\int_p^q y \,.\, dx$
$\dfrac{a}{b+x}$	$a \log_e \dfrac{(b+q)}{(b+p)}$
ax^n	$\dfrac{a}{n+1}(q^{n+1} - p^{n+1})$
$\cos ax$	$\dfrac{1}{a}(\sin aq - \sin ap)$
e^{cx}	$\dfrac{1}{c}(e^{cq} - e^{cp})$

Volume of cylinder $= \pi r^2 h$

Volume of sphere $= \frac{4}{3} \pi r^3$

CHAPTER XII

Statistics

OR

THE ARITHMETIC OF HUMAN WELFARE

TILL the sixteenth century the more primitive use of numbers to enumerate separate objects had played a quite subordinate part in shaping the progress of mathematics. In the ancient world the social statistics of wealth and of human populations for war and taxation involved little beyond simple enumeration, and made no demands on the mathematician except in so far as the need for simple and ready methods of calculation was stimulated by the use of money and the growth of credit. During the past century the need for mathematical devices for dealing with numbers that represent separate objects has acquired a new importance for two reasons. One is increasing attention to statistics of populations in psychology, sociology, and economics, as a basis for laws about man's social behaviour. Many of the numerical devices used in connexion with such problems have been suggested by the mathematical theory of probability, the elements of which will be dealt with in this chapter. There is still much controversy about the relevance of mathematical probability to the circumstances of everyday life, and different views reflect individual beliefs about the nature of knowledge, inductive reasoning and other questions which concern the reader as much as the professional mathematician. Necessarily the attitude of a mathematician whose philosophical inclinations are sympathetic to an idealistic world picture will not be the same as those of the writer, whose outlook is materialistic.

Reference has already been made to the meaning of mathematical probability in Chapter 5. We caught our first glimpse of it in connection with the bizarre and very ancient device of figurate numbers. Such figurate arrangements, like the magic square or the triangular numbers, had very little practical importance till we approach the period in which we are living. In ancient times they were closely associated with mystical beliefs and astrological superstitions. The beginnings of the modern theory of probability were directly related to the cult of games of chance and the rise of insurance. Like the figurate numbers, playing cards are of Chinese origin. Card games became a fashion in European courts in the fourteenth century A.D. The manufacture of cards was probably one of the first commercial uses found for printing from wood blocks, before books were produced from movable type. The first serious contribution to the mathematical theory of probability is contained in a correspondence between two French mathematicians, Fermat and Pascal, about wagers in a game of chance. In 1665 Pascal's posthumous *Treatise on Figurate Numbers* was published. Within a few years the mathematical treatment of risks crops up in a different setting. In 1693 the Philosophical Transactions of the Royal Society of London published a Life Table, based on the births and deaths of the city of Breslau. The object of Halley's Life Table was "an attempt to ascertain the price of annuities upon lives." Today it may seem a far cry from the card table to the insurance corporation. It is still more surprising to see the astrologer in the background of the picture.

The insurance of ships was an important form of financial speculation during the period when ocean trade was expanding in medieval Europe. In the history of Flemish shipping it can be traced to the beginning of the fourteenth century. By the sixteenth century it was a well-established financial transaction, and Sir Nicholas Bacon, addressing Elizabeth's first Parliament, asked "Does not the wise merchant in every adventure give part to have the rest assured?" Earlier writers are by no means so unanimous in associating insurance with the virtue of moral prudence. In its initial stages it was a pure gamble which went hand in hand with less reputable forms of speculation. With these less reputable practices the origins of life insurance are closely associated. Money-lending at financial rates of interest to princes, with a serious prospect of repudiation after a term of years, and credit transactions for business in the medieval fairs were not the only basis for the power which finance began to wield in the fourteenth and fifteenth centuries. Side by side with business loans at the fairs flourished the practice of making wagers on the life of an individual or the birth of a child, and a variety of fantastic speculations. There was frequent legislation during the sixteenth century to restrict the activities of the continental bourses and exchanges to credit operations, while prohibiting various kinds of wager insurance on which the ecclesiastical authorities frowned.

Speaking of the second half of the fifteenth century when the Antwerp Bourse was founded, and the beginning of the sixteenth century when Antwerp supplanted Bruges as the great trade centre of the Netherlands, Ehrenberger (*Capital and Finance in the Renaissance*) says that "in the course of four decades Antwerp developed into a trading centre such as the world has never seen before or since, for never since has there been a market which concentrated to such a degree the trade of all the important commercial nations of the world." Here the merchants "deal chiefly in bills and loans." Commenting on the "extremely speculative" nature of the transactions Ehrenberger lays emphasis on the fact that "astrological prognostications flourished . . . a large part of the dealing was so risky that prophecies of this kind as to the future course of business could obtain credence even with merchants of the first rank." The astrologer Kurz, who used the horoscope to prophesy the prices of pepper, ginger, and saffron a fortnight in advance, was "surrounded with work as a man in the ocean with water."

A sixteenth-century writer complains that "a part of the nobles and merchants . . . employ all their available capital in dealing in money . . . the soil remains untilled, trade in commodities is neglected, there is often increase in prices." With no surer basis than astrology the financial transactions which enriched the merchant princes of the medieval centres were, to a large extent, gambling in the most literal sense. At the medieval fairs merchants with capital would lay wagers on the sex of the unborn child, or the time of a person's death. Examples of these wager insurances, which were the precursors of life insurance, are given by Goris in his study on the southern merchant colonies. Thus there is an extant contract between Domingo Symon Maiar and his brother Bernardo with two women to whom they agree to pay 30 livres if the offspring is a girl on the undertaking that they receive 48 livres in gratitude for the birth of a son. In 1542 Villalon wrote: "Of late in Flanders a horrible thing has arisen, a kind of cruel tyranny which the merchants there have invented among themselves. They wager on the rate of exchange in the Spanish fairs at Antwerp. They call these wagers parturas according to the former manner of winning money at a birth when a man wagers the child shall be a boy. . . . One wagers that the exchange rate shall be at a 2 per cent premium or discount, another at 3 per cent, etc. They promise each other to pay the difference in accordance with the result. This sort of wager seems to me to be like marine insurance business. . . . For dealing of this kind is only common among merchants who *hold much capital*. . . . By their *great capital* and their tricks they can arrange that in any case they have profit." The last sentence anticipates the practical link between a mathematical theory of probability and success in speculation. Numerical devices which had served a long apprenticeship in the practice of magic provided the basis for a theory of mathematical probability when financiers who were gambling in the exchanges required a more certain guidance than the astrologer could give them.

MATHEMATICAL PROBABILITY.—Before beginning the study of mathematical probability you will find it helpful to turn back to the section on Figurate Numbers in Chapter 5, pp. 206–23, and also to read once more the section on the binomial theorem in Chapter 7, pp. 325–30. What mathematicians call probability is sometimes defined in words suggesting that what a mathematician means by probability has some necessary and very definite connexion with the strength of our convictions about the future, the range of our experience of the past, or the extent of our information about the present. All of these things lie outside the province of the mathematician, who is really concerned with the grammar of size and order. It will prevent misunderstanding about the connexion between mathematical probability and what we call probability in everyday life, if we use words which do not suggest any of these things. We shall then be in a better position to understand when the mathematician and the plain man are both talking about the same thing.

Our definition of mathematical probability will be this. If it is possible to perform an action in N ways, of which n can be classified according to some peculiarity, and if there is no known reason why it should be performed more often in one way than in any of the $N - n$ other ways, the mathematical probability that the action will have the peculiarity specified is $\frac{n}{N}$. This definition will not seem so forbidding when an example has been cited. Note carefully that it is one thing to say that we know no reason why an action should be performed in one way rather than another, and it is quite a different thing to say that it actually is performed as often in one way as in another. Thus the actual frequency with which the action is performed in the real world is not yet part of our definition, and the circumstances which justify the use of this ratio in real situations will be discussed later on.

The peculiarity specified about an action may involve the nature of the object involved in the action, persons who did it, things to which it is done, or the quality of the object accomplished. It may also involve the order in which the actions are accomplished. If I spin a coin once the nature of the action can only be classified according to the result accomplished, and there may be two possibilities, it may be a head, or it may be a tail. If I spin it twice (Fig. 186) all the possible modes of action may be classified by the results accomplished, and by the order in which the results occur. *One* class of results is getting *both* a head

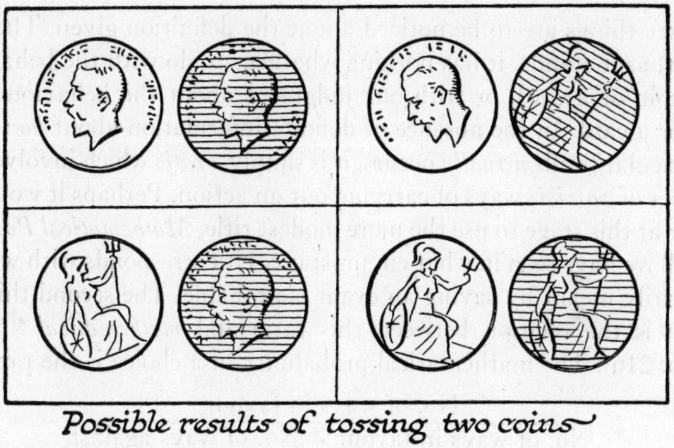

FIG. 186

The four possible results of tossing two coins once or one coin twice are here shown. To distinguish one coin from the other, the second one is shaded.

and a tail. All the N ways in which the action can be carried out are four, namely:

(i) Two heads.
(ii) First a head, then a tail.
(iii) First a tail, then a head.
(iv) Two tails.

Of these four, the number of ways (n) of carrying out the action if it is to have the peculiarity stated is 2. Thus the *mathematical* probability of getting *both* a head and a tail is $\frac{2}{4} = \frac{1}{2}$. The mathematical probability of getting *first* a head, then a tail, is $\frac{1}{4}$, since only one of the four ways ($n = 1$) has this characteristic. In the first case we are only told what sort of objects (a head and a tail) are involved in the action. That is to say, the required result is represented by one of a certain number of combinations. In the second case we are told the order as well as the kind of objects, and the required result is *one* of a certain number of permutations. Drawing four aces from a complete pack is another example which illustrates both ways of classifying the action. The choice of four aces in any order is *one* among $^{52}C_4$ ways of choosing any four different cards from the pack. The choice of four aces in a definite order (e.g. spade, heart, diamond, club) is *one* among $^{52}P_4$ ways of choosing any four different cards in a particular order.

Three things are to be noticed about the definition given. The first is that, as it stands, it has nothing whatever to do with the behaviour of a coin or a card, or with our judgment about the behaviour of a coin or a card. In the absence of definite information about *how often* a particular result *actually* occurs, it is simply a *ratio* which involves the number of *possible* ways of carrying out an action. Perhaps it would be better at this stage to use the more modest title, *Mathematical Possibility*, till we have seen in what circumstances it corresponds with what is ordinarily meant by saying an event is probable. The second thing to notice is the relation between this ratio and *mathematical* "odds" (see p. 216). The mathematical probability of a choice is the ratio

$$\frac{\text{No. of ways in favour}}{\text{No. of ways in favour} + \text{No. of ways against}}$$

Thus the number of ways in favour of and against getting two heads when a coin is tossed twice are 1 and 3. The mathematical probability of this result is $\frac{1}{1+3} = \frac{1}{4}$. The odds in favour of getting it represent the ratio of the number of ways ($n = 1$) in which the action can be carried out to the number of ways ($N - n = 3$) in which it cannot be carried out. These together make $N = 4$, the total number of results which could be obtained if every way of tossing the coin were admitted. If we use p for the mathematical probability that the prescribed result will occur and q for the mathematical probability that it will not occur, we see that

$$p = \frac{n}{N}$$

$$q = \frac{N - n}{N}$$

$$\therefore \quad p = 1 - q$$

Thus the mathematical probability of not getting two heads in tossing a coin twice is $1 - \frac{1}{4} = \frac{3}{4}$.

There are two fundamental principles on which the whole theory of mathematical probability rests. Both can be illustrated by Fig. 187, which shows all the possible ways in which we can draw two balls, one from a bag with 3 white and 2 black ones, the other from a bag containing 2 white and 4 black ones. The first rule is about the probability of two simultaneous results which do not *affect one another.*

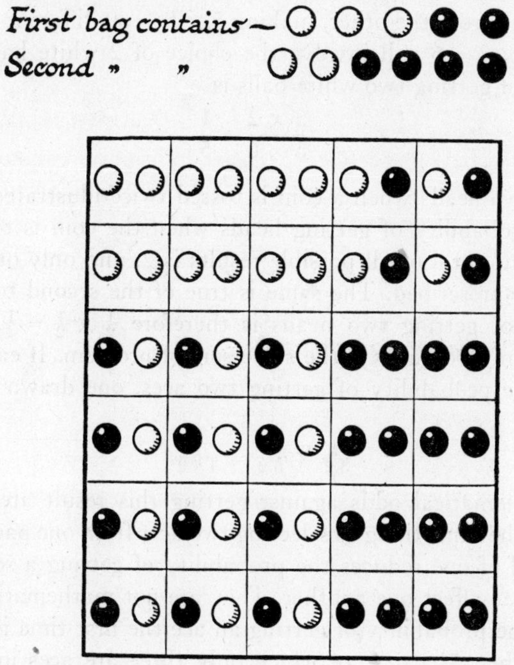

FIG. 187.—CHOOSING ONE BALL FROM EACH OF TWO BAGS

One bag contains 5 balls of which 3 are white. The other contains 6 balls of which 2 are white. Each ball of the first bag can be chosen along with any ball in the second, making in all 30 combinations of different balls. Of these 6 will be all white pairs, 8 will be all black pairs, and the remainder are mixed. Look back at Fig. 25 in Chapter 3, and Fig. 103 in Chapter 7 illustrating multiplication in hieroglyphic form. This will help you to see why (and when) we multiply what the mathematician calls probabilities.

The second is about the probability of a set of simultaneous results when one of the set *excludes* the occurrence of any other.

(*a*) *Simultaneous occurrence of independent results.*—The first principle states that if n is the mathematical probability of one result and m that of another which is independent of it, the probability that both will occur together is the product nm. You will see why this is by looking at Fig. 187. The probability of getting a white ball out of the bag which contains 5 balls in all is $\frac{3}{5}$, since we might choose any one of 5 balls of which only 3 are white. The probability of getting a white ball from the other bag is $\frac{2}{6} = \frac{1}{3}$, since any one of 6 balls may be chosen and only 2 of them are white. Each ball from one bag can be chosen along with each ball from the other, making $5 \times 6 = 30$ different selections. Of these, $3 \times 2 = 6$ will involve the choice of 2 white balls. So the probability of getting two white balls is

$$\frac{3 \times 2}{5 \times 6} = \frac{1}{5}$$

Getting two heads when a coin is tossed twice illustrates the same rule. The probability of getting heads when the coin is tossed once is $\frac{1}{2}$, since the total of all possible results is 2, and only one of these is the result prescribed. The same is true of the second toss. So the probability of getting two heads is therefore $\frac{1}{2} \times \frac{1}{2} = \frac{1}{4}$. Selecting two aces from two packs is the same sort of problem. If each pack is complete the probability of getting two aces, one drawn from each pack is,

$$\frac{4}{52} \times \frac{4}{52} = \frac{1}{169}$$

The mathematical odds against getting this result are 168 to 1. This is not the same thing as selecting two aces from one pack, because the removal of one reduces the probability of getting a second. The two results *do* affect one another. They are not mathematically independent. The probability of getting an ace the first time is $\frac{4}{52} = \frac{1}{13}$. There are then 51 cards, of which only three are aces in the pack. So the probability of getting an ace the second time is $\frac{3}{51} = \frac{1}{17}$. The problem is therefore equivalent to drawing one card from a complete pack of 52 with four aces, and one card from an incomplete pack of 51 with three aces. Thus the probability of getting two aces from one pack is $\frac{1}{13} \times \frac{1}{17} \times \frac{1}{221}$. So the odds against getting two aces if two cards are drawn from a complete pack are 220:1. You can also look at this problem in another way. There are ${}^{52}C_2$ ways of taking two different cards, irrespective of order, from a complete pack. There are ${}^{4}C_2$ ways of taking two aces, irrespective of order, from among all the four aces. So the probability of picking two aces from the pack is

$$\frac{{}^{4}C_2}{{}^{52}C_2} = \frac{4 \cdot 3}{2 \cdot 1} \times \frac{2 \cdot 1}{52 \cdot 51}$$

$$= \frac{1}{221}$$

The principle illustrated in Fig. 187 can be extended to any number of simultaneous results. Suppose we have three bags, each containing a certain number of red balls and a certain number of black balls. If we call a the probability of getting a red ball from bag A, b the probability of getting one from bag B, and c the probability of getting one from bag C, the probability of getting three red balls, if we take one from each, is $a \cdot b \cdot c$. The reason for this lies in the definition. Getting two red balls by taking one ball from bag A and one from bag B is a result which corresponds with a mathematical probability $a \cdot b$. Getting three red balls by drawing one from each bag is the same as getting two red balls from bags A and B and one red ball from bag C. The probability of the first result is $(a \cdot b)$, and of the second, which is independent, is c. The probability of the simultaneous result is $(a \cdot b)c$. By analogy we can look on a human family of any size as a trial in which we can select so many boys and so many girls from a bag with equal numbers of both. We can then say that the *mathematical* probability that any individual in a family will be a female is $\frac{1}{2}$. So the mathematical probability that a family of eight children will be composed of girls only is

$$\frac{1}{2} \times \frac{1}{2} \times \frac{1}{2} \times \frac{1}{2} \times \frac{1}{2} \times \frac{1}{2} \times \frac{1}{2} \times \frac{1}{2} = (\tfrac{1}{2})^8 = \frac{1}{256}$$

Actually the ratio of boys to girls at birth is about 1·06, and the problem is more comparable to drawing red and black balls from a bag which holds 51 red (boys) balls to every 49 black (girls) ones. So the respective probabilities that any child born will be a boy or a girl are 0·51 and 0·49.

(*b*) *Mutually exclusive results.*—The other basic principle on which the theory of probability is built is that if two results are mutually exclusive the probability that the choice will be either one or the other is the sum of their probabilities. The probability that one ball will be black and one white if we draw one from each bag, illustrated in Fig. 187, will make the meaning of this clear. Drawing a black and a white ball involves one of two things. We may draw a white one first and a black one second. In that case we exclude the possibility of drawing a black one first and a white one second. The rule states that if a is the probability of the first choice (i.e. white first and black second), and if b is the probability of the second choice (i.e. black first and then white), the fraction $(a + b)$ is the probability of making *either* the first *or* the second choice. That is to say, $(a + b)$ is the probability of getting both a white and a black irrespective of order. In the illustration we have bag A with five balls, three of which are white, and bag B with six balls, two of which are white. The probability (*a*) of taking a white ball from bag A and a black from bag B is $\frac{3}{5} \times \frac{4}{6} = \frac{2}{5}$. The probability of taking a black ball from bag A and a white ball from bag B is $\frac{2}{5} \times \frac{2}{6} = \frac{2}{15}$. The rule tells us that the probability that the choice will be either one or the other is $\frac{2}{5} + \frac{2}{15} = \frac{8}{15}$. The illustration shows you how the rule works. There are $5 \times 6 = 30$ ways in which we can select from the five different balls in one bag and the six different balls in the other bag. Of these $(2 \times 2 + 4 \times 3) = 16$ are of both sorts, white and black. So the probability of getting both sorts is

$$\frac{16}{30} = \frac{8}{15}$$

The same rule is illustrated in another way by Fig. 187. Every possible result may be classified under three headings which are exclusive of one another, namely, (*a*) both white ($\frac{1}{5}$), (*b*) white and black ($\frac{8}{15}$), (*c*) both black $\frac{4}{6} \times \frac{2}{5} = \frac{4}{15}$. The mathematical probability that one or the other of all three results will occur must be 1, since they include all the possibilities there are. Since the results are exclusive, the probability that one or the other will happen is

$$\frac{1}{5} + \frac{8}{15} + \frac{4}{15} = 1$$

A very important class of problems which will arise later is illustrated by the probability that a single toss with each of five dice (A, B, C, D, E) will result in exactly two sixes. If we consider one die A, the probability of throwing a six is $\frac{1}{6}$. The probability that A and B will both be sixes is $\frac{1}{6} \times \frac{1}{6} = (\frac{1}{6})^2$. The probability that C will not be a six is $1 - \frac{1}{6} = \frac{5}{6}$, and so on for D and E. So the probability that A and B will both turn up sixes and C, D, and E will not is

$$(\tfrac{1}{6})^2 \times (\tfrac{5}{6})^3$$

This is the probability that *a certain pair* (AB) will be sixes and the remainder will not. The total number of different pairs (Fig. 188) which can be selected from the five dice is the number of combinations of five different things taken two at a time, i.e. ${}^5C_2$ (= 10). The probability that *some* pair will be sixes and the other three will turn up some other number is the same as the probability that one or the other of the ${}^5C_2$ different pairs will turn up sixes and the remaining three a different number. It is therefore the sum of ten terms, each being $(\frac{1}{6})^2 (\frac{5}{6})^3$, i.e. ${}^5C_2 (\frac{1}{6})^2 (\frac{5}{6})^3$.

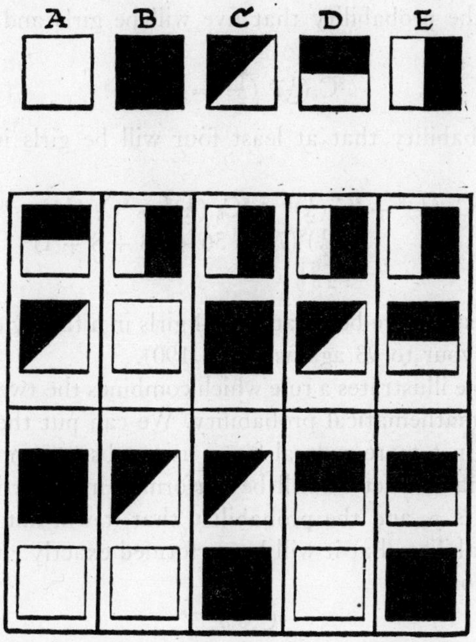

Fig. 188.—Number of Pairs which can be Chosen from Five Different Things Irrespective of Order

All the ten possible combinations are AB, AC, AD, AE, BC, BD, BE, CD, CE, DE.

An analogous problem is the mathematical probability that *at least* four children in a family of eight offspring will be girls. This is the probability that one of five exclusive results will occur, namely,

(*a*) Four boys and four girls
(*b*) Three boys and five girls
(*c*) Two boys and six girls
(*d*) One boy and seven girls
(*e*) No boys and eight girls

The probability that four in a family of eight will be girls and four will be boys is another way of saying that four will be girls and four will be of some other sex. If the probability that any child born will be a boy is taken as $\frac{1}{2}$, it is

$$^8C_4(\tfrac{1}{2})^4\,(\tfrac{1}{2})^4 = {}^8C_4(\tfrac{1}{2})^8$$

Similarly, the probability that five will be girls and three will be boys is

$$^8C_5(\tfrac{1}{2})^5\,(\tfrac{1}{2})^3 = {}^8C_5(\tfrac{1}{2})^8$$

So the probability that at least four will be girls in a family of eight is:

$$\begin{aligned} &{}^8C_4\,(\tfrac{1}{2})^8 + {}^8C_5(\tfrac{1}{2})^8 + {}^8C_6\,(\tfrac{1}{2})^8 + {}^8C_7\,(\tfrac{1}{2})^8 + {}^8C_8\,(\tfrac{1}{2})^8 \\ &= (\tfrac{1}{2})^8(70 + 56 + 28 + 8 + 1) \\ &= \tfrac{163}{256} \end{aligned}$$

The chances of there being at least 4 girls in a family of 8 are therefore 163 in favour to 93 against (Fig. 190).

This example illustrates a rule which combines the two fundamental principles of mathematical probability. We can put the result of the dice problem in a more general form, using abstract numbers. If the probability that an action will be performed in a particular way on any occasion is p, and the probability that it will not be performed is q, the probability that it will be performed exactly r times out of n similar occasions is

$$^nC_r p^r q^{n-r}$$

If you look back to p. 328, and extend the table, you will see that the numbers 70, 56, 28, 8, 1 are terms in the ninth row of Pascal's, or more strictly Omar Khayyám's triangle. When $n = 8$, they are coefficients of the binomial series which corresponds with

$$(p + q)^n$$

The terms in the binomial series which you get when you multiply this out are of the form

$$^nC_r p^r q^{n-r}$$

if we give to r the successive values 8, 7, 6 . . . 3, 2, 1, 0.

So now we have this rule. *If the probability that an action will be performed in a particular way is p, and the probability that it will not be so performed is q, the probabilities that it will be performed on exactly n, $(n-1)$, $(n-2)$ . . . 3, 2, 1, 0 out of n occasions is given by the successive terms of the binomial series:*

$$(p + q)^n = p^n + n.p^{n-1}q + \frac{n(n-1)}{2.1}p^{n-2}q^2 \; . \; . \; .$$

This is illustrated in pictorial form in the next two figures. Fig. 189 shows the mathematical probability of (*a*) getting 0, 1, or 2 heads when we spin a coin twice, (*b*) getting 0, 1, 2, 3 heads when we spin it three times, (*c*) getting 0, 1, 2, 3, 4 heads when we spin it four times. Suppose we spin a coin twice. On each occasion the probability (p)

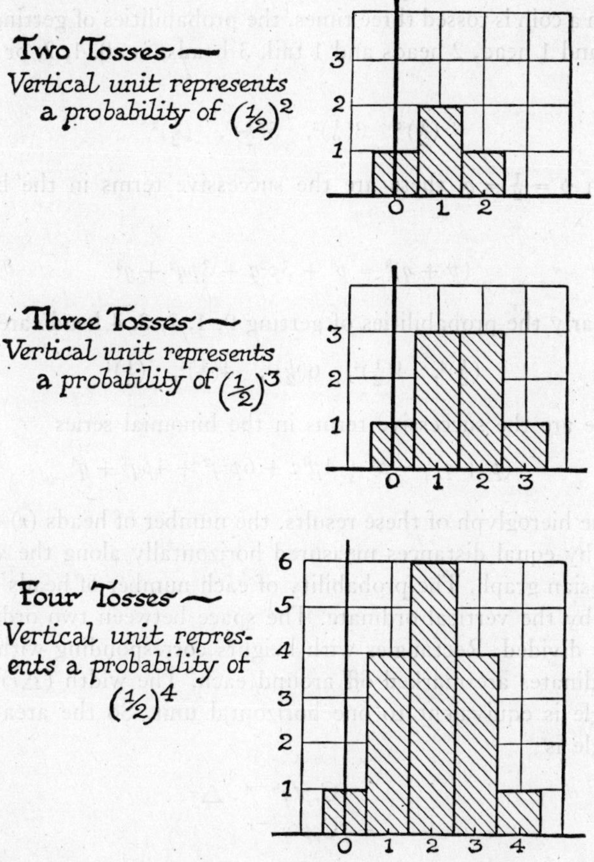

FIG. 189.—HIEROGLYPHIC REPRESENTATION OF THE SPINNING OF A COIN
In each figure one horizontal unit corresponds with a success (i.e. a head)

of getting a tail is $\frac{1}{2}$, that of getting a head (q) is also $\frac{1}{2}$. The probability of getting 2 tails or 0 heads is $(\frac{1}{2})^2$, that of getting one head and one tail $2(\frac{1}{2})\,(\frac{1}{2})$, that of getting two heads or 0 tails $(\frac{1}{2})^2$. So the probabilities of getting 0 heads, 1 head, and 2 heads in a double toss are

$$(\tfrac{1}{2})^2,\ 2(\tfrac{1}{2})^2 \text{ and } (\tfrac{1}{2})^2 \text{ respectively.}$$

If $p = \frac{1}{2} = q$, these are equivalent to

$$p^2, \quad 2pq, \quad q^2$$

which are the terms of $(p + q)^2$

When a coin is tossed three times, the probabilities of getting 3 tails, 2 tails and 1 head, 2 heads and 1 tail, 3 heads, i.e. 0, 1, 2, or 3 heads are:

$$(\tfrac{1}{2})^3, \quad 3(\tfrac{1}{2})^3, \quad 3(\tfrac{1}{2})^3, \quad (\tfrac{1}{2})^3$$

When $p = \frac{1}{2} = q$, these are the successive terms in the binomial series

$$(p + q)^3 = p^3 + 3p^2q + 3pq^2 + q^3$$

Similarly the probabilities of getting 0, 1, 2, 3, 4 heads are:

$$(\tfrac{1}{2})^4, \quad 4(\tfrac{1}{2})^4, \quad 6(\tfrac{1}{2})^4, \quad 4(\tfrac{1}{2})^4, \quad (\tfrac{1}{2})^4$$

These are the successive terms in the binomial series

$$(p + q)^4 = p^4 + 4p^3q + 6p^2q^2 + 4pq^3 + q^4$$

In the hieroglyph of these results, the number of heads (r) is represented by equal distances measured horizontally along the x axis of a Cartesian graph. The probability of each number of heads is represented by the vertical ordinate. The space between two ordinates is equally divided. Rectangles with heights corresponding with successive ordinates are marked off around each. The width (Δr) of each rectangle is equivalent to one horizontal unit. So the area of each rectangle is

$$\begin{aligned} &{}^nC_r p^r q^{n-r} \,.\, \Delta r \\ &= {}^nC_r p^r q^{n-r} \end{aligned}$$

This means that the area of each rectangular element represents the probability of the number of heads corresponding with the mid-point of its base. The area of the entire figure is

$$\begin{aligned} &\sum_0^n {}^nC_r p^r q^{n-r} \Delta r \\ &= \Delta r . \sum_0^n {}^nC_r p^r q^{n-r} \\ &= \Delta r (p + q)^n \end{aligned}$$

Since $p = 1 - q$, $(p + q)^n = 1^n = 1$. Also $\triangle r = 1$ unit. Hence the total area of the whole figure is one unit of surface, and

$$^nC_r p^r q^{n-r} = \frac{^nC_r p^r q^{n-r} \triangle r}{\sum_0^n {^nC_r} p^r q^{n-r} . \triangle r}$$

This means that the probability of getting the number of heads

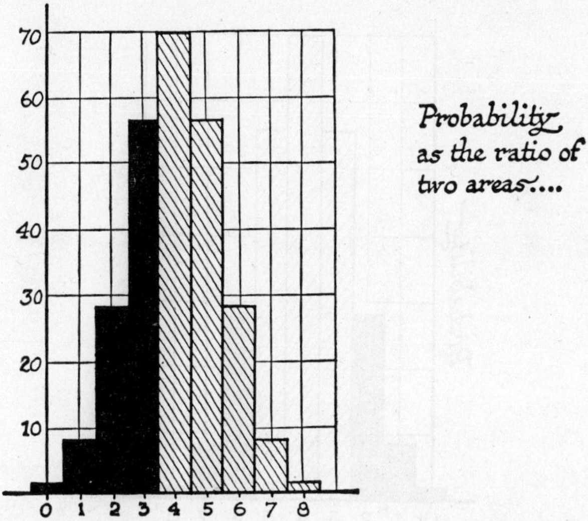

FIG. 190

The explanation is given in the text. The horizontal units represent the number of girls in a family of 8. The vertical unit represents a probability of $(\frac{1}{2})^8$.

r corresponding with the mid-point of the base of a rectangle whose height is $^nC_r p^r q^{n-r}$ is the ratio

$$\frac{\text{Area of rectangle}}{\text{Area of whole figure}}$$

The next figure (Fig. 191) shows the geometrical representation of a more complicated problem, namely, the probability that the number of girls in a family of 8 children will not be less than 3 or greater than 5. The mathematical probability of this result is:

$$\begin{aligned} &(\tfrac{1}{2})^8(^8C_3 + {^8C_4} + {^8C_5}) \\ &= (\tfrac{1}{2})^8(56 + 70 + 56) \\ &= \tfrac{91}{128} \end{aligned}$$

So the mathematical odds are 91 to 37 that the number of girls in a family of 8 will be not more than 5 nor less than 3. The probability that the number will be exactly 4 is

$$^8C_4\left(\frac{1}{2}\right)^8 = \frac{35}{128}$$

This means that if the odds in favour and against any single child's being a girl are equal, the odds in favour and against girls being

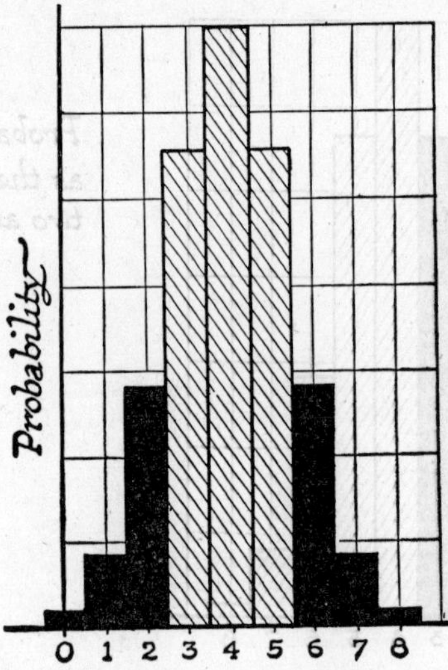

FIG. 191

The units are the same as in the preceding figure. The shaded area in this case stands for the probability that a family of 8 children will have at least 3 and not more than 5 girls.

exactly half a family of 8 are 35:93. To get the odds in favour of girls being *more* than half we require the probability that there will be either 5, 6, 7, or 8 girls in the family, i.e.

$$\left(\frac{1}{2}\right)^8 (^8C_5 + {}^8C_6 + {}^8C_7 + {}^8C_8)$$
$$= \left(\frac{1}{2}\right)^8 (56 + 28 + 8 + 1)$$
$$= \frac{93}{256}$$

That is to say, the odds are 93 for to 163 against getting more than 4 girls in a family of 8.

PROBABILITY IN EVERYDAY LIFE.—When the betting man says that the odds are even or that there is a half-and-half chance, he means that he has reason to believe that the coin turns up heads *as often as* it turns up tails. The justification for this belief is that someone has tried it with the coin which he is about to toss, or that it has been shown to be true of other coins made in the same way, so that there is no reason to suspect the coin has a "bias." When the practical man says that the odds are even, or the chance is half-and-half ($p = \frac{1}{2} = q$), that a coin will turn up heads or tails, he has no justification for believing that exactly 5 heads and exactly 5 tails will always result in a trial of ten tosses. No coin behaves in this way. What we actually find if we toss a coin is illustrated by the following experiment, which was carried out with a penny while writing this paragraph. The first two trials, each of ten tosses, gave 5 and 4 heads respectively, i.e. 50 per cent and 40 per cent heads. The first two trials, each of fifty tosses, gave 48 per cent and 44 per cent heads. The first two trials, each of a hundred tosses, gave 45 per cent and 48 per cent. The percentage of heads in two hundred tosses was 50·5. A study of the behaviour of coins shows that if we toss a very large number our result differs very little from a certain *limiting* proportion. This is in the neighbourhood of 0·5 or $\frac{1}{2}$ in the case of this particular coin, and others which are manufactured in the Mint. If we have established the fact that this is so, we can then say that the *relative frequency* with which heads turn up in a large number of tosses is *numerically* the same as the mathematical probability ($\frac{1}{2}$), as we have used the term so far. *Frequency* is only comparable to *probability* when it refers to experiments based on *large* numbers. The results of applying the mathematical theory to everyday life are *only true in the long run*. The *frequency* which we identify with the probability of the mathematician is based on experience of *large* numbers.

When experiment has established this limiting proportion, we are not yet fully entitled to assume that the mathematical theory of probability, as given so far, gives us a true account of how coins behave when tossed. If a coin always turned up heads when it had turned up tails in the previous toss and vice versa, the relative frequency of heads or tails would still be $\frac{1}{2}$ in an enormous number of tosses; and if a population with equal numbers of families of five and three children proved to have three boys and two girls in every family of five and two girls and one boy in every family of three, the relative frequency of boys or girls would also be $\frac{1}{2}$. The distribution of heads and tails in successive trials of three or five tosses and the distribution of boys and girls in large numbers of families of five or three children would not correspond to the calculations given on pages 586–588. Only experiment can decide whether a correspondence exists. The two hundred tosses of the experiment quoted may be grouped in trials of six at a time. In the first sixteen trials of six tosses the actual frequency with which 0, 1, 2, 3, . . . 6 heads occurred was

Heads ..	0	1	2	3	4	5	6
Frequency	0	2	2	9	3	0	0

The theoretical probability of getting, let us say, four heads is

$$^6C_4\left(\tfrac{1}{2}\right)^6 = \tfrac{15}{64}$$

If mathematical probability were always the same thing as frequency the number of times in which four heads would occur in a trial of sixteen would be

$$\tfrac{15}{64} \times 16 = 3{\cdot}75$$

In this way we might construct a theoretical "distribution" as follows:

Heads ..	0	1	2	3	4	5	6
No. ..	0·25	1·5	3·75	5	3·75	1·5	0·25

Putting the two tables together we have

Heads ..	0	1	2	3	4	5	6
Observed	0	2	2	9	3	0	0
Theoretical	0·25	1·5	3·75	5	3·75	1·5	0·25

This result, which is based on a very small number of trials (sixteen in all), is not very convincing. A better result was obtained when the experiment was continued till 96 trials of six tosses were completed. The results classified as before were then as follows:

Heads ..	0	1	2	3	4	5	6
Observed	1	6	21	28	23	16	1
Theoretical	1·5	9	22·5	30	22·5	9	1·5

You will find it instructive to make such experiments for yourself and compare the results of a small number of trials and of a large number of trials. If you are satisfied that the binomial distribution given on

p. 586 gives a good description of what happens when we spin coins, you will be able to see one way in which the theory of mathematical probability can be applied to practical problems. You must, of course, remember that mathematical probability is a fraction. Calculations based on it usually yield fractions. By its very nature it can rarely fit results which are necessarily whole numbers, and we cannot expect it to give even a good approximation to the results of a simple trial. On the other hand it can give a good representation of a large number of trials. If the observed frequency with which something happens is 3 and the theoretical frequency is 2·5, the excess is 20 per cent. If the observed frequency is 300 and the theoretical frequency differs from the next whole number below it by the same fraction, i.e. if it is 299·5, the excess is only 0·16 per cent, so that the agreement between theory and practice is good. With this reservation we can now see one application of the theory, when we have satisfied ourselves that it furnishes a correct description of the way in which a coin behaves. For instance, you can see how the proprietor of a gaming saloon can adjust his stakes so that a large proportion of his clients get satisfaction, while he makes a steady profit. If he bets that he will get *at least* three heads in a trial of six tosses, the odds are 21 to 11 that he will. With sufficient capital to go on long enough this means that he will succeed in about two-thirds of his wagers and his customers will succeed in about one-third.

If a man sets out to earn a livelihood by wagers like the wager insurances of the Antwerp financiers in the sixteenth century, he can do so provided he has enough capital at the beginning. Taking the proportion of boy and girl births as equal, we see that a very large number of wagers like that of Bernardo and Domingo mean 48 livres return for every 30 paid out, or a net gain of 60 per cent. If the distribution calculated on the assumption that the probability of a male birth is $\frac{1}{2}$ correctly describes how families grow, a man with a capital of 60 livres has a much greater chance of losing it than a man with a capital of 300 livres. If he has 60 he can only make two bets. The probability that both births will be female is $\frac{1}{4}$. Of a very large number of persons with only 30 livres with which to wager one in four will therefore lose all his capital immediately. With a capital of 300 livres ten wagers are possible. The odds in favour of ten successive births being female are 1 to 1023. Of a very large number of people with 300 livres, less than one in a thousand will lose it all before winning a wager. With a large capital the speculator can safely give undertakings in excess of his capital resources to pay if all births were girls without much risk of being bankrupt. So his capital steadily grows while his poorer brethren are ruined, or, if they are not ruined, get a foot on Jacob's ladder themselves. Once he has got together sufficient capital to safeguard himself against any serious likelihood of bankruptcy he can drive his small competitors out of the market by offering more favourable terms. The actual frequency of male births is a little more than half of all. So it is represented by a theoretical probability corresponding with that of drawing balls from a bag in which rather more than half are red. Suppose that the observed frequency of male births is 0·51, based on the entire population. The speculator can then offer to return the premium with a 100 per cent bonus if the bet goes against him, and still make a 2 per cent profit in the long run. Whether he succeeds depends on how long he can go on putting up the capital required. Successful speculation therefore depends on the principle "To him that hath shall be given, and from him that hath not shall be taken away even that which he hath." The great fortunes of finance capitalism have been built up on this basis. While the nobility were gambling away their fortunes by failure to understand the connexion between probability and frequency, their more astute contemporaries realized that there is a surer road to wealth than mere luck or sheer merit. In a period when the wealthier merchants were exploring fresh avenues of enrichment it is easy to see why the correspondence between Pascal and Fermat should awaken interest which extended far afield from the card table.

THE ARITHMETIC MEAN.—In what circumstances the theory of probability can be rightly applied to the interpretation of results obtained in scientific inquiries is still a matter of controversy. There is at least one class of scientific hypotheses about which there is no doubt. Before discussing it, we must examine the significance of a ratio which we have already met in another context. We have already defined the arithmetic mean of two numbers in Chapter 4, p. 159. For a large group of numbers it is obtained by adding all the numbers in the group and dividing by the total number of separate numbers. If there are n numbers, r_1, r_2, r_3, r_4, etc., the arithmetic mean of them is

$$\frac{r_1 + r_2 + r_3 + r_4 \ . \ . \ .}{n}$$

or

$$\frac{1}{n}\Sigma r$$

For instance, the arithmetic mean of 5, 6, 11, 5, 6, 6, 3 is

$$\frac{5 + 6 + 11 + 5 + 6 + 6 + 3}{7}$$
$$= 6$$

When some numbers occur more than once we may write f_r for the frequency of the number r, and the expression for the arithmetic mean becomes

$$\frac{f_1r_1 + f_2r_2 \ . \ . \ . \ f_nr_n}{n}$$
$$= \frac{\Sigma f_s r_s}{\Sigma f_s}$$

In the numerical example just given we may write the result

$$\frac{1(3) + 2(5) + 3(6) + 1(11)}{1 + 2 + 3 + 1}$$
$$= \frac{3 + 10 + 18 + 11}{7}$$
$$= 6$$

Suppose now that we have made a very large number (m) of trials each involving n tosses of a coin, and that the total number of tails obtained is t. The arithmetic mean of tails obtained in all trials each of n tosses is $t \div m$. If q is the relative frequency of tails in this very large sample,

$$q = t \div mn$$
$$\therefore \ t \div m = nq$$

That is to say, nq is the expected arithmetic mean of the number of tails in a large sample of n-fold trials. As you would expect, it is also the mean number of tails in trials of n tosses calculated from the binomial distribution of p. 586, as we see below.

By applying the last formula you will see that the mean proportion of successes in the "binomial distribution" which corresponds mathematically with the *relative* frequency of 0, 1, 2, . . . etc., successes in a trial of n acts of choice is the same for all values of n. The relative frequencies of the binomial series all add up to unity, since $(p + q) = 1$.

$$\therefore \ (p + q)^n = 1$$
$$\therefore \ \Sigma f = 1$$

The relative frequencies of r successes in a distribution such as that illustrated in Figs. 189 and 190, when q is the probability of success may be tabulated thus:

Frequency (f)	Numbers of tails (r)
${}^nC_0p^n$	0
${}^nC_1p^{n-1}q$	1
${}^nC_2p^{n-2}q^2$	2
. . . . .	. . . . .
${}^nC_rp^{n-r}q^r$	r

If M is the arithmetic mean of the number of successes in trials involving n acts of choice:

$$\begin{aligned}
M &= \frac{\Sigma fr}{\Sigma f}\\
&= \frac{\Sigma {}^nC_rp^{n-r}q^r.r}{\Sigma {}^nC_rp^{n-r}q^r}\\
&= \frac{\Sigma {}^nC_rp^{n-r}q^r.r}{(p+q)^n}\\
&= \Sigma {}^nC_rp^{n-r}q^r r\\
&= {}^nC_0p^n(0) + {}^nC_1p^{n-1}q^1(1) + {}^nC_2p^{n-2}q^2(2) + {}^nC_3p^{n-3}q^3(3)\\
&\quad + {}^nC_4p^{n-4}q^4(4) \ . \ . \ .\\
&= 0 + n\cdot p^{n-1}q(1) + \frac{n(n-1)p^{n-2}}{2.1}q^2(2)\\
&\qquad + \frac{n(n-1)\,(n-2)p^{n-3}}{3.2.1}q^3(3)\\
&\qquad\qquad + \frac{n(n-1)\,(n-2)\,(n-3)p^{n-4}}{4.3.2.1}q^4(4) \ . \ . \ .\\
&= n.p^{n-1}q + n(n-1)p^{n-2}q^2 + \frac{n(n-1)\,(n-2)p^{n-3}}{2.1}q^3\\
&\qquad + \frac{n(n-1)\,(n-2)\,(n-3)p^{n-4}}{3.2.1}q^4 \ . \ . \ .\\
&= n.q\left\{p^{n-1} + (n-1)p^{n-2}q + \frac{(n-1)\,(n-2)p^{n-3}}{2.1}q^2\right.\\
&\qquad \left. + \frac{(n-1)\,(n-2)\,(n-3)p^{n-4}}{3.2.1}q^3 \ . \ . \ .\right\}
\end{aligned}$$

Putting $m = (n-1)$, we can write this:

$$\begin{aligned}
&n.q\left\{p^m + m.p^{m-1}q + \frac{m(m-1)p^{m-2}}{2.1}q^2 \ . \ . \ .\right\}\\
&= nq(p+q)^m
\end{aligned}$$

Since $(p + q) = 1$

$$\underline{M = n.q}$$

The problem illustrated in Fig. 191 may now be stated in a different form, which will prove to be useful when we examine the use of statistical hypotheses in science. If the probability (q) that any individual will be a girl is $\frac{1}{2}$, the mean number of girls in a large number of families of n individuals will be $\frac{1}{2}n$. If n is 8, the mean will be 4. The probability that a family of 8 will contain at least 3 and not more than 5 girls is therefore the probability that the number of girls in a family of eight will not differ from the mean number of girls in all families of eight by more than one. It is therefore the probability that the number of girls in a family of eight will lie in the range $\underline{M \pm 1}$.

In Figs. 189–191 the mathematical probability of different combinations of successes and failures in a trial involving some definite number of acts has been illustrated for the particular case when $p = \frac{1}{2} = q$. This condition provides us with a fairly accurate description of the results of numerous experiments with the spinning of a coin. Successive withdrawal of one ball at a time from a bag containing an equal number of red and black balls, if the ball is replaced after its colour has been recorded, or simultaneous withdrawal of one ball from each of a set of similar bags containing red and black balls in the same proportion, could provide an equally appropriate application of the mathematical theory. The law of frequency which governs the selection of balls in such an experiment approximates very closely to the mathematical model, provided that there is no way of identifying the colour of the balls when taking it from the bag. This does not mean that the texture or shape or bulk of every ball in the bag must be the same. The texture, shape, and bulk of no two balls is ever exactly the same. All that matters is that the differences are unrecognizable to the person who carries out the act of selecting them, or, if recognizable, unconnected with the difference of colour. For instance, if half the balls are larger than the remaining half, it will not affect the result so long as the proportion of black and red is the same among the lighter and the heavier ones.

In an experiment of this kind the proportion of red and black balls need not be $\frac{1}{2}$. It may have any value between 0 and 1. Fig. 192 represents the mathematical probabilities of drawing 0, 1, 2, 3, 4 red balls in a single trial which involves taking one ball from each of four bags containing three red balls and one black ball. For each single draw the probability of getting a black ball is $\frac{1}{4}$, ($p = \frac{1}{4}$). The probability of drawing a red ball on any one occasion from any one of the bags is $\frac{3}{4}$, ($q = \frac{3}{4}$). If we draw simultaneously from all four bags the resulting probabilities are:

r	P
0 (0 red, 4 black)	p^4
1 (1 red, 3 black)	${}^4C_1 p^3 q$
2 (2 red, 2 black)	${}^4C_2 p^2 q^2$
3 (3 red, 1 black)	${}^4C_3\ pq^3$
4 (4 red, 0 black)	q^4

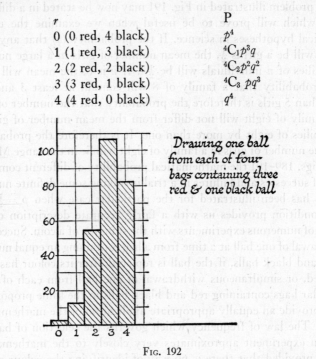

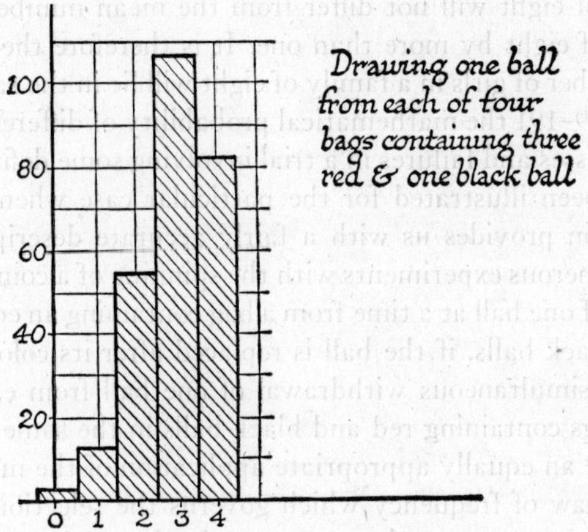

FIG. 192

Number of red balls drawn in a trial of four represented along the horizontal axis. The vertical axis measures relative frequency of each class selected, the unit being $(\frac{1}{4})^4$.

The probabilities of getting 0, 1, 2, 3, or 4 red balls are thus:

$$p^4 \qquad 4p^3q \qquad 6p^2q^2 \qquad 4pq^3 \qquad q^4$$

Putting in the numerical values we have:

$$(\tfrac{1}{4})^4 = \tfrac{1}{256} \qquad 4(\tfrac{1}{4})^3(\tfrac{3}{4}) \; \tfrac{12}{256} \qquad 6(\tfrac{1}{4})^2(\tfrac{3}{4})^2 \; \tfrac{54}{256} \qquad 4(\tfrac{1}{4})\,(\tfrac{3}{4})^3 \; \tfrac{108}{256} \qquad (\tfrac{3}{4})^4 \; \tfrac{81}{256}$$

The mean number of red balls drawn in a trial of 4 is

$$n.q$$
$$= 4 \times \tfrac{3}{4}$$
$$= 3$$

The mean number of black balls drawn in a trial of 4 is

$$n.p = 4 \times \tfrac{1}{4} = 1$$

The probability of getting exactly 3 red balls is

$$\frac{108}{256} = \frac{27}{64}$$

The odds are therefore 37 to 27 against getting the mean value exactly. The probability that the result will not exceed or fall short of the mean by more than one is

$$\frac{54}{256} + \frac{108}{256} + \frac{81}{256} = \frac{243}{256}$$

So the odds in favour of getting at least two red balls are 243 to 13. This is also the probability that the result will not exceed or fall short of the expected mean of black balls by more than 1, because drawing 3 red balls in a trial of 4 is equivalent to drawing 1 black ball in a trial of 4, and so on.

STATISTICAL HYPOTHESIS IN NATURAL SCIENCE.

We may distinguish broadly between three ways in which the mathematical theory of probability is used. The first and without doubt the most fruitful is the construction of *statistical hypotheses* in natural science. Just as we may use the mathematical theory as a paper model of what happens in a game of chance, so we can use what happens in a game of chance as a physical model of natural phenomena. If the conclusions to which we are led by these assumptions are verified by experience, we can use the hypothesis as a guide to conduct. This is the principle which underlies two of the most fertile scientific hypotheses which took shape in the middle of the nineteenth century. One was the kinetic theory of gases. The other was the modern theory of the *gene*. The kernel of the kinetic theory of gases rests on the experimental fact that gases combine to form new chemical entities in constant numerical proportions. This led to the conclusion that gases are made up of discrete units (molecules), of which approximately equal numbers are present in equivalent volumes of all gases at the same temperature and pressure. The beginning of the theory of the gene was Mendel's discovery that hybrids of pure-bred parents belonging to different varieties or strains produce different strains of offspring in definite numerical proportions. This led to the conception that the hereditary constitution of an individual depends on discrete particles (genes) like the molecules of a gas. In the kinetic theory we assume that the speed of different molecules varies in the same way as a smoothed binomial distribution. In the theory of the gène, we assume that whether a particular egg-cell of the mother is fertilized by a particular sperm-cell of the father happens with the same frequency as it would happen if they were coloured balls drawn from a bag.

The use of mathematical probability in the theory of the gene may be illustrated by one of Mendel's original experiments. Mendel crossed pure-bred varieties of the sweet pea, one with yellow seeds, the other with green seeds. The hybrids had yellow seeds. When these hybrids were fertilized with their own pollen, one-quarter of their offspring had green seeds and bred true when self-fertilized. The remainder were yellow. One-third of them, that is to say one-quarter of all the offspring, bred true like their yellow grandparents. The other yellow-seeded offspring, when self-fertilized, had yellow and green offspring in the same proportion as their parents (3:1). Thus a cross between pure stocks resembles a chemical reaction in the two essential features which led to the atomic theory of chemical combination. The first is that the characteristics of the original parents of the hybrids can be recovered in their original purity. The second is that the various combinations of hereditary characteristics occur in constant numerical proportions. The following table shows the results of scientists who have carried out the same experiments with the same varieties of the pea in different countries and on different occasions.

(*a*) Investigator	(*b*) Date	(*c*) Offspring of Yellow Hybrids when Self-fertilized		
		Yellow, Per cent	Green, Per cent	Total Numbers
Mendel ..	1865	75·05	24·95	8,023
Correns ..	1900	75·47	24·53	1,847
Tschermak ..	1900	75·05	24·95	4,770
Hurst	1904	74·64	25·36	1,755
Bateson ..	1905	75·30	24·70	15,806
Lock	1905	73·67	26·33	1,952
Darbishire ..	1909	75·09	24·91	145,246

The experimental results of such a cross lead to two conclusions. The colour of the seed depends on *something* which the individual receives from each of its parents. Green-seeded peas either have two parents which had green seeds, or two parents each of which had green-seeded ancestors. So this *something* which the hybrid gets from

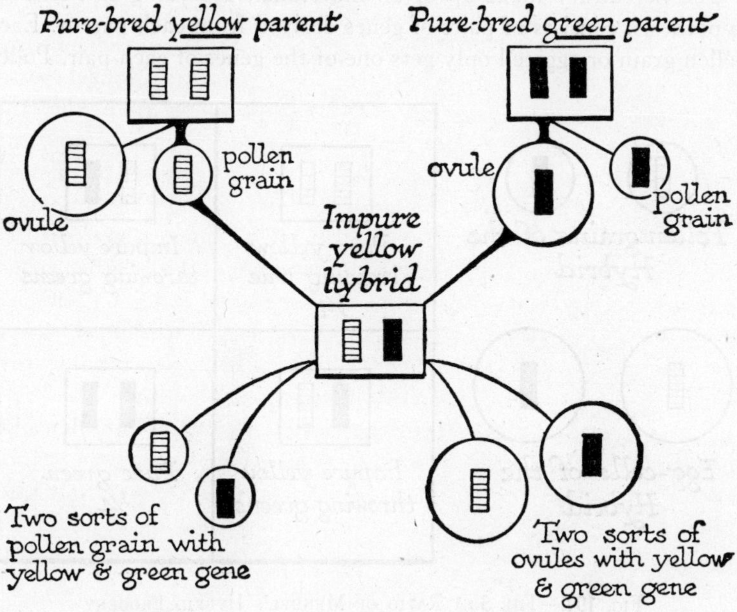

FIG. 193.—DIAGRAM OF THE DISTRIBUTION OF THE GENES WHICH AFFECT SEED COLOUR IN THE PEA

its green parent will only make the seeds green if the individual receives it from both parents. We call this *something* a *gene.* If we suppose that there are particles on which the numerical proportions of hybrid crosses depend, just as there are particles on which the laws of chemical combinations depend, two simple assumptions suffice to explain the manifold results of innumerable experiments in heredity. One is that whether an ovule (egg-cell) has one gene or another does not affect the chance of its getting fertilized by a pollen grain having one gene or another. The second assumption is that when an individual forms pollen grains or egg-cells, each pollen grain or egg-cell gets one gene, but not the other. The yellow hybrids of this experiment get one gene, we call it the yellow gene, from their yellow parent. The other gene, the green gene, comes from their green parent. Half the pollen grains and half the ovules have the gene contributed by one parent in the original cross and half have the other. The application of these two assumptions is exhibited in a diagrammatic form in Figs. 193 and 194.

The hereditary make-up of an individual, according to Mendel's hypothesis, consists of pairs of genes derived from each parent. Each pollen grain or egg-cell only gets one of the genes of each pair. Pollen

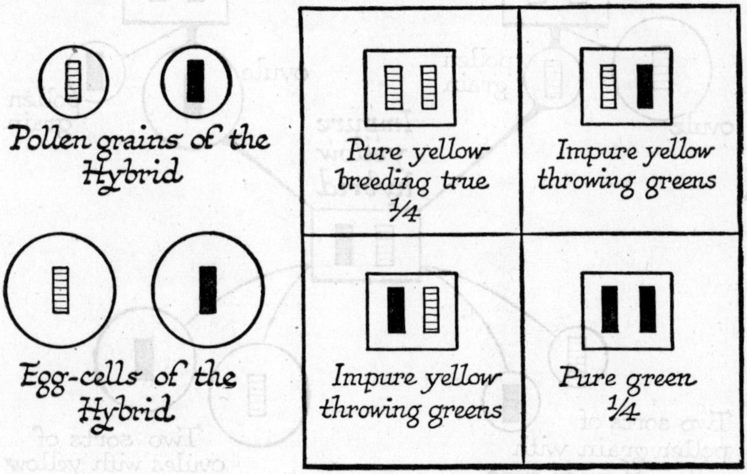

FIG. 194.—THE 3 : 1 RATIO OF MENDEL'S HYBRID PROGENY

grains or egg-cells with one gene or the other of the same pair, such as the green-yellow pair which we are considering, are manufactured with equal frequency. If which sort of pollen fertilizes which sort of egg only depends on the frequency with which the different sorts occur, the proportion of yellows and greens in the offspring will be 3 : 1. This is equivalent to saying that the results obtained are like those we get when we spin a coin twice, or take one ball from each of two bags containing red and black balls in equal numbers. From the table showing the results of other investigators who have repeated the particular cross which has been used to illustrate the elementary theory of the gene, you will see that the numerical proportions of the various kinds of offspring are not absolutely constant. They are only constant in a *statistical sense*.

This saving clause needs very careful scrutiny. In constructing a hypothesis to explain the results, we have chosen a physical model to which the mathematical theory applies. This means that the numbers observed in samples of the same size should differ from the mean of a very large set of observations on similar samples according to the binomial rule. Fig. 195 shows us that in a cross between the impure yellow and the green variety the expectation of either green or impure yellows is $\frac{1}{2}$. Suppose only twelve plants of such a cross are reared in an actual experiment. We should not expect to find exactly six plants

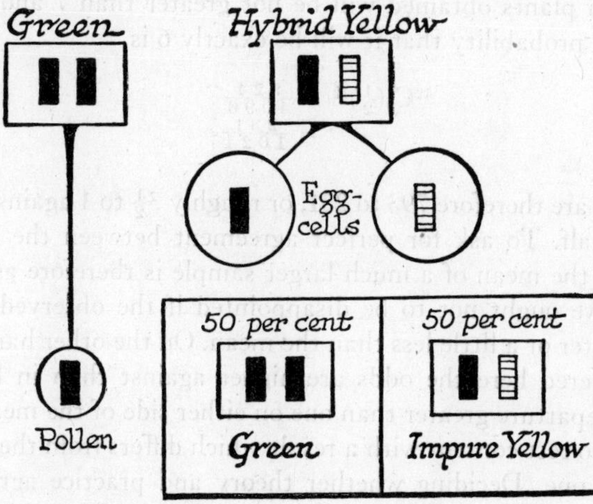

FIG. 195

with green seeds and six with yellow. To get exactly equal numbers would be obviously impossible if the size of the sample were an odd number. In any particular experiment involving only twelve offspring the number of green plants might be anything from 0 to 12. If the kind of physical model we have selected properly describes the results, these numbers will occur with the relative frequency of the binomial terms:

$$^{n}C_0\left(\tfrac{1}{2}\right)^n, \quad {}^{n}C_1\left(\tfrac{1}{2}\right)^n, \ldots \quad {}^{n}C_n\left(\tfrac{1}{2}\right)^n$$

If $q(=\frac{1}{2})$ is the probability that a plant will be green, the mean number of green plants in all samples of twelve should be

$$n.q = 6$$

If a single experiment yields 5 green and 7 yellow, the observed result differs from the mean by 1. The probability that the number will be in the range M ± 1 is

$$ {}^{12}C_5(\tfrac{1}{2})^{12} + {}^{12}C_6(\tfrac{1}{2})^{12} + {}^{12}C_7(\tfrac{1}{2})^{12} $$
$$ = \frac{792 + 924 + 792}{4096} $$
$$ = \tfrac{2508}{4096} $$

Thus the odds are 2,508 to 1,588, or roughly 5 to 3, that the number of green plants obtained will be not greater than 7 and not less than 5. The probability that it will be exactly 6 is

$$ {}^{12}C_6(\tfrac{1}{2})^{12} = \tfrac{924}{4096} $$
$$ = \tfrac{231}{1024} $$

The odds are therefore 793 to 231, or roughly $3\frac{1}{2}$ to 1 against getting exactly a half. To ask for perfect agreement between the observed results and the mean of a much larger sample is therefore asking too much. So we ought not to be disappointed if the observed value is a little greater or a little less than the mean. On the other hand, in the case considered here the odds are higher against than in favour of getting a departure greater than one on either side of the mean. So we ought not to rest content with a result which differs from the mean by more than one. Deciding whether theory and practice agree in the statistical sense thus involves finding a range of values which neither puts theory to too great a strain, nor makes too small a demand upon it.

Strictly speaking, we cannot find a range of whole numbers which meets this case, because in this example the number of offspring is too small. The range M ± 0 is too strict. The range M ± 1 might be regarded as too lax. Experiments in heredity usually involve rearing hundreds or thousands of offspring, sometimes hundreds of thousands. However, the same problem always arises. The numerical proportion which theory proposes is a limiting value to which the result of innumerable experiments should approach. The theory does not tell us the *exact* numbers of the various types in any particular experiment. The number 12 has simply been chosen because the arithmetical calculations which would be necessary to illustrate how a statistical theory is tested would be very laborious for a sample of, say, 700. There are various ways of reducing the amount of arithmetic involved. We shall refer to one later on.

To test an approximately 3 : 1 ratio like that which we get when we cross two impure yellows as in Fig. 194, the physical model of the biological experiment is the simultaneous selection of a ball from a set of bags, all of which contain one black ball and three red ones, as in Fig. 192. Suppose the probability that a plant will have yellow seeds is q, q being in this case $\frac{3}{4}$. The mean number of yellow plants should be

$$n \,.\, q = 9$$

The probability of getting exactly this result would be

$$^{12}C_9(\tfrac{1}{4})^3\ (\tfrac{3}{4})^9$$

The probability that the number of yellow plants would not differ from the mean by more than 1 is

$$^{12}C_8(\tfrac{1}{4})\ ^4(\tfrac{3}{4})^8 + {}^{12}C_9(\tfrac{1}{4})^3\ (\tfrac{3}{4})^9 + {}^{12}C_{10}(\tfrac{1}{4})^2\ (\tfrac{3}{4})^{10}$$

You can work out these values for yourself.

THE THEORY OF ERRORS.—We have dealt first with statistical hypotheses because they illustrate the way in which the theory of probability may be usefully applied in a manner which has led to extremely fruitful results, and is open to no serious criticism.

Historically an earlier application of the theory of probability to science was connected with the discussion of errors of physical measurement, especially in astronomy. This branch of the subject was developed by Laplace and Gauss. Physical measurements of the same thing, as we have repeatedly emphasized, are never absolutely the same. They vary between certain fairly well-defined limits, which depend upon the delicacy of the instruments used and the care taken in controlling the conditions of observation. The same observer making the same measurements repeatedly will not always get precisely the same values. Hence, in dealing with investigations which involve very great accuracy, there arises this question: When the observations of two individuals differ, is the difference one which arises from the nature of the material or from the accuracy of the observer, the delicacy of his instruments, and the conditions of the experiment? Are the differences such as might occur among observations made with the same materials on successive occasions? The answer to such questions is not always obvious, and it is often a matter of great practical importance to find one.

In all the examples of a binomial distribution represented graphically in Figs. 191 and 192 the number of acts of choice which a single trial can involve was taken to be very small. If we use the pictorial form to represent the mathematical theory applied to trials in which n, the number of acts of choice, is very large, we obtain a figure which is very much like the characteristic curve shown in Figs. 196 and 197. By making n as large as possible, we can make the area of the figure differ from the area enclosed by the curve by a quantity so small that we can neglect it. A curve of somewhat similar shape is often met with

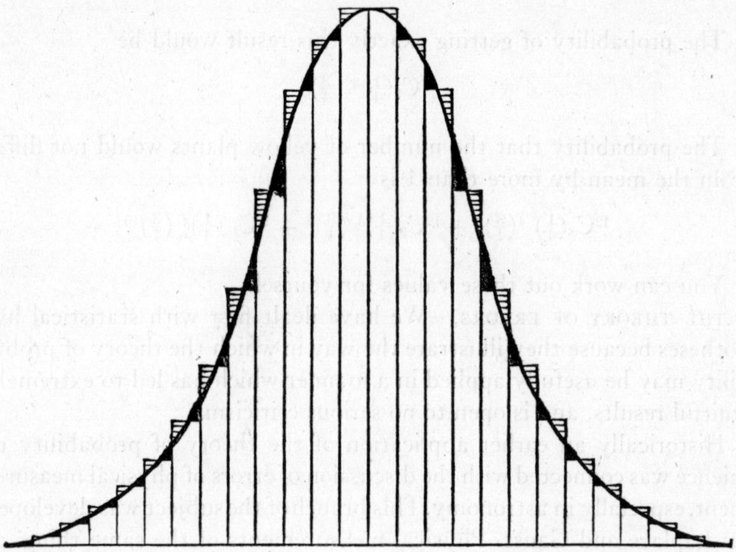

Fig. 196.—The Normal Curve of Error as an Approximation to the Binomial Distribution

if we make a graph of the frequency (y axis) of measurements of different size (x axis) in scientific observations. It is called the *normal curve of error*. The equation of this curve is

$$y = \mathrm{A} \, . \, e^{-bx^2}$$

It is possible to arrive at such an equation by making various assumptions about how y and x are connected. The reader will find an adequate account of them in Caradoc Jones's *Elements of Statistics*, Weld's *Method of Least Squares*, and Feldman's *Biomathematics*. One method is merely an application of the binomial distribution

$$y = {}^n\mathrm{C}_m p^m q^{n-m}$$

If $p = \frac{1}{2} = q$ and n is very large, this becomes (see Appendix 4)

$$y = A \cdot e^{-bx^2}$$

The precise shape of the curve, whether it is relatively steep or relatively flat, as shown in Fig. 197, depends on the constants A and *b*

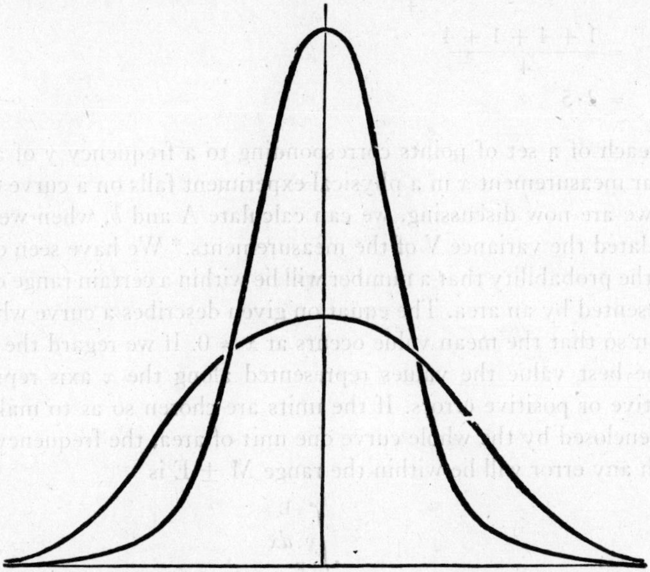

FIG. 197.—THE NORMAL CURVE OF ERROR
The equation of the curve is: $y = A \cdot e^{-bx^2}$
Whether the curve is relatively steep or flat depends on the constants A and *b*

both of which depend on a quantity which can be found from the observations themselves. The quantity on which A and *b* depend plays a very important part in statistics, apart from its interest in connexion with the theory of errors. It is called the "*variance*," and, if n is large, it is the common average of all the quantities formed by squaring the difference between each actual value of x and the arithmetic mean (M) of all (n) the measurements, i.e.

$$V = \frac{\Sigma(M - x)^2}{n}$$

When n is small the denominator is taken as $(n - 1)$, so that for 5 measurements represented by the numbers 6, 7, 8, 5, 4, we have the arithmetic mean 6 and the variance is

$$\frac{(6-6)^2+(6-7)^2+(6-8)^2+(6-5)^2+(6-4)^2}{(5-1)}$$

$$=\frac{(0)^2+(-1)^2+(-2)^2+(1)^2+(2)^2}{4}$$

$$=\frac{1+4+1+4}{4}$$

$$=2\cdot 5$$

If each of a set of points corresponding to a frequency y of a particular measurement x in a physical experiment falls on a curve of the sort we are now discussing, we can calculate A and b, when we have calculated the variance V of the measurements.* We have seen earlier how the probability that a number will lie within a certain range can be represented by an area. The equation given describes a curve which is drawn so that the mean value occurs at $x = 0$. If we regard the mean as the best value the values represented along the x axis represent negative or positive errors. If the units are chosen so as to make the area enclosed by the whole curve one unit of area, the frequency with which any error will lie within the range M $\pm$ E is

$$\int_{-E}^{+E} y\,.\,dx$$

It is not very difficult to show that the area which corresponds with the range M $\pm$ E is exactly half of the curve when

$$E = 0\cdot 675\sqrt{V}$$

This means that errors smaller than $\pm$ E and larger than $\pm$ E occur with equal frequency. In other words, the odds against an error's being greater than E equal the odds in favour. On that account E is usually called the *probable error* of the sample. According to the mathematical theory the means of different samples will fall on a normal curve if the observations in a single large sample do and the

* The actual values of A and b are

$$A = \frac{n}{\sqrt{2\pi V}}$$

$$b = \frac{1}{2V}$$

probable error of the mean obtained from different sets of n observations is

$$E_m = 0{\cdot}675\sqrt{\frac{V}{n}}$$

Similarly the mathematical theory shows that the differences between any two means fall on a normal curve if the individual observations do. The probable error of the difference between two means M_1 and M_2, each obtained from n observations, is

$$0{\cdot}675\sqrt{\frac{V_1 + V_2}{n}}$$

Statisticians advocate different conventions to decide whether the means of two different sets of observations depend upon the material itself. For instance, the odds are about 400 to 1 against the difference between the means of two sets of observations being more than four and a half times the probable error of the difference between the means. Since it is easy to exaggerate the importance of the theory of error in the ordinary practice of scientific inquiry, at least in the laboratory, it is important to recognize two points in connexion with the very common assertion that all scientific laws are "statistical."

The first is that the scientific worker in the laboratory always has two alternatives. We recognized at the very beginning of this book that correct measurements cannot be represented by a single number. A correct measurement is a family of numbers lying between two well-defined physical limits which depend on the delicacy of the instrument, the uniformity of the conditions in which the experiment is carried out, and the competence of the observer. If successive measurements in large numbers of experiments fall on a curve for which the statistician can find an equation, the theory of probability allows him to state the odds against any measurement's lying outside a certain range. If the odds are very large the practical man may draw the conclusion that if such a measurement occurs it cannot be explained by the defects of his method alone. That is to say, it arises from the nature of the material he is studying. What numerical value for the odds justifies such a judgment evidently depends to some extent on his taste and temperament. If he is cautious he is not likely to rest satisfied with a statistical recipe. Instead of relying on a statistical estimate about where a correct measurement *may* lie, he proceeds to devise a more accurate method which will enable him to define narrower limits within which it *must* lie.

Let us take an actual example to make this clear. The existing chemical methods of estimating the small quantity of calcium (i.e. lime salts) in small samples of blood are not capable of giving consistent results which agree within less than 2 per cent. That is to say, estimations of the same solution may differ by as much as 2 per cent, but will not differ by more, if proper precautions are taken. In studying how the blood calcium of a fowl changes when the shell of the egg is being secreted, inaccuracies of this order are negligible, because analysis of a sample of blood taken just before the egg enters the shell gland may show an increase of 200 per cent. Since a fairly crude method is adequate for studying the demands of shell formation on the lime resources of the fowl, the laboratory worker would not put himself to the additional trouble of using or devising more accurate methods than the ones we now have. For the same reason he has no need to call in the help of the statistician. Suppose his problem is a different one. He is studying the increased egg production resulting from keeping fowls in continuous artificial light. He knows that the parathyroid gland regulates the balance of lime salts between the bones and the blood, and he wishes to know whether light and darkness have any effect on its activity. He keeps one set of animals in continuous light and another in continuous darkness, making the diet, temperature, humidity, etc., of both sets as nearly as possible the same. The result of the experiment might be that the *average* lime content of the blood of the two samples differs by about 3 per cent. According to the way in which his estimations are distributed and the numbers he makes, such a result might be statistically significant, or it might not. From the way in which different measurements of one and the same solution differ the statistician will be able to assess the odds against a *mean* difference of this size arising. The statistician may point out the likelihood that a result is significant when casual examination of the figures would lead the practical man to dismiss it. Generally speaking, the experimental worker does not need this sort of encouragement. If he has good reason for expecting a particular result he will try again, using a better method. He is not looking for a statistical law. He wants to be sure. He may decide that the method of blood analysis he is using is not good enough. He will then set about devising one which will give him a higher accuracy, e.g. consistency of measurement within 0·5 per cent. He may repeat the experiment, taking more care to keep his animals in similar conditions, so as to make sure that other factors besides light and darkness do not affect the result. He may select his animals more carefully to make sure that their hereditary constitution does not differ appreciably.

The truth is that the theory of error plays very little part in the practice of the scientific laboratory. The doctrine that all scientific laws are statistical is a statistician's view of what the scientist ought to do. It is not a true description of what the scientific worker actually does. It is one thing to say that all the laws which embody our knowledge of natural phenomena are approximations to the truth. It is another thing to say that they are *statistical*. The scientist is always seeking to get a better approximation. Though he may never hope to find a *single* number which represents the measurability of the thing he is studying, he is always narrowing the range within which it lies. This range is not a statistical convention about betting odds. When we know it we are *certain* that no true value *can* lie outside it.

The second point to remember in connexion with the application of probability to errors of measurement is that any relevance it has must depend upon whether the law of frequency which describes the measurements themselves has been established. To do this on an adequate scale usually involves far more trouble than to devise a more accurate method of measurement. Even when this is not so, the mathematical theory is at best a very rough approximation to the facts themselves. The normal curve of error could only describe measurements encountered in an experiment if an unlimited number of different readings were actually obtainable. Under proper working conditions this is not realized. A comparatively limited number of different readings can be obtained within the range of separate scale divisions which circumscribe competent observations. The mathematical curve which has been studied most has a tail which never quite reaches the x axis (Fig. 197). That is to say, it admits the possibility that errors of any size whatever may occur, though the frequency of very large errors should be exceedingly small. In the practice of a laboratory the occurrence of errors beyond a certain size is not merely a matter of a very small probability. We seek to arrange experiments so that errors beyond a certain size will never occur at all. The experimental scientist does not regard statistics as an excuse for doing bad experiments. Science would stagnate if he did. Gauss, who was prominent among those who elaborated the theory of error associated with the normal curve, assumed the possibility that an indefinitely large number of errors may arise in making a measurement. While it may be true that an indefinitely large number of things may contribute to erroneous observations, it is not true that an indefinitely large number of different measurements (all but one of which are assumed to be erroneous) can actually occur. Indeed the normal curve is only a comparatively good approximation to the distribution of readings made in a very bad experiment. For instance, it is a comparatively good description of very inexpert marksmanship.

The normal curve of error has been used in connexion with statistical hypotheses like that of Mendel to avoid recourse to laborious calculations. To see how it is used in this connexion recall the experiment illustrated in Fig. 195. Suppose we raise 300 plants from a cross between peas with green seeds and hybrid yellows, getting 160 green and 140 yellow offspring. The correct assessment of the probability that the number of green and yellow plants will not differ from the mean (150) by more than 10 is

$$\sum_{r=140}^{160} {}^{300}C_r p^r q^{300-r}$$

In this expression r represents all the whole numbers from 140 to 160 inclusive. The arithmetical translation would involve enormous labour. We assume that the figure such as is shown in Fig. 190 differs very little from the curve shown in Fig. 196, provided that n is fairly large, as it is in this experiment. So we use an integral formula which is equivalent to putting the probability as

$$\int_{140}^{160} A \,.\, e^{-br^2} dr$$

We have seen that A and b both depend on a quantity V, defined already as the mean square deviation from the mean value. By applying the method on p. 596, it is easy to show that for a binominal distribution

$$\begin{aligned} V &= \Sigma^n C_r p^r q^{n-r} (r - M)^2 \\ &= n \,.\, pq \\ &= \frac{n}{4}, \text{ when } p = \tfrac{1}{2} = q \end{aligned}$$

Tables of the value of this integral for different limits which can be used for different values of V have been constructed once and for all. The use of such tables is justified by the fact that it is very tedious to calculate the odds *exactly* when n is large. In any case the value which we attach to an exact statement of the odds is a matter of personal taste. So an approximate estimate is good enough. It is a common convention to rest content if the observed values (in this case 140 and 160) do not differ from the theoretical mean (150) by more than twice the probable error. The probable error for this example is

$$0\cdot675\sqrt{npq}$$
$$= 0\cdot675\sqrt{\frac{300}{4}}$$
$$= 0\cdot675\sqrt{75}$$
$$= 5\cdot85 \text{ (approximately)}$$

In this case the discrepancy is less than twice the probable error. Biologists usually use the same criterion when p and q are not equal. As a matter of fact the theoretical curve which approximately describes the distribution in this case is a different one, and the procedure therefore involves a second approximation.

STATISTICAL THEORY IN SOCIAL SCIENCE.—We have now examined two ways in which the theory of probability is used in natural science. One is the construction of statistical hypotheses, the assumptions of which can be checked by experiment. We can all agree that this is justifiable, and there is no doubt about the usefulness of the results which have arisen from it. The second is the attempt to assess the relative value of different sets of measurements. This may have a limited usefulness if it encourages further experiment by showing where real differences may exist. In the latter part of the nineteenth century a new conception of the use of mathematical probability took shape. The publication of Quetelet's essay on *Social Physics* in 1836 drew attention to the existence of social phenomena which exhibit very striking statistical consistency. At its time this was a very important contribution. For instance, Quetelet's collection of statistics showing the proportion of crime in different countries and classes provided an unanswerable argument against those who advanced the doctrine of free will as an objection to the search for laws which govern man's social behaviour. The statistical regularity which Quetelet exposed in various classes of social phenomena called for a rational explanation, and encouraged closer attention to the statistics of wealth, welfare, and human "faculties." The interpretation of such statistics provides scope for the useful exercise of arithmetical ingenuity. As the study of social statistics grew the defects of social machinery for collecting them became more and more apparent. Since the individual investigator in social statistics cannot himself interfere on a large scale with the social process he is investigating, he is easily tempted to delude himself into believing that the theory of probability can supply him with information which can only be obtained by organized social effort.

In the study of human characteristics and social affairs the most straightforward application of the kind of mathematics included under the term probability arises in connexion with the search for connected quantities, as for instance if we were to ask whether ability to do mental arithmetic is associated with parental income. If we arranged a class of boys and girls first in the order of the marks obtained in an arithmetical test and found the same or reverse order when they were again arranged according to the annual income of their parents, we should conclude that arithmetical facility and economic prosperity are connected in some way. Such complete correspondence would only occur if the effect of all contributory factors were perfectly standardized or negligible, and in practice we should not be discouraged from drawing a positive conclusion if a few names appeared out of place. Drawing a conclusion that a correspondence exists thus depends on adopting some standard for the amount of displacement which can occur when two such "arrays" are compared.

The fundamental measure of displacement when two arrays are compared in this way is called *rank gain* or *loss*. Suppose the arithmetic marks of three boys A, B, C are 75, 52 and 39. Then A, B, C respectively have the ranks 1, 2, 3 in descending order of proficiency. If their parents' incomes are £500, £320 and £450 their ranks are 1, 3, 2. The rank of A is the same (1) in each array. The rank of B has increased by 1 and that of C has decreased by 1. The total rank gains and losses must always be the same, and the total number of either can be used as a criterion of correspondence. The number of all possible ways of arranging three things is $3! = 6$, viz.:

A	A	B	B	C	C
B	C	A	C	A	B
C	B	C	A	B	A

If we take any one of these as the standard order there will be a net loss (or gain) of rank when any of the other five are compared with it. If we take the first as the standard the orders of rank are:

A	1	1	2	2	3	3
B	2	3	1	3	1	2
C	3	2	3	1	2	1

The rank gains (positive sign) and losses (negative) are:

..	0	+1	+1	+2	+2
..	+1	−1	+1	−1	0
..	−1	0	−2	−1	−2

This makes the total gains 8 and the total losses 8. So when a group of 3 objects are successively arranged in all the 6 possible ways in which they can be arranged, the total rank loss is 8 and the mean for all possible ways is $\frac{8}{6}$. If l is the loss (negative sign) of rank in any compartment of the last table, the mean rank loss for a rearrangement of n objects when equal value is given to every possible order is therefore

$$\frac{\Sigma l}{n!} = \mathrm{S}$$

If the total rank loss (T) when two arrays are compared does not differ greatly from the mean rank loss when all possible arrangements are given the same value, we have no reason to suspect that there exists any connexion between the marking or measurements on which the order of the arrays depends. An index which indicates the correspondence in the following way is called Spearman's rank coefficient:

$$\mathrm{R} = 1 - \frac{\mathrm{T}}{\mathrm{S}}$$

If the total rank loss is equivalent to the mean rank loss $\mathrm{R} = 0$, and if the total rank loss is zero $\mathrm{R} = 1$. So values of R between 1 and 0 indicate greater or less correspondence. To use this formula we only need to know how to find S for an array composed of a fairly large number of items. The expression is,

$$\mathrm{S} = \frac{n^2 - 1}{6}$$

Thus when there are 3 objects, $\mathrm{S} = \frac{9-1}{6} = \frac{8}{6}$, as we have already found. The formula for S can be built up from the structure of the table:

1	1	.	2	2	.	3	3
2	3	.	1	3	.	1	2
3	2	.	3	1	.	2	1

As indicated before there are $n!$ possible arrangements of n items, and the number of rank gains is the same as the number of rank losses. Looking at the top row you will see that the number of times each of the n numbers occurs is the number of arrangements of the remaining $(n - 1)$ numbers, i.e. each number occurs $(n - 1)!$ times. The highest number (n) can lose rank by 0, 1, 2 on to $(n - 1)$ and each loss occurs $(n - 1)!$ times. The next highest $(n - 1)$ can lose rank 0, 1, 2 on to $(n - 2)$ and each loss occurs $(n - 1)!$ times. So all rank losses can be tabulated thus:

nth number	$(n - 1)!\,[0 + 1 + 2 \ldots + (n - 1)]$
$(n - 1)$th number	$(n - 1)!\,[0 + 1 + 2 \ldots + (n - 2)]$
lowest number but two	$(n - 1)!\,[0 + 1 + 2$
lowest number but one	$(n - 1)!\,[0 + 1$
lowest number	$(n - 1)!\,[0$

The sum of all the items of this table when the addition is rearranged according to the vertical columns is

$$(n - 1)!\,[n(0) + (n - 1)(1) + (n - 2)(2) + (n - 3)(3) \ldots]$$
$$= (n - 1)!\,[(0 + n + 2n + 3n \ldots) - (0 + 1^2 + 2^2 + 3^2 \ldots)]$$

In each of the two series in this expression there are n terms beginning with 0, hence ending with $n - 1$ and $(n - 1)^2$. So we may rewrite it:

$$(n - 1)!\,[n(1 + 2 + 3 \ldots n - 1) - (1^2 + 2^2 + 3^2 \ldots + (n - 1)^2)]$$

We have met the summation of the first n whole numbers and their squares on pp. 326–7. Substituting $(n - 1)$ for n in these expressions the sum of the first $(n - 1)$ numbers and of their squares are respectively $\frac{n(n-1)}{2}$ and $\frac{n(n-1)(2n-1)}{6}$. So we may rewrite the total as

$$(n - 1)!\left\{\frac{n.n(n-1)}{2} - \frac{n(n-1)(2n-1)}{6}\right\}$$
$$= n(n-1)!\left(\frac{n^2-1}{6}\right)$$
$$= n!\left(\frac{n^2-1}{6}\right)$$

This is the total rank loss. To get the mean we have to divide by $n!$. So the mean rank loss is, as stated:

$$\frac{n^2-1}{6}$$

As an illustration of the use of the Spearman coefficient we will suppose that the marks for scripture (i) and parents' income (ii) of 8 boys are as follows:

	(i)	(ii)		(i)	(ii)
A	70	£720	E	60	£250
B	80	£800	F	55	£500
C	21	£750	G	24	£300
D	42	£450	H	30	£200

The ordinal position of the boys on the two scales is

	(i)	(ii)	Rank difference		(i)	(ii)	Rank difference
A	2	3	− 1	E	3	7	− 4
B	1	1	0	F	4	4	0
C	8	2	+ 6	G	7	6	+ 1
D	5	5	0	H	6	8	− 2

The total rank gains (or losses) are $\pm$ 7. The mean rank loss is $\frac{8^2 - 1}{6} = \frac{63}{6}$. Substituting in the formula

$$R = 1 - \frac{7 \times 6}{63} = 0 \cdot \dot{3}$$

Thus the ordinal correspondence is 33 per cent as measured by this index.

Considerations arising from the theory of probability have led to the construction of various numerical indices, which have merits of their own, and can often be used to summarise quantitative data without regard to their special significance in mathematical theory. One of these, the variance (or its square root, called the standard deviation) of a group, is a useful check on drawing wrong conclusions from the comparison of common averages. Look below at the annual incomes of the two groups of people A and B given below:

A	B
£75	
£100	£950
£350	£1,050
£600	£1,075
£4,000	

The arithmetic mean of the incomes or "average" income of both these groups is the same, namely, £1,025. Taken by itself this figure provides no useful information about the prosperity of these two groups, one of which consists of three individuals with roughly the same amount of money to spend, the other of five individuals representing extremes of poverty and prosperity. If the two groups happen to be families the members of which pool their resources, so that what counts is the *total* family income and the number of persons to spend it, the mean figure tells us that both groups are equally well off. Otherwise the information imparted is useless. If we have two groups like those of the last example, the arithmetic mean tells us nothing about which is the more prosperous one unless we also know something about the internal organization of the group, i.e. how the incomes are distributed. Compare, for example, the following:

A	C
£75	£750
£100	£650
£350	£800
£600	£700
£4,000	

The average (arithmetic mean) income of the first is £1,025, which is roughly 40 per cent greater than £725, that of the second. On the other hand, every member of the second group is better off than 80 per cent of the members of the first. Thus the average income in the numerical sense is a very different thing from the income of the "average" man in the language of everyday life. When we talk about the average man we usually mean the majority of men. The overwhelming majority of group A in this example are not so well off as any of the members of group C.

The usefulness of the Variance (or its square root, which is called the standard deviation or standard error) lies in the fact that it is large when the measurements (e.g. income) of a group differ widely. Conversely it is small when the measurements differ very little. Comparing groups A and B in the last example but one, we get the variance by the formula already given, namely,

$$V = \frac{\Sigma(M - m)^2}{n - 1}$$

Since the value of n is generally large in statistics it is usual to take $(n - 1)$ as equal to n, and to replace it by n in the denominator.

Applying this to the figures already given, we may tabulate (M − *m*) thus:

A		B	
$(1025 - 75)^2$	= 902500		
$(1025 - 100)^2$	= 855625	$(1025 - 950)^2$	= 5625
$(1025 - 350)^2$	= 455625	$(1025 - 1050)^2$	= 625
$(1025 - 600)^2$	= 180625	$(1025 - 1075)^2$	= 2500
$(1025 - 4000)^2$	= 8850625		
Total	11245000		8750

This gives us the following values:

$$V_A = \frac{11245000}{4} = 2811250$$

$$V_B = \frac{8750}{2} = 4375$$

The corresponding standard deviations (denoted in statistical books by the Greek letter σ) will therefore be

$$\sigma_A = \sqrt{2811250} = 1680 \text{ (approx.)}$$
$$\sigma_B = \sqrt{4375} = 65 \text{ (approx.)}$$

Whether we use the variance or the standard deviation, the big difference which these figures reveal shows that although the mean income of groups A and B is the same, the discrepancy between individual incomes and the mean is much greater in one group than in the other. This is another way of saying that the average income is a much better indication of what the "average" man of one group gets than of what the average man of the other group gets. So, unless all incomes are pooled, a low variance corresponds with a relatively higher level of general prosperity when there is no considerable difference in the mean income. If the means differ considerably this is not necessarily so. Take, for instance, the following numbers:

D	E
65	650
70	700
85	850

You will see at once that in each group the ratio of corresponding numbers to the mean of the group is the same. The variability is proportionately the same in each group. The mean of one group is ten times that of the other, and so is the standard deviation. To compare the variability, or, as statisticians sometimes say, the dispersion of the two groups when the means are very different, it is therefore customary to express the standard deviation as a percentage of the mean. This percentage is called the Coefficient of Variation. Calling it C we have

$$C = \frac{100\sigma}{M}$$

The coefficient of variation is the same in the last two samples. Evidently it is a better test of the variability of two groups than the variance or the standard deviation taken alone. Comparing the two groups A and C tabulated above with mean incomes £1,025 and £725 respectively, we get:

$$V_A = 2811250$$
$$V_C = 4167$$

$$C_A = 100 \times \frac{\sqrt{2811250}}{1025} = 164$$

$$C_C = 100 \times \frac{\sqrt{4167}}{725} = 8 \cdot 9$$

Thus the variability of group C is much less than that of group A. Hence the mean of group C, though somewhat smaller than the mean of group A, is a better index of what the "average" man gets. In cases like this the variance (or any other of the many statistical measures of dispersion which we may use) is a danger signal to warn us against drawing silly conclusions from averages like the arithmetic mean. When both are taken together we have a useful and very condensed summary of what we want to know about a group. Measures of dispersion are not always a sufficient safeguard as two illustrations will show.

A common argument advanced by professors of economics against a rationally planned society illustrates the danger of taking averages too seriously. They first tell us that the average income per head is such and such. Then they proceed to deduce that no one would be particularly well off if everyone had the same income. In reality the average income of a community is of no interest to anyone except the tax collector, and then only if all incomes are taxed to the same extent.

A fundamental change in the distribution of income would entail a fundamental change in the way in which human labour is organized and applied to exploit the resources of nature. The possibility of organizing a higher general level of human enjoyment has nothing to do with the average income of individuals who have the misfortune to live in a society which fails to use natural science to exploit nature efficiently and fails to develop a psychological technique for enlisting individuals in the necessary social effort to bring this about.

Another example is provided by figures which have been quoted by eugenists as an argument against extending educational opportunities. Several investigations have shown that the average marks obtained in intelligence tests by children of professional parents are somewhat higher than the average marks of children whose parents belong to classes engaged in manual work. Apart from the fact that such tests are certainly not a straightforward measure of inborn ability, the use of mere averages in the discussion of a question like this defeats the real use of statistical methods. A difference between two averages in this case means that the *proportion* of children in a higher grade is greater in one group than in the other. Since there are far more children with working-class parents than children with professional parents the actual *number* of the former in a higher grade may be far greater, even if the *proportion* is far less. This is a good example of the difference between the use of arithmetic by the experimental scientist to change the world and its use by the arm-chair philosopher to interpret the world. The eugenist does not wish to change the existing distribution of opportunities for a good education. The arithmetic mean serves his purpose admirably by giving a figure which he can use to delude himself into believing that society is organized so that the child with the better average intelligence gets better facilities. This congenial conclusion is the same sort of fallacy as confusing the income of the average man with the average income. If the eugenist were really concerned with applying human intelligence to plan a society which makes the best use of all the brains it has, he would want a statistical method which can tell us how much ability is wasted by our present arrangements. A comparison of class averages gives us absolutely no information of this nature.

When the average measurements of two groups like the foregoing do not differ by a relatively large amount, statisticians usually calculate the variance or standard deviation for each group. From these the probable error of the mean itself or of the difference between two means is computed. If the difference between two means is more than three times its probable error, it is taken to be significant in the statistical sense. That is to say, the difference indicated by the means represents a difference which we should expect to find if we took the mean of the entire groups of which our statistics usually represent a comparatively small sample. This is done as a check against the possibility that the differences observed might simply be differences which could often occur if we took successive samples of the same size from one and the same group we are considering. The assumption made is that the frequency of the measurements of different individuals, if represented graphically, would fall approximately on some statistical curve like the normal curve of error. So what we mean when we say that a difference is *significant in the statistical sense* is that it would not *often* happen that the mean of different samples taken from the same group would differ by as much as the difference which our statistics show. If the frequency distribution has actually been shown to correspond approximately with a known statistical curve, we can form an estimate of *how often* a mean difference of a particular size would be found if two samples were taken from the same group. If we find that it would only happen *very rarely*, we are led to suppose that the difference observed arises because we are dealing with two different groups. What we mean by very rarely—once in twenty times, or once in two hundred times—is a purely arbitrary decision in so far as it justifies our judgement. Such an estimate makes certain assumptions which are difficult, and often impossible, to prove. No doubt it is a helpful check against drawing rash conclusions. At the same time it is a poor substitute for information which could be got if we took as much trouble to standardize all our conditions as we expect to take in carrying out a physical experiment. While recognizing its merit for what it is worth, we must guard against the error of assuming that a difference the statistician calls significant has any real significance from the social standpoint. In the last example the socially important feature of the statistics cannot be represented by an average; so a difference between two such averages may be statistically significant and socially insignificant.

To a large extent the correct use of social statistics depends on common sense and simple arithmetic. The interpretation of death-rates calls for the same kind of intelligence as devising a good experiment. If we wish to examine the effect of public-health measures, a large number of factors have to be taken into consideration. First of all we have to reckon with the fact that two communities which differ in their public-health policy may also differ with regard to the economic status of the individuals concerned and external conditions such as climate. When we have taken these facts into consideration, there are others which are not so obvious. For instance, females have a lower mortality than males at most ages. So the proportion of females and males in two communities will influence the rate at which people die irrespective of what measures are taken to keep them alive. More important still is the fact that people do not die as frequently at some ages as at others. The proportion of individuals who die during the first year of life is enormously high compared with the proportion of people who die during the eleventh year of life. So, too, it need hardly be said, the proportion of people who live to be eighty and die before they are eighty-five is enormously high compared with the proportion of people who live to be ten and die before they are fifteen. So if the proportion of people who are either very old or very young is different in two communities, the apparent effect of a health policy may be greatly exaggerated or totally obscured. There is a simple numerical device for getting over this difficulty and at the same time presenting a picture of the true state of affairs concisely. Instead of comparing the crude death-rates of two communities, i.e. the number of deaths from all causes in a year per 1,000 of the population irrespective of age and sex, we can use what are called standardized mortality rates.

A standardized mortality rate tells us what the death-rate would be if the ages and sexes of the individuals in the community bore the same proportion as in some fixed or standard population. The necessary social machinery is a separate record of deaths for either sex at different ages. In British statistics the standard population to which mortality rates are referred is based on the age and sex composition of England and Wales in the year 1901. To calculate the standardized mortality rate for any other year the deaths per 1,000 for each year of life or five-year period of males and females are needed. If we multiplied these by the proportions of individuals of the sex and age group in the population we are studying and added them all together, the result would be the same as the crude death-rate (total deaths per thousand of the entire population), and would not be comparable with the crude death-rate of a population having a different sex and age composition. If we multiply the death-rates of each age and sex group by the proportion of individuals of the same age and sex group in the standard population, we have a standardized mortality rate which may be slightly higher or slightly lower than the crude death-rate and is strictly comparable as far as sex and age affect the result with any other standardized death-rate calculated on the same basis.

Corrections of this kind may be useful in a variety of ways. For instance, if we are anxious to know what effect poverty or climate has on the liability to a particular disease we can place no reliance on crude death-rates. Thus, infantile diarrhoea only affects mortality in the early years of life. Cancer chiefly affects mortality at the latter end. Puerperal fever only affects the death of females during the child-bearing period. So comparing the crude death-rates, i.e. annual number of deaths per 1,000 of the whole population, resulting from any of these three diseases might lead to totally false conclusions if the age and sex compositions of the populations compared were widely different. A good example of this is provided by the cancer statistics of England and Ireland in the five-year period 1869–73. The crude death-rate from cancer in Ireland was higher than that of England. The standardized death-rate of England was even more conspicuously higher than that of Ireland. Such standardized death-rates give us a very compact picture of the way in which physical environment and factors which can be socially controlled affect mortality in different communities or at different periods in the history of a community. A complete picture of the health record of a society is presented in the life table from which insurance companies calculate the risks which fix the price of annuities. As we have already mentioned, the first life table was compiled by Halley during a period when corporations were endeavouring to secure royal charters for insurance and the experience of the Great Plague and the American emigrations had focused interest on statistics of deaths and births. Although the use of the life table in the practice of insurance has provided material for applying the mathematical theory of probability, and its discussion has played an important part in the development of the mathematical theory, a life table is really nothing more than a record of how many people survive to a particular age and does not depend on the mathematical theory which emerged from the same social context.

A life table essentially consists of two columns. One gives the number of years of age (1, 2, 3, etc.) to which individuals referred to survive. The other column tells us the proportion of individuals in the community, or the number per thousand born (N_1, N_2, N_3, etc.) who survive to a given number of years. An example of an abridged life table given by Kuczynski for Germany, 1924–26, is the following:

Years of Age	Female Survivors
0	1,000
1	906·23
5	882·19
10	874·50
15	868·87
20	858·24
25	842·92
30	826·14
35	808·61
40	789·34
45	767·06
50	739·70

The construction of a table like this from information supplied by the registrar of births and deaths only requires a knowledge of elementary arithmetic and the application of common sense. At first sight it might seem sufficient to count the number of children who attain their fifth year, let us say, in 1933, and the number of children born in 1928, or the number of children who attain their tenth year in 1933 and the number born in 1923, and so on. This would be quite useless for a reason which is not difficult to see. The number of people of any age in a community is affected by emigration and immigration. There is also a more subtle objection. A life table is constructed to convey information about the way in which conditions prevailing at some particular time are affecting the survival of people to a given age. In a sense this is a fiction, though a useful fiction because it allows us to make calculations on more or less plausible assumptions, such as the supposition that conditions are not going to become worse over the period to which our calculations refer. If we were to base our calculations on determinations of the proportion of people who survive to the age of fifty or to the age of one on the number of births which occurred fifty years or a year ago, we should be recording the effect of very different sets of conditions on the proportion of people who survive to a given age. So the life table is actually constructed from the death statistics of some one particular year.

Let us suppose we can estimate Q_x, the proportion (expressed as a fraction of unity) of individuals of exactly x years of age who will die without attaining exactly $x + 1$ years of age. The fraction of people of exactly x years of age who will reach the age of $x + 1$ years is then

$1 - Q_x$. So if N_0 is a number of people born in a given year and N_1 is the number of those who will survive at least to their first year under the conditions of mortality prevailing in that year,

$$N_1 = N_0 (1 - Q_0)$$

Similarly, if N_2 is the number who would survive to be at least two years at the existing mortality rates

$$\begin{aligned} N_2 &= N_1(1 - Q_1) \\ &= N_0(1 - Q_0)(1 - Q_1) \end{aligned}$$

Similarly,

$$\begin{aligned} N_3 &= N_0(1 - Q_0)(1 - Q_1)(1 - Q_2) \\ N_4 &= N_0(1 - Q_0)(1 - Q_1)(1 - Q_2)(1 - Q_3) \end{aligned}$$

etc.

So all we have to determine is a set of fractions Q_x, which represent the proportion of individuals of exactly x years of age who will die without reaching the age of $x + 1$ years. Suppose that in the middle of the year in question there are y people between the ages of x and $x + 1$, and that during this year the number of deaths between x and $x + 1$ is z.

Then z represents the number of deaths of a group of y people whose mean age at the census on June 30th, half-way through the year, is $(x + \frac{1}{2})$ years. This group of y are the survivors of a group of average age x at the beginning of the year. Of this group $z/2$ have died during the half-year preceding the census date. So z deaths in that year occur among $y + z/2$ people with an average age of x at the beginning of the year, i.e.

$$Q_x = \frac{z}{y + \frac{z}{2}}$$

Although the life table was originally designed to provide profits for insurance corporations, it has many applications of general social importance. For example, a comparison of life tables compiled at different periods during the last two centuries gives a clear indication of changes in social well-being as it is reflected in the survival of the bulk of the population. Another very important use of the life table to throw light on social changes is illustrated by its use in the measurement of population growth. Entirely false ideas about the way in which populations are now growing have been spread by Malthusian propagandists who attribute the manifest evils which result from economic maladjustment in an age of plenty to a supposedly excessive rate of population growth. Such misunderstanding rests upon a fallacious use of crude birth-rates and death-rates, the misuse of which is clearly set forth in Enid Charles's book *The Twilight of Parenthood*.

A clear conception of how a population is growing can be obtained by the use of two indices. The first is called the gross reproduction rate. To get this we tabulate the number of births per 1,000 women of a given age for every year of the child-bearing period. If we add all these together we get the number of children which would be born to 1,000 women during the whole of the child-bearing period if fertility remained unchanged. By multiplying this by the proportion of females among all children born and dividing by 1,000 we get the number of girls which would be born per woman if fertility remained at its existing level during their lives. Clearly if this number, the *gross reproduction rate*, is less than unity, a population is bound to dwindle away unless something happens to raise it. This is true however much may be done to diminish the risk of death to mother and child.

The other index of population growth is obtained by multiplying the birth-rates for each maternal age by the number of survivors of that age given in the life table. On adding the products and multiplying the result by the proportion of females in all births and dividing by 1,000 we get the average number of girls who will themselves survive to become mothers born per woman in the population. Existing statistics show that this index is less than unity in most industrialized countries. That is to say, these communities are not capable of maintaining themselves at existing rates of mortality and fertility. In older industrialized countries even the gross reproduction rate has sunk below unity. So such populations cannot hope to maintain themselves by any reduction in mortality alone. Meanwhile science is now producing the necessities of life in an abundance beyond the imagination of Malthus and his contemporaries. Thus the position is just the reverse of what we have been told by Malthusian propagandists.

APPENDIX TO CHAPTER XII

STATISTICAL INDICES

1. MEDIAN AND MODE

In addition to the arithmetic mean, which has been discussed, two other statistical constants are sometimes used to describe the characteristics of a distribution. If a number of individuals differ with respect to a measurable characteristic, they can be arranged in order corresponding to the order of magnitude of the characteristic observed. The *median* can then be defined as the value of the characteristic which corresponds to the individual in the middle of the series. There will thus be equal numbers of individuals having values of the characteristics higher and lower than the median. Where the individuals are so numerous that they are grouped in classes, the position of the midmost individual can generally be found by interpolation, if the limits of the characteristic for the group are known. When there is an even number of individuals, the value of the median is taken to be half-way between the values of the characteristic pertaining to the two individuals who stand nearest to the middle of the series.

The *mode* is the most fashionable value of the variable character observed. When the character measured changes by a comparatively small number of clearly separated steps, for example the number of blooms to a stem in sweet peas, the mode is easily determined. When the character changes by steps as small as can be measured, and there are large numbers of individuals for each measured step, the mode is less easily found by inspection. In these cases it may be defined as the value of a variable x which corresponds to a maximum value of the other variable y. There may thus be more than one mode in a distribution. When a distribution is *symmetrical*, for example, one which corresponds closely to the normal curve of error, mean, mode and median correspond, but when the distribution is "skew" they do not. So that the position of the median or mode relative to the mean is a useful way of describing the skewness of a distribution. The following measures of skewness have been suggested:

$$\text{skewness} = \frac{(\text{mean} - \text{mode})}{\sigma}$$

$$\text{or} = \frac{3(\text{mean} - \text{median})}{\sigma}$$

In the examples given on p. 618 the mean income of series A is £1,025, while the median income is £350. In series C, on the other hand, both the mean and the median income are the same, i.e. £725.

2. THE CORRELATION COEFFICIENT

An arithmetical device used like Spearman's rank coefficient for describing the resemblance between the way in which two sets of observations vary is called the coefficient of correlation, and is nearly always represented by the letter *r*. It is used in three ways—(*a*) as an index of social welfare to indicate whether two sets of numbers or measurements are connected, e.g. whether the frequency of crime and the percentage of unemployment are connected, or whether the weight of school children is connected with their parents' wages. It is used (*b*) as an index of reliability to represent the correspondence of different measurements made on the same group of individuals on successive occasions, and hence of the reliability of the measuring instrument or test, or of the stability of the characteristic measured between successive tests. For instance, we may give marks to individuals for the answers they give to a set of questions about their political opinions; *r* can be used to measure how far the marks obtained by individuals on two successive occasions tally with one another. If they tally well we must conclude that their attitude is not much affected by anything that has happened between the two tests and that the test represents the attitude of the individuals concerned in a definite sense. The two issues can be separated by varying the period between the tests. It is used (*c*) as an index of resemblance. If we take pairs of individuals who share some common influence, such as similar environment or similar heredity, we may use *r* to represent how some measurable characteristics tally when made on two members of such pairs. For instance, the numerical value of *r* for measurements of the height of "identical twins" may be compared with the value of *r* for measurements of the height of non-identical twins. Thus we can say how far differences of height are affected by heredity and family environment within certain limits because we know that identical twins have the same hereditary make-up and non-identical twins have not.

The index is so constructed that its values lie between ± 1. If the measurements tally perfectly, one set increasing as the other increases, *r* may be as great as $+1$. If *r* is -1 the two sets of measurements tally perfectly, one increasing as the other decreases. If *r* is 0

TABLE I

Year	Employed Percentage (Trade Unions) (*a*)	Marriage Rate per 1,000 of Population, England and Wales (*b*)	Year	Employed Percentage (Trade Unions) (*a*)	Marriage Rate per 1,000 of Population, England and Wales (*b*)
1860	98·15	17·1	1895	94·00	15·0
1861	96·30	16·3	1896	96·65	15·7
1862	93·95	16·1	1897	96·55	16·0
1863	95·30	16·8	1898	97·05	16·2
1864	98·05	17·2	1899	97·95	16·5
1865	98·20	17·5	1900	97·55	16·0
1866	97·35	17·5	1901	96·65	15·9
1867	93·70	16·5	1902	95·80	15·9
1868	93·25	16·1	1903	95·00	15·6
1869	94·05	15·9	1904	93·60	15·2
1870	96·25	16·1	1905	94·75	15·3
1871	98·35	16·7	1906	96·30	15·6
1872	99·05	17·4	1907	96·05	15·8
1873	98·85	17·6	1908	91·35	15·1
1874	98·40	17·0	1909	91·30	14·7
1875	97·80	16·7	1910	94·90	15·0
1876	96·60	16·5	1911	96·95	15·2
1877	95·60	15·7	1912	96·85	15·6
1878	93·75	15·2	1913	97·90	15·7
1879	89·30	14·4	1914	96·75	15·9
1880	94·75	14·9	1915	99·00	19·4
1881	96·45	15·1	1916	99·55	14·9
1882	97·65	15·5	1917	99·40	13·8
1883	97·40	15·5	1918	99·30	15·3
1884	92·85	15·1	1919	97·50	19·8
1885	91·45	14·5	1920	97·45	20·2
1886	90·45	14·2	1921	84·45	16·9
1887	92·85	14·4	1922	82·80	15·7
1888	95·85	14·4	1923	87·50	15·2
1889	97·95	15·0	1924	90·90	15·3
1890	97·90	15·5	1925	88·95	15·2
1891	96·60	15·6	1926	87·30	14·3
1892	93·80	15·4	1927	90·40	15·7
1893	92·30	14·7	1928	89·30	15·4
1894	92·80	15·0	1929	89·60	15·8

From W. H. Beveridge, *Unemployment*.

it means that the two measurements we are comparing do not tally. The figures have no connexion, the test has no reliability, or a general resemblance does not exist. The use of the correlation coefficient and the method of determining it can best be illustrated by a concrete example. In *Unemployment* by W. H. Beveridge, statistical supplement, Table XLVII, p. 460, will be found a series of statistics relating to unemployment. In two columns are given (*a*) the Employed Percentage (Trade Unions), and (*b*) the Marriage Rate per 1,000 of Population, for England and Wales from 1860 to 1929, as shown in Table I.

If (*a*) and (*b*) are plotted as two separate curves against the number of years since 1860, it will be seen that the curves show a series of ups and downs, and that on the whole the turning-points in the unemployment curve correspond to turning-points in the marriage curve either in the same year or a year or two later. This connexion is best seen in the earlier years. From 1914 onwards the course of both curves is more erratic. For the present we shall confine ourselves to the years 1860 to 1914. The first step is to group the values into a convenient number of classes. We make a table, and in each square of the table place a dot for each value which falls in that square. This is shown in Table II.

TABLE II

Employment Percentage

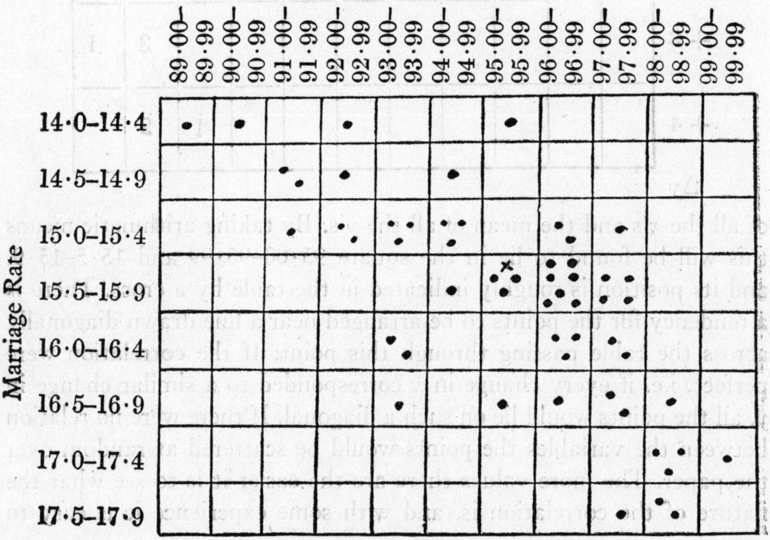
89·00–
89·99
90·00–
90·99
91·00–
91·99
92·00–
92·99
93·00–
93·99
94·00–
94·99
95·00–
95·99
96·00–
96·99
97·00–
97·99
98·00–
98·99
99·00–
99·99
Marriage Rate
14·0–14·4
14·5–14·9
15·0–15·4
15·5–15·9
16·0–16·4
16·5–16·9
17·0–17·4
17·5–17·9

From such a table as the foregoing it is possible to see the nature of the correlation. If we call the Unemployment Percentage the *x* variable and the Marriage Rate the *y* variable, the centre of greatest density of all the points will lie at a point corresponding to the mean

TABLE III

y \ *x*	−6	−5	−4	−3	−2	−1	0	+1	+2	+3	+4 Δ*x*
−3	1	1		1			1				
−2			2	1		1					
−1			1	2	3	3		2	1		
0						1	3	7	4		
+1					2			3	2		
+2					1		1	1	2	1	
+3										3	1
+4									1	2	
Δ*y*											

of all the *x*'s and the mean of all the *y*'s. By taking arithmetic means this will be found to lie in the square 95·00–95·99 and 15·5–15·9, and its position is roughly indicated in the table by a cross. There is a tendency for the points to be arranged near a line drawn diagonally across the table passing through this point. If the correlation were perfect, i.e. if every change in *x* corresponded to a similar change in *y*, all the points would lie on such a diagonal. If there were no relation between the variables the points would be scattered at random over the paper. The more values there are the easier it is to see what the nature of the correlation is, and with some experience it is easy to make a good approximate estimate of the amount of correlation from such a diagram.

To obtain a more refined measure we must substitute for the table of single values a table of frequencies. We have already found the approximate location of the mean x and y, and we can now disregard the actual values of the variables and carry out the rest of our calculations in terms of class units, taking the class in which the mean is situated as the origin.

The correlation coefficient can now be defined as follows. Let the deviations of the variable x from the mean x as origin be denoted by $\triangle x$, and the deviations of the variable y from the mean y as origin be denoted by $\triangle y$. Then if p is the mean of all the product pairs $\triangle x \triangle y$,

$$r = \frac{p}{\sigma_x \sigma_y} \quad . \quad . \quad . \quad . \quad . \quad . \quad . \quad . \quad . \quad . \quad . \quad . \quad . \quad \text{(i)}$$

If n is the total number of observations, this is equivalent to saying that

$$r = \frac{\dfrac{\Sigma \triangle x \triangle y}{n}}{\sqrt{\left\{\dfrac{\Sigma(\triangle x)^2}{n} \times \dfrac{\Sigma(\triangle y)^2}{n}\right\}}} \quad . \quad . \quad . \quad . \quad . \quad \text{(ii)}$$

This reduces to
$$r = \frac{\Sigma \triangle x \triangle y}{\sqrt{\{\Sigma(\triangle x)^2 \times \Sigma(\triangle y)^2\}}} \quad . \quad . \quad . \quad . \quad . \quad \text{(iii)}$$

In our Table we have grouped single values together in classes so that each value of $\triangle x$ and $\triangle y$ has a given frequency, and our formula can be written

$$r = \frac{\Sigma f \triangle x \triangle y}{\sqrt{\{\Sigma f(\triangle x)^2 \times \Sigma f(\triangle y)^2\}}} \quad . \quad . \quad . \quad . \quad . \quad \text{(iv)}$$

No attempt will be made to give a complete mathematical explanation of the formula for r. It is easy to see that p is a measure of the relationship between x and y. When the deviations of x and y have the same sign, their product will be positive. When they have opposite signs, their product will be negative, so that if every change in y was equally likely to be accomplished by a change in the same or in an opposite direction, the positive and negative products would balance each other, and r would be zero, or nearly so. By dividing p by the standard deviations of the two variables we eliminate the effect of different variabilities. In actual practice we seldom take the origin exactly at the mean. In the example we are considering, the origin has been taken at the centre of the class $x = 95{\cdot}00 - 95{\cdot}99$ and $y = 15{\cdot}5 - 15{\cdot}9$. Actually the mean x and mean y are respectively

0·054 and 0·2 class units on the positive sides of this point.* We shall see later how to correct for this, but in practice it seldom makes a big difference to the value of *r*, and it is always best to calculate an approximate value or *r* first and correct later, thus checking the arithmetical work.

The next step in the calculation of *r* is set forth in Table IV.

TABLE IV

(1) Δx	(2) Δy	(3) f	(4) $f\Delta x$	(5) $f\Delta y$	(6) $f\Delta x^2$	(7) $f\Delta y^2$	(8) $f\Delta x\Delta y$
− 6	− 3	1	− 6	− 3	36	9	+ 18
− 5	− 3	1	− 5	− 3	25	9	+ 15
− 4	− 2	2	− 8	− 4	32	8	+ 16
− 4	− 1	1	− 4	− 1	16	1	+ 4
− 3	− 3	1	− 3	− 3	9	9	+ 9
− 3	− 2	1	− 3	− 2	9	4	+ 6
− 3	− 1	2	− 6	− 2	18	2	+ 6
− 2	− 1	3	− 6	− 3	12	3	+ 6
− 2	+ 1	2	− 4	+ 2	8	2	− 4
− 2	+ 2	1	− 2	+ 2	4	4	− 4
− 1	− 2	1	− 1	− 2	1	4	+ 2
− 1	− 1	3	− 3	− 3	3	3	+ 3
− 1	0	1	− 1	—	1	—	—
0	− 3	1	—	− 3	—	9	—
0	0	3	—	—	—	—	—
0	+ 2	1	—	+ 2	—	4	—
+ 1	− 1	2	+ 2	− 2	2	2	− 2
+ 1	0	7	+ 7	—	7	—	—
+ 1	+ 1	3	+ 3	+ 3	3	3	+ 3
+ 1	+ 2	1	+ 1	+ 2	1	4	+ 2
+ 2	− 1	1	+ 2	− 1	4	1	− 2
+ 2	0	4	+ 8	—	16	—	—
+ 2	+ 1	2	+ 4	+ 2	8	2	+ 4
+ 2	+ 2	2	+ 4	+ 4	8	8	+ 8
+ 2	+ 4	1	+ 2	+ 4	4	16	+ 8
+ 3	+ 2	1	+ 3	+ 2	9	4	+ 6
+ 3	+ 3	3	+ 9	+ 9	27	27	+ 27
+ 3	+ 4	2	+ 6	+ 8	18	32	+ 24
+ 4	+ 3	1	+ 4	+ 3	16	9	+ 12
Total		55	+ 3	+ 11	297	179	+ 167

Table IV is derived thus from the frequency table (Table III).

* These means were obtained from the frequency table, not from the original values.

In column (1) we put first the lowest value of Δx, and next to it in column (2) the successive values of Δy corresponding to this value of Δx with the appropriate frequency in column (3). We continue in the same way with all the values of Δx. Column (4) is obtained by multiplying (1) and (3), column (5) by multiplying (2) and (3), column (6) by squaring (1) and multiplying by (3), column (7) by squaring (2) and multiplying by (3), and column (8) by multiplying (1), (2), and (3) together.

A first approximation for r can now be got from formula (iv), i.e.

$$r = \frac{167}{\sqrt{(297 \times 179)}}$$
$$= 0{\cdot}724$$

To correct for the fact that our origin is not exactly at the mean we must go back to formula (ii) and rewrite it as follows:

$$r = \frac{\dfrac{\Sigma f\Delta x\Delta y}{n} - \dfrac{\Sigma f\Delta x}{n}.\dfrac{\Sigma f\Delta y}{n}}{\sqrt{\left\{\dfrac{\Sigma f(\Delta x)^2}{n} - \dfrac{(\Sigma f\Delta x)^2}{(n)^2}\right\}\left\{\dfrac{\Sigma f(\Delta y)^2}{n} - \dfrac{(\Sigma f\Delta y)^2}{(n)^2}\right\}}}$$

$$r = \frac{\dfrac{167}{55} - \dfrac{3}{55}.\dfrac{11}{55}}{\sqrt{\left\{\dfrac{297}{55} - \dfrac{(3)^2}{(55)^2}\right\}\left\{\dfrac{179}{55} - \dfrac{(11)^2}{(55)^2}\right\}}}$$
$$= 0{\cdot}726$$

We have thus arrived at the conclusion that there is a fairly high degree of correlation between the two phenomena considered.

The correlation coefficient as used in this example is a measure of statistical resemblance. It does not throw any light on the mechanism connecting two phenomena. It is only a recipe for action in the sense that it points the way to further investigation or experiment.

The same principle of simplifying computation can be used in determining the standard deviation alone. A convenient point fairly near the mean is taken as origin. Deviations are measured from this origin and corrected for the distance between the origin and the mean.

Examples on Chapter 12

1. What is the probability of throwing a six in three throws of a single die?

2. What is the probability of getting thirteen spades in a hand at bridge?

3. If one partner at bridge has the ace and king of a given suit, what is the probability of his partner having the queen and knave?

4. In Andalusian fowls, black and white plumage colour behaves similarly to yellow and green seed colour in peas, except that impure blacks are blue. So the offspring of two blue Andalusians are black, blue and white in the ratios 1:2:1. In a batch of 20 chickens raised from two blue Andalusians, what is the probability that exactly half will be blue? What are the chances of getting at least 8 blue chickens?

5. In fowls, the types of comb known as rose and pea each depend on a dominant gene which behaves in a similar way to the yellow seed gene. In the absence of either gene the comb is single, and when both are present a type of comb called walnut is seen. The offspring of a single and a walnut-combed fowl mated among themselves gave the following offspring:

walnut comb	211	rose comb	71
pea comb	68	single comb	24

Interpret this.

6. From the table of Area and Population of the World by Continents in *Whitaker's Almanack* determine the mean density of population with its standard deviation and coefficient of variation for each continent.

7. From the table of Expectation of Life in *Whitaker's Almanack* find approximately your chance of living to be eighty.

8. From *Whitaker's Almanack* find the correlation between the density of population in the English counties and the proportion of Conservative (or Labour) votes.

Epilogue on Science

OR

MATHEMATICS AND THE REAL WORLD

In Chapter 3 we discussed how to translate everyday speech into the idiom of mathematical diction. Everyone who has learned a little French knows that translating from French into English and from English into French are tasks with their own special difficulties. For instance, you need a larger vocabulary for the one, and a more thorough grasp of grammatical rules for the other. After this book had been sent to press a friendly critic suggested that something ought to be said about translating mathematical phraseology back into the vernacular. There are, in fact, several pitfalls to avoid when we do this. Hence what follows.

One, and the most obvious, is forgetting that statements about the world in the language of mathematics, like statements made about the world in everyday speech, are only approximately true. Suppose we have made experiments on a gas to find the connexion between:

(*a*) The temperature and the pressure when the volume is kept constant.

(*b*) The temperature and the volume when the pressure is kept constant.

(*c*) The pressure and the volume when the temperature is kept constant.

We might then decide that our observations are consistent with the following verbal statements:

(i) When the volume of a fixed weight of gas is kept the same, the pressure increases or decreases in direct proportion to the increase or decrease of temperature ($p \propto t$).

(ii) When the pressure of a fixed weight of gas is kept the same, the volume increases or decreases in direct proportion to the temperature ($v \propto t$).

(iii) When the temperature is kept constant the pressure and volume of a fixed weight of gas are inversely proportional (pv = const.).

These simple statements, which fit the facts very closely if temperature is measured on the "*absolute*" scale, for which the freezing point of water is 273° and the boiling point 373°, are all included in the more compact rule:

$$\frac{pv}{t} = \mathrm{R}$$

This may be written:

(*a*) $p = \frac{\mathrm{R}}{v} \cdot t$, which is the same as (i) when v is a fixed number.

(*b*) $v = \frac{\mathrm{R}}{p} \cdot t$, which is the same as (ii) when p is a fixed number.

(*c*) $pv = \mathrm{R}t$, which is the same as (iii) when t is a fixed number.

You see that the second statement can be used as a recipe for action if translated, "raise the temperature of a gas at fixed pressure so much to increase its volume by so much"; and there is nothing in the form of the equation to prohibit you from translating it "raise the volume of a gas at fixed pressure so much to increase its temperature so much." Experience tells you that the latter statement is meaningless. So a first caution to bear in mind is that a mathematical statement can only be used to prescribe a correct course of action if it is supplemented by *additional* knowledge derived from experience of how a process actually occurs in the real world.

If you know from experience how to apply the rule, when expressed in mathematical terms, and have carried out experiments to get a good average value of R, you can then use it to calculate any one of the three quantities p, v or t when the other two are known. For instance, if the gas is hydrogen and its weight is n grams, you will find that R is approximately 0·0025 n, i.e.

$$\frac{pv}{t} = 0{\cdot}0025n$$

Although this statement is more suggestive, more compact and more explicit, it is not in any other sense more exact than its verbal alternatives. When we say that the pressure is inversely proportional to the volume at fixed temperature we mean that, when we have arranged an experiment to keep the temperature as steady as we can, and measured the volume and pressure of a gas with vessels as accurate as we can make them and scales divided as finely as we can divide them, the product of pressure and volume does not vary by more than we should expect from the discrepancies between successive measurements of volume at the same pressure (as far as we can get it to remain the same) or successive measurements of pressure when the volume shows no change (which we can detect). This is on all fours with the corresponding statement that the various values of R which we get when we make a number of observations at different pressures, volumes, and temperatures are as close as we can expect with instruments which are liable to the margin of error which it is part of a good experiment to ascertain.

In other words, we can only use the mathematical statement with the reservation that the results calculated with the help of it will not differ from what we should actually find by a margin of error greater than our instruments could be relied on to detect. This was true at the time when the rule just given was established in the seventeenth and eighteenth centuries by the experiments of Hooke, Mariotte, Charles, and Gay Lussac. It is not true today, because we have better instruments. On the other hand, the results obtained by applying it to the behaviour of ordinary gases like air or hydrogen differ from observation by less than 1 per cent over a wide range of temperatures and pressures. So although a more accurate rule (called van der Waals' equation) has now been established, it is still a safe guide for all kinds of conduct which do not require greater accuracy than 1 per cent within this range. In translating backwards, therefore, another caution to bear in mind is this. *The great precision with which the rules of mathematical discourse are stated does not imply that a description of nature is necessarily more exact because the language used to describe it is mathematical.* Exact science, as the term is usually employed, is a misnomer. Science is as exact as it *can* be with the instruments available or *need* be for the uses to which it is put. Otherwise it is not science, and using mathematical devices does not make it more or less exact.

A second caution is specially important when we come to apply mathematics to social life or biological processes. It is emphasized in Bell's stimulating book *The Search for Truth*, which did not come into the writer's hands till after this one had been written. Though the gas rule just given is as accurate as could be expected to describe the experiments its discoverers made with the instruments they possessed, it would not have been as accurate as they could have expected with the instruments at their disposal, had they known how to produce very low temperatures in the neighbourhood of the point at which air liquefies under high pressure. In this region the rule becomes grossly inaccurate. Any rule about the real world is only correctly stated, verbally or mathematically, when we are told in what circumstances it holds good, and to apply it with confidence we may need to know in what circumstances it does not. The example chosen embodies experience of how gases behave within certain limits of temperature and pressure. Provided we keep within those limits, we can use it as a guide for correct conduct.

Many people express the correspondence between rule and observation by saying that a scientific law shows you how to *predict* a result. If they really mean that it *prescribes* what *to do* in order *to get* a result, there is no objection to this way of putting it. They often mean something very different. Seemingly it is equally a "prediction" to say that the sun's declination (see Chapter 8) will not be more than a quarter of a degree off $23\frac{1}{2}°$ N. at noon on June 21, 1938, or that the earth will be warm enough to maintain vegetation for five million million years more. In reality the two statements are not analogous. The first tells me at what angle to fix a sextant if I want to see the sun dip at noon on that date. It is justified by measurements carried out over a period of five thousand years to show how much variation in the calculable position of the sun occurs in short intervals like that between the time of writing this page and the date mentioned. It deals with a sample of time which experience has taught us to be small enough to handle. We have no such knowledge of how the earth cools in a period of five million million years, and we can put statements about samples of such a size to no use which would check their credibility. Between the two types of statements illustrated there is a gulf between two different attitudes which people adopt to what they call knowledge. One is the social view which regards knowledge as an instrument for active participation in the work of reshaping the world in conformity to human needs. The other is that of the isolated intellectual with the tradition of a leisured class, passively reflecting upon a world without the disposition to change it.

In physical and biological science the distinction is not very important, because the extrapolations of astronomers and geologists do most harm to their own reputations. Since Kelvin's colossal blunder about the rate of cooling of the earth was exposed by Madame Curie's discovery of radium, specialists in natural science treat similar exploits as an amusing and permissible branch of fiction. In the study of human society the position is different. Professors of economics still believe that it is legitimate to argue that prosperity will return because they can draw graphs which show how depressions and booms have alternated in the past. They believe this because a real scientist draws graphs to suggest "formulae" which convey simple rules, as explained in Chapter 9. Whether expressed hieroglyphically by the graph or in "dictionary" language by the formula, the rule describes the conditions of the experiment as the scientist arranges them, and can only be used as a safe guide of conduct if he can arrange similar conditions. The trade cycle graphs of the economist refer to changing conditions, which the economist cannot fix, and, unlike the astronomer, he has no long scale experience of the results of acting on the assumption that certain features recur with unfailing regularity. When graphs are used in real science, the person who uses them *interpolates* points within the range covered by observations made under prescribed conditions. Extrapolating, i.e. reading off points from where a curve is presumed to continue beyond this range is not science. It is mere guesswork.

This does not mean that people who study social institutions should not draw graphs or that they should not record their results in numbers. The estimates of Enid Charles show that if the fertility of England and Wales as a whole remains at its present level, there will only be about half a dozen survivors four hundred years hence. This is useful information because it shows that we have got to do something if we wish to prevent the extinction of a population or its replacement by its more fertile elements, e.g. Roman Catholics. The rule we have chosen shows at what temperature a sealed bottle of air will burst, if it cannot stand a pressure of more than 10 atmospheres. So if we do not wish the bottle to burst, we know below what limit to keep the temperature. In the same way comparison of statistics drawn from different populations may show us some of the things which discourage parenthood, and hence help us to get rules which show us how to encourage it.

In translating backwards we have now stated two cautions. One is that you must not think the use of mathematical language makes a rule, or the subject-matter of a science, any more exact. So introducing graphs of supply and demand in a fictitious free-exchange economy does not make economics an exact science. The other is that if a rule is a true statement of nature it embodies a specification of the conditions which must be observed when you use it. So the full translation of a rule involves the further statement "if such and such conditions are maintained." A third caution which is worth adding is that the *form* of a mathematical statement does not necessarily tell you anything about the *process* it describes. All it does is to tell you how to calculate a result.

A very crude example will illustrate this pitfall. It might conceivably happen that year to year statistics of infantile mortality (m), rainfall (r) and income (i) per head in some community varied so that the first was directly proportional to the second and inversely proportional to the third. Their connexion could then be expressed by the formula $mi \div r =$ constant. This has exactly the same form as the gas rule $pv \div t =$ constant. Although no one would be so silly as to argue that the connexion between income, infantile deaths, and the fall of rain *must* therefore be due to gaseous reactions, very similar reasoning has been used, and still is used, in popular expositions of science, and often in expositions by gifted and responsible people.

At any stage in the history of science we have to distinguish between two sorts of beliefs which are called scientific. One includes beliefs about regularities of nature based on observation. The other consists of mathematical fictions or metaphors suggested by, or used to suggest, the calculating devices which are employed in dealing with them. The first are the enduring bricks of science. The second is the temporary scaffolding used and discarded at different stages of the building. The repeated swing of the pendulum from materialistic to idealistic fashions in philosophy has much to do with the habit of confusing them. A metaphor assumes the aspect of a regularity of nature. When it is seen for what it is, people who are content to interpret the world without reshaping it welcome the invention of a new instrument of calculation as a proof that science is merely a by-product of human consciousness. Several of these metaphorical bubbles have been burst in our generation, and a flood of pietistic obsequies has issued forth. All that has happened is that new calculating devices have been invented, because the old ones are not good enough to deal with all the newly discovered enduring facts about a world which existed before there were any philosophers, theologians, Gifford Lecturers, or newspaper editors.

The *luminiferous ether* is one which has vanished into the void of illuminating metaphors from which it came. While it lasted it was a picturesque way of stating that you can calculate the path of a beam of light through empty space by using the same kind of mathematical formulae as the ones which are used for tracking a wave of compression through an elastic jelly. That the picture of empty space gorged with an all pervading blancmange is less suggestive, when you encounter new phenomena to which you can apply the mathematics used for describing the trajectory of bullets from a machine gun, does not mean that the world is merely a succession of human metaphors. The statement that the wave length of the D-lines in the sodium spectrum is ·00005893 ± ·00000003 centimetre is just as true as it was before. All that has happened is that you may now prefer to call it the "interference limit," "path difference" or some other name which smells as sweet. Much of what is called popular science consists of scaffoldings of metaphor like this, and conveys the impression that when the scaffolding is removed the building is about to collapse. The truth is that the scaffolding is removed because the building has grown too big and strong for it.

Unhappily scientific men themselves do not always distinguish between two ways in which they use the word *law*, when they talk of laws of nature, and it is applied indiscriminately to both of them in most current textbooks of science. One is for *observed regularities of nature* as a basis for correct social conduct, such as navigating a ship into port on time, getting the maximum yield of ripe apples with a high vitamin C content before the first autumn frosts, or producing structural materials by the use of bone or clay with the minimum of human effort. If you do not know what these observed regularities are a book about science can tell you. Good popular science gives you information of this kind. The second way in which scientists use the word law is very difficult to convey without help of an actual example. When we say that *action and reaction are equal and opposite* is a scientific "law," we convey no information about newly observed regularities of nature or guidance for the correct conduct of anybody except a mathematician. What we really do is to state briefly in general terms the kind of symbolic conventions we intend to adopt in applying the kind of mathematics we intend to use when making measurements upon the sort of situation about which we are speaking. If we must use the word law for statements of this class, we should call them bye-laws, implying our right to repeal them.

We shall never make the world outlook of science an open Bible until we remove this source of confusion, and we can only do so by democratizing mathematics. Most observing teachers must have recognized a difficulty which many school children or first-year students experience when they begin mechanics. One of their first exercises in applying Galilean principles is the problem of the inclined plane. They are then expected to take kindly to a statement like the following, taken from a textbook in general use:

"The resolved part of the weight perpendicular to the inclined plane is balanced by the reaction of the plane, since the body has no acceleration perpendicular to the plane."

Few of them, in fact, do take kindly to it. The beginner's reaction is that this assertion is plain nonsense. The force normal to the plane has just been put in to make the answer agree with the result of Galileo's experiments.

To take a simpler case of the third "law" of Newton, imagine that I am about to drop on to a chair built to stand my weight. Actually the chair stays where it was, and so do I, when I reach it. In technical language a "state of equilibrium is reached." Since we have agreed to represent force by change of momentum, we can only describe the fact that no visible movement exists by inventing another force to counterbalance it. If you are new to the game, you are fully entitled to raise a very proper objection at this stage. My push is something very tangible. It could have burst a toy balloon, put in the same place as the chair, or splashed water on to the wallpaper, if there had been a bucket instead of a seat in the same place. On the other hand, a strong chair does not change in any obvious way when I drop on it. Its resistance is not something tangible as far as crude observation can reveal, and from that standpoint it is put in to signify the algebraical conventions used in an equation which correctly describes a state of equilibrium in accordance with the results of experiments made on equilibrium states.

It is a mathematical, and extremely useful, trick. None the less, it is a trick for all that. Our first reaction is to believe that we have a grievance, because we have been tricked. In a sense we have one. Our real grievance is not that we have been tricked, but that no one explained the difference between rules of grammar and laws of nature. The result is that one of two things happens. Some of us decide we are stupid and acquire a distaste which makes the subject unnecessarily difficult. Others (the bright ones) accept what they are told with becoming humility, and stop examining the implications of the scientific outlook on the world. Later on they become professors.

We have to make "laws" of discourse to regulate the communication of laws which are made without our help. The latter are the real laws of nature, and they do not change because Einstein is a better mathematician than Newton was. Indeed, when Einstein applied a different sort of mathematics to the mechanical problems for which Newton's system was devised a party of scientists had to trek half-way across the earth to decide whether it really made any difference. The difference it did make may have a big yield in so far as it guides the search for the recognition of new and unsuspected regularities of nature. Up to date, it is not a very big one. Newton's system remains a good enough equipment of calculating tricks for communicating the real laws of Nature revealed by any observations which had been made till long after his death. Probably we shall continue to use it for most purposes, as we use the law of Boyle and Charles, because for most purposes it will be good enough.

Einstein's robust common sense has not prevented his disciples from erecting his teaching into a new system of theological apologetics. The followers of Mach, who anticipated some of Einstein's criticisms of Newton's mechanics, had already anticipated their exploits. The sequel was a comic controversy about whether science is a true picture of the world. Science is not a picture of anything. It is an ordnance map to direct our efforts in changing the world. The world view of science is not a by-product of human cerebration. The mountains and the valleys remain, when we use a new colour scale to paint in the altitudes. The ether does not remain. It is the ink used in the nineteenth-century edition of the map. Both parties were right, and both were wrong. One argued as if mathematical symbols were eternal, and the other, as if regularities of nature did not exist before Pithecanthropus became extinct. Controversies of this sort will continue, until we make the language of science part of the language of mankind, and realize that the future of the human reason lies with those who are prepared to face the task of rationally planning the instruments of communication. Many people talk as if we had reached the limit of the educability of mankind. In Bacon's words, they prefer to extol the powers of their own minds instead of seeking "the true helps" by which intelligent citizenship can be encouraged. If we ask what true helps exist we need not look far afield for new materials. When the educational powers of the cinema have been adopted to visualizing the use of mathematical symbols anything which can be achieved by books and blackboards will seem trivial by comparison.

Appendices

APPENDIX 1

SINE FORMULA FOR SPHERICAL TRIANGLES (p. 380)

We can adapt Fig. 124 to demonstrate the sine formula directly as follows. As we unfold the model in Fig. 123 the moving point A_1 revolves about the line OQ describing a circular arc in a plane at right angles to this line OQ and to the plane OQP till it comes to the position A.

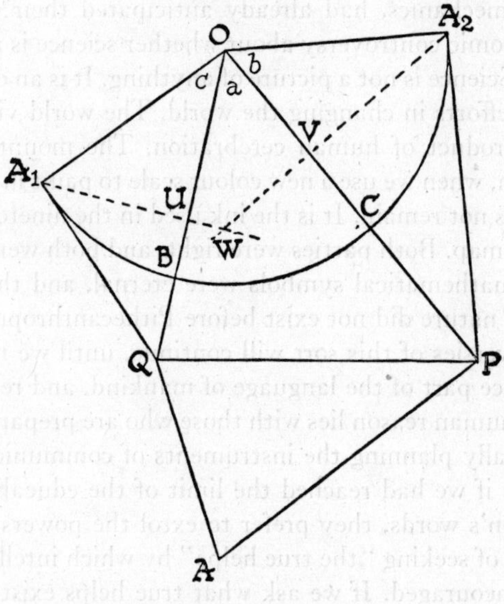

Similarly it describes a circular arc about the line OP till it comes to the position A_2. So

$$A_1UO = 90° = A_2VO$$

When the figure is folded back into its original position A is directly above a point W in the plane OQP and W is the point where the generating radii A_1U and A_2V meet. From the first figure we see that:

$$\text{(i)} \qquad \frac{A_1U}{A_1O} = \sin c; \text{ and } \frac{A_2V}{A_2O} = \sin b.$$

$$\therefore \quad A_1U = AO \sin c; \text{ and } A_2V = AO \sin b.$$

The angle AUW is the angle between the planes which include the arcs AB and BC respectively. Hence AUW is equivalent to $\angle B$ of the spherical triangle. From the second figure we see that:

$$\text{(ii)} \qquad \frac{AW}{A_1U} = \sin B; \text{ and similarly } \frac{AW}{A_2V} = \sin C.$$

$$\therefore AW = A_1U \sin B; \text{ and } AW = A_2V \sin C.$$

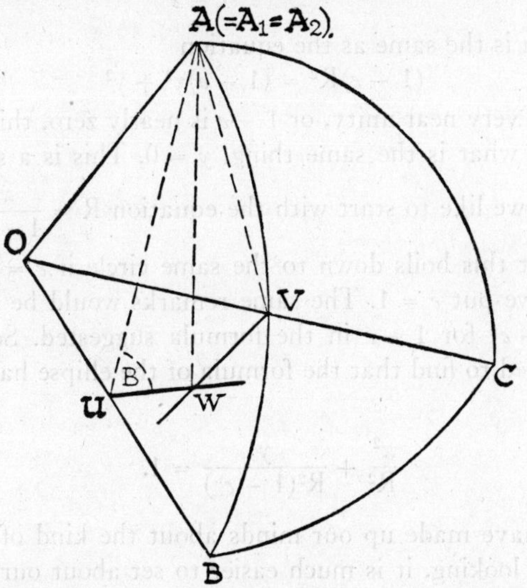

Combining (i) and (ii)

$$AO \sin c \sin B = AW = AO \sin b \sin C.$$

$$\therefore \frac{\sin c}{\sin C} = \frac{\sin b}{\sin B}$$

In the same way each is equal to $\sin a/\sin A$.

APPENDIX 2

THE EQUATION OF THE ELLIPSE (p. 427)

When he is faced with a problem like this the mathematical detective has two kinds of clue to help him. He asks himself whether the figure for which he wants a formula is like any figure for which he already has one, and then recalls how someone else got the latter. The ellipse is related to two figures for which we hold the formulae. If its eccentricity is indefinitely near unity, it becomes a straight line. If its eccentricity is indefinitely small it becomes a circle. So the formula for which we are looking must boil down to the formula of the line or circle according as we make one quantity in it indefinitely near unity or zero. We can therefore say in advance what *sort* of formula it will be. If we make e very small, the equation of the circle is the same as

$$R^2 = x^2 + \frac{y^2}{1 - e}$$

This equation is the same as the equation

$$(1 - e)R^2 = (1 - e)x^2 + y^2$$

and when e is very near unity, or $1 - e$ is nearly zero, this boils down to $y^2 = 0$, or, what is the same thing, $y = 0$. This is a straight line, the x-axis. If we like to start with the equation $R = \frac{x^2}{1 - e} + y^2$, we shall find that this boils down to the same circle if $e = 0$, but gives the y-axis if we put $e = 1$. The same remarks would be equally true if we put $1 - e^n$ for $1 - e$ in the formula suggested. So we should not be surprised to find that the formula of the ellipse had some such form as

$$\frac{x^2}{R^2} + \frac{y^2}{R^2(1 - e^n)} = 1.$$

When we have made up our minds about the kind of formula for which we are looking, it is much easier to set about our job. This is a very important thing to realise. At school we are often warned against the wickedness of cooking a result. Cooking a result is really the way in which higher mathematics is often carried on. What we now have to do is to recall anything we know about getting a formula of this sort. The clue has been given to us by the circle. So we proceed to try out where we get by using Pythagoras' theorem. Remember, of course, that an ellipse has two separate foci in place of the single fused focus of the circle. Remember too that we want to get e into the result along with some quantity like R in the equation of the circle.

APPENDIX 3

BINOMIAL DEMONSTRATION OF THE EXPONENTIAL PROPERTY (p. 487)

There is another way of demonstrating the rule that

$$e^x = 1 + x + \frac{x^2}{2!} + \frac{x^3}{3!} + \ldots$$

It is suggested originally by a study of compound interest tables. From such tables let us make a list of the amounts to which £1 has grown after nx years at a rate of interest $\frac{100}{n}$%. Here are a few values for $x = 1$.

Number of Years, n	Rate of Interest	Amount to which Capital has grown
20	5 %	£2·653
25	4	2·666
40	$2\frac{1}{2}$	2·685
50	2	2·692
100	1	2·705

We notice that the amounts in the last column are nearly equal, and that they are bigger for larger values of n. What happens if n is made indefinitely large? That is, what is the value of $\left(1 + \frac{1}{n}\right)^n$ when n is made indefinitely large? The answer is $e = 2{\cdot}718$, and we write this answer mathematically in the form

$$\underset{n \to \infty}{\text{Limit}} \left(1 + \frac{1}{n}\right)^n = e.$$

Try this out for other values of x; if you take $x = 1/2$ you will find the capital has grown to about £$e^{\frac{1}{2}}$ after $\frac{1}{2}n$ years at $\frac{100}{n}$%.

We are thus tempted to examine the value of $\left(1 + \frac{1}{n}\right)^{nx}$ when n becomes indefinitely large, or $\frac{1}{n}$ becomes indefinitely small. As a final step we shall put $\frac{1}{n} = 0$.

Using the binomial series

$$\left(1 + \frac{1}{n}\right)^{nx} = 1 + nx\cdot\left(\frac{1}{n}\right) + \frac{nx(nx-1)}{2}\cdot\left(\frac{1}{n^2}\right) + \frac{nx(nx-1)(nx-2)}{2.3}\cdot\left(\frac{1}{n^3}\right) + \ldots$$

$$= 1 + x + \frac{1}{2!}x\left(x - \frac{1}{n}\right) + \frac{1}{3!}x\left(x - \frac{1}{n}\right)\left(x - \frac{2}{n}\right) + \ \ldots$$

So if $x = 1$, we see that

$$\left(1 + \frac{1}{n}\right)^n = 1 + 1 + \frac{1}{2!}1\left(1 - \frac{1}{n}\right) + \frac{1}{3!}1\left(1 - \frac{1}{n}\right)\left(1 - \frac{2}{n}\right) + \ \ldots$$

But we can write $\left(1+\frac{1}{n}\right)^{nx} = \left\{\left(1+\frac{1}{n}\right)^{n}\right\}^{x}$, so that

$$\left[1+x+\frac{1}{2!}x\left(x-\frac{1}{n}\right)+\frac{1}{3!}x\left(x-\frac{1}{n}\right)\left(x-\frac{2}{n}\right)+\ .\ .\ .\right]$$

$$=\left[1+1+\frac{1}{2!}1\left(1-\frac{1}{n}\right)+\frac{1}{3!}1\left(1-\frac{1}{n}\right)\left(1-\frac{2}{n}\right)+\ .\ .\ .\right]^{x}$$

Now put $\frac{1}{n} = 0$, and we find

$$1+x+\frac{x^2}{2!}+\frac{x^3}{3!}+\ .\ .\ .\ =\left[1+1+\frac{1}{2!}+\frac{1}{3!}+\ .\ .\ .\right]^{x} = e^x$$

APPENDIX 4

TO SHOW THAT IF n IS VERY LARGE

$y = {}^nC_m p^m q^{n-m}$ LEADS TO $y = Ae^{-bx^2}$ (p. 607)

If we toss a penny n times, we get a distribution represented by rectangles as in Fig. 196, giving the chance of having 0, 1, 2, .., n heads. Now suppose each head counts a small amount $-\frac{1}{2}c$ and each tail $+\frac{1}{2}c$; so that the rectangle of height ${}^nC_m p^m q^{n-m} = {}^nC_m(\frac{1}{2})^n$, which is the chance of getting exactly m heads, corresponds to an amount, or "error"

$$x = -\tfrac{1}{2}c\,.\,m + \tfrac{1}{2}c\,.\,(n-m) = \tfrac{1}{2}c(n-2m)$$

In the same way the rectangle of height ${}^nC_{m-1}(\frac{1}{2})^n$ corresponds to an error

$$x = -\tfrac{1}{2}c(m-1) + \tfrac{1}{2}c(n-m+1) = \tfrac{1}{2}c(n-2m) + c$$

But we are making the rectangles narrow, of width c (small), so we must increase their heights to make sure that the total area of all the rectangles is still 1, corresponding to certainty—the error is certain to have some value, which may, of course, be zero. Suppose each is multiplied by k in height.

Then the height y, which depends on x, is such that when

$$x = x_0 = \tfrac{1}{2}c(n-2m), \qquad y = y_0 = \frac{k}{2^n}{}^nC_m$$

and when

$$x = x_1 = \tfrac{1}{2}c(n-2m)+c,\ y = y_1 = \frac{k}{2^n}{}^nC_{m-1} = \frac{k}{2^n}{}^nC_m\,\frac{m}{n-m+1}$$

so that $\dfrac{\Delta y}{\Delta x} = \dfrac{y_1 - y_0}{x_1 - x_0} = \dfrac{k}{2^n}\,{}^nC_m\left(\dfrac{m}{n-m+1} - 1\right) \div c$

Now if we take c small and n large, this can be taken to be the value of $\dfrac{dy}{dx}$ at the point half way between (x_0, y_0) and (x_1, y_1). At this point

$$x = \tfrac{1}{2}(x_0 + x_1) = \tfrac{1}{2}c(n - 2m + 1)$$

$$y = \tfrac{1}{2}\frac{k}{2^n}{}^nC_m\left(\frac{m}{n-m+1} + 1\right) = \tfrac{1}{2}\frac{k}{2^n}{}^nC_m\frac{n+1}{n-m+1}$$

so

$$\frac{dy}{dx} = \frac{k}{2^n}{}^nC_m\frac{2m-n-1}{n-m+1} \div c$$

$$= \frac{k}{2^n}{}^nC_m\frac{n+1}{n-m+1}\cdot\frac{-\tfrac{1}{2}c(n-2m+1).2}{(n+1)c^2}$$

$$= 2y\frac{-2x}{(n+1)c^2}$$

Now we can make c small and $n + 1$ large in such a way that $\tfrac{1}{2}(n+1)c^2$ is constant, say $1/b$. For example, if $b = 20$; take $c = \tfrac{1}{100}$, and $n = 999$, or take $c = 10^{-6}$, and $n + 1 = 10^{11}$ and so on. Then

$$\frac{dy}{dx} = y(-2bx)$$

or

$$\frac{1}{y}\frac{dy}{dx} = -2bx$$

or

$$\log_e y = -bx^2 + D$$

or

$$y = Ae^{-bx^2} \quad \text{if} \quad A = e^D$$

APPENDIX 5

ON POSITION FINDING BY MEANS OF SUB-CELESTIAL POINTS

In these times many readers will be more interested in the technique of position finding in air than at sea or on land. The ensuing notes are for those who have grasped the principles of navigation and cartography set forth in Chapter VIII; and would like to understand the underlying principles involved in their application to the peculiar difficulties of navigating at a speed which precludes protracted computations or delayed observation. By means of the spherical triangle formulae on pp. 378–379, we can get our latitude and longitude *on land* from simultaneous measurements (p. 58) of the altitude and azimuth of a single celestial body at any moment referable to Greenwich time. For various reasons, it is not practicable to determine the azimuth of a celestial body accurately in a ship or other vehicle. As far as possible, the ship's navigator therefore makes use of meridian

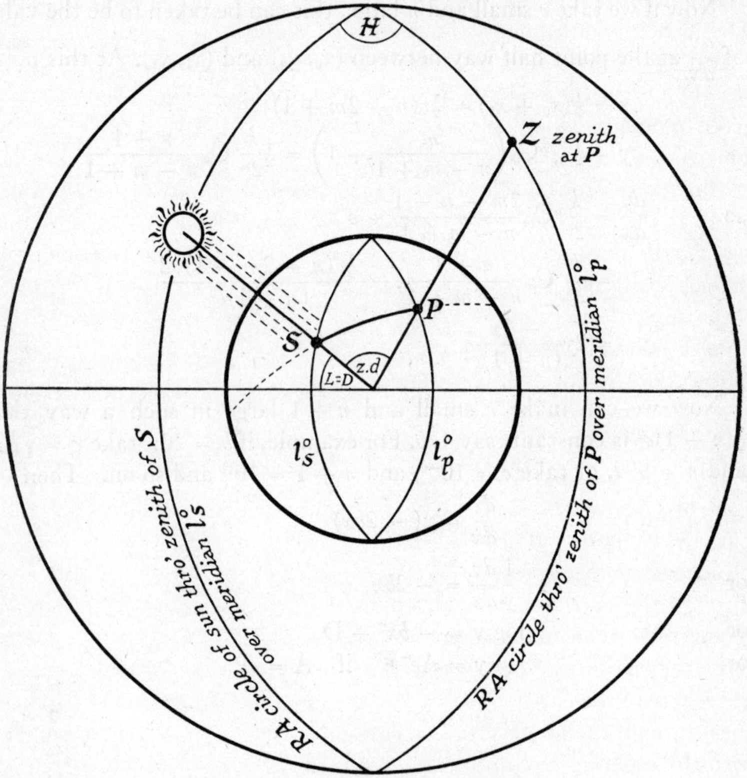

FIG. 1.—THE SUBSOLAR POINT

The sun's R.A. circle is directly over the meridian of longitude l_s on which the *subsolar point* lies at latitude L = D (sun's declination). P is the position of a ship on another meridian l_p. The hour angle H between P and S is the angular difference between the sun's R.A. circle and the R.A. circle passing through the zenith (Z) of P, and is therefore also the difference of longitude between P and S. The line joining S to the earth's centre gives the direction of the sun's rays, since the sun is at the zenith above S, and the inclination of the sunbeams to the line through P, its zenith (Z) and the earth's centre is the z.d. of the sun at P. This is therefore the angular measure of the arc of the great circle passing through P and S.

altitudes (pp. 356–361). At night the officer can use any star not concealed by clouds at the time when it crosses the meridian, but we can rely on only one celestial body—the sun—during the daytime. If clouds conceal the sun at local noon, the usual method of observing the value of the sun's maximum altitude and the Greenwich time at which it is at its highest point in the heavens fails us. To get his latitude and longitude the mariner has to fall back on Sumner's method. The principle of Sumner's method is as follows:

Any star of declination D is a zenith star of any place at latitude L = D. On the latitude circle L there is therefore some spot at any given moment, where a star of declination D = L is at the zenith. This spot whose latitude is L is called the *substellar* point of the star at this moment; and it lies on the meridian of longitude in the same plane as the star's R.A. circle at that moment. What is true of a star is also true of any celestial body, e.g. the sun. At any given moment there is a subsolar point where the sun is directly overhead. Its latitude is the sun's declination and since the sun is on the meridian its local time is noon. If the chronometer gives Greenwich time as x hours (after noon) its local time is x hours behind, and its longitude is $15x°$ west of, Greenwich (p. 358). Let us suppose that Greenwich time is 10 a.m., and that our nautical almanack gives the sun's declination as + 18°. The subsolar point is then $(15 \times 22)° = 330°$ West, i.e. 30° East of Greenwich. Hence the subsolar point at that moment is at Lat. 18° N. Long. 30° E.

Since the line which joins the zenith to the observer also goes through the earth's centre (p. 166), the subsolar point has a simple geometrical relation to our postion on the earth's surface. The sun's rays lie in the direction of the line joining the subsolar point to the centre of the earth, and the angle between this line and that which goes through the observer and the earth's centre is the angle it makes with the observer's plumbline, i.e. the local zenith distance of the sun (Fig. 1). In other words, the sun's z.d. = $Z_1°$ is the angular distance between the observer and the *subsolar point.* One degree at the earth's centre subtends an arc of approximately 69 *land* miles (p. 376) along any great circle. In what follows we shall take this value as correct for illustrative purposes. We can therefore say that the observer's position is 69 Z_1 land miles by great circle sailing from the subsolar point. Any point on a circle of radius 69 Z_1 miles with the subsolar point as centre fulfils this condition. From one observation of the sun's z.d. all we can therefore tell is that we are somewhere on a particular circle which we can trace out on the globe.

Having traced out this circle 69 Z_1 miles by great circle sailing from a point 18° N. 30° E., we can take a second reading when the sun's z.d. is $Z_2°$. Let us suppose that the chronometer then gives Greenwich time as 4 p.m. and tables give the sun's declination as 18.05°. Our position is somewhere on a circle whose radius is a great circle arc of Z_2° with its centre at the subsolar point, now 18.05 N. 60 W. If we trace this second circle on the globe it must cut the first one at two points; and if we have kept at the same position during the time between the two observations, our position must be somewhere on both

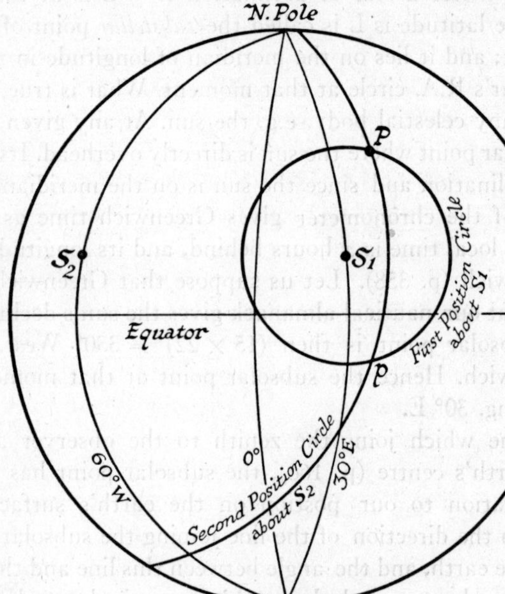

FIG. 2.—POSITION FINDING FROM TWO SUBSOLAR POINTS

S_1 and S_2 are successive subsolar points at times t_1 and t_2 respectively. The radii of the two position circles Z_1 and Z_2 being respectively the sun's z.d. at time t_1 and t_2 at the ship's position. The ship is somewhere on both these circles and must therefore be either at P or *p*. If we have a rough idea from knowledge of the ship's course, we know that it cannot be at one of them (say *p*) and must therefore be at the other. Anyway, a rough estimate of the sun's azimuth at P settles the question.

of these circles. Therefore it must be at one of these two points (Fig. 2). We could decide in favour of the correct one by a *rough* estimate of the sun's azimuth at any one reading which gives us an estimate of our latitude and longitude; but this is rarely necessary. We know which to choose from what we know about the ship's course by dead reckoning, since the last previous fix on a previous day with propitious weather.

In real life a ship does not stick to the same spot P between successive observations at times t_1 and t_2. It moves from P_1 where the sun's z.d. is Z_1 to P_2 where the sun's z.d. is Z_2; but it is a simple matter to reconstruct what would have happened if the ship had kept its station at either its initial or its final position. All we need is a correction for its z.d. at t_1 on the assumption that the ship was then at P_2. On that assumption its z.d. would have been the z.d. of all places on a great circle with its centre at the subsolar point and with P_2 somewhere on its circumference. Now the arc of a great circle joining the subsolar point to P_1 is the meridian bearing of the subsolar point with reference to P_1, and this is also the sun's azimuth at P_1 when the time is t_1. If P_2 is y miles beyond P_1 on the same arc $(y \div 69)°$ is the required correction; and y is the number of miles through which the ship has to sail to get from P_1 to P_2 if its track coincides with the meridian bearing of the subsolar point at time t_1. If the ship's course sticks to this great circle we can therefore put in the circle which connects all points where the sun's z.d. would have been the same as at P_2 at time t_1. Since P_2 is on this circle and also on the position circle of radius Z_2 from the substellar point at t_2, our final position P_2 is one of the points of intersection of the two circles. Now we know how far it is from P_1 to P_2 by dead reckoning, if we know the ship's speed. If we also know its direction by compass bearing, we know the inclination of its track to the bearing of the subsolar point at P_1 at time t_1; and if it has moved m miles at an inclination of $a°$, $y = m \cdot \cos \cdot a$.

We might use a star in exactly the same way. If we know the R.A. of a star we know (p. 359) how many hours elapse between its transit and local noon at any given spot. Thus we can find (pp. 356 and 359) the latitude and longitude of the substellar point of any star at a particular moment of Greenwich time, as given by the chronometer. On a ship there is little to gain from tracing two position circles based on successive z.d. measurements of a single star. If there are not too many clouds to prevent two such observations, there will not be too many clouds to prevent a single determination of the transit of one of the many easily recognisable stars which are south in the hours of darkness. Still, we can—if need arises—adapt the principle of Sumner's method to take advantage of a short period of cloudlessness in a night otherwise overcast.

This adaptation is the basis of position finding on a night flight, when no beam control is available. A ship does not move very far during the intervals between occasions when some recognisable star is in transit; but an aeroplane can do so. Consequently, it is advantageous for the air pilot to have a means of location which does not involve waiting for the transit of some star which he can recognise for reference in tables of declination and R.A. If we take simultaneous observations of the z.d. of *two* stars we can trace a position circle around the substellar point of each, and we can choose the two stars to give circles whose points of intersection are a thousand or more miles apart. We have therefore no doubt about which of the two points of intersection of the two position circles is the one which specifies the observers's position.

To trace out a position circle of $x°$ radius from a subsolar or substellar point on the globe, it is merely necessary to lay off a circle with the same radius as a parallel of latitude $(90 - x)°$. We can do this roughly by means of a pin, a thread and a pencil, or with compass constructed to draw circles on a spherical surface; but to get our position correct within a mile, we should need a very large globe, much too large for a ship and *a fortiori* much too large for a plane. To determine the appropriate point of intersection of two position circles in real life, the sea or sky pilot has to work with a chart. In the neighbourhood of the dead reckoning position on a large-scale chart, the arc of an actual position circle about a given sub-celestial point does not appreciably differ from its own tangent, i.e. from a *straight* line. All position circles about a given point on the globe are concentric, and if the angular radius of the position circle is large, i.e. if the z.d. of the star is over 15°, all corresponding arcs on a large-scale chart appear to be *parallel straight lines*.

Since the radius of the position circle around the sub-celestial point is also the z.d. of the celestial body at the same moment, a difference of 1° between the radii of two position circles corresponds to a z.d. difference of 1° between places situated on one or the other. This means that places on parallel position lines drawn 69 land miles apart on our chart are places where the z.d. difference is 1°. Conversely, if the difference between the z.d. of a star in two places on our chart is $x°$, the two places lie on two parallel lines 69 x miles apart. If we know the bearing of *one* of them, we can therefore draw the other with the *same* bearing at the appropriate distance from it. To draw our actual position line with as little delay as possible, we therefore need a *reference* line joining places of the same *known* z.d. at the moment when we determine the actual z.d. of the star. Thus our problem is how to put on the chart such a reference line—or rather two such reference lines, one for each of the two stars we use to get the point of intersection of two actual position lines.

On the surface of the globe an arc joining a reference point of known z.d. to the substellar point cuts the meridian on which the reference point itself lies at an angle which is the azimuth, or meridian bearing, of the substellar point with reference to the observer's position. On our large-scale chart the arc is a straight line which cuts the meridian on which the reference point lies at the same angle. This line represents the radius of the position circle through the reference point. The position line being tangent to the position circle at this point, is at right angles to it. We can therefore draw our reference line if we have two data: (1) the location of *any* point of known z.d. at the moment when we make our observation of the actual z.d. of the appropriate star; (2) the meridian bearing or azimuth of the substellar point at the same place.

Suppose we chose *any* point of *specified* latitude and longitude near our dead reckoning position at a given moment when we propose to find the actual z.d. of a star. Such a point is one apex of a spherical triangle (Fig. 3) of which two sides are its co-latitude and the co-declination of the star chosen. The included polar angle is the hour angle or difference of longitude between the substellar point and the reference point. We can therefore solve for the remaining side and remaining angles by use of the spherical triangle solution formulae on pp. 374 and 380; or by recourse to tables based on them. Now the third side which joins the reference point to the substellar point (Fig. 1) is the z.d. of the star at the reference point at the moment specified, and the angle between this side and the side which joins the reference point to the pole along the meridian of the latter is the azimuth, i.e. meridian bearing, of the substellar point, and of the star itself, at the reference point. For any point of *assumed* latitude and longitude near our dead reckoning position at any *assumed* time we can therefore specify the z.d. of a star and its meridian bearing. To do so, we merely reverse the procedure for getting latitude and longitude from direct observation of the azimuth of a star, its z.d. and standard time.

For instance, we may reckon that we are going to be somewhere near $54\frac{1}{3}^{\circ}$ N. $10^{\circ}\frac{1}{4}$ E. at 8.45 p.m. chronometer time, ten minutes later, when we propose to check up our position accurately by making simultaneous sextant measurements of the z.d. of Aldebaran and z.d. of Altair. To do this we can lay off position lines for the substellar points of these two stars at 8.45 p.m. chronometer time passing through a point 54° N. and 10° E. To get these lines we merely need the meridian bearing of their substellar points at 54° N. and 10° E. and 8.45 p.m. chronometer time. Having got the two angles from the solution of the corresponding triangles we put the bearings on the chart and draw the position lines at right angles to them. Our solution also gives us the z.d. of the two stars on the position line at the moment of observation and our observations (at 8.45 p.m.) show us by how much (x_1 and x_2) the z.d. of each star at our actual position

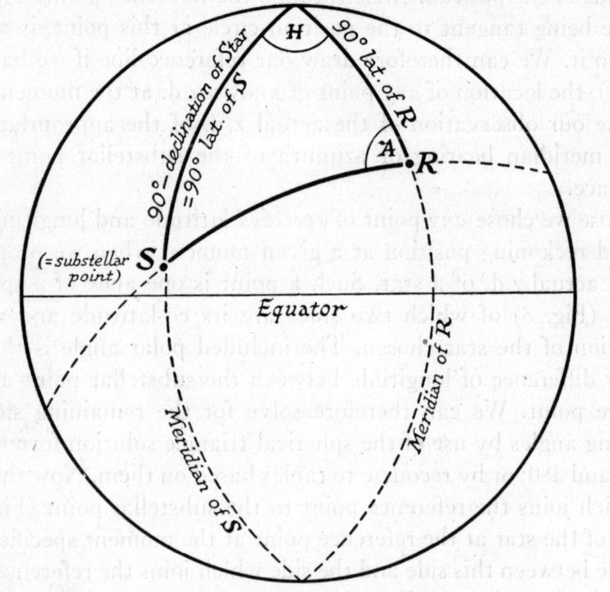

FIG. 3.—SPHERICAL TRIANGLE OF REFERENCE POINT (R) OF KNOWN LATITUDE AND LONGITUDE

A = azimuth of subsolar point (S) with reference to R.
H = hour angle of S with reference to R (= difference of longitude between R and S).

differs from the z.d. of the corresponding stars at our reference point or "assumed position." All that remains is to lay off lines parallel to our two reference lines 69 x_1 and 69 x_2 miles apart from them, and to read off the latitude and longitude of the point at which they intersect. This is our real position.

To plot our actual position line correctly we have to take a more accurate value than 69 miles for the length of a circular arc which subtends 1° at the earth's centre. Needless to say, our chronometer reading gives us Greenwich *mean* time, and we have to use Greenwich *local* time to get the hour angle of the celestial body at our assumed position at the appropriate moment. We do this as explained in *Science for the Citizen* (p. 63) by reference to tables of the "equation of time." To take advantage of tabulated solutions of spherical triangles, when making necessary computations for laying off reference lines we have to choose the latitude of our assumed position as a *whole* number of degrees and a longitude so as to make integral the hour angle of the substellar point w.r.t. the reference point.

To simplify the preceding explanation, we have considered our two observations on the z.d. of the two stars as simultaneous. In practice, accuracy demands the mean of several values of each. The interval between completing the two sets is of no significance, if the vehicle is a ship; and two officers can co-operate on a large ship to make truly simultaneous observations, if the need for such arises. For air transport, the interval is sufficient to permit a displacement of say 15 miles. So the air pilot's problem at night is on all fours with the mariner's problem by day. To get the required point of intersection he does not use his actual position line at t_1. He shifts the first position line in the direction of the plane's flight. The amount depends on the inclination a of the plane's course to the meridian bearing of the substellar point of the first star. If s is the ground speed, the distance traversed in the plane's track during the interval is $s \cdot (t_1 - t_2) = m$ miles, and the required shift is $m \cdot \cos a^\circ$ along the meridian bearing.

Tables

NOTES ON USING THE TABLES

I. In Table I are given some of the more useful relations connecting weights and measures. In the metric system the units of length, weight, and capacity are the metre, gramme, and litre. Each of these is subdivided in the same way. A hundredth part has the prefix centi-, a thousandth part has the prefix milli-, and a thousand times has the prefix kilo-.

III. The use of the difference column has already been explained. Values between those shown in the difference column can be found by proportional parts. For example, we may want the square of 28·756. The table gives the square of 28·75 as 826·5. In this part of the difference column a difference of 1 in the number to be squared corresponds to a difference of 7 in the square. Therefore a difference of 0·6 will correspond approximately to a difference of $7 \times 0{\cdot}6$, i.e., about 4. The square required is thus 826·9. Table III can also be used to find square roots. For example, we may want to find the square root of 123·2. By inspection we can see that the square root of this number lies between 11 and 12. In the tables we see that 1232 occurs twice, first corresponding to the digits 111, and then corresponding to the digits 351. The square root of 123·2 is thus 11·1. If we had wanted the square root of 12·32 it would clearly have been 3·51.

IV. In most tables of sines, etc., the parts of a degree are given in minutes, so that the steps are 6′, 12′, etc. The custom of expressing the steps as decimal fractions of a degree is, however, gradually being introduced.

The table of sines can also be used to find cosines by using the formula $\cos A = \sin (90° - A)$, e.g. to find cos 31·5°, look up sin 58·5°.

VI. A table of antilogarithms has been omitted for reasons of economy. Table VI can be used for finding numbers from their logarithms by simply reversing the process of finding the logarithm of a number. For directions for using the table see p. 506 and the note on Table III.

I

ENGLISH WEIGHTS AND MEASURES

1,760 yards	= 1 mile
4,840 square yards	= 1 acre
640 acres	= 1 square mile
112 lbs.	= 1 cwt.
20 cwts.	= 1 ton
8 pints	= 1 gallon
1 gallon	= 277 cubic inches
1 cubic foot	= 6·23 gallons

METRIC WEIGHTS AND MEASURES

10 millimetres	= 1 centimetre
100 centimetres	= 1 metre
1,000 metres	= 1 kilometre
1,000 grammes	= 1 kilogramme
100 centilitres	= 1 litre
1 litre	= 1,000 cubic centimetres

METRIC AND ENGLISH EQUIVALENTS

1 inch	= 2·54 centimetres
1 lb.	= 454 grammes
1 metre	= 1·09 yards
1 kilometre	= 0·621 mile
1 kilogramme	= 2·20 pounds
1 litre	= 0·22 gallon

II

CONSTANTS

$\pi = 3 \cdot 1416$ $\log_{10} \pi = 0 \cdot 4971$

1 radian = 57·296 degrees

$e = 2 \cdot 7183$ $\log_{10} e = 0 \cdot 4343$

$\log_e N = 2 \cdot 3026 \log_{10} N$

$\log_{10} N = 0 \cdot 4343 \log_e N$

Earth's mean radius = 3,960 miles = $6 \cdot 371 \times 10^8$ centimetres

$g = 32 \cdot 2$ feet per second per second, or 981 centimetres per second per second.

1 cubic centimetre of water at 4° C. weighs 1 gramme.

III

SQUARES

	0	1	2	3	4	5	6	7	8	9	1	2	3	4	5	6	7	8	9
10	1000	1020	1040	1061	1082	1103	1124	1145	1166	1188	2	4	6	8	10	13	15	17	19
11	1210	1232	1254	1277	1300	1323	1346	1369	1392	1416	2	5	7	9	11	14	16	18	21
12	1440	1464	1488	1513	1538	1563	1588	1613	1638	1664	2	5	7	10	12	15	17	20	22
13	1690	1716	1742	1769	1796	1823	1850	1877	1904	1932	3	5	8	11	13	16	19	22	24
14	1960	1988	2016	2045	2074	2103	2132	2161	2190	2220	3	6	9	12	14	1.	20	23	26
15	2250	2280	2310	2341	2372	2403	2434	2465	2496	2528	3	6	9	12	15	19	22	25	28
16	2560	2592	2624	2657	2690	2723	2756	2789	2822	2856	3	7	10	13	16	20	23	26	30
17	2890	2924	2958	2993	3028	3063	3098	3133	3168	3204	3	7	10	14	17	21	24	28	31
18	3240	3276	3312	3349	3386	3423	3460	3497	3534	3572	4	7	11	15	18	22	26	30	33
19	3610	3648	3686	3725	3764	3803	3842	3881	3920	3960	4	8	12	16	19	23	27	31	35
20	4000	4040	4080	4121	4162	4203	4244	4285	4326	4368	4	8	12	16	20	25	29	33	37
21	4410	4452	4494	4537	4580	4623	4666	4709	4752	4796	4	9	13	17	21	26	30	34	39
22	4840	4884	4928	4973	5018	5063	5108	5153	5198	5244	4	9	13	18	22	27	31	36	40
23	5290	5336	5382	5429	5476	5523	5570	5617	5664	5712	5	9	14	19	23	28	33	38	42
24	5760	5808	5856	5905	5954	6003	6052	6101	6150	6200	5	10	15	20	24	29	34	39	44
25	6250	6300	6350	6401	6452	6503	6554	6605	6656	6708	5	10	15	20	25	31	36	41	46
26	6760	6812	6864	6917	6970	7023	7076	7129	7182	7236	5	11	16	21	26	32	37	42	48
27	7290	7344	7398	7453	7508	7563	7618	7673	7728	7784	5	11	16	22	27	33	38	44	49
28	7840	7896	7952	8009	8066	8123	8180	8237	8294	8352	6	11	17	23	28	34	40	46	51
29	8410	8468	8526	8585	8644	8703	8762	8821	8880	8940	6	12	18	24	29	35	41	47	53
30	9000	9060	9120	9181	9242	9303	9364	9425	9486	9548	6	12	18	24	30	37	43	49	55
31	9610	9672	9734	9797	9860	9923	9986				6	13	19	25	31	38	44	50	57
31								1005	1011	1018	1	1	2	3	3	4	5	5	6
32	1024	1030	1037	1043	1050	1056	1063	1069	1076	1082	1	1	2	3	3	4	5	5	6
33	1089	1096	1102	1109	1116	1122	1129	1136	1142	1149	1	1	2	3	3	4	5	5	6
34	1156	1163	1170	1176	1183	1190	1197	1204	1211	1218	1	1	2	3	3	4	5	6	6
35	1225	1232	1239	1246	1253	1260	1267	1274	1282	1289	1	1	2	3	4	4	5	6	6
36	1296	1303	1310	1318	1325	1332	1340	1347	1354	1362	1	1	2	3	4	4	5	6	7
37	1369	1376	1384	1391	1399	1406	1414	1421	1429	1436	1	2	2	3	4	5	5	6	7
38	1444	1452	1459	1467	1475	1482	1490	1498	1505	1513	1	2	2	3	4	5	5	6	7
39	1521	1529	1537	1544	1552	1560	1568	1576	1584	1592	1	2	2	3	4	5	6	6	7
40	1600	1608	1616	1624	1632	1640	1648	1656	1665	1673	1	2	2	3	4	5	6	6	7
41	1681	1689	1697	1706	1714	1722	1731	1739	1747	1756	1	2	2	3	4	5	6	7	7
42	1764	1772	1781	1789	1798	1806	1815	1823	1832	1840	1	2	3	3	4	5	6	7	8
43	1849	1858	1866	1875	1884	1892	1901	1910	1918	1927	1	2	3	3	4	5	6	7	8
44	1936	1945	1954	1962	1971	1980	1989	1998	2007	2016	1	2	3	4	4	5	6	7	8
45	2025	2034	2043	2052	2061	2070	2079	2088	2098	2107	1	2	3	4	5	5	6	7	8
46	2116	2125	2134	2144	2153	2162	2172	2181	2190	2200	1	2	3	4	5	6	7	7	8
47	2209	2218	2228	2237	2247	2256	2266	2275	2285	2294	1	2	3	4	5	6	7	8	9
48	2304	2314	2323	2333	2343	2352	2362	2372	2381	2391	1	2	3	4	5	6	7	8	9
49	2401	2411	2421	2430	2440	2450	2460	2470	2480	2490	1	2	3	4	5	6	7	8	9
50	2500	2510	2520	2530	2540	2550	2560	2570	2581	2591	1	2	3	4	5	6	7	8	9
51	2601	2611	2621	2632	2642	2652	2663	2673	2683	2694	1	2	3	4	5	6	7	8	9
52	2704	2714	2725	2735	2746	2756	2767	2777	2788	2798	1	2	3	4	5	6	7	8	9
53	2809	2820	2830	2841	2852	2862	2873	2884	2894	2905	1	2	3	4	5	6	7	9	10
54	2916	2927	2938	2948	2959	2970	2981	2992	3003	3014	1	2	3	4	5	7	8	9	10

Find the position of the decimal point by inspection.

SQUARES

	0	1	2	3	4	5	6	7	8	9	1	2	3	4	5	6	7	8	9
55	3025	3036	3047	3058	3069	3080	3091	3102	3114	3125	1	2	3	4	6	7	8	9	10
56	3136	3147	3158	3170	3181	3192	3204	3215	3226	3238	1	2	3	5	6	7	8	9	10
57	3249	3260	3272	3283	3295	3306	3318	3329	3341	3352	1	2	3	5	6	7	8	9	10
58	3364	3376	3387	3399	3411	3422	3434	3446	3457	3469	1	2	4	5	6	7	8	9	11
59	3481	3493	3505	3516	3528	3540	3552	3564	3576	3588	1	2	4	5	6	7	8	10	11
60	3600	3612	3624	3636	3648	3660	3672	3684	3697	3709	1	2	4	5	6	7	8	10	11
61	3721	3733	3745	3758	3770	3782	3795	3807	3819	3832	1	2	4	5	6	7	9	10	11
62	3844	3856	3869	3881	3894	3906	3919	3931	3944	3956	1	3	4	5	6	7	9	10	11
63	3969	3982	3994	4007	4020	4032	4045	4058	4070	4083	1	3	4	5	6	8	9	10	11
64	4096	4109	4122	4134	4147	4160	4173	4186	4199	4212	1	3	4	5	6	8	9	10	12
65	4225	4238	4251	4264	4277	4290	4303	4316	4330	4343	1	3	4	5	7	8	9	10	12
66	4356	4369	4382	4396	4409	4422	4436	4449	4462	4476	1	3	4	5	7	8	9	11	12
67	4489	4502	4516	4529	4543	4556	4570	4583	4597	4610	1	3	4	5	7	8	9	11	12
68	4624	4638	4651	4665	4679	4692	4706	4720	4733	4747	1	3	4	5	7	8	10	11	12
69	4761	4775	4789	4802	4816	4830	4844	4858	4872	4886	1	3	4	6	7	8	10	11	13
70	4900	4914	4928	4942	4956	4970	4984	4998	5013	5027	1	3	4	6	7	8	10	11	13
71	5041	5055	5069	5084	5098	5112	5127	5141	5155	5170	1	3	4	6	7	9	10	11	13
72	5184	5198	5213	5227	5242	5256	5271	5285	5300	5314	1	3	4	6	7	9	10	12	13
73	5329	5344	5358	5373	5388	5402	5417	5432	5446	5461	1	3	4	6	7	9	10	12	13
74	5476	5491	5506	5520	5535	5550	5565	5580	5595	5610	1	3	4	6	7	9	10	12	13
75	5625	5640	5655	5670	5685	5700	5715	5730	5746	5761	2	3	5	6	8	9	11	12	14
76	5776	5791	5806	5822	5837	5852	5868	5883	5898	5914	2	3	5	6	8	9	11	12	14
77	5929	5944	5960	5975	5991	6006	6022	6037	6053	6068	2	3	5	6	8	9	11	12	14
78	6084	6100	6115	6131	6147	6162	6178	6194	6209	6225	2	3	5	6	8	9	11	13	14
79	6241	6257	6273	6288	6304	6320	6336	6352	6368	6384	2	3	5	6	8	10	11	13	14
80	6400	6416	6432	6448	6464	6480	6496	6512	6529	6545	2	3	5	6	8	10	11	13	14
81	6561	6577	6593	6610	6626	6642	6659	6675	6691	6708	2	3	5	7	8	10	11	13	15
82	6724	6740	6757	6773	6790	6806	6823	6839	6856	6872	2	3	5	7	8	10	12	13	15
83	6889	6906	6922	6939	6956	6972	6989	7006	7022	7039	2	3	5	7	8	10	12	13	15
84	7056	7073	7090	7106	7123	7140	7157	7174	7191	7208	2	3	5	7	8	10	12	14	15
85	7225	7242	7259	7276	7293	7310	7327	7344	7362	7379	2	3	5	7	9	10	12	14	15
86	7396	7413	7430	7448	7465	7482	7500	7517	7534	7552	2	3	5	7	9	10	12	14	16
87	7569	7586	7604	7621	7639	7656	7674	7691	7709	7726	2	4	5	7	9	10	12	14	16
88	7744	7762	7779	7797	7815	7832	7850	7868	7885	7903	2	4	5	7	9	11	12	14	16
89	7921	7939	7957	7974	7992	8010	8028	8046	8064	8082	2	4	5	7	9	11	13	14	16
90	8100	8118	8136	8154	8172	8190	8208	8226	8245	8263	2	4	5	7	9	11	13	14	16
91	8281	8299	8317	8336	8354	8372	8391	8409	8427	8446	2	4	5	7	9	11	13	15	16
92	8464	8482	8501	8519	8538	8556	8575	8593	8612	8630	2	4	6	7	9	11	13	15	17
93	8649	8668	8686	8705	8724	8742	8761	8780	8798	8817	2	4	6	7	9	11	13	15	17
94	8836	8855	8874	8892	8911	8930	8949	8968	8987	9006	2	4	6	8	9	11	13	15	17
95	9025	9044	9063	9082	9101	9120	9139	9158	9178	9197	2	4	6	8	10	11	13	15	17
96	9216	9235	9254	9274	9293	9312	9332	9351	9370	9390	2	4	6	8	10	12	14	15	17
97	9409	9428	9448	9467	9487	9506	9526	9545	9565	9584	2	4	6	8	10	12	14	16	18
98	9604	9624	9643	9663	9683	9702	9722	9742	9761	9781	2	4	6	8	10	12	14	16	18
99	9801	9821	9841	9860	9880	9900	9920	9940	9960	9980	2	4	6	8	10	12	14	16	18

Find the position of the decimal point by inspection.

IV

NATURAL SINES

	·0°	·1°	·2°	·3°	·4°	·5°	·6°	·7°	·8°	·9°
0°	·0000	0017	0035	0052	0070	0087	0105	0122	0140	0157
1	·0175	0192	0209	0227	0244	0262	0279	0297	0314	0332
2	·0349	0366	0384	0401	0419	0436	0454	0471	0488	0506
3	·0523	0541	0558	0576	0593	0610	0628	0645	0663	0680
4	·0698	0715	0732	0750	0767	0785	0802	0819	0837	0854
5	·0872	0889	0906	0924	0941	0958	0976	0993	1011	1028
6	·1045	1063	1080	1097	1115	1132	1149	1167	1184	1201
7	·1219	1236	1253	1271	1288	1305	1323	1340	1357	1374
8	·1392	1409	1426	1444	1461	1478	1495	1513	1530	1547
9	·1564	1582	1599	1616	1633	1650	1668	1685	1702	1719
10	·1736	1754	1771	1788	1805	1822	1840	1857	1874	1891
11	·1908	1925	1942	1959	1977	1994	2011	2028	2045	2062
12	·2079	2096	2113	2130	2147	2164	2181	2198	2215	2233
13	·2250	2267	2284	2300	2317	2334	2351	2368	2385	2402
14	·2419	2436	2453	2470	2487	2504	2521	2538	2554	2571
15	·2588	2605	2622	2639	2656	2672	2689	2706	2723	2740
16	·2756	2773	2790	2807	2823	2840	2857	2874	2890	2907
17	·2924	2940	2957	2974	2990	3007	3024	3040	3057	3074
18	·3090	3107	3123	3140	3156	3173	3190	3206	3223	3239
19	·3256	3272	3289	3305	3322	3338	3355	3371	3387	3404
20	·3420	3437	3453	3469	3486	3502	3518	3535	3551	3567
21	·3584	3600	3616	3633	3649	3665	3681	3697	3714	3730
22	·3746	3762	3778	3795	3811	3827	3843	3859	3875	3891
23	·3907	3923	3939	3955	3971	3987	4003	4019	4035	4051
24	·4067	4083	4099	4115	4131	4147	4163	4179	4195	4210
25	·4226	4242	4258	4274	4289	4305	4321	4337	4352	4368
26	·4384	4399	4415	4431	4446	4462	4478	4493	4509	4524
27	·4540	4555	4571	4586	4602	4617	4633	4648	4664	4679
28	·4695	4710	4726	4741	4756	4772	4787	4802	4818	4833
29	·4848	4863	4879	4894	4909	4924	4939	4955	4970	4985
30	·5000	5015	5030	5045	5060	5075	5090	5105	5120	5135
31	·5150	5165	5180	5195	5210	5225	5240	5255	5270	5284
32	·5299	5314	5329	5344	5358	5373	5388	5402	5417	5432
33	·5446	5461	5476	5490	5505	5519	5534	5548	5563	5577
34	·5592	5606	5621	5635	5650	5664	5678	5693	5707	5721
35	·5736	5750	5764	5779	5793	5807	5821	5835	5850	5864
36	·5878	5892	5906	5920	5934	5948	5962	5976	5990	6004
37	·6018	6032	6046	6060	6074	6088	6101	6115	6129	6143
38	·6157	6170	6184	6198	6211	6225	6239	6252	6266	6280
39	·6293	6307	6320	6334	6347	6361	6374	6388	6401	6414
40	·6428	6441	6455	6468	6481	6494	6508	6521	6534	6547
41	6561	6574	6587	6600	6613	6626	6639	6652	6665	6678
42	·6691	6704	6717	6730	6743	6756	6769	6782	6794	6807
43	·6820	6833	6845	6858	6871	6884	6896	6909	6921	6934
44	·6947	6959	6972	6984	6997	7009	7022	7034	7046	7059

	·0°	·1°	·2°	·3°	·4°	·5°	·6°	·7°	·8°	·9°
45°	·7071	7083	7096	7108	7120	7133	7145	7157	7169	7181
46	·7193	7206	7218	7230	7242	7254	7266	7278	7290	7302
47	·7314	7325	7337	7349	7361	7373	7385	7396	7408	7420
48	·7431	7443	7455	7466	7478	7490	7501	7513	7524	7536
49	·7547	7559	7570	7581	7593	7604	7615	7627	7638	7649
50	·7660	7672	7683	7694	7705	7716	7727	7738	7749	7760
51	·7771	7782	7793	7804	7815	7826	7837	7848	7859	7869
52	·7880	7891	7902	7912	7923	7934	7944	7955	7965	7976
53	·7986	7997	8007	8018	8028	8039	8049	8059	8070	8080
54	·8090	8100	8111	8121	8131	8141	8151	8161	8171	8181
55	·8192	8202	8211	8221	8231	8241	8251	8261	8271	8281
56	·8290	8300	8310	8320	8329	8339	8348	8358	8368	8377
57	·8387	8396	8406	8415	8425	8434	8443	8453	8462	8471
58	·8480	8490	8499	8508	8517	8526	8536	8545	8554	8563
59	·8572	8581	8590	8599	8607	8616	8625	8634	8643	8652
60	·8660	8669	8678	8686	8695	8704	8712	8721	8729	8738
61	·8746	8755	8763	8771	8780	8788	8796	8805	8813	8821
62	·8829	8838	8846	8854	8862	8870	8878	8886	8894	8902
63	·8910	8918	8926	8934	8942	8949	8957	8965	8973	8980
64	·8988	8996	9003	9011	9018	9026	9033	9041	9048	9056
65	·9063	9070	9078	9085	9092	9100	9107	9114	9121	9128
66	·9135	9143	9150	9157	9164	9171	9178	9184	9191	9198
67	·9205	9212	9219	9225	9232	9239	9245	9252	9259	9265
68	·9272	9278	9285	9291	9298	9304	9311	9317	9323	9330
69	·9336	9342	9348	9354	9361	9367	9373	9379	9385	9391
70	·9397	9403	9409	9415	9421	9426	9432	9438	9444	9449
71	·9455	9461	9466	9472	9478	9483	9489	9494	9500	9505
72	·9511	9516	9521	9527	9532	9537	9542	9548	9553	9558
73	·9563	9568	9573	9578	9583	9588	9593	9598	9603	9608
74	·9613	9617	9622	9627	9632	9636	9641	9646	9650	9655
75	·9659	9664	9668	9673	9677	9681	9686	9690	9694	9699
76	·9703	9707	9711	9715	9720	9724	9728	9732	9736	9740
77	·9744	9748	9751	9755	9759	9763	9767	9770	9774	9778
78	·9781	9785	9789	9792	9796	9799	9803	9806	9810	9813
79	·9816	9820	9823	9826	9829	9833	9836	9839	9842	9845
80	·9848	9851	9854	9857	9860	9863	9866	9869	9871	9874
81	·9877	9880	9882	9885	9888	9890	9893	9895	9898	9900
82	·9903	9905	9907	9910	9912	9914	9917	9919	9921	9923
83	·9925	9928	9930	9932	9934	9936	9938	9940	9942	9943
84	·9945	9947	9949	9951	9952	9954	9956	9957	9959	9960
85	·9962	9963	9965	9966	9968	9969	9971	9972	9973	9974
86	·9976	9977	9978	9979	9980	9981	9982	9983	9984	9985
87	·9986	9987	9988	9989	9990	9990	9991	9992	9993	9993
88	·9994	9995	9995	9996	9996	9997	9997	9997	9998	9998
89	·9998	9999	9999	9999	9999	1·000	1·000	1·000	1·000	1·000

V

NATURAL TANGENTS

	·0°	·1°	·2°	·3°	·4°	·5°	·6°	·7°	·8°	·9°
0°	0·0000	0017	0035	0052	0070	0087	0105	0122	0140	0157
1	0·0175	0192	0209	0227	0244	0262	0279	0297	0314	0332
2	0·0349	0367	0384	0402	0419	0437	0454	0472	0489	0507
3	0·0524	0542	0559	0577	0594	0612	0629	0647	0664	0682
4	0·0699	0717	0734	0752	0769	0787	0805	0822	0840	0857
5	0·0875	0892	0910	0928	0945	0963	0981	0998	1016	1033
6	0·1051	1069	1086	1104	1122	1139	1157	1175	1192	1210
7	0·1228	1246	1263	1281	1299	1317	1334	1352	1370	1388
8	0·1405	1423	1441	1459	1477	1495	1512	1530	1548	1566
9	0·1584	1602	1620	1638	1655	1673	1691	1709	1727	1745
10	0·1763	1781	1799	1817	1835	1853	1871	1890	1908	1926
11	0·1944	1962	1980	1998	2016	2035	2053	2071	2089	2107
12	0·2126	2144	2162	2180	2199	2217	2235	2254	2272	2290
13	0·2309	2327	2345	2364	2382	2401	2419	2438	2456	2475
14	0·2493	2512	2530	2549	2568	2586	2605	2623	2642	2661
15	0·2679	2698	2717	2736	2754	2773	2792	2811	2830	2849
16	0·2867	2886	2905	2924	2943	2962	2981	3000	3019	3038
17	0·3057	3076	3096	3115	3134	3153	3172	3191	3211	3230
18	0·3249	3269	3288	3307	3327	3346	3365	3385	3404	3424
19	0·3443	3463	3482	3502	3522	3541	3561	3581	3600	3620
20	0·3640	3659	3679	3699	3719	3739	3759	3779	3799	3819
21	0·3839	3859	3879	3899	3919	3939	3959	3979	4000	4020
22	0·4040	4061	4081	4101	4122	4142	4163	4183	4204	4224
23	0·4245	4265	4286	4307	4327	4348	4369	4390	4411	4431
24	0·4452	4473	4494	4515	4536	4557	4578	4599	4621	4642
25	0·4663	4684	4706	4727	4748	4770	4791	4813	4834	4856
26	0·4877	4899	4921	4942	4964	4986	5008	5029	5051	5073
27	0·5095	5117	5139	5161	5184	5206	5228	5250	5272	5295
28	0·5317	5340	5362	5384	5407	5430	5452	5475	5498	5520
29	0·5543	5566	5589	5612	5635	5658	5681	5704	5727	5750
30	0·5774	5797	5820	5844	5867	5890	5914	5938	5961	5985
31	0·6009	6032	6056	6080	6104	6128	6152	6176	6200	6224
32	0·6249	6273	6297	6322	6346	6371	6395	6420	6445	6469
33	0·6494	6519	6544	6569	6594	6619	6644	6669	6694	6720
34	0·6745	6771	6796	6822	6847	6873	6899	6924	6950	6976
35	0·7002	7028	7054	7080	7107	7133	7159	7186	7212	7239
36	0·7265	7292	7319	7346	7373	7400	7427	7454	7481	7508
37	0·7536	7563	7590	7618	7646	7673	7701	7729	7757	7785
38	0·7813	7841	7869	7898	7926	7954	7983	8012	8040	8069
39	0·8098	8127	8156	8185	8214	8243	8273	8302	8332	8361
40	0·8391	8421	8451	8481	8511	8541	8571	8601	8632	8662
41	0·8693	8724	8754	8785	8816	8847	8878	8910	8941	8972
42	0·9004	9036	9067	9099	9131	9163	9195	9228	9260	9293
43	0·9325	9358	9391	9424	9457	9490	9523	9556	9590	9623
44	0·9657	9691	9725	9759	9793	9827	9861	9896	9930	9965
45	1·0000	0035	0070	0105	0141	0176	0212	0247	0283	0319
46	1·0355	0392	0428	0464	0501	0538	0575	0612	0649	0686
47	1·0724	0761	0799	0837	0875	0913	0951	0990	1028	1067
48°	1·1106	1145	1184	1224	1263	1303	1343	1383	1423	1463
49	1·1504	1544	1585	1626	1667	1708	1750	1792	1833	1875
50	1·1918	1960	2002	2045	2088	2131	2174	2218	2261	2305
51	1·2349	2393	2437	2482	2527	2572	2617	2662	2708	2753
52	1·2799	2846	2892	2938	2985	3032	3079	3127	3175	3222
53	1·3270	3319	3367	3416	3465	3514	3564	3613	3663	3713
54	1·3764	3814	3865	3916	3968	4019	4071	4124	4176	4229
55	1·4281	4335	4388	4442	4496	4550	4605	4659	4715	4770
56	1·4826	4882	4938	4994	5051	5108	5166	5224	5282	5340
57	1·5399	5458	5517	5577	5637	5697	5757	5818	5880	5941
58	1·6003	6066	6128	6191	6255	6319	6383	6447	6512	6577
59	1·6643	6709	6775	6842	6909	6977	7045	7113	7182	7251
60	1·7321	7391	7461	7532	7603	7675	7747	7820	7893	7966
61	1·8040	8115	8190	8265	8341	8418	8495	8572	8650	8728
62	1·8807	8887	8967	9047	9128	9210	9292	9375	9458	9542
63	1·9626	9711	9797	9883	9970	*0057*	*0145*	*0233*	*0323*	*0413*
64	2·0503	0594	0686	0778	0872	0965	1060	1155	1251	1348
65	2·1445	1543	1642	1742	1842	1943	2045	2148	2251	2355
66	2·2460	2566	2673	2781	2889	2998	3109	3220	3332	3445
67	2·3559	3673	3789	3906	4023	4142	4262	4383	4504	4627
68	2·4751	4876	5002	5129	5257	5386	5517	5649	5782	5916
69	2·6051	6187	6325	6464	6605	6746	6889	7034	7179	7326
70	2·7475	7625	7776	7929	8083	8239	8397	8556	8716	8878
71	2·9042	9208	9375	9544	9714	9887	*0061*	*0237*	*0415*	*0595*
72	3·0777	0961	1146	1334	1524	1716	1910	2106	2305	2506
73	3·2709	2914	3122	3332	3544	3759	3977	4197	4420	4646
74	3·4874	5105	5339	5576	5816	6059	6305	6554	6806	7062
75	3·7321	7583	7848	8118	8391	8667	8947	9232	9520	9812
76	4·0108	0408	0713	1022	1335	1653	1976	2303	2635	2972
77	4·3315	3662	4015	4373	4737	5107	5483	5864	6252	6646
78	4·7046	7453	7867	8288	8716	9152	9594	*0045*	*0504*	*0970*
79	5·1446	1929	2422	2924	3435	3955	4486	5026	5578	6140
80	5·671	5·730	5·789	5·850	5·912	5·976	6·041	6·107	6·174	6·243
81	6·314	6·386	6·460	6·535	6·612	6·691	6·772	6·855	6·940	7·026
82	7·115	7·207	7·300	7·396	7·495	7·596	7·700	7·806	7·916	8·028
83	8·144	8·264	8·386	8·513	8·643	8·777	8·915	9·058	9·205	9·357
84	9·51	9·68	9·84	10·02	10·20	10·39	10·58	10·78	10·99	11·20
85	11·43	11·66	11·91	12·16	12·43	12·71	13·00	13·30	13·62	13·95
86	14·30	14·67	15·06	15·46	15·89	16·35	16·83	17·34	17·89	18·46
87	19·08	19·74	20·45	21·20	22·02	22·90	23·86	24·90	26·03	27·27
88	28·64	30·14	31·82	33·69	35·80	38·19	40·92	44·07	47·74	52·08
89	57·29	63·66	71·62	81·85	95·49	114·6	143·2	191·0	286·5	573·0

Where the integer changes, the numbers are italicised.

VI

LOGARITHMS

	0	1	2	3	4	5	6	7	8	9	1	2	3	4	5	6	7	8	9
10	·0000	0043	0086	0128	0170	0212	0253	0294	0334	0374	4	8	12	17	21	25	29	33	37
11	·0414	0453	0492	0531	0569	0607	0645	0682	0719	0755	4	8	11	15	19	23	26	30	34
12	·0792	0828	0864	0899	0934	0969	1004	1038	1072	1106	3	7	10	14	17	21	24	28	31
13	·1139	1173	1206	1239	1271	1303	1335	1367	1399	1430	3	6	10	13	16	19	23	26	29
14	·1461	1492	1523	1553	1584	1614	1644	1673	1703	1732	3	6	9	12	15	18	21	24	27
15	·1761	1790	1818	1847	1875	1903	1931	1959	1987	2014	3	6	8	11	14	17	20	22	25
16	·2041	2068	2095	2122	2148	2175	2201	2227	2253	2279	3	5	8	11	13	16	18	21	24
17	·2304	2330	2355	2380	2405	2430	2455	2480	2504	2529	2	5	7	10	12	15	17	20	22
18	·2553	2577	2601	2625	2648	2672	2695	2718	2742	2765	2	5	7	9	12	14	16	19	21
19	·2788	2810	2833	2856	2878	2900	2923	2945	2967	2989	2	4	7	9	11	13	16	18	20
20	·3010	3032	3054	3075	3096	3118	3139	3160	3181	3201	2	4	6	8	11	13	15	17	19
21	·3222	3243	3263	3284	3304	3324	3345	3365	3385	3404	2	4	6	8	10	12	14	16	18
22	·3424	3444	3464	3483	3502	3522	3541	3560	3579	3598	2	4	6	8	10	12	14	15	17
23	·3617	3636	3655	3674	3692	3711	3729	3747	3766	3784	2	4	6	7	9	11	13	15	17
24	·3802	3820	3838	3856	3874	3892	3909	3927	3945	3962	2	4	5	7	9	11	12	14	16
25	·3979	3997	4014	4031	4048	4065	4082	4099	4116	4133	2	3	5	7	9	10	12	14	15
26	·4150	4166	4183	4200	4216	4232	4249	4265	4281	4298	2	3	5	7	8	10	11	13	15
27	·4314	4330	4346	4362	4378	4393	4409	4425	4440	4456	2	3	5	6	8	9	11	13	14
28	·4472	4487	4502	4518	4533	4548	4564	4579	4594	4609	2	3	5	6	8	9	11	12	14
29	·4624	4639	4654	4669	4683	4698	4713	4728	4742	4757	1	3	4	6	7	9	10	12	13
30	·4771	4786	4800	4814	4829	4843	4857	4871	4886	4900	1	3	4	6	7	9	10	11	13
31	·4914	4928	4942	4955	4969	4983	4997	5011	5024	5038	1	3	4	6	7	8	10	11	12
32	·5051	5065	5079	5092	5105	5119	5132	5145	5159	5172	1	3	4	5	7	8	9	11	12
33	·5185	5198	5211	5224	5237	5250	5263	5276	5289	5302	1	3	4	5	6	8	9	10	12
34	·5315	5328	5340	5353	5366	5378	5391	5403	5416	5428	1	3	4	5	6	8	9	10	11
35	·5441	5453	5465	5478	5490	5502	5514	5527	5539	5551	1	2	4	5	6	7	9	10	11
36	·5563	5575	5587	5599	5611	5623	5635	5647	5658	5670	1	2	4	5	6	7	8	10	11
37	·5682	5694	5705	5717	5729	5740	5752	5763	5775	5786	1	2	3	5	6	7	8	9	10
38	·5798	5809	5821	5832	5843	5855	5866	5877	5888	5899	1	2	3	5	6	7	8	9	10
39	·5911	5922	5933	5944	5955	5966	5977	5988	5999	6010	1	2	3	4	5	7	8	9	10
40	·6021	6031	6042	6053	6064	6075	6085	6096	6107	6117	1	2	3	4	5	6	8	9	10
41	·6128	6138	6149	6160	6170	6180	6191	6201	6212	6222	1	2	3	4	5	6	7	8	9
42	·6232	6243	6253	6263	6274	6284	6294	6304	6314	6325	1	2	3	4	5	6	7	8	9
43	·6335	6345	6355	6365	6375	6385	6395	6405	6415	6425	1	2	3	4	5	6	7	8	9
44	·6435	6444	6454	6464	6474	6484	6493	6503	6513	6522	1	2	3	4	5	6	7	8	9
45	·6532	6542	6551	6561	6571	6580	6590	6599	6609	6618	1	2	3	4	5	6	7	8	9
46	·6628	6637	6646	6656	6665	6675	6684	6693	6702	6712	1	2	3	4	5	6	7	7	8
47	·6721	6730	6739	6749	6758	6767	6776	6785	6794	6803	1	2	3	4	5	5	6	7	8
48	·6812	6821	6830	6839	6848	6857	6866	6875	6884	6893	1	2	3	4	4	5	6	7	8
49	·6902	6911	6920	6928	6937	6946	6955	6964	6972	6981	1	2	3	4	4	5	6	7	8
50	·6990	6998	7007	7016	7024	7033	7042	7050	7059	7067	1	2	3	3	4	5	6	7	8
51	·7076	7084	7093	7101	7110	7118	7126	7135	7143	7152	1	2	3	3	4	5	6	7	8
52	·7160	7168	7177	7185	7193	7202	7210	7218	7226	7235	1	2	2	3	4	5	6	7	7
53	·7243	7251	7259	7267	7275	7284	7292	7300	7308	7316	1	2	2	3	4	5	6	6	7
54	·7324	7332	7340	7348	7356	7364	7372	7380	7388	7396	1	2	2	3	4	5	6	6	7

	0	1	2	3	4	5	6	7	8	9	1	2	3	4	5	6	7	8	9
55	·7404	7412	7419	7427	7435	7443	7451	7459	7466	7474	1	2	2	3	4	5	5	6	7
56	·7482	7490	7497	7505	7513	7520	7528	7536	7543	7551	1	2	2	3	4	5	5	6	7
57	·7559	7566	7574	7582	7589	7597	7604	7612	7619	7627	1	2	2	3	4	5	5	6	7
58	·7634	7642	7649	7657	7664	7672	7679	7686	7694	7701	1	1	2	3	4	4	5	6	7
59	·7709	7716	7723	7731	7738	7745	7752	7760	7767	7774	1	1	2	3	4	4	5	6	7
60	·7782	7789	7796	7803	7810	7818	7825	7832	7839	7846	1	1	2	3	4	4	5	6	6
61	·7853	7860	7868	7875	7882	7889	7896	7903	7910	7917	1	1	2	3	4	4	5	6	6
62	·7924	7931	7938	7945	7952	7959	7966	7973	7980	7987	1	1	2	3	3	4	5	6	6
63	·7993	8000	8007	8014	8021	8028	8035	8041	8048	8055	1	1	2	3	3	4	5	5	6
64	·8062	8069	8075	8082	8089	8096	8102	8109	8116	8122	1	1	2	3	3	4	5	5	6
65	·8129	8136	8142	8149	8156	8162	8169	8176	8182	8189	1	1	2	3	3	4	5	5	6
66	·8195	8202	8209	8215	8222	8228	8235	8241	8248	8254	1	1	2	3	3	4	5	5	6
67	·8261	8267	8274	8280	8287	8293	8299	8306	8312	8319	1	1	2	3	3	4	5	5	6
68	·8325	8331	8338	8344	8351	8357	8363	8370	8376	8382	1	1	2	3	3	4	4	5	6
69	·8388	8395	8401	8407	8414	8420	8426	8432	8439	8445	1	1	2	2	3	4	4	5	6
70	·8451	8457	8463	8470	8476	8482	8488	8494	8500	8506	1	1	2	2	3	4	4	5	6
71	·8513	8519	8525	8531	8537	8543	8549	8555	8561	8567	1	1	2	2	3	4	4	5	5
72	·8573	8579	8585	8591	8597	8603	8609	8615	8621	8627	1	1	2	2	3	4	4	5	5
73	·8633	8639	8645	8651	8657	8663	8669	8675	8681	8686	1	1	2	2	3	4	4	5	5
74	·8692	8698	8704	8710	8716	8722	8727	8733	8739	8745	1	1	2	2	3	4	4	5	5
75	·8751	8756	8762	8768	8774	8779	8785	8791	8797	8802	1	1	2	2	3	3	4	5	5
76	·8808	8814	8820	8825	8831	8837	8842	8848	8854	8859	1	1	2	2	3	3	4	5	5
77	·8865	8871	8876	8882	8887	8893	8899	8904	8910	8915	1	1	2	2	3	3	4	4	5
78	·8921	8927	8932	8938	8943	8949	8954	8960	8965	8971	1	1	2	2	3	3	4	4	5
79	·8976	8982	8987	8993	8998	9004	9009	9015	9020	9025	1	1	2	2	3	3	4	4	5
80	·9031	9036	9042	9047	9053	9058	9063	9069	9074	9079	1	1	2	2	3	3	4	4	5
81	·9085	9090	9096	9101	9106	9112	9117	9122	9128	9133	1	1	2	2	3	3	4	4	5
82	·9138	9143	9149	9154	9159	9165	9170	9175	9180	9186	1	1	2	2	3	3	4	4	5
83	·9191	9196	9201	9206	9212	9217	9222	9227	9232	9238	1	1	2	2	3	3	4	4	5
84	·9243	9248	9253	9258	9263	9269	9274	9279	9284	9289	1	1	2	2	3	3	4	4	5
85	·9294	9299	9304	9309	9315	9320	9325	9330	9335	9340	1	1	2	2	3	3	4	4	5
86	·9345	9350	9355	9360	9365	9370	9375	9380	9385	9390	1	1	2	2	3	3	4	4	5
87	·9395	9400	9405	9410	9415	9420	9425	9430	9435	9440	0	1	1	2	2	3	3	4	4
88	·9445	9450	9455	9460	9465	9469	9474	9479	9484	9489	0	1	1	2	2	3	3	4	4
89	·9494	9499	9504	9509	9513	9518	9523	9528	9533	9538	0	1	1	2	2	3	3	4	4
90	·9542	9547	9552	9557	9562	9566	9571	9576	9581	9586	0	1	1	2	2	3	3	4	4
91	·9590	9595	9600	9605	9609	9614	9619	9624	9628	9633	0	1	1	2	2	3	3	4	4
92	·9638	9643	9647	9652	9657	9661	9666	9671	9675	9680	0	1	1	2	2	3	3	4	4
93	·9685	9689	9694	9699	9703	9708	9713	9717	9722	9727	0	1	1	2	2	3	3	4	4
94	·9731	9736	9741	9745	9750	9754	9759	9763	9768	9773	0	1	1	2	2	3	3	4	4
95	·9777	9782	9786	9791	9795	9800	9805	9809	9814	9818	0	1	1	2	2	3	3	4	4
96	·9823	9827	9832	9836	9841	9845	9850	9854	9859	9863	0	1	1	2	2	3	3	4	4
97	·9868	9872	9877	9881	9886	9890	9894	9899	9903	9908	0	1	1	2	2	3	3	4	4
98	·9912	9917	9921	9926	9930	9934	9939	9943	9948	9952	0	1	1	2	2	3	3	4	4
99	·9956	9961	9965	9969	9974	9978	9983	9987	9991	9996	0	1	1	2	2	3	3	3	4

Answers to some of the Exercises

Remember that some of the numerical answers are only approximate, so that you need not agree with them exactly, but, of course, you should not be far out.

Chapter 3 (page 112).

Exercise No.

6. (*a*) $x^2 + 3xy + y^2$, (*b*) $6x + 6y + 10z$,
(*c*) $3a^2 + 12a + 12 = 3(a + 2)^2$, (*d*) $2x - 3$,
(*e*) $a^2 - 2ab - b^2$, (*f*) $x^2yz + xy^2z + xyz^2 = xyz(x + y + z)$,
(*g*) $6a^3b^4$, (*h*) $2x^6$, (*i*) $-a^2 - 4x^2$, (*j*) $\frac{1}{2}xy^3$, (*k*) $3ab$, (*l*) $\frac{1}{3}ad$.
8. (*a*) 12, (*b*) 12, (*c*) 14, (*d*) 5, (*e*) 2, (*f*) 6, (*g*) 3, (*h*) $\frac{1}{2}$, (*i*) 3, (*j*) 18,
(*k*) 1, (*l*) 5, (*m*) 2, (*n*) $6a$, (*o*) $2a + b$, (*p*) $a - b$.
9. £285, £255. 10. £342, £171, £114.
11. $1\frac{1}{2}$ hours from the time Tom starts. 12. 12.
13. For 6000 miles A requires 212 gallons and B 165 gallons.
14. 1s. 6d. per peck.

Chapter 4 (page 185).

7. $3x + 7y$, $2a - 5b$, $4a - 9b$, $a + 3$, etc.
9. $(x - 1)(x + 1)$, $(a + b - c)(a + b + c)$, $(a + b - c)(a - b + c)$,
$(a - b)(a + b)(a^2 + b^2)$, $(9 - x)(9 + x)$, $(a - b - c)(a + b + c)$,
$(x + y - 1)(x + y + 1)$, $(x - y)(x + y)(x^2 + y^2)(x^4 + y^4)$,
$(a + b - 1)(a + b + 1)$, $(x + y - 2)(x + y + 2)$, $3(2x + 1)$.
10. (i) 90°, (ii) 60°, (iii) 50°, (iv) 10°, (v) 78°. 12. 60°, 49°, $38\frac{1}{2}$°.
13. $46\frac{1}{2}$°, $43\frac{1}{2}$°; $57\frac{1}{2}$°, $32\frac{1}{2}$°; 68°, 22°. 15. $3\sqrt{3} \doteqdot 5{\cdot}2$ feet, 6 feet.
16. 68·2°. 17. $3\sqrt{3} \doteqdot 5{\cdot}2$ feet. 18. 45·14°. 20. 42 yards.

Chapter 5 (page 229).

1. 5·196, 4·243, 3·464, 4·899, 3·162, 5·477. 2. $\frac{1}{4}\sqrt{7}$, $\frac{1}{3}\sqrt{5}$, $\frac{3}{5}$.
5. $l = f + (n - 1)d$, etc. 7. (i) $2n - 1$, n^2, (ii) $3n - 2$,
$\frac{1}{2}n(3n - 1)$, (iii) $5n$, $5n(n + 1)/2$, (iv) $\frac{1}{2}n$, $\frac{1}{4}n(n + 1)$,
(v) $4n - 10$, $2n^2 - 8n$, (vi) $-(n - 2)a$, $\frac{1}{2}a(3n - n^2)$,
(vi) $\frac{1}{3}(14 - 5n)$, $(23n - 5n^2)/6$; 3, 2. 8. $\frac{1}{2}n(n + 1)$.
9. $7\frac{4}{5}$, $9\frac{3}{5}$, $11\frac{2}{5}$, $13\frac{1}{5}$. 10. $1\frac{1}{2}$, 2, $2\frac{1}{2}$.
11. The difference between successive terms is $(l - f)/(n + 1)$.
14. (i) 2^{n-1}, $2^n - 1$, (ii) $(0{\cdot}9)^n$, $10\left\{0{\cdot}9 - (0{\cdot}9)^{n+1}\right\}$,
(iii) $3/2^{n+1}$, $\frac{3}{2}(1 - 1/2^n)$,
(iv) $a^{n-1}x^{6-n}$, $x^{6-n}(x^n - a^n)/(x - a)$, (v) 3^{n-1}, $\frac{1}{2}(3^n - 1)$. 15. 25, 125.

Exercise
No.

16. 2/9, 4/27, 8/81. 17. The ratio of successive terms is $\left(\frac{1}{f}\right)^{1/(n+1)}$

20. 2/3, 25/99, 791/999. 21. 2, $1\frac{1}{4}$.
22. (*a*) $n^3 - (n-1)^3 = 3n^2 - 3n + 1$, $n(2n-1)$, (*b*) $n(3n-2)$.
23. 4! = 24, 8! = 40320, 12! = 479001600, 16!.
24. 56, 495, 4368. 25. 720. 26. 16, 26.
27. 5040, 720, 48, 24. 28. 15, 3.

Chapter 6 (page 281).

11. 1·57 miles. 12. About 5,110 yards. 13. 60·9 feet.
14. 13·65 miles. 15. 9 miles.
16. $\sin 2A = 2 \sin A \cos A$,
$\sin 3A = 3 \sin A \cos^2 A - \sin^3 A = 3 \sin A - 4 \sin^3 A$,
$\cos 2A = \cos^2 A - \sin^2 A$,
$\cos 3A = \cos^3 A - 3 \cos A \sin^2 A = 4 \cos^3 A - 3 \cos A$.
22. QK = 7,813 miles, KP = 5,117 miles, PQ = 11,962 miles.
23. AM = 2,996 miles, AZ = 4,863 miles, MZ = 1,890 miles.
25. 4,133 miles. 26. 42·4 miles. 27. 33° $53\frac{1}{2}'$ or 28° $6\frac{1}{2}'$.
30. (*a*) $\frac{3}{4}\{1 - (-3)^n\}$, (*b*) $\frac{1}{6}\{1 - (-2^{-n}\}$, (*c*) $\frac{27}{20}\{1 - (-\frac{2}{3})^n\}$,
(*d*) $\frac{3}{5}\{1 - (-\frac{2}{3}^n\}$. 31. $-ar^{2n-1}$, ar^{2n}.

Chapter 7 (page 337).

2. (*a*) $(a+4)(a+6)$, (*b*) $(p+2)(p+3)$, (*c*) $(x-1)(x-2)$,
(*d*) $(m+1)(m+3)$, (*e*) $(x-2)(x-8)$, (*f*), $(f+5)(f-4)$,
(*g*) $(t+5)(t-8)$, and so on.
3. (*a*) $(x+6)(x-6)$, (*b*) $(3x+5)(3x-5)$, (*c*) $4(x+5)(x-5)$,
(*d*) $25(2y+1)(2y-1)$, etc.
(*i*) $(16t+13s)(16t-13s)$, . . ., (*o*) $(\sqrt{3}+x)(\sqrt{3}-x)$,
(*p*) $(\sqrt{2}+\sqrt{3x})(\sqrt{2}-\sqrt{3x})$, etc.
4. (*a*) $(x+3)(3x+1)$, (*b*) $(2x+5)(3x+2)$, (*c*) $(2p+1)(3p+1)$,
(*d*) $(t+5)(3t+7)$, . . ., (*f*) $(2q-1)(3q-2)$, . . .,
(*h*) $(4x^2+1)(5x^2-1)$, (*i*) $(3+2x)(5-2x)$,
(*j*) $(2n-3)(3n+4)$, etc.
5. (*a*) $(2a+3x)(3a-x)$, (*b*) $(3a-5bc)(5a+3bc)$,
(*c*) $(a-7b)(6a+5b)$, (*d*) $(a+b)(2a-9b)$, etc.
6. (*a*) and (*b*) $1/(x+y)$, (*c*), (*d*) and (*e*) $1/(x-y)$, (*f*) $3x/4z$,
(*g*) $(x+1)/(x+3)$, (*h*) $(x+1)/(x+2)$, (*i*) $(x+1)/(2x+5)$,
(*j*) $(3x+7)/(x+7)$, (*k*) $b(a+b)/a$, (*l*) $(4a^2+2a+1)/(2a-1)$,
(*m*) $(2x-3)/(x-2)$.

Exercise
No.

7. (*a*) $a(b + c)/bc$, (*b*) ab, (*c*) $-2x + 3y$, (*d*) $a^2/(a - 2b)$,
(*e*) $5a/4(x + 1)$, (*f*) $(a + 17b)/12$, (*g*) $a/4(x + 2y)$,
(*h*) $y^2(y - x)/(y + x)$.
8. (*a*) $2x/(x^2 - 1)$, (*b*) $- 2/(x^2 - 1)$, (*c*) $2b/(a^2 - b^2)$,
(*d*) $(a^2 + 2ab - b^2)/(a^2 - b^2)$, etc., (*h*) $2/(y - 4)(y - 6)$,
(*i*) $2x/(x + y)$, . . ., (*k*) $12/(t - 1)(t + 3)(t - 5)$, etc.
10. (*a*) 19, (*b*) $a + 2b$, (*c*) 12/13, (*d*) $2\frac{1}{2}$, (*e*) — 4/3, (*f*) 10/7.
11. (*a*) $4\frac{1}{3}$ miles, (*b*) 30 miles, (*c*) 3·59%.
12. (*a*) 10, – 21, (*b*) 11, – 8, (*c*) $1\frac{1}{4}$, – $1\frac{1}{3}$, (*d*) 2/3, – 3/8,
(*e*) 8, – 17/3, (*f*) 1, – $\frac{1}{2}$, (*g*) a, $b - a$, (*h*) 2, – 4.
13. (*a*) 5, 6, 7, or – 7, – 6, – 5, (*b*) $\frac{1}{2}(3 + \sqrt{2081})$ feet,
(*c*) $2\frac{6}{11}$, $2\frac{17}{44}$ feet,
14. (*a*) $x = 10$, $y = 2$, (*b*) 3, 4, (*c*) 6, 2, (*d*) 9, 15, (*e*) 11, 12, 13,
(*f*) 3, 6, 1.
15. (*a*) $20\frac{4}{7}$, (*b*) – 17/64, (*c*) $l = 18$, $b = 12$ feet, (*d*) 25, (*e*) 30.
16. (i) $n(2n - 1)$, (ii) $\frac{1}{2}n^2(n + 1)$, (iii) $n(3n^2 - 2)$, (iv) $3n^2 - 3n + 1$.
(v) $\frac{1}{2}(3n^2 - 3n + 2)$, (vi) $2n^2 - 2n + 1$.
18. (i) 1·1249, (ii) 0·9039, (iii) 1·5735, (iv) 128·7876.

Chapter 8 (page 390).

3. Lat. 50° N., Long. $5\frac{3}{8}$° W. approximately.
4. 20 h. 28 m., 8.1 p.m., $48\frac{1}{2}$° W. 5. 46° N.
7. September 23rd. 8. Thin waning crescent, 5.8 a.m., 11.8 a.m.
10. About 7,900. 11. North Devon. 12. About September 24th.
18. 57·7°, 7.33 p.m.
19. About 6.40 a.m., 5.20 p.m., at Gizeh, 7 a.m., 5 p.m. at New York,
7.28 a.m., 4.32 p.m. at London.

Chapter 9 (page 456).

2. (*a*) $x^2 + y^2 = 16$, (*b*) $x^2 + y^2 - 4x - 6y = 3$.
8. (*a*) 45°, (*b*) 60°. 9. Parallel and equally spaced. 11. $y = C$.
17. $l = 100t^2$. 19. (*a*) $x = 0$, $y = 3$ or $x = 4$, $y = 0$,
(*b*) $x = 3$, $y = 4$, or $x = 4$, $y = 3$, (*c*) $x = 2$, $y = 1$, or $x = 3$,
$y = 2$ or $x = - 3$, $y = - 2$ or $x = - 2$, $y = - 1$.
26. (i) 1 or – 1·4, (ii) $\frac{3}{4}$ or – $\frac{1}{2}$, (iii) 1·2 or – 1.

Chapter 10 (page 508).

1. (i) 4118, (ii) 30288, (iii) 1992, (iv) 99·18.
2. 6227, 9692, 0·01950, 45·82, 1·009, 0·4181. 3. 2, 3, 3/2.

Exercise No.

5. (i) 125,930, (ii) $0 \cdot 968$, (iii) $1 \cdot 111$.
6. (i) £265, (ii) between 7 and 8 years, (iii) £84.
7. $0 \cdot 0010$, $0 \cdot 3466$, $8 \cdot 240$.

Chapter 11 (page 568).

1. Hint:—$\log_e (1 + \frac{1}{80}) = 4 \log_e 3 - 4 \log_e 2 - \log_e 5$,
   $\log_e (1 - \frac{1}{25}) = 3 \log_e 2 + \log_e 3 - 2 \log_e 5$, and so on.
6. $1 - 1/x^2$. 7. $3 \cdot 6x^{2 \cdot 6}$, $5/2\sqrt{x}$, $-1\frac{1}{2}x^{-2\frac{1}{2}}$, $\frac{7}{2}x^{5/2}$, $\frac{1}{3}x^{-8/9}$.
8. $5x^4 - 15x^2 + 10x - 4$. 10. $x = -1, y = 2$, and $x = 1, y = -2$.
11. $8/\pi$ cubic feet. 12. $10x = 3y = \frac{1}{2}c$.
14. (i) $x^4 + C$, (ii) $3 \log_e x + C$, (iii) $\{ \frac{1}{4}x^{n+1}/(n+1) \} + C$,
    (iv) $\frac{2}{3}x^{3/2} + C$, (v) $x^3 + x^2 + x + C$.
15. (i) $\frac{1}{3}x^3 + Ax + B$, (ii) $\frac{5}{2}x^2 + Ax + B$, (iii) $\frac{4}{15}x^{5/2} + Ax + B$.
16. $p = 11 \cdot 41 + 500v^{-1 \cdot 4}$.
17. (i) $-a^2 \sin a^2x$, (ii) $12 \cos 3x$, (iii) $na \cos nx - nb \sin nx$.
20. $A = 2x^2 + 3x + C$; (i) 108, (ii) 216, (iii) 25. 21. $274\frac{2}{3}$.
22. (i) $223\frac{1}{3}$, (ii) $\frac{2}{3}a + 2c$, (iii) $4\frac{1}{2}$, (iv) 56, (v) 2.
23. (i) $20266\frac{2}{3}$, (ii) $19994\frac{2}{3}$, (iii) $19993 \cdot 6$ exactly.
24. 14. 26. 1,1900 ft. lb. wt. 27. 100π cu. in. 28. 369π cu. in.
30. (i) 1, (ii) 0, (iii) $[\sin x - x \cos x]_0^\pi = \pi$.
31. (i) $x \cos x + \sin x$, (ii) $\cos x \sec^2 x - \sin x \tan x = \cos x$,
    (iii) $6x^2 + 6x + 4$.
32. (i) $-1/(x+1)^2$, (ii) $(x \cos x - \sin x)/x^2$, (iii) $-\sin x/\cos^2 x$,
    (iv) $\sec^2 x$.
33. (i) $\frac{1}{2} \cos x/\sqrt{\sin x}$, (ii) $na(ax + b)^{n-1}$, (iii) $a \cos (ax + b)$,
    (iv) $(2ax + b)/(ax^2 + bx + c)$.
35. (i) $y = A \cos 2x + B \sin 2x$, (ii) $y = Ae^{2x} + Be^{-2x}$.
    Second part: (i) $y = 5 \cos 2x + 2 \sin 2x$,
    (ii) $y = \frac{1}{2}(7e^{2x} + 3e^{-2x})$.

Chapter 12 (page 636).

1. $1 - (5/6)^3 = 91/216$. 2. $13!\,39!/52! = 1/635013559600$.
3. 2/19, provided that the first partner has neither.
4. 46189/262144, 910596/1048576. 5. In the ratios 9, 3, 3, 1.

Index

E

H

M

U

V